The Steam Locomotive

The Steam Locomotive

Edgar A. Haine

Cornwall Books
New York ● London ● Toronto

Associated University Presses
440 Forsgate Drive
Cranbury, NJ 08512

Associated University Presses
25 Sicilian Avenue
London WC1A 2QH, England

Associated University Presses
2133 Royal Windsor Drive
Unit 1
Mississauga, Ontario
Canada L5J 1K5

Library of Congress Cataloging-in-Publication Data

Haine, Edgar A., 1908–
  The steam locomotive.

  Bibliography: p.
  Includes index.
  1. Locomotives—History.   I. Title.
TJ603.H28   1990   625.2'61'09   82-46082
ISBN 0–8453–4763–2 (alk. paper)

Printed in the United States of America

This book is dedicated
to the memory of my wife,
Helen Davenport Haine

CONTENTS

PREFACE

THIS BOOK IS A PICTORIAL HISTORY OF THE steam locomotive in forty-eight different parts of the world, not including the United States, Canada, or Great Britain. The 1,130 accompanying photographs, sketches, and drawings document the advent, development, and utilization of the railway steam engine in each country or region. I have attempted to select typical, contemporary locomotive pictures depicting a range of uses from the initial introduction of the "iron horse" in the nineteenth century to its demise around the middle of the twentieth century. The illustrations are arranged chronologically for each country. In most cases the photographs are generously supported by appropriate captions and technical information. The principal sources of steam locomotive pictures were cooperating railway companies in various locations; secondary origins were libraries and railway, transportation, and science museums. Picture sources are acknowledged under individual entries.

The forty-eight geographic locales are arranged alphabetically in this compilation. Each chapter begins with a brief summary of the history of railroading and steam locomotion in that country or area. The captions accompanying the illustrations often provide additional historical detail.

This steam locomotive treatise was not intended to be all-inclusive; however, in some areas, such as South Africa, Italy, France, New Zealand, and parts of Australia, the pictorial record is quite extensive. Many other important national entities, such as those behind the iron curtain, miscellaneous Asian and African countries, the republics of Central America, and some nations in South America, were not incorporated because most requests to those countries for photographs and information went completely unheeded. For all countries, the magnitude of the presentation was determined almost solely by availability of photographs as well as pertinent historical and technical data.

ACKNOWLEDGMENTS

A BOOK THIS WIDE IN SCOPE COULD NOT HAVE been prepared without the valued assistance of a large number of supporting individuals. I am especially beholden to Malcolm Nicolson, librarian with the Mitchell Library, Glasgow, Scotland, for his splendid assistance in locating a vast array of steam locomotive photographs, plus attendant specification information, applicable to some of the countries covered in this pictorial history. I am grateful to Arthur Engelland of Fort Lauderdale, Florida, for the use of his extensive collection of National Geographic Society maps. Special thanks go to Antonio Urbani of Fort Lauderdale for his enduring help in translating and interpreting difficult technical documents bearing on Italian steam locomotives. The generous cooperation of Ellen Magaline of Fort Lauderdale is also gratefully acknowledged for translating numerous letters and technical data relating to steam locomotives used in Germany. The important support of Ruth S. Burkhart of Harrisburg, Pennsylvania, is also recognized for her assistance and encouragement attending the final phases of this book.

The following railway officials and authorities rendered valuable contributions in the form of locomotive pictures and caption information covering railroads in the countries indicated:

J. R. Renshaw, Traffic Manager—Rail, State Transport Authority, Adelaide, South Australia

E. M. Wilson, Public Relations Officer, Western Australian Government Railways, Perth, Australia

Boon lorm Davivongsna Ayudhya, Chief, Public Relations, State Railway of Thailand, Bangkok, Thailand

Alida Siregar, Chief General Administration, Indonesian State Railways, Bandung, Indonesia

Sebastian Jacobi, Swiss Federal Railways, Bern, Switzerland

Marion Pohl, Publicity Dept., Danish National Railways, Copenhagen, Denmark

Pasquale della Valle, Foto Attualita, Rome, Italy

Marie-Anne Asselberghr, Stichtina Nederlands Spoorwegmuseum, Utrecht, The Netherlands

Dr. Americo Ramalho, Public Relations Manager, Caminhos de Ferro Portugueses, Lisbon, Portugal

H. M. Ali, General Manager's Office, Sudan Railways Corp., Atbara, Sudan

C. A. Alrenius, Swedish State Railways Museum, Gävle, Sweden

Dr. Vaszko Akos, Acting General Director, Museum of Transport, Budapest, Hungary

John C. Clayson, Museum of Transport, Glasgow, Scotland

Ibrahim Episen and Halil Ertan, Turkey State Railways, Ankara, Turkey

Juan Agustin Isetto, National Railroad Museum, Buenos Aires, Argentina

Alison Henwood, University of Rhodesia Library, Salisbury, Zimbabwe

M. D. Mutsamwira, National Archives, Salisbury, Zimbabwe

J. G. H. Loubser, Director General, South African Railways, Johannesburg, South Africa

M. Diane Brenner, Museum Archivist, Anchorage Historical and Fine Arts Museum, Anchorage, Alaska

Klaus Matzka, Perchtoldsdorf, Austria

W. Van Gestel, Public Relations Officer, Soc.

Nationale des Chemens de Fer Belges, Brussels, Belgium

Fernando J. Abelha Salles, Chefe do Dept. Geral de Comm. Social da RFFSA, Rio de Janeiro, Brazil

Seija Petman, Press Office, Finnish State Railways, Helsinki, Finland

Susan Shaner, Archivist, Public Archives, State of Hawaii

Malene F. Dodds, Port Washington, New York

Satoo Horike, International Department, Japanese National Railways, Tokyo, Japan

Zainal Abidn Bin A. Talib, Malayan Railway, Kuala Lumpur, Malaysia

Ivan G. Holland, New Zealand Railways, Wellington, New Zealand

E. Fjeldselh, Public Relations Dept., Norwegian State Railways

Nan S. Chong, Panama Collection Librarian, Panama Canal Commission

Pandora G. Aleman, Chief Records Management Branch, Panama Canal Commission

Alex de A. Freitas Cruz, National Library, Lisbon, Portugal

Eduardo Guerrero Sanchez, Public Relations, State Railways of Spain

Y. S. Pin, Taiwan Railway Administration, Taipei, Taiwan

A. K. Ghosh, National Library, Calcutta, India

Fritz Lehmann, University of British Columbia, Vancouver, B.C., Canada

Mr. Peter Schriver, Copenhagen, Denmark

Fred Westing, Railway Historian, Drexel Hill, Pennsylvania

Tom E. Matsalia, Public Relations Officer, Kenya Railways, Nairobi, Kenya

I will be forever grateful for the personal and dedicated assistance rendered by my wife, Helen Davenport Haine, who passed away before this book was completed. As ever, the editorial work provided by my daughter, Vicki Haine Loiodice, of Grenoble, France, was greatly appreciated.

INTRODUCTION
THE DEVELOPMENT OF STEAM
LOCOMOTION

THE EARLY EXPERIMENTS OF NICOLAS CUGNOT, William Jessop, Charles Vignoles, William Hedley, Richard Trevithick, George and Robert Stephenson, Oliver Evans and Colonel John Stevens, William Morris, M. W. Baldwin, Thomas Rogers, and many others, form a history of endless trials and tribulations leading to eventual progress. Their years of work eventually gave birth to a steam-powered mechanical marvel, the forerunner of thousands of railway steam engines that blazed a trail of achievement and success all over the globe. More than any other form of transportation, the steam locomotive, and its ability to pull a connected string of cars carrying prodigious quantities of commerce as well as people, had a profound and positive impact on world trade. The majestic era of the railway steam engine, barely extending over a hundred years, was one of worldwide attention, outstanding technical accomplishment, and tremendous progress in opening up and conquering the major land masses of this planet. The arrival of the steam locomotive was most aptly described in the 28 June 1860 issue of the *Natal Mercury* in South Africa: "The march of the locomotive is a march of progress. Before the approach of the 'steam horse,' all retrogressive influences vanish and give way. Wherever the almighty engine secures a footing, civilization inevitably follows and enterprise of every kind fructifies and spreads."

The indomitable steam locomotive, society's first and greatest medium of mass transportation, not only contributed to a fabulous increase in commercial activity, it assured man's liberation from the debilitating confinements of a localized existence. Moreover, no other human invention has engendered the same degree of esteem, reverence, and devotion as the legendary railway steam engine. Indeed, the advent of this great machine was a significant milestone in the industrial progress of mankind; the steam locomotive worked momentous changes, transporting both people and commerce at almost unbelievable speeds.

The advance in steam locomotion, from the early rudimentary, frail machines of the nineteenth century to the monsters of the mid-twentieth century, was a tale of energetic, systematic research and development in many countries. In some areas, private enterprise carried out the pioneer locomotive work. More often, since the major railways of the world were largely state-owned and controlled, or were retained and managed by large corporate bodies, plenty of financial resources, technological expertise, and political clout were usually available for building faster, more efficient, and more powerful locomotives. While engineers and inventors were making progress with engines and the rights-of-way, railway management began to appreciate the fact that the great value of this new form of transportation lay not in short hauls on a local level but in connections between widely separated locations.

From many endeavors, private as well as institutional, all over the globe came important improvements in steam motive power. The Allan straight-link motion was invented by Alexander Allan, Superintendent of the Scottish Central Railway, at Perth in 1855. On 12 May 1863, Robert F. Fairlie patented a type 0–6–0 + 0–6–0 four-cylinder locomotive whose principal feature was that the boiler had two barrels with a common central firebox fired from the side. The cab was in the center of the engine. Two power bogies supported the boiler and also carried the buffing and draw gear. A Belgian, Alfred Belpaire (1820–93) was the inventor, in 1878, of the famous locomotive firebox that bore his name. Egide Walschaerts (1820–1901), another Belgian, in 1844 originated the most efficient and widely used valve gear on steam locomotives. The celebrated German, Dr. Wilhelm Schmidt, patented his outstanding superheater in 1896, which was used worldwide, until the very decline of railway steam engines. The eminent French engineer Anatole Mallet (1837–1919) was awarded a patent in June 1885 for an articulated locomotive, which made him famous. Dr. Rudolf Diesel (1858–1913), the great inventor of the diesel internal combustion engine in 1891, hastened the decline of the steam locomotive. H. W. Garratt first designed his articulated type of steam engine in 1909; these engines were used all over the world, with the notable exception of the United States, where the Mallet jointed machine was preferred.

Over the years, steam locomotives developed into ever more efficient and complex machines, thanks to such technical refinements as compounding, automatic stokers, exhaust steam feedwater heaters, mechanical lubricators, multitube boilers, thermic syphons, tractive boosters, roller bearings, steam blowers, mechanical boiler cleansers, steam, hydraulic and vacuum power brakes, standard car connectors, blast pipes, steam-operated reversing gear, soot blowers, steam injectors, spark arrestors, speed recorders, electric generators and headlamps, power-operated fire doors, firebox drench pipes, piston valves, intermediate combustion chambers, automatic warning devices, safety pop valves, and compensated spring gear on coupled drive wheels.

Hand in hand with the design and construction of better steam locomotives came advanced erection methods, new materials, and improved mechanical shop procedures. As steam engines grew larger, more powerful, and heavier, supporting members had to be stronger. Forged frames eventually were replaced by steel castings, often formed as composite units with integral crosspieces and cylinders. Drive-wheel technology discarded the old-type spoked sections in favor of newly designed and fashioned wheel centers. Bogie wheels, originally assembled from separate frames and bolsters, were now cast in one piece. Various unusual alloys were created to strengthen and enhance the longevity of many locomotive parts, including the boilers. To assist in keeping engine axle-loads within permissible limits, various auxiliary components such as ash pans, cabs, side platforms and foot plates, were fabricated from aluminum. With improved construction methods and harder, stronger materials came a better understanding of lubrication. Welding gradually superseded old-fashioned, laborious riveting procedures in construction and maintenance of locomotives.

The development of the railway steam engine was a story of extensive trial and error, of many omissions and commissions, of continued improvement in design and operational technology. Countless performance problems had to be resolved through a long succession of tough technical and engineering determinations in the great struggle to build machines with greater and greater pulling power and operational efficiency. Further examination of some of the difficulties overcome by those who designed, built, and operated the steam locomotives will, I feel, help create a worthwhile understanding of this extraordinary mechanical invention.

Basically, the steam locomotive consisted of a boiler, in which steam was produced, carried on a steel framework or chassis to which the engine cylinders were attached. Springs and axle boxes transferred the weight of the engine to the axles and wheels. The forces generated by the drive wheels on the track were normally transmitted through the engine's rear drawbar and thence to the tender, if any, and on to the train.

To most students of the railway steam engine, its straightforward mechanics are relatively easy to observe, understand, and appreciate. Even a novice knows that as fire heated water in the engine boiler, the resulting steam pressure, when turned loose, moved the cylinder pistons, which in turn drove the connecting rods that turned the engine wheels. In more definitive terms, the ordinary locomotive consisted of a pair of direct-acting horizontal or partially inclined engines (cylinders) fixed in a rigid frame under the front end of the boiler. As the steam in the cylinder drove the piston, the piston pushed the main piston rod (and possibly connecting rods) back and forth. The rod moved the crosshead (a heavy steel block that slid freely along steel guides), which propelled the main rod. The main rod pushed on a pin connected to the main drive wheel, thus turning the wheel. From this primary drive wheel, connecting rods transmitted force to other crank pins on adjoining drive wheels, and all the wheels turned in unison.

In order to direct steam pressure alternately to the two sides of the cylinder pistons, generating indispensable reciprocating motion, a valve gear was required to synchronize the movement of these pistons with the driving wheels. The primary function of this valve was to admit live steam to one end of the cylinder during the first part of the piston stroke, while at the same time releasing from the other end of the cylinder the expanded or exhaust steam from the previous stroke in the opposite direction. The whole process would then be reversed and repeated. By controlling the valve gear, the engineer could allow the engine to move forward or backward, slow or fast, and then exhaust the steam after all the work was performed. Actually, synchronization was accomplished by action of the drive wheels and crossheads, to which were attached eccentrics that pushed and pulled the valve rods and so controlled the movement and position of the valves and, through them, the admission and discharge of steam. In the early days of railroading, the valve motion was almost universally that invented by Stephenson. Later on, by far the most popular type of valve gear, widely used in Europe and most other countries, was one designed by Walschaerts. This was generally mounted outside the wheels, where the working of this simple and graceful linkage of valve-gear rods, deriving its motion and guidance in part from the driving wheel axle and in part from the crosshead, could be closely observed.

The expanded steam, after it had performed its work in the cylinders, was used to provide a draft for the fire before finally being directed to a chimney outlet. In the process, the rush of exhaust steam carried heat from the firebox through the elements of the tubular boiler, thereby enhancing the generation of the original steam.

In addition to the driving wheels, auxiliary wheels (or bogies) of a smaller diameter were normally provided to carry the weight and to help guide the locomotive smoothly around curves and across inequalities in the right-of-way. Baldwin helped smooth out track movement with his invention of the flexible beam truck, an arrangement by which each pair of driving wheels could partially shift sideways, independent of other wheels, as the train went around a curve. These supplementary wheels also reduced track wear as well as reducing wheel flange attrition, especially on the leading drive wheels.

Fuel Combustion. A big problem in the development and efficient use of the steam locomotive was proper combustion of fuels such as wood and various types and grades of coal. There were never-ending battles against high clinker and ash content (and correspondingly low calorific value) in coal. Out of this effort came new types and arrangements of fireboxes, firegrates, firebars, tubes, ash pans, etc. Much study went into improving the performance and longevity of the fireboxes; this included special flexible side and roof straps, and brick linings and arches that helped prevent boiler deterioration. It was found that a thin layer of fire spread over a larger and wider grate would burn more air and less coal, thereby enhancing combustion efficiency. To make fireboxes larger and wider, the locomotive engineers resorted to moving them out from between the last pair of drivers and placing them over a low axle supported by a pair of small trailing wheels.

At first, it was believed that the size of the steam cylinder was the principal factor in estimating engine power. About the beginning of the twentieth century, however, steam engineers determined that improved firebox design, resulting in more effective combustion, actually was the crucial factor in developing more powerful locomotives. In the United States, many boilers were adapted to burn finely granulated coal. Pulverization enabled refuse grades of coal to be utilized with substantial reduction in the generation of smoke, cinders, live sparks, and fire hazards.

Superheating. The practice of superheating was probably the greatest step toward improving efficiency and performance. Dr. Wilhelm Schmidt's superheater, developed in Germany in 1896, indicated to railroad engineers that enhanced thermal efficiency, theoretically possible with compound expansion, could be more reliably and effectively achieved by elevating the temperature of the steam. The reheating process consisted of conveying the saturated, or wet, steam back through the hot flues of the boiler to raise its temperature to as high as

600 or 700 degrees Fahrenheit. Higher temperatures were feasible, but there was a practical limit beyond which lubrication problems developed, leading to undue wear of pistons, valves, etc. Superheated steam allowed the generation and use of practical working boiler pressures as high as 250 pounds per square inch. It was claimed in many areas that superheaters gave 10 to 20 percent savings in fuel costs, and reduced water use 15 to 25 percent.

The early practice of superheating brought about many new problems, and the first German engines were not too successful. The true virtue of the Schmidt superheater was first demonstrated in England, with outstanding results, about ten years after Dr. Schmidt's invention was announced.

The extraordinary value of superheating was due to the fact that high-temperature steam acts as a gas under pressure and can perform a large amount of work before condensing to the liquid state. The superheater added greatly to boiler steaming efficiency and counteracted many difficulties associated with firing locomotives to maintain adequate pressure, especially in the later phases of the steam era, when really huge machines had been developed. Failure to use superheaters resulted in a loss of engine haulage power and increased coal and water consumption. However, in some conditions, superheaters were intentionally omitted, since it was inefficient where there were many short and steep gradients or when frequent stops were involved. Nonetheless, it gradually became apparent that the superheater offered the most practical means of enhancing steam locomotive power.

Braking. From the earliest days of the steam locomotive, the exasperating difficulty of slowing and stopping such a large moving mass was immediately apparent. No phase of railway practice has received closer attention and more minute study than that of braking a train, especially as it applied to continuous brakes, i.e., braking all vehicles simultaneously. It soon became clear that a heavy train moving at twenty-five to fifty miles per hour could only be arrested in some reasonable and safe distance by bringing a powerful force to bear for the shortest possible period of time.

The first Stephenson engines had hand brakes fitted to the tender only. These wooden blocks were the only brakes on the train at that time, the rest of the cars being unbraked. In the case of tank engines, a similar system of wooden brake blocks was operated by hand from the engine cab or the footplate. These wooden blocks disintegrated all too easily due to the frictional heat of braking. Some blocks, fitted with teak plugs, gave much better service. In general, during the pioneer period, iron brake blocks did not last even as long as certain wooden blocks.

Subsequently, many brake inventions were tried—brakes actuated by fluids, air, steam, vacuum, or worked by mechanical action through chains. Clarke's chain brake was used between 1874 and 1896, giving moderately satisfactory results. The chain brake used a system of chains and pulleys to operate an arrangement of wheel brakes by remote hand power. Starting about 1896, simple vacuum brakes served as reserve brakes until they were considerably refined later on. Many early trains utilized steam brakes on the engines and hand brakes on the cars.

In modern locomotive engineering, two general systems of braking have been employed: the automatic vacuum brake and the compressed-air brake, invented by George Westinghouse in 1868. The vacuum brake was widely used in Great Britain, South America, Japan, Norway, Denmark, South Africa, Rhodesia, India, Pakistan, Spain, and Portugal. The compressed-air system was standard in the United States, Canada, and on most European railways. In modern times, the latter arrangement was universally applied on electric and diesel railways.

Automatic vacuum braking involved maintaining a vacuum in a continuous pipe throughout the train and in individual auxiliary cylinders on each train vehicle. Vacuum was provided by two ejectors on the engine, one small unit exhausting continuously and a large one utilized to restore vacuum in the system after a major brake application. So long as vacuum was maintained in the system, the brakes were held in a released position. The train engineer applied the brakes by lowering the vacuum level; i.e., by admitting air to the train pipe, causing the brake cylinder piston to move the brakes to the "on" position. By restoring the vacuum, the brake cylinders were emptied of air, and the pistons shifted back to the "off brake" position.

The compressed-air brake employed a similar, though opposite, principle, pumping compressed air through a locomotive compressor and an auxiliary reservoir on each train unit. Brakes were held in their released position as long as adequate air pressure was maintained. If there was any disruption or reduction of this pressure, either intentional or due to an accidental break in the air connections, the escape of air immediately and automatically applied all brakes. Actually, a reduction of pressure allowed the compressed air in the auxiliary reservoirs to pass into the brake cylinders, pushing the pistons outward and thus applying the brakes. In this setup, brakes were withdrawn by reapplying full air pressure, after which so-called triple valves came into play, closing the connection between the auxiliary reservoir and the brake cylinder, then opening a port to allow compressed air to escape. A heavy spring then pulled back the piston and released the brakes. A practical advantage of compressed-air braking was that leaks that interfered with its efficiency were more readily detected than similar failures in the vacuum system could be.

Boiler feed water. A perpetual problem with steam locomotives worldwide has been the poor quality and the unreliable supply of boiler water. In order to prevent or minimize corrosion, pitting, and scale formation on boiler heating surfaces, many schemes and processes were originated to remove the harmful inorganic chemicals found in hard water. Ultimately, ion exchanges were used. For years, on railway engines in all countries, zinc plates were suspended in boiler barrels in the belief that this would combat boiler corrosion. That method was eventually proven ineffective, and most water was instead first treated to produce near-zero hardness and impart a degree of alkalinity sufficient to prevent or reduce boiler problems. Often water had to be filtered and clarified to eliminate gross levels of contaminants even before it could be chemically treated. In areas with superior-quality water, steel fireboxes were satisfactory; otherwise, with impure water and no water treatment, fireboxes were fabricated of copper.

Various other means were used to minimize boiler scale formation. One such method was "continuous blowdown"; blasting water out of the boiler while the engine was running, which seemed to remove alkaline sludge. The French railways had long-term success with feeding calculated amounts of appropriate chemicals regularly into the feed water to prevent deposit of hard scale on boiler heating surfaces. Solutions of sodium and potassium salts, intermixed with colloids, were used to precipitate the calcium and manganese deposits. Oxygen dissolved in the boiler water was absorbed by alkaline additives and various reducing agents. In all of the above methods, which involved treatment while the boiler was operating, the various precipi-

tates collected at the bottom of the boiler and were removed periodically by blowdown methods. Such processes greatly reduced time lost to maintenance stops in running sheds and substantially extended the intervals between major engine overhauls. Also, the number of treatment plants in France was reduced by one-half after the blowdown process was instituted.

Standardization. A tremendous problem during the reign of the mighty steam locomotive was inadequate standardization of engine parts. South African Railways, for example, in 1911 had thirteen hundred locomotives of seventy different types, whereas it was estimated that fifteen models would be adequate to cover all the railroad's varying requirements. Here, a new philosophy was initiated in 1914, when a new and more powerful goods engine was needed. Rather than following their traditional course of testing new technical refinements through a series of engines, each one an improvement on the previous design, the South African Railways decided to design their new engine all in one big step. The earlier practice of step-by-step development had led to the unnecessary types. The same principle was applied later to carriages, wagons, permanent way, bridges, culverts, signals, and other railroad equipment. South African Railways instituted a similar policy for all workshop repair facilities and practices. They also took a great step forward when they achieved a basic standardization of locomotive boilers, finally settling on three or four types that could be fitted to all steam engines.

One of the great innovators of standardization was John Ramsbottom, Locomotive Superintendent of the London and North Western Railway (1861–71). He perfected reliable standards of locomotive design and construction that sustained the railways of Great Britain over a period of forty years; he also instituted a determined works organization having an outstanding productive capacity, a superior administration, and a high level of labor cooperation.

Eventually, all the principal railways of the world attained a high degree of standardization and interchangeability of parts.

Rotating and reciprocating oscillations. In the early years of the steam locomotive, considerable engineering concern was directed toward the damaging effects of the rotating and reciprocating forces generated when the locomotive was in operation. It was necessary to mechanically limit serious and dangerous oscillations by counterbalancing the stresses produced in heavy rotating and reciprocating machinery. Rotational oscillation due to the weight of crank pins, the wheels, and the driving and side rods, was totally eliminated by properly adjusting the weight balance of the coupled drive wheels and the other parts involved. As to reciprocating forces, engineers determined that only partial balancing was needed, since at high speeds excessive balance caused the drive wheels to lift several inches off the rails, then drop back, exerting a terrific force of up to several tons. This was described as "vertical hammer blow." On the other hand, insufficient reciprocating balance caused a negative, harmful degree of lateral vibration, or oscillation. Accordingly, reciprocating balances had to be determined with extreme precision. On some railroads, the proportion of balanced reciprocating parts had to be reduced to about 20 percent, in which case the vertical hammer blow, at fifty miles per hour, produced a force of 0.9 tons on any drive wheel. A figure of one ton per wheel at forty-five miles per hour was finally considered a normal, safe standard for coupled driving wheels.

Higher speeds. The advent of the steam locomotive brought almost immediate demands for higher operating speeds. As early as 1850, maximum speeds of sixty miles per hour were attained on some railways, but with adverse degrees of swaying, rolling, and other undesirable consequences. This phenomenon was, of course, less noticeable on wider-gauge tracks, which afforded greater lateral stability. The need for increased speeds and accompanying locomotive power led to using larger boilers and drive wheels, with consequent design problems. The larger drive wheels and boilers raised the center of gravity, aggravating the rolling and swaying at high speed. One solution was the French Crampton locomotive, which placed a single pair of driving wheels at the rear of the engine, allowing the forward installation of a low-slung boiler over a set of carrying wheels.

One long-held fallacy, especially in England, was the belief that a single pair of drive wheels (2–2–2 wheel arrangement) gave greater freedom of mechanical action at high speeds and that multiple-coupled drive wheels somehow hindered smooth operation at higher revolutions. Actually, it was demonstrated that, with properly designed and constructed components plus adequate lubrication, locomotives with 4–6–8–10 coupled wheels could run just as fast and effortlessly, with the added ad-

vantage of greater adhesion and better acceleration from a standstill.

Of course, faster freight and passenger service was a continuing demand on all the world railways. This led to a larger diameter drive wheel, which cut the wear and tear on locomotive machinery at higher speeds. As engine designers and builders increased the diameter of the coupled drive wheels, however, they had to deal with subsequent problems of wheel spacing and other contingencies. Once these questions were resolved and larger drivers were installed, they noticed a consequent reduction in tractive power. Therefore, the horsepower had to be increased by fitting larger cylinders or increasing boiler pressures, or both. In general, the final results allowed more mileage between major repairs, lower repair costs per mile traveled, and higher speed once suitable rights-of-way were also made available.

Axle loading. Often locomotive design and development activities were completely out of phase with the railway track systems. Axle loading restrictions due to lightweight rail, bridges with insufficient weight-carrying capacity, and other operating limitations of the permanent way, posed horrendous difficulties for the design engineer. Frequently, improved types of locomotives were available to fill required work assignments but could not be operated on a given set of tracks due to constraints imposed by the right-of-way. Most railway systems had standards of maximum weight allowable on a single locomotive axle. Twenty to twenty-one tons in Great Britain and thirty to thirty-two tons in the United States. Of course, in many countries even lower limits were mandatory due to lighter rail.

Axle loading was not the only factor that had an adverse effect on the track, culverts, bridges, etc. The "dynamic augment" effect of the balance weights used to make the locomotive run smoothly, could increase the loading on the rails 50 percent over the dead weight of the wheels. After long-term studies, engineers devised ways to eliminate most dynamic augment, and heavier basic axle loadings then became acceptable.

In cases where locomotives of exceptional tractive force were required, and particularly where the track, bridges, and curves did not allow further development of existing designs due to axle loading limitations, the number of coupled wheels required demanded articulated types of locomotives. Thus, most Garratt-type articulated engines in South Africa had high tractive forces but with maximum axle loads of only thirteen or fourteen tons. Narrow-gauge railways—two feet, for example—consequently got a new lease on life, as articulated engines enabled train load limits and carrying capacities to be virtually doubled without strengthening the tracks and bridges.

Overdesign. A host of problems have been produced in the world of steam locomotives by zealous designers who often went overboard and departed from the premise that simplicity was the basic design objective for any mechanical contrivance. There were unfortunate instances, too, of a tendency to experiment with and arbitrarily alter successful existing steam engine designs.

Derailments—Smooth-Riding Locomotives. The fear that steam locomotives, with their unavoidably high center of gravity, would be too top-heavy and would tip over was long a restricting influence in the minds of locomotive designers. South Africa adopted an arbitrary rule requiring that the boiler centerline be no higher than twice the width of the track gauge. This precept had a long-term effect on locomotive design; for example, it limited clearance between boiler barrels and larger diameter (five-foot) drive wheels. In some cases in South Africa, design engineers resorted to cutting the boiler shell and fitting specially shaped pockets to obtain necessary wheel clearances. In 1903, South African locomotives had a maximum boiler center height of seven feet six inches, yet engines in the United States and Europe safely rode the rails with centers of ten feet and over. Between 1903 and 1935, the height of South African locomotives increased in small increments, to a maximum of nine feet three inches. Eventually, it became apparent that high-pitched boilers actually had steadier riding qualities and caused less railside wear than those with a lower center of gravity.

The problem of running railway locomotives steady and true on all kinds of rail, curved and straightaway, without danger of derailment received considerable attention and study. It was discovered early on that guidance and stability could be enhanced by placing a two-wheeled or four-wheeled bogie or truck at the forepart of the engine, mounted with a center bolt or pivot to its frame. Radial axles also increased stability. These axles, were set either at the front or back of the engine. By allowing their axle boxes to slide laterally between circular guides as the locomotive rounded the curves, they maintained a radial position at right angles to the rails.

One trouble with early steam locomotives, running over the rough and uneven tracks of that time, was the difficulty of keeping the proper weight balanced over the drive wheels. Too much weight might fall on the leading pivot truck, where no power was being applied, and not enough on the spinning wheels. The equalizing lever, which kept the weight distributed, was invented in 1837 by Joseph Harrison.

Locomotives with a larger number of drive wheels naturally had a more difficult time negotiating severe curves. The use of the flangeless driving wheels, usually the leading pair, helped somewhat. As locomotive speeds increased, the possibility of derailments also increased, and reducing this hazard required a tremendous amount of work. Some railroads had an epidemic of tender derailments, since these relatively short vehicles, with bogies spaced close together, were rather unstable. Such tendencies were corrected by a combination of rigid wheels and pivoted bogies, greater attention to spring compensation, placement of bogie side-friction pads, and better alignment of the bogies in the first place.

Aids to forward visibility. A long-standing, but perhaps minor, problem with steam locomotives was limited visibility due to exhaust steam and combustion products from the firebox beating down from the chimney on the engineer's cab. This was eventually solved by various means, one of which was the use of internal steam jets with a blast pipe to force exhaust materials higher into the sky. Another contrivance consisted of special smokestacks with several circular chimney rings and internal louvers that induced upward surges of air, carrying the exhaust wastes clear of the driver's lookout.

Spark arrestors. Grass and forest fires ignited by live embers emitted from steam locomotive smokestacks were a common problem in all areas of the world. Eventually, smokebox wire netting and many other types of spark arrestors were fitted to these engines, which greatly diminished the hazards.

Mountain and other traction problems. A major difficulty on most world railways was negotiating the severe grades and curves encountered in mountainous terrain. Speed was decreased on all grades due to the extra work required, which also mandated power cutbacks to reduce mechanical strain or breakdown, resulting in immediate and negative effects on railway operating efficiency. Getting over the mountains with a meaningful tonnage at reasonable speeds taxed the ingenuity and patience of locomotive designers all during the steam era. More powerful, more effective engines were gradually developed, mainly by upgrading the tractive forces and providing multiple drive wheels with increased track adhesion. On steeply graded rail lines where adhesion locomotives could not operate, rack-and-pinion systems were installed using various special engines adapted to the Abt, Riggenbach, or other tracks.

Naturally, adhesion problems were not all confined to climbing mountains. Wet rails due to rain or dew lowered the wheel-to-track friction and caused traction problems. Greased-rail conditions often stalled trains on even moderate grades when engines were loaded at or near their mechanical limits. From the very beginning of the steam locomotive era, sanding was used to assist train starts and acceleration, especially when the locomotive was under heavy load. The use of tank locomotives, where the added weight of the water and fuel in the engine improved adhesion, prolonged the life of this type of machine some forty to sixty years in many countries.

Articulated locomotives. Of the three well-known types of articulated locomotives—Garratt, Mallet, and Fairlie—that were extensively tested in South Africa, the Garratt engines performed best. South African Railway practice was to incorporate standard frames, wheels, cylinders, and accessories in the designs as far as practical. The boiler in a Garratt engine was carried in a cradle suspended on pivot centers attached to the frames, each of which was free to align itself to the track curvature. Flexible connections were required for steam and exhaust pipes.

Use of such articulated locomotives could double the capacity of a line without requiring strengthening of the track, bridges, and culverts, and without improving curves. These engines were free-running and capable of safe speeds at least comparable to nonarticulated types having similar coupled wheel diameters. Experience showed that they were equally trackworthy and immune from breakdown as nonarticulated machines. Their operating economy, since they required only one engine crew for what was practically a double engine, was quite obvious. Also, the Garratt ran equally well in both directions. The firebox design allowed a better shape and depth than that of ordinary locomotives, and thus maximum boiler power

was obtained with the simplest construction. The unusually great length of the Garratt locomotive was a definite advantage where weight spread-over was necessary due to restricted load limits on bridges. The Garratts also worked out best on the many narrow-gauge rail lines in South Africa.

Extensive comparisons between the Garratt and Mallet locomotives showed the superiority of the Garratt types for the South African railways. For one thing, the Garratts, with their four high-pressure cylinders, avoided the problems associated with compounding; the Mallets used two high-pressure and two low-pressure cylinders. The Mallets seemed to "choke up" above certain speeds, which difficulty was traced to compounding and to the exceptionally long steam pipes and tortuous steam passages between boiler and engine. The Mallets also had considerable condensation problems in the low-pressure cylinders and the South African Railways staff referred to them as "water bellies." Tests showed that the Garratt engines handled greater loads, made better time, and consumed less water and coal.

Compounding. Toward the end of the nineteenth century, engineers were increasingly faced with the need to enhance the thermal efficiency of the steam locomotive. By this time, the application of two-stage and three-stage steam expansion in various marine engines had been successfully demonstrated. The idea was consequently adapted to the railway steam engine, with marginal advantages at first. A big problem was how to skillfully blend theory and practice in working out the ideal proportion of high- and low-pressure steam volumes in the respective cylinders.

Compounding involved double use, or expansion, of the same boiler steam to operate multiple engine cylinders. In a compound locomotive, steam was first directed into one or two high-pressure cylinders and then, in an expanded condition, into larger low-pressure cylinders, where it powered additional work before finally being exhausted to the outside. One objective of compounding was to more completely utilize the available heat energy from what was notably and historically a most inefficient operation. By keeping the cylinders at a more uniform higher temperature throughout the cycle, heat losses were minimized and thermal efficiency was consequently enhanced.

In France, compounding was widely and successfully applied by de Glehn, whose work was continued with excellent results by du Bousquet. The de Glehn principle of compound propulsion was first used at the turn of the century, and for many years afterward, on the Northern Railway of France, where Atlantic- and Pacific-type locomotives established high performance standards on the fast trains between Paris and Calais. The de Glehn compound system achieved the most success with two high-pressure cylinders outside and two low-pressure cylinders inside, with the drive divided between two coupled axles. On some 4–4–0 engines, this arrangement led to unexplained differential slippage between the forward and after pair of coupled wheels, which buckled the coupling rods. The temporary solution was to have the low- and high-pressure cylinders drive separate and uncoupled axles. The permanent solution was to use four-cylinder 4–6–0 coupled locomotives, which gave a long and distinguished record of service on French railroads.

In the United States, Mallet compound locomotives were highly favored over the Garratt noncompound types. Mallet engines normally had two high-pressure cylinders mounted on the main frames at the trailing end, and two low-pressure cylinders, much larger in diameter, on the front rotating chassis. In South Africa, compounding never achieved substantial successes or gained any engineering adherents, possibly due to the limitations imposed on locomotive widths by the prevalent 3-foot 6-inch gauge tracks. Ultimately, the superheater permitted high performance locomotion without the complications of using cylinders in a compounding arrangement.

Mechanical Boiler Stoker. As steam locomotives became larger and more powerful, a crew of one or two firemen proved inadequate to service the firebox and maintain steam pressure. Railway management turned to mechanical stokers to supply fuel to the boiler, thus removing most of the back-breaking manual work. Of course, the many types of mechanisms that appeared were hampered by the limited space between the tender and the locomotive and by the complexity required to achieve the desired automation. One such contraption, the Street mechanical stoker, was used on a class MG, Mallet-type 2–6–6–2 locomotive in South Africa in 1911:

The mechanical operations of the "Street" stoker started with a coal crusher fitted to the front left-hand footplate of the tender and powered by a small steam engine mounted behind the brake pillar. A fireman fed the crusher by hand, which reduced the coal to a suitable size for the stoker. The crushed coal fell by gravity into the chute which discharged into a receiver installed below the hind buffer beam of the locomotive. From there a bucket conveyor belt, moving in a large pipe, delivered the coal into a central receiver above the firehole door. From this receiver the coal was directed by means of a cone-shaped tray to fall either to the center, right- or left-hand sides, where circular orifices were provided, connected to which were three feeders fitted with steam pipes. As coal fell in front of each orifice it was blown into the firebox by jets of steam supplied by cocks actuated by adjustable cams. The bucket conveyor was driven by a second auxiliary engine located on top of the firebox. (T. J. Espitalier and W. A. Day, in *South African Railways & Harbours Magazine* [April 1945]: 276.)

This type of mechanical stoker was very complicated, to say the least. The fireman had to attend to two auxiliary engines in addition to handling the same amount of coal, since every pound of fuel had to be transferred by hand into the crusher. The noise created by this mechanism was deafening: first the rapidly grinding crusher, next the noisy circulation of the conveyor belt, and finally the sharp reports of the steam jets controlling the feeding. Early experiences with mechanical stoking in South Africa were not successful, but the trials did show the advantage of such a device for large locomotives.

Later on, advanced mechanical stokers on large Garratt locomotives were capable of delivering fifteen thousand pounds of coal at each loading, ensuring a high firing rate when required. The stoker, in this case, was driven by a totally enclosed double-acting two-cylinder variable speed reversing steam engine located on the hind pivot casting of the tender and operated from the locomotive cab. The coal bunker had sloping sides so coal could easily gravitate to the stoker conveyor screw trough that extended the full length of the bunker.

Improvements in design of mechanical stokers progressed so far that, in the latter period of steam locomotion, it would have been indefensible not to fit them where high locomotive performance was necessary.

Streamlining. In the terminal stages of the steam locomotive era, considerable attention was devoted to streamlining these machines. The fad was partly aesthetic, partly in the honest belief that streamlining could increase speed. In general, on most railroads the effort and added expense of streamlining was rarely justified except with speeds approaching one hundred miles per hour. At lower speeds, say sixty miles per hour, savings were estimated to be only about 2 percent, at best. Difficulties with increased costs and added engine weight, plus reduced accessibility to working parts, rendered streamlining an unnecessary and complicated luxury. Some railroads also ran into problems with the thin covering sheets, which often became distorted or tore loose.

The demise of the steam locomotive is a topic that deserves considerable explanation and discussion. In railway operations, a primary aim was efficiency: the maximum proportion of the motive power performing useful work, i.e., revenue-producing service. Conversely, relatively little effort should have to be devoted to keeping the machinery in good running shape.

It was not surprising that the successes of the internal combustion engine on the highways should have spread eventually to the railways. Moreover, it is generally held that the most efficient energy source for railway operations, and ultimately the most economical, is electricity, given a reasonably priced and reliable supply.

Electric and diesel locomotives do not require several hours of "lighting up," as does the steam locomotive. Likewise, crew members on a diesel or electric engine do not have to spend a major part of their time cleaning the fire and attending to a host of related chores. The newer sources of tractive power do not require taking on water periodically. Fuel sufficient for a really extended run of two or three thousand miles can be carried with diesel engines. Like electric traction, the diesel engine has a far higher starting tractive effort than does steam locomotion; thus, it can handle heavier loads and does not need assistance going up long mountain grades. Coupling diesel power units together can be accomplished easily, and the combination can be handled as a single locomotive by only one crew.

Replacing steam with diesel power makes possible a considerable reduction in the number of independent locomotive units needed to work any given train service. Since all axles of a diesel locomotive can be powered, axle loading can be kept to a minimum; thus, expenditures for a new track and bridge construction to carry heavier and heavier steam locomotives, could be avoided altogether by replacing steam with diesel power.

Environmental concerns, which were mounting in the last years of steam, also subsided to a considerable extent once diesel traction was substituted.

In many countries, steam locomotive development reached the maximum limits imposed by conditions of the permanent way, i.e., the heights and widths of tunnels, bridges, and other confined spaces. In general, the diesel engine permitted a more economical use of oil compared with a steam locomotive that burned it in its firebox—the most wasteful way possible. The diesel locomotive could also be used on continuous runs of one to two thousand miles without any changes, a practical impossibility with steam locomotives. Employment conditions also had an influence on the increasing popularity of diesel. The crew of a diesel engine had relatively clean and comfortable work conditions with regular hours compared to the hard and dirty work involved in firing, operating, and cleaning a steam locomotive.

A fundamental reason for the displacement of the steam locomotive was its inherently low overall thermal efficiency. The use of the exhaust steam provide the required draft for the fire wasted a huge amount of energy as heat drawn through the tubes by suction of the locomotive blast was dispensed, unused, through the smokestack. It has been estimated the fuel efficiency in a steam locomotive was in the order of about 8 to 10 percent. Of course, many efforts were made to better utilize the heat energy produced by the combustion of coal on the firegrate. Changes in the boiler and attendant machinery have been referred to earlier. One aim was to economize on fuel and water by making better use of the expansive properties of steam. Some attempt was made to replace the reciprocating motion of the traditional cylinders with steam turbines; however, the high cost of such a radically different system, which only raised the thermal efficiency to around 13 or 14 percent, was not too appealing at a time when steam power was on the decline due to advances in electric and diesel traction.

For these reasons, and many others, innovative attempts to delay the demise of the steam locomotive met with little success, and inevitably this great servant of mankind was relegated to near oblivion.

ALASKA

THE FIRST WORKABLE RAIL SYSTEM IN ALASKA, the narrow-gauge hundred-mile line from Skagway, Alaska, to Whitehorse, Canada, known as the White Pass & Yukon Railroad, was constructed between April 1890 and July 1900 and has operated ever since. In 1903 an American syndicate from Seattle financed the standard-gauge Alaska Railroad, which was planned to run about 114 miles from Seward to the coal fields in the vicinity of the present city of Anchorage. Only 70.8 miles of this road were ever laid down. The system suffered serious financial losses, and the holdings were sold in 1910 to a different set of financiers, at which time the line was renamed the Alaska Northern Railroad. Between 1909 and 1916, another group of American capitalists constructed the Tanana Valley Mine Railroad, a forty-five-mile line running northwest from Fairbanks to the Chatanika mining district. Original expenditures totaled $867,000 for this narrow-gauge system.

In August 1912, the federal government changed the status of Alaska to that of a United States Territory and authorized an Alaskan legislature. An act of Congress on 14 March 1914 granted approval for building a government railroad connecting an ice-free port on the Gulf of Alaska with the Yukon interior, at a cost not to exceed $35 million. During May 1914, the Alaska Engineering Commission, provided for in the Alaska Railroad Act, was appointed by President Woodrow Wilson. The commission's first responsibility was to investigate and recommend a railroad route running north from Seward to the navigable winter-bound rivers of in-terior Alaska. The topographic survey was completed in October 1914 and, on 10 April 1915, President Wilson approved a route for the first government-sponsored railway in Alaska. By executive order, he also extended the duties of the Alaska Engineering Commission to include supervision of the construction of the proposed rail system.

The Alaska rail project called for immediate acquisition of the Alaska Northern Railroad and the Tanana Valley Mine Railroad. Base headquarters and a supply depot for the Alaska Railroad were established at Anchorage. Vast quantities of materials and equipment were shipped in from the United States and also from Central America, where the Panama Canal had been completed in August 1914. Initial construction on the Alaska Railroad (ARR) commenced at Anchorage on 29 April 1915. The actual construction was performed by subcontractors, with manpower recruited from a horde of prospective workers who had arrived from the states.

Construction proceeded apace despite the many problems posed by the severe northern weather and the rough topography. Work was finished in July 1923. Peak employment, early in 1917, was 4466 men. With the United States' entry into World War I, total employees declined to 2500 by 1919. The 471-mile Alaska Railroad from Seward to Anchorage to Fairbanks was dedicated by President Warren Harding, in person, on 15 July 1923. The final cost of the project was $60 million, or about $25,000 per mile, including acquisition costs for the Alaska Northern and Tanana Valley railroads plus related equipment, rolling stock, and real estate.

The Alaska Railroad operated in the red for its first fifteen years. During World War II, the rail line was of tremendous logistical importance in delivering military and other supplies to Russia; consequently, its financial picture improved substantially. After World War II, however, owing to the deterioration of track and rolling stock, the railroad soon reached state of virtual collapse, until the United States Congress provided a $34 million rehabilitation appropriation. The Alaska earthquake of 1964 wrecked parts of the rail system, and $25 million was required to repair the damage. Despite many operating problems due to its far northern latitude, the Alaska Railroad remains a very viable and profitable communications entity in the general growth of Alaska and a vital link in the defense of the United States.

Details of the Alaska Railroad are discussed in my 1979 book, *Seven Railroads*, listed in the Bibliography.

Steam Locomotives in Alaska

The Alaska Railroad locomotive story starts with

rail equipment originally used on the two early railroads: the Alaska Northern Railroad and the Tanana Valley Mine Railroad. Three pictures are available of the locomotives used on the narrow-gauge Tanana Valley Mine Railroad.

When these two early rail systems were acquired by the Alaska Engineering Commission in April 1915 as part of the Alaska Railroad project, various items of rolling stock were used during construction of the U.S. government's Alaska Railroad. Included in these transfers were several steam locomotives previously used on the standard-gauge Alaska Northern Railroad. Two of these engines were assigned ARR classifications and are described as ARR class F1, type 4–4–0 tender locomotives. These engines were built early in the twentieth century, but the manufacturers are not known. The engines were reactivated at Seward in 1915, and appear to be American-type locomotives built by Baldwin with the following specifications:

Cylinders	24-inch stroke
Drive wheels	63-inch diameter
Boiler working pressure	135 pounds per square inch
Tractive force	14,150 pounds
Operating weight	133,000 pounds (engine plus tender)
Tender capacities	3500 gallons water; 6 tons coal.

The ARR class D1, type 4–6–0 ten-wheeler en-

Steam locomotive no. 450, formerly of the Tanana Valley Railroad of Alaska is shown here working on the construction of the Alaska Railroad. This picture was taken on 13 October 1917 at a gravel pit about 1½ miles from Fairbanks. The records of the Alaska Railroad do not document the origin nor the specifications of this engine.
(Courtesy: Alaska Railroad)

Pictured is a wood-burning dinkey steam engine, type 0–4–0, used on the Tanana Valley Mine Railroad in Alaska. This is a 1916 picture after the above rail line was acquired by the Alaska Railroad Commission for use in the construction process.
(Courtesy: Anchorage Historical & Fine Arts Museum)

Pictured is an old type 0–4–0 dinkey steam locomotive used on the Tanana Valley Mine Railroad of Alaska. This picture was taken about 1903 near Fairbanks. No specification data was available.
(Courtesy: Anchorage Historical & Fine Arts Museum)

gine with tender, was put in active service at Seward in 1916. The engine was originally constructed by the Rhode Island Locomotive Works and had these specifications:

Cylinders	19 by 24 inches
Drive wheels	55-inch diameter
Boiler heating surface	1579 square feet
Boiler working pressure	175 pounds per square inch
Tractive force	8950 pounds
Operating weight	200,800 pounds (engine plus tender)
Tender capacities	3500 gallons water; 6 tons coal.

With the completion of the Panama Canal in August 1914, various steam locomotives were transferred to the government's rail construction job in Alaska. Some of these engines were ARR class M1, Mogul 2–6–0 tender locomotives. Sixteen of these Panama Railroad engines were placed in service at Anchorage in 1916 and 1917. The engines were originally constructed by the American Locomotive Company, Cooke Works, in 1906. See various illustrations, all of which list the engine specifications.

ARR class M2, Mogul 2–6–0 tender locomotives were also shipped up from Panama. These were originally built by the American Locomotive Company for five-foot gauge tracks in 1906. Six such engines were placed in service at Anchorage in 1919 and used on standard-gauge tracks after the necessary adjustments. Specifications for engine no. 610 were:

Pictured is a class M1 Mogul type 2–6–0 tender locomotive, no. 265, one of sixteen machines transferred from the Panama Railroad to the Alaska Railroad in 1916–17. These engines were originally manufactured by the American Locomotive Company for use in building the Panama Canal. They were operated on 5 foot gauge tracks in Panama and had to be changed to conform to the standard 4 foot 8½ inch gauge tracks on the Alaska Railroad. Specifications were as follows:

Cylinders	19 by 24 inches
Drive wheels	54-inch diameter
Boiler	
Heating surface	1560 square feet
Working pressure	100 pounds per square inch
Length	24 feet 10⁵⁄₁₆ inch
Diameter	5 feet 2 inches
Number of tubes	236
Length of tubes	11 feet 8 inches
Diameter of tubes	2 inches
Tractive force	23,980 pounds at 10 miles per hour
Hauling capacity	3317 tons on level track
Valve gear	Stephenson link plus Richardson balanced slide valve
Operating weight	233,400 pounds (engine plus tender)
Tender capacity	4000 gallons water; 11 tons coal.

(Courtesy: Anchorage Historical & Fine Arts Museum)

Shown is another class M1 Mogul type 2–6–0 steam locomotive, no. 239, which had been transferred from Panama to Alaska in 1917. For specifications see the previous illustration.
(Courtesy: Anchorage Historical & Fine Arts Museum)

Pictured is another Mogul type 2–6–0 steam locomotive, no. 225, used in building the Alaska Railroad after its transfer from Panama in 1916. See an earlier illustration for specifications.
(Courtesy: Anchorage Historical & Fine Arts Museum)

Pictured is still another Mogul type 2–6–0 steam engine, No. 152, transferred from Panama to the Alaska Railroad job on 1916.
(Courtesy: Anchorage Historical & Fine Arts Museum)

Cylinders	20 by 26 inches
Coupled drive wheels	63-inch diameter
Boiler heating surface	2200 square feet
Boiler working pressure	100 pounds per square inch
Tractive force	24,690 pounds at 10 miles per hour
Operating weight	256,000 pounds (engine plus tender)
Tender capacities	4700 gallons water; 12 tons coal.

The tender locomotive, type 2–8–0, no. 151, from the narrow-gauge Tanana Valley Mine Railroad, has not been identified. It is pictured.

In constructing the Alaska Railroad, various saddle-type tank locomotives were used. Engine no. 1, is shown on a monument site in front of the ARR administration building at Anchorage. Two type 0–

Shown is engine no. 151 which was transferred in 1915 to the U.S. Government Alaska Railroad project from the narrow gauge Tanana Valley Mine Railroad. The origin and specifications on this locomotive were not available.
(Courtesy: Anchorage Historical & Fine Arts Museum)

The above engine monument, located at Anchorage, Alaska, in front of the Alaska Railroad Administration building, displays one of the original steam locomotives used in the construction of the Alaska Railroad during the period April 1915 to July 1923. This monument was dedicated on 17 November 1952. The 0–4–2 saddle tank engine, built at the Rogers Works of the American Locomotive Company, was placed in service at Anchorage in 1916. Specifications of the class A1 tank engine were as follows:

Cylinders	14 by 22 inches
Drive wheels	3-foot 8-inch diameter
Tractive power	15, 350 pounds
Boiler	
Working pressure	165 pounds
Heating surface	650 square feet
Length	12 feet 2⁶/₁₆ inches
Diameter	43 inches
Number of tubes	106
Length of tubes	11 feet 8 inches
Diameter of tubes	2 inches
Engine weight	82,000 pounds
Hauling capacity	2320 tons on level track
Water capacity	1700 gallons.

See attached schematic drawing.
(Courtesy: Alaska Railroad)

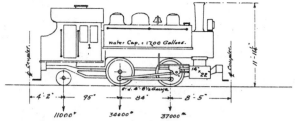

A.R.R. - CLASS A1 - SADDLE TANK LOCOMOTIVE.

- SPECIFICATIONS -

Purchased from	- American Locomotive Company.
New Equipment.	
Placed in Service	- Anchorage 1916.
Estimated Life	- 20 Years.
Type	- Saddle Tank. 0-4-2.
Builder	- American Locomotive Company - Rogers Works.
Cylinders	- 14" x 22"
Dia. of Drivers	- 44"
Wt. on Drivers	- 71000 #
Total Wt. Engine	- 82000 #
Tractive Power	- 13350 #
Hauling Capacity	- 2320 Tons on level Track.
Valve Gear	- Link Valve Gear with Sliding Valve.
Driving Wheel Base	- 7'-0"
Total Eng. Wheel Base	- 14'-11"
Driving Journals	- 7" x 8"
Maximum Height	- 11'-11¼"
Maximum Width	- 8'-8"
No Tender - Saddle Tank. - Capacity : 1700 Gallons.	
Couplers	- M.C.B. "Tower" Pocket.

Train Length	- 27'-6"
Pilot	- None.
Fuel	- Bituminous.
Engine is equipped with Automatic Air Brakes,	
Steel Cab, Steel Tired Truck Wheels, W.I. Frames,	
Hand Sander for forward and Reverse and other	
usual Accessories,	
Oil Headlight.	
BOILER -	
Working Pressure	- 165 Lbs.
Heating Surface	- 660 Sq.Ft. Approx.
Length	- 12'-2 5/16"
Diameter	- 43"
Number of Tubes	- 106
Length of Tubes	- 11'-8"
Dia. of Tubes	- 2"

This is a drawing of the class A1 saddle tank locomotive used in the early days of constructing the Alaska Railroad. See original engine pictured in an earlier illustration.
(Courtesy: Alaska Railroad)

Pictured is another saddle-type 0–4–0 tank engine, no. 19, originally used in the construction of the Alaska Railroad over the period 1915–23.
(Courtesy: Anchorage Historical & Fine Arts Museum)

Shown is a saddle-type 0–4–0 tank locomotive used in
constructing the Alaska Railroad during the period
1915–23. No technical or other data was available.
(Courtesy: Anchorage Historical & Fine Arts Museum)

Pictured is a locomotive no. 701, a Baldwin Mikado
type engine, pulling a passenger train on a trestle near
Moose Pass, Alaska, on 11 July 1948. Specifications
and an engineering drawing are shown.
(Courtesy: Alaska Railroad)

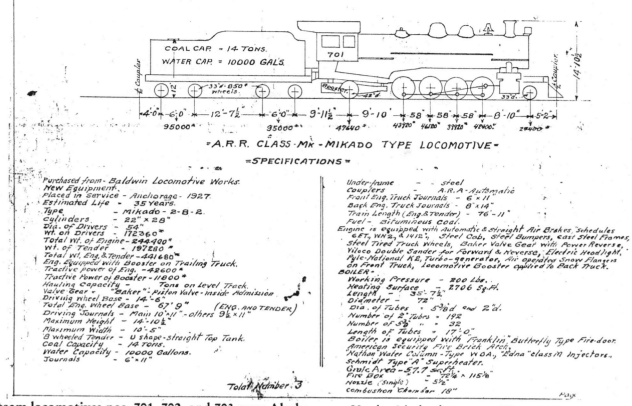

COAL CAP. = 14 TONS.
WATER CAP. = 10000 GAL'S.

701

=A.R.R. CLASS · Mᴋ · MIKADO TYPE LOCOMOTIVE=

=SPECIFICATIONS=

Purchased from - Baldwin Locomotive Works.
New Equipment.
Placed in Service - Anchorage - 1927.
Estimated Life - 35 Years.
Type - Mikado - 2-8-2.
Cylinders - 22" × 28"
Dia. of Drivers - 54"
Wt. on Drivers - 172360 #
Total Wt. of Engine - 244400 #
Wt. of Tender - 197280 #
Total Wt. Eng. & Tender - 441680 #
Eng. Equipped with Booster on Trailing Truck.
Tractive Power of Eng. - 42600 #
Tractive Power of Booster - 11800 #
Hauling Capacity - ____ Tons on Level Track.
Valve Gear - "Baker" - Piston Valve - Inside Admission
Driving Wheel Base - 14'-6"
Total Eng. Wheel Base - 67'9" (ENG. AND TENDER)
Driving Journals - Main 10"×11" - others 9½×11"
Maximum Height - 14'-10½"
Maximum Width - 10'-5"
8 wheeled Tender - U shape - straight Top Tank.
Coal Capacity - 14 Tons.
Water Capacity - 10000 Gallons.
Journals - 6"×11"

Under-frame - - steel
Couplers - A.R.A - Automatic
Front Eng. Truck Journals - 6"×11"
Back Eng. Truck Journals - 8"×14"
Train Length (Eng. & Tender) - 76'-11"
Fuel - Bituminous coal.
Engine is equipped with Automatic & Straight Air Brakes, schedules 6ET, WN2, & 1412's, Steel Cab, Steel Bumpers, cast Steel Frames, Steel Tired Truck Wheels, Baker Valve Gear with Power Reverse, Viloco Double Sander for Forward & Reverse, Electric Headlight, Pyle-National K2, Turbo-generator, Air operated Snow Flangers on Front Truck, Locomotive Booster applied to Back Truck.
BOILER -
Working Pressure - 200 Lbs.
Heating Surface - 2706 Sq. Ft.
Length - 35'-7½"
Diameter - 72"
Dia. of Tubes - 5⅜"d. and 2"d.
Number of 2" Tubes - 192
Number of 5⅜ " - 32
Length of Tubes - 17'-0"
Boiler is equipped with "Franklin" Butterfly Type Fire-door.
American Security Fire Brick Arch,
Nathan Water Column - Type WOA, "Edna" class M Injectors,
Schmidt Type "A" Superheater.
Grate Area - 57.7 Sq. Ft.
Fire Box - 72¼" × 115⅛"
Nozzle (Single) - 5½"
Combustion Chamber - 18"

Total Number 3

Steam locomotives nos. 701, 702, and 703 were Alaska Railroad class Mk, Mikado 2–8–2 type. These three engines were purchased from the Baldwin Locomotive Works and placed in service at Anchorage in 1927. Specifications on these locomotives were as follows:

Cylinders	22 by 28 inches
Drive wheels	54-inch diameter
Boiler	
Working pressure	200 pounds
Grate area	57.7 square feet
Heating surface	2706 square feet
Length	35 feet 7.5 inches
Diameter	6 feet
Fire box	75.25 by 115 ⅛ inches
Number 2-inch tubes	192
Number 5 ⅜-inch tubes	32
Length of tubes	17 feet
Fire door	Franklin "Butterfly" type
Fire brick	American Security
Superheater	Schmidt type "A"
Engine weight	244,800 pounds
Tender weight	197,280 pounds
Tractive power (engine)	42,600 pounds
Valve gear	Baker
Tender capacity	10,000 gallons water; 14 tons coal
Length (engine plus tender)	76 feet 11 inches.

See attached schematic drawing.
(Courtesy: Alaska Railroad)

Shown is a locomotive no. 703, a type 2–8–2 Baldwin, hauling a freight train on the Alaska Railroad near Clear, Alaska, on 30 July 1948. See earlier specifications plus an engineering drawing.
(Courtesy: Alaska Railroad)

Shown is one of a series 700, class Mk Mikado type 2–8–2 tender locomotive used on the Alaska Railroad starting in 1927. Specifications are set forth in an earlier illustration.
(Courtesy: Anchorage Historical & Fine Arts Museum)

Locomotive no. 401, Lima type 2–8–0, shown is rounding a curve on a loop trestle on the Alaska Railroad on 20 May 1949. Specifications and a drawing were given earlier.
(Courtesy: Alaska Railroad)

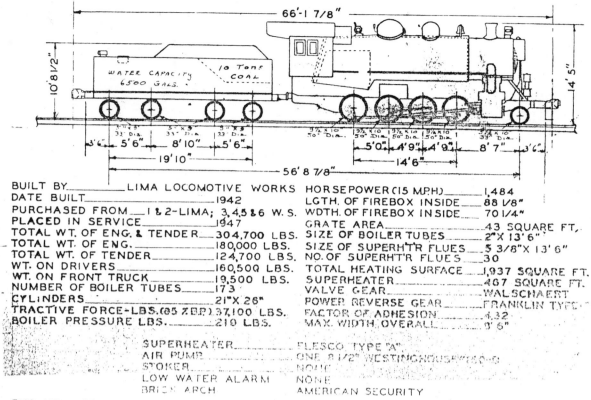

BUILT BY_____LIMA LOCOMOTIVE WORKS
DATE BUILT_____1942
PURCHASED FROM___I & 2-LIMA; 3,4,5 & 6 W.S.
PLACED IN SERVICE_____1947
TOTAL WT. OF ENG. & TENDER___304,700 LBS.
TOTAL WT. OF ENG._____180,000 LBS.
TOTAL WT. OF TENDER_____124,700 LBS.
WT. ON DRIVERS_____160,500 LBS.
WT. ON FRONT TRUCK_____19,500 LBS.
NUMBER OF BOILER TUBES_____173
CYLINDERS_____21"X 26"
TRACTIVE FORCE-LBS.(@5 ZBP)37,100 LBS.
BOILER PRESSURE LBS._____210 LBS.

HORSEPOWER (15 M.P.H.)_____1,484
LGTH. OF FIREBOX INSIDE____88 1/8"
WDTH. OF FIREBOX INSIDE____70 1/4"
GRATE AREA_____43 SQUARE FT.
SIZE OF BOILER TUBES_____2"X 13'6"
SIZE OF SUPERHT'R FLUES___5 3/8"X 13'6"
NO. OF SUPERHT'R FLUES___30
TOTAL HEATING SURFACE___1,937 SQUARE FT.
SUPERHEATER_____467 SQUARE FT.
VALVE GEAR_____WALSCHAERT
POWER REVERSE GEAR_____FRANKLIN TYPE "B"
FACTOR OF ADHESION_____4.32
MAX. WIDTH OVERALL_____9' 6"

SUPERHEATER_____ELESCO TYPE "A"
AIR PUMP_____ONE 8 1/2" WESTINGHOUSE 150-0
STOKER_____NONE
LOW WATER ALARM_____NONE
BRICK ARCH_____AMERICAN SECURITY

ENG 403 — OIL-1800 GALS.

The class 400 consolidation type locomotives, used on the Alaska Railroad, were built in 1942 by the Lima Locomotive Works and were placed in service in 1947. Specifications on these 2–8–0 locomotives were as follows:

Cylinders	21 by 26 inches
Drive wheels	50-inch diameter
Horsepower	1484 at 15 miles per hour
Tractive force	37,100 pounds at 85 percent boiler pressure
Firebox length inside	88⅛ inches
Firebox width inside	70¼ inches
Number of tubes	173
Length of tubes	13.5 feet
Diameter of tubes	2 inches
Boiler pressure	210 pounds
Superheater	Elesco type "A"
Number of flues	30
Size of flues	5⅜ inches by 13½ feet
Heating surface	467 square feet
Total heating surface	1937 square feet
Grate area	43 square feet
Valve gear	Walschaert
Power reverse gear	Franklin type "B"
Engine weight	180,000 pounds
Tender weight	124,700 pounds
Tender capacity	6500 gallons water; 10 tons coal
Weight on drivers	16,000 pounds
Weight on front truck	19,500 pounds.

See attached schematic drawing for class 400 Alaska Railroad locomotives.
(Courtesy: Alaska Railroad)

Illustrated is an Alaska Railroad freight train being pulled by locomotive no. 404, a Lima 2–8–0 type on 28 September 1951. Specifications were shown earlier.
(Courtesy: Alaska Railroad)

Nº 551, 552, 554, 555, 556, 557, 558, 559, 560, 561, 562

BUILT BY - BALDWIN LOCO. WORKS
YEAR BUILT - 1943
TYPE - CONSOLIDATION
WEIGHT ON DRIVERS - WORKING ORDER - 191,000 LBS.
WEIGHT ON FRONT TRUCK - WORKING ORDER - 21,500 LBS.
WEIGHT ON BACK TRUCK - WORKING ORDER - NONE
TOTAL WEIGHT OF ENG. WORKING ORDER - 162,500 LBS.
TOTAL WEIGHT OF TENDER LOADED - 126,450 LBS.
TOTAL WEIGHT OF ENG. & TENDER LOADED - 288,950 LBS.
CYLINDERS - 19" X 26"
DIA. OF DRIVERS - 57"
TRACTIVE POWER (85% BOILER PRESS.) 31,500 LBS.
FACTOR OF ADHESION - 4.4
MAXIMUM WIDTH OVERALL - 8' 11½"
FUEL - BITUMINOUS COAL
BRICK ARCH - AMERICAN SECURITY

BOILER PRESSURE - 225 LBS.
LENGTH OF FIREBOX INSIDE - 84 ⅛"
WIDTH OF FIREBOX INSIDE - 70¼"
GRATE AREA - 41.04 SQ. FT.
SIZE OF BOILER TUBES - 2" X 13'-6"
NUMBER OF BOILER TUBES - 150
SIZE OF SUPERHEATER FLUES - 5 ⅜" X 13'-6"
NUMBER OF SUPER HEATER FLUES - 30
TOTAL HEATING SURFACE - 1773 SQ. FT.
SUPERHEATER - 480 SQ. FT.
SUPERHEATER - ELESCO - TYPE A
STOKER - NONE
LOW WATER ALARM - NONE
VALVE GEAR - WALSCHAERT
POWER REVERSE GEAR - BALDWIN
AIR PUMP - ONE 9½" WESTINGHOUSE
AIR PUMP - ONE 11" WESTINGHOUSE (557 ONLY)

Consolidation class 500, Baldwin locomotive, 2–8–0 type, used on the Alaska Railroad for freight and passenger service between 1943 and 1957.

Eleven Consolidation class 2–8–0 Baldwin locomotives were placed in service on the Alaska Railroad during 1943. These engines had the following specifications:

Cylinders	19 by 26 inches
Drive wheels	57-inches diameter
Tractive power	31,500 pounds at 85 percent boiler pressure
Working steam pressure	225 pounds per square inch
Firebox length inside	84⅛ inches
Firebox width inside	70¼ inches
Grate area	41.04 square feet
Number of boiler tubes	150 (size 2 inches by 13.5 feet)
Superheater	Elesco type "A"
Number of superheater flues	30 (size 2 inches by 13.5 feet.)
Surface area	480 square feet
Total heating surface	1773 square feet
Valve gear	Walschaert
Power reverse gear	Baldwin
Engine	162,500 pounds
Tender weight	126,450 pounds
Weight on drivers	191,000 pounds
Weight on front truck	21,500 pounds
Tender capacity	6500 gallons water; 10 tons coal.

See schematic drawing.
(Courtesy: Alaska Railroad)

This illustration shows engine no. 502, Consolidation type 2–8–0 Baldwin steam locomotive on the Alaska Railroad in 1943. Specifications are given in the previous illustration.
(Courtesy: Anchorage Historical & Fine Arts Museum)

The last operating passenger steam locomotive on the Alaska Railroad was no. 557. This was a Consolidation type 2–8–0 engine built in 1943 by the Baldwin Locomotive Works of Philadelphia, Pa. The locomotive pictured was one of eleven like engines (nos. 551, 552, 554, 555, 556, 557, 558, 559, 560, 561, and 562). Technical specifications are detailed with the drawing presented elsewhere.
(Courtesy: Alaska Railroad)

This is locomotive no. 556, a Baldwin Consolidation type engine used on the Alaska Railroad after 1943. Specifications are set forth with the drawing, part of an earlier illustration.
(Courtesy: Alaska Railroad)

4–0 tank engines are shown but no information on their origin or specifications is available.

The Alaska Railroad was completed in July 1923. A wide variety of steam locomotives were used for passenger and freight service on the newly completed rail line, starting with various Mogul-type engines left over from construction of the road. In 1927, new ARR class Mk, Mikado 2–8–2 tender locomotives were introduced. Three machines, numbered 701, 702, and 703, were purchased from the Baldwin Locomotive Works. Their characteristics are extensively set forth. Also included are photographs of series 700 Mikado-type steam locomotives used on the Alaska Railroad.

The series 400 Consolidation 2–8–0 tender locomotives, with superheaters, were built in 1942 by the Lima Locomotive Works for use on the Alaska Railroad. A drawing and specifications are given. Also illustrated are two series 400 locomotives.

In 1943, thirteen additional units—series 500,

Consolidation 2–8–0 tender locomotives—were supplied by the Baldwin Locomotive Works. Pertinent specifications are included. Three additional illustrations are photographs of these series 500 locomotives, including engine no. 557, the last operating steam locomotive, as it looked in 1949.

By the end of the 1960s, steam locomotion in Alaska had been displaced by diesel tractive power.

ARGENTINA

IN THE INITIAL YEARS OF INDEPENDENT ARGEN-
tina, the professional army, the immigrants, and
the railways were the means used to subjugate the
aggresive gauchos of the pampas and defeat the Indians. These actions finally brought peace and order to the country and permitted the establishment
of a structured society based on the European pattern.

Some early railroads fostered and built by the
British had profits guaranteed by the Argentine national government, which in some cases granted
land subsidies and purchased shares in the rail enterprises. In general the state had hoped to avoid
the use of overseas capital, becoming thereby less
dependent on foreign investors. One expedient in
Argentina was to tax trade through the busy port of
Buenos Aires, thus generating the necessary
finances to support some rail construction, but this
plan was only partially successful. Private Argentine interests projected and built various railways
such as the early Central Argentine Railway; other
rail lines were constructed by provincial authorities, connecting population centers such as
Córdoba, Tucuman, Santiago del Estero, and Mendoza with the ocean ports.

The first railway line in Argentina ran several
miles from Parque to Floresta. This railroad
opened on 30 August 1857, with 5-foot 6-inch
gauge tracks. Its first locomotive, named "La
Portena," was constructed in 1857 by E. B. Wilson
and Company of Leeds, England.

As it finally turned out, Britain became Argentina's principal trading and investment partner
from the mid-nineteenth century until World War
II. The British-built lines spread out from Buenos
Aires and, to a lesser extent, from Rosario and
Bahía Blanca. A 460-mile rail link between Rosario
and Córdoba was completed in 1870, which
ushered in several decades of vigorous railroad construction by various British companies. In most
right-of-way concessions, the British acquired a
three-mile strip of land on both sides of the railroad
track, used largely by Argentina to promote colonization. A famous English railway builder,
Thomas Brassey, worked on various Argentine rail
projects in 1864. The first major rail line, the Central Argentine Railway, now known as the Mitre,
ran from Rosario to Córdoba. It was extended to
Tucumán in 1876, to Jujuy in 1900, and on to the
Bolivian border in 1908. The most significant railway expansion took place in the 1880s in those
areas adjacent to Buenos Aires where British investors built and managed three major rail systems
centered on that port: the Great Southern (today
the Roca); the Western (now the Sarmiento); and
the Pacific (now the San Martín).

By 1890 Argentina had 5,900 miles of railroads,
owned and operated by twenty-two different
firms. The Southern Railway in 1897 extended a
line from Bahía Blanca to Rio Colorado and on to
Neuquen in 1899. In 1900 there were thirty different companies involved in rail operations on ten
thousand miles of track. In 1910 there were seventeen thousand miles of rail, extending in spiderweb
fashion from Buenos Aires into the pampas and
most other parts of the country.

The British remained a major factor in the railway fortunes of Argentina until 1943, by which

time there were nine railway companies in existence. When Perón came to power, he established a program of "economic independence," with expropriation of the British railway interests as his administration's prime objective. On 16 November 1943, the Argentine government named a three-man commission to study the financial operations of the British-owned enterprises. This proved to be the first step in a protracted series of transactions, eventually culminating in the takeover of all railroads in Argentina. On 13 February 1947, $600 million of Argentine credits, frozen in Britain during World War II, were exchanged for the British rail properties, and expropriation became an established fact.

Argentina has the second longest dead-straight stretch of railroad track in the world, on the Buenos Aires & Pacific Railway: a 205-mile-long track between Junín and MacKenna on the 5-foot 6-inch-gauge Buenos Aires–Mendoza line. At Mendoza this railway connects with the famous South Transandine line across the towering Andes to Valparaiso, Chile.

The four highest summits on the rail lines in Argentina are: Tres Cruces, on a meter-gauge railway, at 12,116 feet above sea level; Pumahuasi at 11,654 feet; Iturbe at 10,965 feet; Diego de Almagro at 10,840 feet.

The most southerly railway in the world is located at the South Atlantic port of Deseado in Argentina, 47° 45′ south latitude. This is the terminus of the 5-foot 6-inch gauge railway from Colonia la Heras.

The most serious railroad disaster in Argentina occurred on 4 February 1970, near Buenos Aires, a collision that brought death to 236 people.

ARGENTINE RAILWAY ROUTES IN ACTIVE SERVICE, 1975

Region	Gauge (meters)	Route length (kilometers)
Roca	1.676	8,159
Roca	0.750	403
Mitre	1.676	6.174
San Martín	1.676	4,625
Sarmiento	1.676	3,830
Urquiza	1.435	3,086
Belgrano	1.000	13,461
	Total	39,738

Steam Locomotives in Argentina

It has been difficult to reconstruct the history of the steam locomotive in Argentina. The first Argentine railway, from Parque to Floresta, which opened 30 August 1857, had 5-foot 6-inch gauge tracks and used a small engine built by E. B. Wilson of Leeds, England. Generally, British-built engines were used throughout the early days of railroading in Argentina.

Starting in 1884, Baldwin supplied various class 8–20–C, "American"-type locomotives with a 4–4–0 wheel arrangement for passenger and freight service on the Argentine railways. In 1888 Neilson Reid furnished a number of 0–6–0 engines. In 1893 the North British Locomotive Company (NBLC) provided various locomotives for the Argentine railways, including the type 4–6–0 tender engine shown.

In 1905 the North British Locomotive Company supplied a number of 2–6–2 tank engines and 4–6–0 and 4–4–0 passenger engines. Koppel of Germany built a few shunting engines in 1910. Also in 1910, Maffei of Germany supplied twenty-eight Pacific type 4–6–2 engines, of which four were still in service in 1972 on the Belgrano suburban lines. In 1911 Argentina received several shunting engines, type 2–8–2, from the Hanover Machine Works of Germany. In 1916 the Central Railway of Argentina used a number of passenger engines (4–6–2) manufactured by the North British Locomotive Company. Various NBLC engines, with a 2–6–2 wheel arrangement, were being employed by 1918 on the Argentine portion of the Transandine Railway.

In 1920 Baldwin delivered twenty-five Mikado type 2–8–2 engines that had been constructed to strict Argentine design specifications. Then in 1921, Baldwin filled its largest foreign order ever for steam locomotives: eighty-five engines for the Argentine State Railways, consisting of twenty-five Pacifics (4–6–2), ten Santa Fe types (2–10–2), and fifty Mountains (4–8–2). Also in 1921, Alco furnished a number of heavy Mikado 2–8–2 engines and Henschel supplied some 2–10–2 types.

The North Central Railway in 1922 initiated a series of type 2–8–2 locomotives built by Hanover Machine Works (Hannover Maschinenbau) of Germany. Also in 1922, Henschel supplied twenty-four engines and Baldwin twelve engines, all type 2–8–2, for the 2-foot 6-inch gauge railway in

This illustration covers a Baldwin type 4–4–0 locomotive built in 1884 for the 5-foot 6-inch gauge Western Railway of Buenos Aires. The engine, named *La Plata*, is believed to have had the following specifications:

Cylinders   13 by 22 inches
Drive wheels   57-inch diameter
Operating weight engine   56,000 pounds
Tender capacity   1400 gallons water
Baldwin class 8–20–C.

(Courtesy: Frederick Westing collection)

Shown is a North British Locomotive Company locomotive constructed in 1893 for the 5-foot 6-inch gauge Buenos Aires Great Southern Railway. This was a type 4–6–0 tender engine with the following specifications (no. 44):

Cylinders	17 by 24 inches
Drive wheels	4-foot 9-inch diameter
Front wheels	3-foot diameter
Boiler	
Fire grate area	17 square feet
Heating surface (tubes)	1051 square feet
Heating surface (firebox)	85 square feet
Heating surface (total)	1136 square feet
Working pressure	160 pounds per square inch
Feed	Two injectors plus one pump
Tractive force	14,602 pounds at 75 percent boiler working pressure
Operating weights	
Engine	45 tons plus 4 hundred weights
Drive wheels	30 tons plus 9 hundred weights
Tender	37 tons plus 16 hundred weights
Tender capacities	3000 gallons water; 250 cubic feet coal.

(Courtesy: Science Museum, London)

Pictured is a type 2–6–2 tank locomotive furnished by the North British Locomotive Company to the 5-foot 6-inch guage Buenos Aires Great Southern Railway in 1905. Engine no. 394 had the following specifications:

Cylinders	18 by 26 inches
Drive wheels	5-foot 2-inch diameter
Front and rear wheels	3-foot 5-inch diameter
Boiler	
Grate area	27 square feet
Heating surface (tubes)	1517 square feet
Heating surface (firebox)	143 square feet
Heating surface (total)	1660 square feet
Working pressure	180 pounds per square inch
Feed	Two injectors
Tractive force	18,342 pounds at 75 percent boiler working pressure
Operating weight	73 tons plus 15 hundred weights
Operating weight on drive wheels	48 tons plus 19 hundred weights
Tank capacity	1200 gallons
Fuel space	100 cubic feet.

(Courtesy: Science Museum, London)

Shown is a type 4–4–0 tender locomotive supplied to the 5-foot 6-inch gauge Buenos Aires Western Railway in 1905. Specifications were:

Cylinders	18 by 24 inches
Coupled drive wheels	6-foot diameter
Bogie wheels	3-foot 2-inch diameter
Boiler	
Grate area	22.7 square feet
Heating surface (tubes)	1178.3 square feet
Heating surface (firebox)	108 square feet
Heating surface (total)	1236.3 square feet
Working pressure	160 pounds per square inches
Feed	Two injectors
Tractive force	12,960 pounds at 75 percent boiler working pressure
Operating weights	
Engine	47 tons plus 16 hundred weights
Drive wheels	30 tons plus 14 hundred weights
Tender	37 tons plus 17 hundred weights
Tender capacities	3000 gallons water; 170 cubic feet coal space.

(Courtesy: Science Museum, London)

Pictured is a steam locomotive, no. 555, used on the Southern Railway of Argentina in the early Twentieth century. This type 4–6–0 engine was built by North British Locomotive Company in 1906 and had the following specifications:

Cylinders	483-millimeter diameter
Wheels	
Drivers	1829-millimeter
Leading	965-millimeter diameter
Tender	965-millimeter diameter
Boiler	
Diameter	1638-millimeters
Length	3727-millimeters
Operating Weights	
Engine	67,135 kilograms
Tender	48,770 kilograms.

(Courtesy: Ferrocarriles Argentinos)

Illustrated is an old steam locomotive used in the early twentieth century on the North Central Railway of Argentina. This engine, no. AX 5, was built by Koppel of Germany in 1910. Specifications were as follows:

Cylinders	259-millimeter diameter
Drive wheels	650-millimeter diameter
Boiler	
Diameter	700-millimeters
Length	1585-millimeters.

(Courtesy: Ferrocarriles Argentinos)

Pictured is a type 2–8–2 locomotive, no. 749, used on the North Central Railway of Argentina. No. 749 was built by the Hanover Machine Works of Germany in 1911. Technical data were not available.
(Courtesy: Ferrocarriles Argentinos)

Shown is a type 4–6–2 locomotive, no. 140, used on the Central Railway of Argentina. This engine was built by the North British Locomotive Company in 1916. Specifications were:

Cylinders	507-millimeter diameter
Wheels	
Drivers	1727-millimeter diameter
Leading	965-millimeter diameter
Trailing	1245-millimeter diameter
Tender	965-millimeter diameter
Boiler	
Diameter	1721-millimeter
Length	4137-millimeter
Operating weights	
Engine	78,450-kilograms
Tender	71,323-kilograms.

(Courtesy: Ferrocarriles Argentinos)

This illustration shows a British-made steam locomotive, type 2–6–2, employed on the Argentina portion of the Transandean Railway in 1918. No technical information available.
(Courtesy: Ferrocarriles Argentinos)

In 1921 Baldwin filled the largest foreign order ever for steam locomotives—a consignment of eighty-five railway engines for use on the Argentine State Railways as follows: ten Santa Fe type, fifty Mountain type, and twenty-five Pacific type. These engines are pictured in the following illustrations:

Santa Fe type (2–10–2)

Cylinders	22 by 24 inches
Coupled drive wheels	48-inch diameter
Engine weight	195,800 pounds

Mountain type (4–8–2)

Cylinders	19 by 24 inches
Coupled drive wheels	50-inch diameter
Engine weight	170,800 pounds

Pacific type (4–6–2)

Cylinders	20 by 26 inches
Coupled drive wheels	60-inch diameter
Engine weight	170,000 pounds.

The above order followed a successful delivery in 1920 of twenty-five Mikado type locomotives, built according to Argentina's design and specifications. The latter engines had cylinders eighteen by twenty-two inches, drive wheels forty-two inches in diameter, with engine weights of 131,300 pounds.
(Courtesy: Frederick Westing collection)

Pictured is a type 4–8–2 steam locomotive, no. 819, used on the North Central Railway of Argentina. The engine was built by Baldwin in 1921. Specifications were as follows:

Cylinders	482-millimeter diameter
Drive wheels	1270-millimeter diameter
Boiler	
Diameter	1644-millimeters
Length	5902-millimeters
Operating weights	
Engine	77,500 kilograms
Tender	42,820 kilograms.

(Courtesy: Ferrocarriles Argentinos)

Shown is a 3-foot 3⅝-inch narrow gauge Pacific type 4–6–2 Baldwin locomotive built in 1921 for the Argentine State Railways. This engine had what the manufacturer called an "Exhibition Finish" with its prominent boiler jacket bands and a clean-cut paint job. Specifications were as follows:

Cylinders	20 by 26 inches
Drive wheels	60-inch diameter
Boiler	
Type	Belpaire
Diameter	66 inches
Grate area	44 square feet
Superheater	648 square feet
Total heat surface	2592 square feet
Working pressure	200-pounds per square inch
Operating weight	266,950 pounds (engine plus tender)
Tender capacity	
Water	4500 gallons
Fuel oil	2000 gallons.

(Courtesy: Frederick Westing collection)

Pictured is a tank locomotive used on the Central
Railway of Argentina. This FCCA engine, type 4–8–4,
no. 501, was built by the Armstrong Whitworth
Company in 1927. Specifications were:

Cylinders	571-millimeter diameter
Wheels	
Drivers	1574-millimeter diameter
Leading	965-millimeter diameter
Trailing	965-millimeter diameter
Boiler	
Diameter	1718 millimeters
Length	4545 millimeters
Operating weight (engine)	111,965 kilograms.

(Courtesy: Ferrocarriles Argentinos)

This steam locomotive, no. 3201, named *General Roca*
was used on the Southern Railway of Argentina.
Beyer Peacock manufactured this type 4–6–0 engine
sometime in the 1930s. Specifications were as follows:

Cylinders	483-millimeter diameter
Wheels	
Drivers	1727-millimeter diameter
Leading	965-millimeter diameter
Tender	483-millimeter diameter
Boiler	
Diameter	1524 millimeters
Length	3728 millimeters
Operating weight	
Engine	63,512 kilograms
Tender	44,716 kilograms.

(Courtesy: Ferrocarriles Argentinos)

Illustrated is a type 4–6–0 locomotive, no. 3884, named *Ciervo,* which found service on the North Central Railway of Argentina in the 1930s. The name of the builder was not available. Specifications were:

Cylinders	711-millimeter diameter
Wheels	
Drivers	1829-millimeter diameter
Leading	965-millimeter diameter
Tender	965-millimeter diameter
Boiler	
Diameter	1524 millimeters
Length	3727 millimeters.
Operating weights	
Engine	73,409 kilograms
Tender	53,392 kilograms.

(Courtesy: Ferrocarriles Argentinos)

This type 4–6–0 steam locomotive, no. 3905, named *Alberti,* was used on the Southern Railway of Argentina sometime in the 1930s. The name of the manufacturer was not available. Specifications were as follows:

Cylinders	483-millimeter diameter
Wheels	
Drivers	1829-millimeter diameter
Leading	965-millimeter diameter
Tender	965-millimeter diameter
Boiler	
Diameter	1645 millimeters
Length	3727 millimeters
Operating weight	
Engine	75,965 kilograms
Tender	66,196 kilograms.

(Courtesy: Ferrocarriles Argentinos)

Shown is locomotive no. 881, type 4–8–2, used on the North Central Railway of Argentina in the 1930s. This engine was built by Henschel and Sohn of Germany in 1938. General specifications were as follows:

Cylinders	500-millimeter diameter
Drive wheels	1270-millimeter diameter
Boiler	
Diameter	1646 millimeters
Length	3904 millimeters
Operating weight	
Engine	79,450 kilograms
Tender	68,800 kilograms.

(Courtesy: Ferrocarriles Argentinos)

southern Argentina on the General Roca line.

The Armstrong Whitworth Company in 1927 built a few type 4–8–4 tank locomotives for use on the Central Railway. In 1928 and 1929 six type 4–8-0 engines were furnished by Kerr Stuart. During the 1930s the Argentine railways continued to purchase a great variety of locomotives from Baldwin, Henschel, Beyer Peacock, the North British Locomotive Company, and from Krupp. Some of these engines are shown.

Baldwin and American Locomotive, in 1948, constructed sixty heavy type 4–8–2 Mountain engines for the Belgrano system. Also in 1948, Ferrocarriles Argentino ordered fifteen heavy 2–10–2 engines from the Skoda Works to be used on the newly constructed Salta line over the Andes to the Chilean border at Socompa.

In modern times Argentina ranked with India, South Africa, and China in having a superabundance and variety of railway steam engines. In 1969 the three main railways in Argentina carried about 1740 locomotives on their active rosters, comprising a tremendous assortment of subclasses and about seventeen different wheel arrangements, but by 1978 steam locomotion on the Argentine railways was being rapidly phased out in favor of diesel power.

AUSTRALIA

MANY OF THE EARLY RAILWAYS IN AUSTRALIA were laid within two hundred miles of the coast, with occasional lines penetrating the interior to tap pastoral, agricultural, and mining resources. Unfortunately, various rail systems originated independently and with too little foresight. The railways were centered about their respective state capitals and used different rail gauges. Lines in Victoria and South Australia used the broad Irish 5-foot 3-inch track. Those in New South Wales used standard gauge, i.e., 4 feet 8½ inches. In Queensland, Western Australia, and Tasmania, narrow-gauge 3-foot 6-inch tracks were utilized. These differences in rail gauge, plus occasional interstate rivalry and suspicion, led to rail systems with serious passenger and freight delays and tedious changes in carriers at the break-points—all of which adversely affected long-term and long-distance railway development in Australia. For example, until about 1960, the 3485-mile trip from the Indian Ocean to the Pacific Ocean was split into six sections, with all attendant difficulties, nuisance, and delay in transferring freight and passengers between the various rail systems.

The early authorities in Australia were influenced by a long-established respect for and loyalty to the steamship, and prejudices against the railway steam engine were deep-rooted. Still, the great advantages of rail transportation for inland routes soon became evident and eventually steps were taken to utilize the iron horse even though the early Australian railways simply would not compete economically with steamships on coastal and river waterways.

The first steam locomotive line in Australia was the small 5-foot 3-inch gauge Melbourne & Hobson's Bay Railway in Victoria, which opened 12 September 1854, and ran 2½ miles between Melbourne and Port Melbourne. South Australia got its first steam-operated railway in 1856, Queensland in 1865, and Tasmania and Western Australia in 1871. All this rail activity occurred before federation in 1901, at which time Australia had six separate railway systems, one for each state. A seventh system, the Commonwealth Railways, came into existence with the building of a line between Port Augusta in South Australia and Kalgoorlie in Western Australia in 1917. All the state railway systems except those in Queensland and Western Australia started as private companies. All of them, however, soon ran into financial difficulties and the respective state governments were obliged to take them over.

Between 1875 and 1891 the state governments of Australia participated in a wild railroad-building boom, borrowing vast sums in England. Rail lines were laid down to race courses, to gold towns, and to distant pastoral and mining communities. The rails were spreading everywhere, and in Victoria and New South Wales there were fears that because of over expansion the steam monster might devour its masters. However, one fortunate circumstance became apparent. In eastern Australia the pioneering railways had already battled their way across the most difficult, costly, mountainous terrain. The inland plains, on the other hand, had no ranges to tunnel, no rivers to bridge, and few viaducts or embankments to construct. Thus, the decision to use narrow-gauge tracks, plus the easier topography, afforded far more economical railroads.

The first railways running inland, to accommodate the shipment of pastoral products, reached Echuca, Victoria, in 1864; Toowoomba, Queensland, in 1867; and Goulburn, New South Wales, in 1869. Of course, the many goldfield discoveries also merited other inland railways from the late 1850s on. Thus, while rail development was at first quite slow in the early 1850s, real progress commenced when the Victoria government in 1862 pushed the iron track to two gold towns: one running east to Ballarat and one north to Bendigo.

In the 1880s the governments that ran the four largest railway systems in Australia found it necessary to hand over the detailed administration of their railways to independent commissioners, usually experts from England. In general, government railways in this country were unduly extravagant in prosperous years, and in depression years their revenue was inadequate to pay the bondholders in England, which meant that the various states had to cover the losses from their general treasuries.

The break-in-gauge problem met its severest test at the border between Victoria (3-foot 6-inch gauge) and New South Wales (4-foot 8½-inch gauge). Nevertheless, the six hundred-mile railroad from Sydney to Melbourne was inaugurated on 14 June 1883. In 1889, when Australia's most expensive bridge was built over the wide Hawkesbury estuary between Sydney and Newcastle, the four largest Australian cities (Adelaide, Melbourne, Sydney, and Brisbane) were linked by 1800 miles of railway with three distinct rail gauges.

Railways increased in Australia from 1,600 miles in 1875 to 4,000 miles in 1881, to 10,000 miles in 1891, and to 26,000 miles in 1921. By this time, one could travel from Cairns in northern Queensland south across New South Wales and Victoria to a distant city in South Australia. Travel still had some serious discontinuities, though, since there were fourteen different public rail systems, with gaps varying between a mile and hundreds of miles. In other locations, busy railway lines were joined together but still with variation in rail gauges, to the annoyance of military men, politicians, and railway officials. By the 1920s, as isolated railways were linked and the era of track laying came to an end, travelers could journey from Western Australia to the most distant railway station in tropical North Queensland but they could not avoid the eternal nuisance of having to change trains at five different locations. In World War II, these movement obstructions more than ever proved a real nightmare to logistics planners.

In general, Australia's infant economy received a substantial amount of strength and drive from its railways during the late nineteenth century. These rail systems handled countless trainloads of important export commodities that could not have been transported otherwise. The railroads also moved thousands of immigrants into virgin areas that would not have been settled and developed without the help of the rail carrier. In times of drought, sheep stations near a rail line could send the sheep on the railroad to other fertile areas or could bring in hay and fodder until the rains came. Long railroads eventually opened the inland wheat regions of New South Wales, Western Australia, and southern Queensland, which enabled Australia to become a major supplier to markets all over the world. The railroads prolonged the life of the early, inaccessible inland zinc, lead, copper, silver, and gold centers. The rail lines also carried coke, coal, and timber inexpensively to the inland smelting and mining industries, then transported the refined mineral products to the coastal ports. Despite the huge debts created by railway construction, the Australian state governments recognized the great economic benefits of supporting and expanding their rail networks. The demand for locomotive fuel stimulated the coal mines. From the 1870s on, many foundries in Australia turned out rail, carriages, and locomotives, fostering a native iron industry. Moreover, railroad construction provided employment for a brawny, roving army of navvies. In the minds of most historians, the railways were the most sacred and significant symbols of progress in Australia.

With the formation of the commonwealth of the six Australian states in 1910, the decision was made to lay down a single-gauge rail line between South Australia and Western Australia, known as the Trans-Australian Railway. This standard-gauge line of 1,051 miles from Port Augusta in South Australia to Kalgoorlie in Western Australia was started in the fall of 1912 and was completed in October 1917. It turned out to be one of the most formidable construction projects in the whole history of railroading, mainly due to logistic problems rather than to engineering difficulties. The railroad was laid through desperately arid and uninhabited country, devoid of all natural running water. There were subzero temperatures in winter but summer temperatures soared to above 120 degrees Fahrenheit. Camels were used extensively during construction in the desert sections. The center of the route included 450 miles of track through the featureless Nullarbor Plain (plain of no trees), having the longest stretch of continuous straight track in the world—297 miles. The line had no tunnels and only a few cuttings were necessary. Rails were bolted to imported hardwood sleepers known as jarrah. On 27 October 1917, for the first time, passengers were able to make the long, hot journey between Kalgoorlie and Port Augusta without changing cars, although there were breaks in the rail gauge at both ends of the Trans-Australian Railway.

A railroad running north from Port Augusta, of a 3-foot 6-inch gauge, known as the Central Australian Railway, was constructed in the early twentieth century. This first ran to Oodnadatta in the state of South Australia. The line was acquired by the commonwealth of Australia in 1911 but was at once leased back to South Australia to operate. Control reverted to the Commonwealth Railways in 1926. The railroad was extended north to Alice Springs in Northern Territory in 1929, a distance from Port Augusta of about 650 miles.

From the north coast of Australia the first tracks south were constructed in 1888 along a right-of-way from Darwin to Pine Creek, about 110 kilometers (68 miles). Three thousand Chinese navvies were imported to work on this railroad. By 1911 the commonwealth had acquired possession of the rail line, which was then managed by the Northern Territory administration. In accordance with the Pine Creek & Katherine Railway Act of 1912, an extension was started south from Pine Creek. This rail system, later known as the North Australian Railway, became part of the Commonwealth Railways in 1918. The extension to Birdum was finished in 1929. At present there are no plans to extend the 320-kilometer (199-mile) rail connection between Darwin and Birdum across central Australia to join the southern railways at Alice Springs, a distance of 1,030 kilometers (640 miles).

In 1930 the standard-gauge system in New South Wales was extended from Sydney to Brisbane in Queensland. In 1962 Sydney and Melbourne were joined by standard-gauge tracks, and in 1969 the final 380-mile link of standard-gauge track was finished connecting Sydney and Perth in Western Australia.

The following railroad mileage figures were extracted from *Janes World Railways 1980–81*:

Authority	Gauge (meters)	Route length (kilometers)	(miles)
New South Wales	1.435	9,756	6,062
Queensland	1.435	9,796	6,087
Victoria	1.600	6,645	4,129
	1.435	332	206
	0.762	13	8
South Australia	1.600	142.38	88
Western Australia	1.067	439	273
	Dual-Gauge	148	92
Australian National	1.435	2,140	1,330
Railways	1.067	869	540
	1.600	511	318
Totals		32,020.38	19,897

NEW SOUTH WALES

The first railway line in New South Wales was a 13½-mile stretch of 4-foot 8½-inch track opened on 26 September 1855 between Sydney and Parramatta. It was built by the Sydney Railway Company, which had been formed by a government act in 1849, but was taken over by the New South Wales government before it opened on 3 September 1855. The first locomotive used on this rail line is pictured. Four of these units were supplied by Robert Stephenson in England. Actually, the line was operated for the first twelve months, on authority of the New South Wales government, by the construction contractor, Mr. William Randle.

With Sydney surrounded by rocky terrain and mountain ranges, the railway engineering problems were extreme, to say the least. The chief engineer, Mr. John Whitton, who held that position from 1857 to 1890, was the major guiding force in designing and installing 2,100 miles of New South Wales railways through countless financial and constructional aggravations, all the while steadfastly promoting the desirability of standard-gauge tracks.

Early rail construction in New South Wales included sections running west from the coast at Newcastle. In 1857 the first twenty-mile portion of the Great Northern Railway, following an inland route roughly parallel to the Pacific Ocean, was opened, and this was extended to the Queensland border at Wallangarra in 1887.

Another early New South Wales project was to

lay down a rail line running 130 miles west from Parramatta to the rich community of Bathurst. Unfortunately, the intervening Blue Mountains presented a stupendous obstacle. The mountain ridges, at 3,600 feet above sea level, were finally won by Whitton-designed zigzags, one of which, constructed near Lithgow in 1869, brought worldwide acclaim. The section between Penwith and Bathurst proved to be a tremendous ten-year task, completed in 1876. In 1910 heavy traffic necessitated a major renovation of the route over the Blue Mountains. Accordingly, ten new short tunnels plus a regrading program eliminated the Lithgow zigzag and changed the ruling gradient from 1 in 42 to 1 in 90.

While the rail route west from Sydney was under construction, the Great Southern Railway moved southward over some difficult grades, reaching Goulburn, about 120 miles distant, in 1869; Wagga Wagga, about 150 miles further along in 1879; and the Victoria border at Albury, about an additional 80 miles, in February 1881. Earlier, Victoria had advanced her steel rails 187 miles northeast from Brisbane to the small community of Wodonga close to the New South Wales border.

Major rail progress was experienced in New South Wales during from 1880 to 1885, when about a thousand miles of railway were laid. One major obstacle to a connection between Sydney and its northern neighbor city, Newcastle, was the Hawkesbury estuary. Not until May 1889 was Australia's most costly bridge, with a length of 2,900 feet, finally constructed over that waterway.

The richest territory for encroaching railway

Two illustrations show the first locomotive used in New South Wales in September 1855 to pull the first train on the newly opened line between Sydney and Granville (Parramatta). This was a type 0–4–2 engine on which no technical data was available.
(*Courtesy: O. S. Nock:* **The Dawn of World Railways, 1800–1850**)

promoters from other states was in New South Wales. The vast expanses of this state and the long distance from its port city of Sydney allowed rail lines from Victoria and South Australia, without crossing the New South Wales border, to tap into the lucrative inland commerce. In 1876 a private company from Victoria did open forty-five miles of railway across the plains, from Echuca at the north-central Victoria border to Deniliquin in New

This illustration shows a New South Wales Railway, class C36, type 4–6–0, locomotive on heavy-duty freight service.
(Courtesy: New South Wales Government Railway)

Pictured is one of the most successful locomotives used on the New South Wales Government Railways (class C38, type 4–6–2). Also shown is a portion of the famous Hawkesbury Bridge opened in 1889 which finally connected the cities of Sydney and Newcastle in this part of Australia.
(Courtesy: New South Wales Government Railway)

South Wales. This tied in with all kinds of Victoria rail traffic to the south, until a competing New South Wales government railway was extended from Sydney in about 1900.

In the late 1880s there appeared in New South Wales Australia's most profitable railway built by private investments. This was the thirty-six mile narrow-gauge railroad from the silver mines at Broken Hill in western New South Wales to the South Australia border, connecting with a South Australian railroad to Port Pirie. The Silverton Tramway Company paid dividends of 30 percent in poor years and 50 percent in good years.

By 1890 a New South Wales railroad stretched northwest more than five hundred miles from Sydney to Bourke. Also in 1890, railroads became big business indeed when the New South Wales government employed about twelve thousand men. The organization was haphazardly managed by political appointees, however, and it soon became necessary, in the interest of the railway's salvation, to turn the management over to independent commissioners enlisted from the major British railway companies. By this time, long railways had opened the inland wheat belts of New South Wales, contributing to Australia's development as a worldwide grain supplier.

All early steam locomotives for the New South Wales railways were procured from British manufacturers, but, as in other parts of Australia, by the 1870s local foundries started producing engines and rolling stock. A principal Australian builder was the Clyde Engineering Works, which together with Baldwin of Philadelphia, Penn. furnished a large number of successful locomotives. The first Baldwin locomotives for New South Wales were constructed in 1877. In 1879, four twelve-ton tramway motors were built on order of the New South Wales Government. These were intended for use on grades of 6 percent running from the railway terminus to the Sydney Exhibition Grounds. More tramway motor orders followed from Sydney. During 1905 Baldwin supplied twenty ten-wheeler locomotives constructed to specifications furnished by the South Wales government railways. These had many special features, including plate frames and Allen valve motion. In 1892 New South Wales Railways engineer W. Thow provided a type 4–6–0 engine design (class P6) that was widely produced over the next nineteen years by Beyer Peacock and

This is a model of a North British Locomotive Company engine, type 2–8–0, gauge of 4 feet 8½ inches. The original engine, built in 1916, was used on the New South Wales Railways. It had the following specifications:

Cylinders	22 by 26 inches
Coupled drive wheels	4-foot 3-inch diameter
Boiler	
Grate area	30 square feet
Feed	Two number 10 injectors
Heating surface	
Tubes	1,660 square feet
Superheater	464 square feet
Firebox	172 square feet
TOTAL	2296 square feet
Working pressure	150 pounds per square inch
Tractive force	27,750 pounds at 75 percent boiler working pressure
Operating weight	
Engine	67 tons plus 13 hundred weights
Tender	40 tons plus 15 hundred weights
Tender capacities	
Water	3650 gallons
Coal	225 cubic feet
Wheel base (engine plus tender)	51 feet 10 inches.

(Courtesy: Museum of Transport, Glasgow)

three other builders. These versatile engines were used for all types of transport services. One of these class P6 (later designated class C32) engines performed the last ritual steam-traction job, pulling an express train in New South Wales in 1971.

Mr. Thow also designed the class T524, later class D50, locomotive in 1896 (type 2–8–0), of which about 280 units were constructed. Later, 310 units of an improved version (classes D53 and D55) satisfied the long-term need for freight-hauling engines in New South Wales.

In 1910 about 190 units of a class D53, type 2–8–0 shunting engine were constructed. These saw long service in New South Wales, and a few survived up to the final demise of the railway steam engine in this part of Australia in the early 1970s. Various other classes of steam locomotives were also used, such as the class Z19, type 0–6–0 tender locomotive and the class C30, type 4–6–4 tank engines built during World War II, some of which were rebuilt between 1928 and 1933 as class C30, 4–6–0 tank machines.

Class D57 engines, type 4–8–2 with three cylinders, were placed in heavy freight service in 1925. The original class P6 (C32), type 4–6–0 locomotives were largely replaced by new type 4–6–0 engines in the 1930s, i.e., classes C35 and C36. By 1943 class 38, type 4–6–2 Pacifics were being successfully used on the most demanding long-distance routes in New South Wales. After World War II, Baldwin filled an order for twenty class D59 Mikado locomotives, type 2–8–2

In 1952 Beyer Garratt's class AD60, type 4–8–4 + 4–8–4 engines, the most powerful ever used in

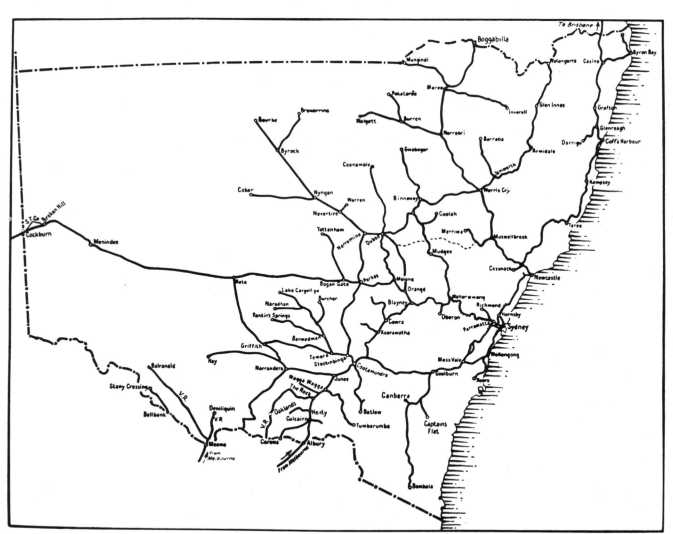

Railway map of New South Wales.
(*Courtesy:* Janes World Railways)

An old locomotive on a monument site in Canberra, New South Wales, Australia is pictured. This type 4–4–0 tank engine was built in 1878 by Beyer Peacock. *(Courtesy: Australian News & Information Bureau)*

Australia, were introduced into New South Wales. These "big boy" locomotives of which forty-two were originally constructed, were among the very last steam locomotives to survive in Australia. Also holding out to the end of the steam age were several class D53, type 2–8–0 engines built in 1910.

Steam operations in New South Wales were shut down in 1973 as diesel tractive power took over. The management of the New South Wales Government Railways followed a general Australian policy of preserving a representative number of old steam locomotives. Some of these engines are used occasionally on steam excursions. (See map of New South Wales rail network. See also the illustration, showing an 1878 locomotive on display on a Canberra monument.)

QUEENSLAND

With the attainment of self-government in Queensland in 1859, attention turned to the great need for railway transportation The first rail line (of 3-foot 6-inch gauge) was soon authorized from Ipswich to the Darling Downs area, a distance of about eighty miles. The first section, twenty-one miles to Grandchester was completed on 31 July 1865. After surmounting the difficult Liverpool and Main ranges, the railroad reached Toowoomba, about sixty miles from Ipswich, on 1

May 1867. A twenty-mile connection from Iipswich to the capital at the Brisbane was opened in 1876.

Then followed the construction of an assortment of independent, unconnected rail systems extending inland at various points from the east coast of Queensland. Some of these were as follows: from Townsville south and southwest to Charters Towers, 1880–1882; a short rail section westward from Rockhampton, 1867; another west from Mackay in 1885, and west from Maryborough and Bundaberg in 1888.

Construction of the long 3-foot 6-inch gauge coastal railroad from Brisbane to Cairns started in 1887. This entailed tremendous engineering difficulties, especially through the fifteen-mile Barron Gorge, which had many tight curves, fifteen tunnels, fifty-nine timber trestles, and six iron viaducts. Approximately three hundred miles of the line were originally constructed by the Chillagoe Company to connect with their various mining areas. These independent coastal railroads were eventually joined in 1903. The Queensland government in 1910 authorized the completion of a rail link all the way to Cairns, which was finished in 1924.

In general, with a low level of financial support, the Queensland railroads were developed on a very frugal, shoestring basis, and rails, rolling stock, locomotives, and attendant equipment were acquired as inexpensively as possible. This resulted in small railroad engines, medium-sized carriages and wagons, lightweight tracks, and a conservative schedule of public service. However, the savings resulting from using a narrow-gauge system greatly outweighed any concern about losses resulting from tardy movement of people and commodities. Despite their frugal approach, through the years the Queensland railways had many difficult periods and serious operating problems, caused mainly by their long and lightly railed 6,600 miles of track, which served only a sparse population.

The original railroads in Queensland used several steam locomotives weighing about twenty-two tons, type 2–4–0, manufactured by the Avonside Engine Company. Later, type 0–4–2 locomotives of about twenty tons were constructed by Neilson

for operations on the Queensland Government Railway tracks. In 1867 three Fairlie engines, type 0–6–6–0, were tried, but these failed to meet performance standards. Subsequently in 1885 some type 4–4–0 engines were purchased from Baldwin. In general, the light forty-two-pound per yard rail used on Queenland railways led to the widespread use of the 4–6–0 type locomotives. Various engines in service between 1883 and 1924 included classes B13, B15, PB15, R, Rx, and C17 (see Illustration

Here is a Baldwin type 4–4–0 locomotive used on the 3-foot 6-inch gauge tracks of the Government of Queensland Railways starting in 1885. Specifications were as follows:

Cylinders	10 by 20 inches
Drive wheels	45-inch diameter
Operating weight	36,000 pounds (engine)
Weight on drive wheels	21,000 pounds
Tender capacity	1000 gallons water.

(Courtesy: Queensland Railways)

Pictured is a class PB 15, type 4–6–0, locomotive and passenger train on a high trestle on the Queensland Government Railway.
(Courtesy: Australian News & Information Bureau)

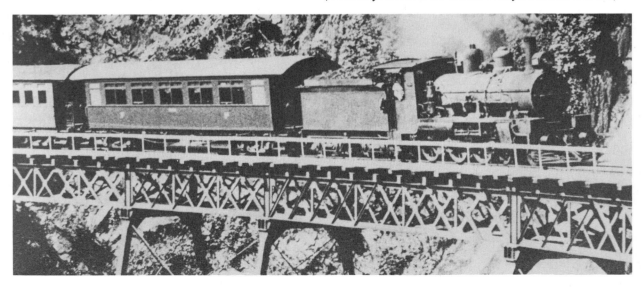

A small wood-burning tank engine used to haul sugar cane from the fields to a sugar mill in Queensland, Australia in the early part of the twentieth century is pictured here.
(Courtesy: Australian News & Information Bureau)

In 1926 the first of eighty-three class B 18¼ locomotives were manufactured at the Ipswich shops of the South Queensland Railways using the Pacific type 4–6–2 wheel arrangement. These engines were used on all types of railroad service. Specifications were as follows:

Cylinders	18.25 by 24 inches
Coupled wheels	4-foot 3-inch diameter
Boiler	
Grate area	25 square feet
Heating surface	1957 square feet
Steam pressure	160 pounds per square inch
Tractive effort	22,648 pounds at 85 percent steam pressure
Operational weight	
Engine	93.25 tons
Tender	91.1 tons
Tender capacity	
Water	3050 gallons
Coal	7.7 tons.

The above picture shows a large operating model used to haul children on a 5-inch gauge track, sixty-seven feet in diameter. This small engine was arbitrarily named *Polly,* which name, of course, never showed on the original engines.
(Courtesy: Queensland Railways)

A type 4–8–2 plus 2–8–4 Beyer-Garratt engine, one of thirty acquired for heavy duty service on the railroads of Queensland, is shown.
(*Courtesy: Queensland Railways*)

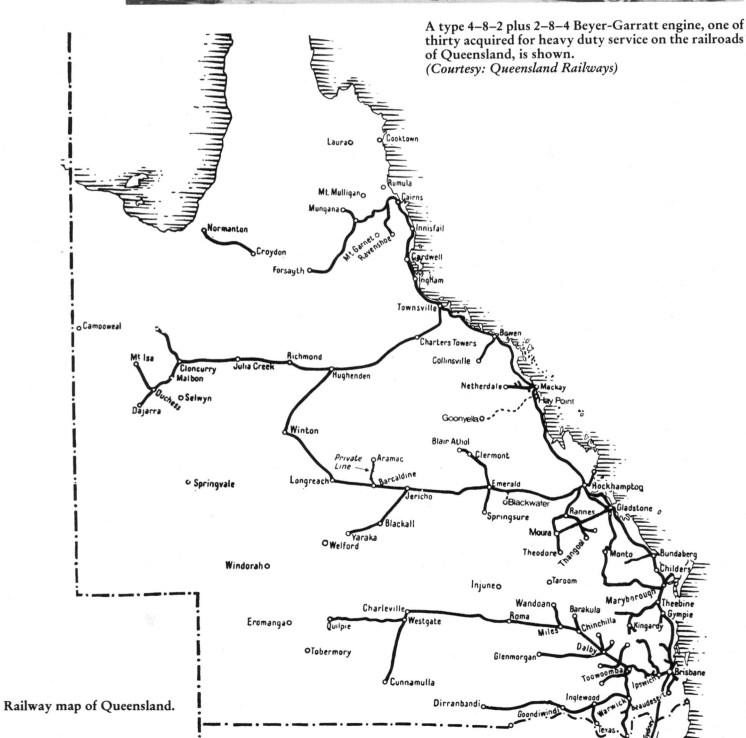

Railway map of Queensland.

showing Class PB15 locomotive). Some of the latter engines were provided by Kitson of Leeds, England, but most were built in the Ipswich workshops of the Queensland Government Railways or by other Queensland firms. Illustrated is an early twentieth-century locomotive used in the sugarcane fields of Queensland. The class C17 engines, type 4–8–0, were introduced in 1920 for heavy freight services. Additional heavy passenger and freight engines, class B18¼, type 4–6–2 (Pacific), appeared in 1926, and an improved version, class BB¼, was constructed in 1951. Also in 1951, Beyer Garratt type 4–8–2 + 2–8–4 steam locomotives saw use on various suburban lines near Brisbane.

All steam traction was suspended in Queensland in 1969, except for certain specialized operations such as mining, logging, and tourist excursions.

SOUTH AUSTRALIA

After the foundation of the state of South Australia in 1836, plans were immediately formulated to construct an 11.7-kilometer railway between Adelaide and Port Adelaide to speed the movement of people and goods between the capital city and its adjoining seaport. On 26 March 1847, the first ordinance was passed for regulating and constructing railways. This act did not authorize the construction of any specific rail system but set out, in considerable detail, the conditions, responsibilities, limitations, and privileges applying to any companies that might be empowered by "special acts" to build and operate railways.

The Adelaide City & Port Adelaide Railway Company, a private organization, was soon authorized by a government act to construct and operate a railway between the inland city and the seaport. The selected gauge was 4 feet 8½ inches. The government reserved the right to eventually purchase the rail line and placed a limitation upon the grant of lands. However, negotiations failed shortly thereafter and the project was abandoned.

In October 1851 the rail proposal was renewed when the South Australia governor and legislative council approved the construction of the Adelaide–Port Adelaide railroad using public funds. This action actually laid the foundation for an extensive system of state-owned railways throughout Australia. The newly proposed railway in South Australia had a gauge fixed at 5 feet 3 inches instead of 4 feet 8½ inches. Rails were the same type that Brunel had used on the seven-foot gauge Great

This is an old sketch of Isambard Kingdom Brunel, eminent engineer, bridge builder, and railroad entrepreneur in England who fostered the use of the broad gauge 7-foot 0¼-inch tracks on railroads in England and other locations around the world. *(Courtesy: Science Museum, London)*

Western line in England. They weighed sixty-three pounds per yard and were laid on longitudinal timbers. A "Board of Undertakers" supervised the construction, assisted by Benjamin H. Babbage, a local chief engineer, and by Isambard K. Brunel (see illustration), chief engineer of the Great Western Railway Company, as agent and consulting engineer. The longitudinal sleepers, showing signs of decomposition a few years later, were replaced in 1868–69 with regular wooden ties. The Adelaide & Port Railway was officially opened on 21 April 1856.

Subsequent railway expansion in South Australia was north and east from Adelaide. In 1870 the 5-foot 3-inch gauge line was pushed approximately one hundred miles north to the copper mining center at Burra. By 1880 this line was extended approximately another forty-five miles to Terowie. In 1883, taking an easterly course, the wide-gauge tracks ran twenty-two miles to Aldgate, and in 1885 the railroad reached another one hundred miles to the South Australia–Victoria border at Wolseley. By 1887 construction on the same 5-foot 3-inch gauge tracks in Victoria had reached its western border with South Australia, which permitted the incorporation of Intercolonial Express.

(Locomotives and rolling stock were operated on a joint ownership basis in the Intercolonial Express, an arrangement which has remained in force to this day.)

Based on the knowledge that narrow-gauge rail lines were cheaper to build and operate, in the late 1860s the South Australian government made an unfortunate decision to revert to this type of construction in all future railroads. Eight such lines subsequently originated at various isolated ports on the coast, running into the wheatland areas. These small systems were later merged into four primary operating conglomerates, one of which was the Western Railway centered at Port Wakefield at the head of Gulf St. Vincent. The Northern Railway started at Port Pirie on Spencer Gulf in 1875, and ran about forty miles northeast to inland Peterborough by 1881.

With the discovery of silver in the Silverton and Broken Hill areas of western New South Wales, and with the closest seaport at Port Pirie, the South Australian government extended the narrow-gauge line from Peterborough about 120 miles to Cockburn on the border. Over this route many fortunes traveled from the silver mines to the smelters at Port Pirie. Traffic to and from Broken Hill, four years after the railway was installed, yielded for the South Australian government about a half-million pounds sterling of annual income, or 44 percent of the entire revenue of its railways; this was a small sum compared with the vast wealth the ore trains would generate in subsequent periods.

Railway development in South Australia had been jointly carried out by South Australian Railways (SAR) and by various private railway companies. In 1899, however, South Australian Railways became the sole operator in this part of Australia. In 1975 the State Transport Authority was formed, absorbing the former South Australian Railways, and in 1978 this change went a step further when all railways service and freight operations in the state were handed over to the Australian National Railways Commission. Today the State Transport Authority operates all rail passenger service in the metropolitan area of Adelaide.

SOUTH AUSTRALIA RAILWAY CONSTRUCTION TIMETABLE

1856   Adelaide to Port Adelaide
1857   Adelaide to Gawler
1857   Adelaide to Northfield
1868   Port Adelaide to Dry Creek
1873   Adelaide–Glenelg (closed 1929; now tramway)
1878   Semaphore Road Line (closed 1978)
1879   Glenelg and South Coast Tramway (closed 1880)
1880   Holdfast Bay Railway (Adelaide–Glenelg closed 1929)
1882   Woodville to Grange
1883   Adelaide–Bridgewater
1894   Grange to Henley Beach
1908   Glanville to Outer Harbor
1913   Goodwood to Marino
1915   Marino to Willunga (Hallett Cove to Willunga closed 1969)
1940   Albert Park to Hendon
1940   Woodville to Finsbury
1914   Salisbury to Penfield
1976   Port Stanvac to Christie Downs
1978   Christie Downs to Noarlunga Centre

Steam Locomotives in South Australia

The development of steam locomotives in South Australia can be described as a prodigious trial-and-error evaluation of a vast assortment of steam engine types, examples, designs, and classes.

With the opening of the Adelaide & Port Railway on 21 April 1856, the three pioneer locomotives, manufactured by Fairbairns of Manchester, England, were named "Adelaide," "Victoria," and "Albert." These engines arrived in Australia on the brig *Theodore* after a long voyage (3 July 1855 to 1 November 1855). The locomotives were assembled at Port Adelaide under the guidance of a Fairbairns representative, and their names placed on the side of the boiler in large brass letters on a red background. The boiler case was painted green and the smoke funnel was bright copper. These engines, designed in England by I. K. Brunel, had the following specifications:

Cylinders	15-inch diameter; 24-inch stroke
Drive wheels	5-foot 3-inch diameter
Lead wheels	3-foot 4-inch diameter
Operating weight	23 tons (engine)
Boiler working pressure	80 pounds per square inch
Fuel consumption	135 pounds wood or 65 pounds coal per mile.

These locomotives were similar to the SAR locomotive no. 1 pictured; the tender was added in

Pictured is steam locomotive no. 1, first used on the railways of South Australia. It was a type 2–4–0 tank engine which started service in 1856. The builder was Fairbairn. The machine was converted to a tender type in 1869 and withdrawn from service in 1871. Cylinders were fifteen by twenty-four inches, and the working boiler pressure was eighty pounds per square inch.
(Courtesy: South Australian Railways)

Shown is a tender engine, no. 4, class B, type 2–4–0, used on the South Australian Railways starting in 1856. This engine was converted to a tank type in 1875; note water tank under engine cab. The locomotive was transformed into a railroad crane in 1887 and was condemned in 1938. Specifications were:

Cylinders	14 by 20 inches
Drive wheels	5-foot 6-inch diameter
Boiler working pressure	130 pounds per square inch
Tractive effort	6560 pounds
Operating weight	31.80 tons
Capacities	500 gallons water; 75 hundred weights coal
Overall length	26 feet 6.5 inches.

Two class B tender locomotives were originally im-

ported from Robert Stephenson for working the lightly laid track between Adelaide and Gawler, and it was no. 4 that hauled the official opening train to Gawler on 5 October 1857. The two engines continued to work the Gawler line for some years, but were also used on the Port line. After rebuilding as tank engines in the mid-1870s, both engines were used extensively on Port line trains. As later rebuilt, with a radial crane mounted behind the cab, and with the cab removed, the two engines finished their days as shunting engines at the SAR Islington workshops.
(Courtesy: South Australian Railways)

Illustrated is engine no. 18, type 4–4–0, class D. Two units were built by Robert Stephenson and placed in service in 1859 to work the lightly constructed Gawler-Kapunda line which opened in 1860. The leading four wheeled bogie made this type of engine most useful on light lines, and further orders were placed up to 1867. During 1904–05 it was decided to overhaul four of the engines and use them for working the Tailem Bend-Pinnaroo railway. These engines were last condemned in 1928. Specifications were:

Cylinders	15.5 by 22 inches
Drive wheels	5-foot 4-inch diameter
Boiler working pressure	130 pounds per square inch
Tractive effort	9130 pounds
Operating weight	47 tons (engine plus tender)
Capacities	1500 gallons water; 83.25 hundredweights coal
Overall length	42 feet 11.5 inches.

(Courtesy: South Australian Railways)

Two class C locomotives, built by Robert Stephenson, were the second group of engines imported for use on the Gawler line in 1856. Pictured is engine no. 6, type 2–4–0. Both engines gave satisfactory service for many years and were last condemned in 1926. Both had been rebuilt in the period 1884–85, acquiring at the same time "Thow" cabs with circular windows. They were long used on the Northern lines of South Australia. Specifications were as follows:

Cylinders	14 by 20 inches
Drive wheels	4-foot 6-inch diameter
Boiler working pressure	130 pounds per square inch
Tractive effort	8020 pounds
Operating weight	42 tons (engine plus tender)
Capacities	1060 gallons water; 75.75 hundredweights coal
Overall length	42 feet 10 inches.

(Courtesy: South Australian Railways)

Illustrated is engine no. 19, class A, type 2–4–0, of which several units were placed in service on the South Australian Railways in the period 1868–73. These engines were manufactured by Robert Stephenson & Company. This engine was unique in that it only pumped water into the boiler when running. The first two class A locomotives were imported for use on the light Roseworthy-Tarlee railway, but on arrival proved to be too heavy and too rigid for the track. They were then transferred to duties on the Port line; here they proved successful and consequently a third machine was introduced. Throughout their life they worked suburban passenger and goods trains, although one was stationed at Strathalbyn for a short period to work Milang trains. Specifications were:

Cylinders	14 by 22 inches
Drive wheels	5-foot diameter
Boiler working pressure	130 pounds per square inch
Tractive effort	7940 pounds
Operating weight	30.20 tons
Capacities	225 gallons water; 13.75 hundredweights coal
Overall length	26 feet 6 inches.

(Courtesy: South Australian Railways)

Pictured is a class E tank locomotive, type 2–4–0, placed in service during the period 1862 to 1882. Specifications were as follows:

Cylinders	15 by 21 inches
Drive wheels	5-foot 6-inch diameter
Boiler working pressure	130 pounds per square inch
Tractive effort	7910 pounds
Operating weight	31.5 tons
Capacities	600 gallons water; 12 hundredweights coal
Overall length	26 feet 4 inches.

As purchased, all class E locomotives were built by Slaughter, Gruning & Company, or as the firm was later known, the Avonside Engine Company. Three of these locomotives were imported for the Melbourne and Essendon Railway, Victoria, but as traffic had declined, only one was retained (B.no. 458), one was sold to the SAR (no. 459), while a third (no. 488) was sold to the Lyttleton & Christchurch Railway of New Zealand. Following the eventual failure of the Melbourne & Essendon Railway Company in 1865, their engine was purchased by the SAR. Meanwhile the engine sold to New Zealand had proven successful, and a further three were purchased by that system from the builder. When the New Zealand government decided to convert the broad gauge Lyttleton Christchurch Railway to a 3-foot 6-inch gauge, the locomotives and rolling stock were offered for sale. A total of nine engines of various classes were purchased by the SAR and were loaded aboard the vessel "Hyderabad" for shipment to Port Adelaide. Unfortunately this ship ran aground off the coast of New Zealand, but the engines and rolling stock were later recovered and brought on to South Australia. In service the class E engines worked passenger and goods trains and performed shunting duties in the suburban area.
(Courtesy: South Australian Railways)

Illustrated are the class F tank locomotives, type 4–6–2, which were most commonly used on local passenger traffic in South Australia. A total of forty-four machines were built at the James Martin shops, Gawler, at the Perry Engineering Works, and at the Islington workshops of the SAR. These engines were introduced in 1902 and were finally withdrawn in 1967. Specifications were as follows:

Cylinders	17.5 by 24 inches
Drive wheels	5-foot 3-inch diameter
Boiler working pressure	185 pounds per square inch
Tractive effort	18,340 pounds
Operating weight	59 tons
Capacities	1160 gallons water; 45 hundredweights coal
Overall length	40 feet 7 inches.

There were two series of class F engines. The first two locomotives were originally purchased to operate goods trains over the lightly constructed Roseworthy-Tarlee line, a railway designed in the first place to use horse traction. The first of the second series of class F engines, no. 167, was built by the Islington workshops as a pattern engine for working Adelaide suburban trains. The design was so successful that large orders for additional engines were placed as indicated above. In service the class F engines became known as "Dollys" and worked all suburban lines, including the South line to Belair. Also, for a long time they worked some trains to Hamley Bridge and Willunga, and in the 1920s one was stationed at Strathalbyn to handle Milang line trains.
(Courtesy: South Australian Railways)

Pictured is another class F, type 4–6–2 tank locomotive, the type most commonly seen on local passenger service in South Australia between 1902 and the time of their withdrawal in 1967. This was one of a total of forty-four such machines which were built starting in 1902. Pictured is engine no. 239 which was converted to oil burning in 1952. It is shown with a consist of "dog box" carriages on the Sempahore Road line which was closed on 29 October 1978 after one-hundred years of use.
(Courtesy: South Australian Railways)

Illustrated is tank engine no. 165, type 4–0–0, class GE which was manufactured by Beyer Peacock & Company in 1891. Two similar units, first used in 1881, were taken over from the Glenelg & Suburban Railway Company in 1899. Specifications were as follows:

Cylinders	13 by 18 inches
Drive wheels	4-foot diameter
Boiler working pressure	145 pounds per square inch
Tractive effort	7810 pounds
Operating weight	29 tons
Capacities	460 gallons water; 16 hundredweights coal
Overall length	25 feet 7 inches.

(Courtesy: South Australian Railways)

Shown is a type 0–4–0, class I (first series) tank locomotive built by Neilson for the Canterbury Railway of New Zealand in 1873. The engine was one of several salvaged from the shipwrecked "Hyderabad." It was purchased by the SAR from New Zealand in 1879 and was condemned in 1905. Specifications were:

Cylinders	9 by 16 inches
Drive wheels	2-foot 11-inch diameter
Boiler working pressure	130 pounds per square inch
Tractive effort	4100 pounds
Operating weight	12 tons
Capacities	160 gallson water; 4.5 hundredweights coal
Overall length	18 feet 2 inches.

(Courtesy: South Australian Railways)

Pictured is a class I, type 0–4–0 tank locomotive built by Beyer Peacock in 1888 for the engineer in charge. The engine was taken over by the SAR in 1910 and condemned in 1929. Specifications were:

Cylinders	12 by 18 inches
Drive wheels	3-foot diameter
Boiler working pressure	145 pounds per square inch
Tractive effort	8870 pounds
Operating weight	22 tons
Capacities	500 gallons water; 10 hundredweights coal
Overall length	21 feet 5 inches.

(Courtesy: South Australian Railways)

Pictured is engine no. 32, type 0–6–0, class J built by Beyer Peacock and placed in service in 1874. Specifications were:

Cylinders	17 by 24 inches
Drive wheels	5-foot diameter
Boiler working pressure	130 pounds per square inch
Tractive effort	12,770 pounds
Operating weight	57 tons (engine plus tender)
Capacities	1535 gallons water; 91 hundredweights coal
Overall length	43 feet 9 inches.

The two class J locomotives were the only 0-6-0 engines in service on the SAR For most of their working life they worked over the lines from Adelaide to Port Adelaide, Kapunda, and Terowie, although one was based at Murray Bridge for working trains over the Murray Lands lines for some time.
(Courtesy: South Australian Railways)

Engine no. 52, type 0–6–4, class K tank locomotive which was built by Dubs & Company in 1884 is shown here. These engines were condemned in 1938. Specifications were:

Cylinders	16.5 by 20 inches
Drive wheels	4-foot diameter
Boiler working pressure	130 pounds per square inch
Tractive effort	12,540 pounds
Operating weight	43 tons
Capacities	1060 gallons water; 38 hundredweights coal
Overall length	32 feet 6 inches.

The first of the class K locomotives were introduced to work the Morgan line which opened in 1878. Further engines were introduced during the 1880s and worked between Adelaide and Port Adelaide, and Adelaide and Terowie. The acquisition of the Gelelg lines in 1899 gave the class K locomotives additional territory, but they were permitted to work only over the South Terrace line. During the early years of the Murray Mallee lines east of Tailem Bend, up to the introduction of the big power in the 1920s, the class K engines, with one or two exceptions, gave satisfactory service on these lines.
(Courtesy: South Australian Railways)

Engine no. 39, type 4–4–0, class L tender locomotive built by Beyer Peacock and placed in service in 1880 is pictured. It was originally constructed as a tank engine but prior to service in South Australia was converted to the tender type. These were last condemned in 1934. Specifications were as follows:

Cylinders	16 by 22 inches
Drive wheels	5-foot diameter
Boiler working pressure	130 pounds per square inch
Tractive effort	10,370 pounds
Operating weight	57.75 tons
Capacities	2040 gallons water; 99 hundredweights coal
Overall length	46 feet 3 inches.

The four class L tank locomotives were introduced to handle the rapidly increasing traffic between Adelaide and Port Adelaide. As built, however, their axle loading was too heavy, and it was necessary to rebuild them as tender engines. It was in this form that they were issued to service for working the North line. With the opening of the Intercolonial Railway as far as Nairne in 1883, these engines were used for hauling trains over the heavily graded sections and continued this work until the introduction of the larger class Q locomotives two years later. In subsequent years they worked around Port Adelaide and Dry Creek, and were finally allotted to Murray Bridge for working Mallee line trains.
(*Courtesy: South Australian Railways*)

Shown is the first type 0–4–2, class M tank locomotive built by the Avonside Engine Company for the Canterbury Railways Company of New Zealand. Specifications were as follows:

Cylinders	12.5 by 16 inches
Drive wheels	4-foot 7-inch diameter
Boiler working pressure	130 pounds per square inch
Tractive effort	5020 pounds
Operating weight	22 tons
Capacities	580 gallons water; 16.75 hundredweights coal
Overall length	23 feet 3 inches.

Originally five such engines were brought from New Zealand. The earliest models were nos. 44 and 46 which featured well-tanks. Nos. 43, 45, and 47 were newer locomotives and had longer side tanks but small bunkers. In service these engines first worked the Port line and for a short period worked over the private Largs Bay line. In later years they operated trains to Henley Beach, Outer Harbour, and Semaphore, and were also used for working goods trains on the North line. A second series of class M engines were acquired from the Melbourne suburban electrification organization; their class E engines were converted to class M's on the SAR, and these worked suburban trains. The latter engines only survived a few years and were replaced by larger engines in 1926.
(Courtesy: South Australian Railways)

Illustrated is a type 4–6–0, class N tender locomotive built by the Baldwin Locomotive Works in 1881. This engine was subsequently rebuilt in the Islington workshops in 1904. Specifications were as follows:

Cylinders	19 by 24 inches
Drive wheels	5-foot diameter
Boiler working pressure	130 pounds per square inch
Tractive effort	15,900 pounds
Operational weight	(missing)
Capacities	3000 gallons; 106.35 hundredweights coal
Overall length	52 feet.

The two class N engines imported from Baldwin in the United States were intended for use on the steep grades of the Intercolonial Railway between Adelaide and Murray Bridge. Both seemed to perform well, however the failure of the governor's special opening train to Aldgate on 14 March 1883, cast suspicion not only on the quality of the engines, but upon the entire railway administration. However the N's continued to work trains over the Hills line until displaced by class Q and class R engines. Thereafter they saw little service for some years, until they were eventually rebuilt.
(Courtesy: South Australian Railways)

Pictured is a type 4–6–0, class N locomotive built by
Baldwin in 1881. This is a picture of a Hill's Run passenger train on a trestle in 1901 near the Adelaide
suburbs. See a previous illustration for class N details.
(Courtesy: South Australian Railways)

Illustrated is a tank engine, type 2–4–0, class P manufactured in 1884 by Beyer Peacock for use on the railroads of South Australia. Additional units were built
in 1893 by J. Martin & Company of Gawler, Australia.
This engine was withdrawn from service in 1957.
Specifications were:

Cylinders	16 by 20 inches
Drive wheels	5-foot diameter
Boiler working pressure	145 pounds per square inch
Tractive effort	10,520 pounds
Operating weight	33.5 tons
Capacities	600 gallons water; 30 hun- dredweights coal
Overall length	28 feet 5 inches.

Increased traffic over the Port line was responsible
for the introduction of the P class locomotive in the
first place. All these engines were initially involved in
suburban operations, principally working passenger
trains to Semaphore and Glenelg. In later years these
locomotives were more active in shunting duties at
Port Adelaide and Tailem Bend.
(Courtesy: South Australian Railways)

A view of a type 4–6–0, class Rx locomotive at the Adelaide station in 1980 is shown here. Previously this engine was known as class R, introduced in 1886 for hauling freight trains over the heavily graded sections of the Intercolonial Railway. The original engines were built by Dubs & Company. The design proved successful and in the period 1890–95 additional machines were constructed by J. Martin & Company of Gawler. Class R machine no. 102 was the first locomotive manufactured in South Australia. The thirty engines built in South Australia worked heavy goods trains over all the main broad gauge lines in the state. In 1899 the first class R engine to be rebuilt with a Belpaire firebox boiler was outshopped, and at the same time the "Thow" type cab was altered. All class R engines were subsequently rebuilt and designated class Rx, and later on when it became necessary to construct additional heavy goods engines, the class Rx design was chosen. Engines built as Rx were provided with eight-wheel bogie tenders compared with six-wheel tenders on the class R units. In addition to working heavy goods trains, the class R and class Rx engines worked the Adelaide-Melbourne expresses between Adelaide and Murray Bridge, usually double heading, and occasionally with a third banking engine pushing. When the big engines replaced the Rx locomotives on the heavy work in 1926, the latter were transferred to branch line operations and were active on the Murray Mallee and light lines such as Spaulding and Truro. The class Rx locomotives lasted well into the diesel era, and even in the mid-1960s they were the principal shunting power at most Adelaide and country marshalling yards. In the period 1909 to 1915 fifty-four class Rx units were built at the Islington workshops in South Australia, by North British Locomotive Company, and by Walkers, Ltd in Queensland. Specifications on the class Rx locomotives were:

Cylinders	18 by 24 inches
Drive wheels	4-foot 6-inch diameter
Boiler working pressure	175 pounds per square inch
Tractive effort	21,420 pounds
Operating weight	88.5 tons
Capacities	3750 gallons water; 156 hundredweights coal
Overall length	57 feet 11.75 inches.

(Courtesy: South Australian Railways)

Pictured is an old class Rx, type 4–6–0 locomotive, no. 207, built in 1913. This photograph was taken 26 April 1981 when the Port Adelaide to Port Dock railway celebrated its 125th birthday. For the occasion, the Australian Historical Society ran a special excursion using engine no. 207. The train carried end-loading carriages which had the familiar American clerestory roof bodies. See previous illustrations for additional data on the class Rx locomotives.
(Courtesy: South Australian Railways)

Illustrated a passenger train crossing the Hamley Bridge in South Australia with a society holiday special to Spalding on 19 October 1974. Engine no. 207, type 4–6–0, class Rx, was built by the North British Locomotive Company and entered service 12 May 1913. All maintenance since 1968 has been furnished by the society.
(Courtesy: Australian Railway Historical Society)

A 1905 picture of the Adelaide station is shown—in the foreground is the Melbourne Express headed by a class Rx locomotive on the right and a class R engine on the left.
(Courtesy: South Australian Railways)

This is a head-on view of another class Rx locomotive. See a previous illustration for details.
(Courtesy: South Australian Railways)

Shown is a side view of a class Rx, type 4–6–0 tender locomotive which was built by Dubs & Company in 1886. See an earlier illustration technical details.
(Courtesy: South Australian Railways)

Illustrated is a class T tender locomotive, type 4–8–0, used on the narrow 3-foot 6-inch gauge railways of the SAR. These engines were built over the period 1903–17 by James Martin & Company of Gawler, Walkkers Ltd., Queensland, and by the Islington workshops of the SAR. Specifications were:

Cylinders	16.5 by 22 inches
Drive wheels	3-foot 7-inch diameter
Boiler working pressure	185 pounds per square inch
Tractive effort	78 tons
Capacities	2418 gallons water; 160 hundredweights coal
Overall length	54 feet.

A class T engine. no. 180, was originally constructed as a pattern engine for a more powerful type of narrow-gauge engine to handle increasing traffic on the Northern narrow-gauge lines of the SAR. The design proved to be most useful, and large orders were placed for more class T locomotives. At first they operated over the Northern lines, and the first was seen in the southeast in 1935. A number were also transferred to the Eyre Peninsula system. The only narrow-gauge lines not worked by class T engines were the Glencoe lines and the terminal parts of the Beachport and Kingston lines in the southeast. During World War II, a number of these engines were loaned to the Commonwealth Railways for working to Alice Springs. On the Southeast system they worked until the gauge was widened to Mount Gambier and Millicent. On the Eyre Peninsula system the class T engines were gradually displaced by 830 diesels during the 1960s, and on the Peterborough Division, they were active up to the time of conversion of the Port Pirie-Broken Hill line in January 1970. Five class T locomotives were converted to 5-foot 3-inch gauge and reconverted to 3-foot 6-inch gauge in 1922–23 and 1949 respectively.
(Courtesy: South Australia Railways)

Shown is a class S, type 4–4–0 tender locomotive built by James Martin & Company in 1894 and 1903 for express service on the SAR railroads. When first introduced the class S engines hauled the Melbourne Express between Murray Bridge and Serviceton, often double-heading with a class Q, or in later years another class S engine. They also worked express trains between Adelaide and Terowie. After the introduction of the class 600 Pacifics, the class S locomotives were displaced to lighter duties and worked on secondary lines such as those to Barmera, Victor Harbour, or Moonta. Although not ideally suited to shunting with their large driving wheels, some were to be found shunting at Tailem Bend and Mile End during the 1950s. Specifications were as follows:

Engine no.	134
Cylinders	18 by 24 inches
Drive wheels	6-foot 6-inch diameter
Boiler working pressure	150 pounds per square inch
Tractive effort	12,710 pounds
Operating weight	82 tons
Capacities	3750 gallons water; 156 hundred weights coal
Overall length	57 feet.

(Courtesy: South Australian Railways)

Pictured is engine no. 146, class V, type 0–4–4, used on 3-foot 6-inch gauge tracks of the SAR. These tank units were built in the period 1877 to 1893 by Beyer Peacock and by J. Martin & Company of Gawler, Australia. The last engine of this class was condemned in 1953. Specifications were as follows:

Cylinders	9.5 by 15 inches
Drive wheels	3-foot diameter
Boiler working pressure	130 pounds per square inch
Tractive effort	4150 pounds
Operating weight	15.7 tons
Capacities	300 gallons water; 12 hundred-weights coal
Overall length	21 feet 3 inches.

The first engines of this class were placed in service on the light Kingston line, which had previously been operated by horse traction. They were not entirely successful on mainline work and were relegated to shunting duties when the class W locomotives were introduced on the line in 1878. In later years all class V engines were employed as shunt locomotives and worked at Port Wakefield, Port Pirie, and Wallaroo. The last two surviving members of this class, nos. 9 and 146, shunted at the Peterborough Locomotive Depot until the 1950s.
(Courtesy: South Australian Railways)

Pictured is a class Y tender locomotive, type 2–6–0, built by Beyer Peacock, by J. Martin & Company, Gawler, and by the SAR workshops at Islington over the period 1885–98. Numerically this was the largest class on the SAR, a total of 137 machines having been constructed for use on the 3-foot 6-inch gauge tracks. Specifications (engine no. 179) were as follows:

Cylinders	14.5 by 20 inches
Drive wheels	3-foot 3-inch diameter
Boiler working pressure	185 pounds per square inch
Tractive effort	17,000 pounds
Operating weight	50 tons
Capacities	1600 gallons water; 40 hundred-weights coal
Overall length	39 feet 3 inches.

Following the poor performance of the class X locomotives it was decided to seek further English machines to provide the additional necessary motive power required for the spreading narrow-gauge network. The engine was designed by Beyer Peacock and the initial group showed that they were well suited to the requirements of hauling goods and passenger trains. At first they remained confined to the Northern lines and worked trains to Cockburn and Oodnadatta, as well as handling most of the traffic over the shorter lines of the network. The first class Y engine in the southeast arrived in 1914, and this class of engine could work all lines there but the Kingston line. During the first quarter of the twentieth century most of the Martin engines were rebuilt with larger boilers and classified Yx and were used on the Eyre Peninsula system.
(Courtesy: South Australian Railways)

This illustration shows a goods tank engine, type 0–6–0, built in 1885 by Kitson & Company for use on the railway between Goolwa and Port Elliot which opened in 1854 and used horse traction. No specification data was available. This was withdrawn in 1923.
(Courtesy: South Australian Railways)

This is a historic picture of the famous "Coffee Pot" steam motor coach, one of two built by Kitson & Company in 1906. These were used on the 3-foot 6-inch gauge Port Augusta to Marree line. One engine, in 1981, was being restored by the Pichi Richi Railway at Quorn. The other had been condemned in 1935.
(Courtesy: South Australian Railways)

A class 500 Mountain, type 4–8–4 locomotive used on the Melbourne Express is shown. This picture was taken in March 1934 in a railroad roundhouse in South Australia. These engines were constructed starting in 1926 by William Armstrong-Whitworth Company. They were converted to class 500B during the period 1929–36. The 500s were withdrawn from service in 1963. No technical data was available.

When Mr. W. A. Webb became Commissioner of the South Australian Railways in 1922, he set about rehabilitating the State Railway system and soon placed orders for thirty large and powerful locomotives. The largest of this series were the class 500, popularly known as the Mountain type engines, and these were introduced for working heavy trains through the Adelaide Hills. For many years they worked most heavy trains, including the "Overland" between Adelaide and Tailem Bend. They also saw service on some other lines, mainly Terowie, Port Pirie, and Victor Harbour. As rebuilt with boosters and four-wheel trailing trucks they became known as class 500B. They continued to work the Adelaide Hills line until replaced by the class 900 and class 930 diesel-electric locomotives in the 1950s.
(Courtesy: South Australian Railways)

This is another class 500 Mountain type 4–8–4 locomotive.
(Courtesy: South Australian Railways)

Three views of the class 520, type 4–8–4 locomotive, designed and constructed in the SAR workshops at Islington over the period 1943–47 are shown. Engine no. 520, first of the series, entered service on 11 October 1943. It was restored in 1972 at a cost of twenty thousand dollars and refinished in black livery; it was repainted green in 1975. In 1978 the Society (Australian Railway Historical) spent a further thirty thousand dollars on tender rebuilding and repainting. It is used presently on holiday runs during the summer months, known as the "Steamranger." Specifications were:

Cylinders	20.5 by 28 inches
Drive wheels	5-foot 6-inch diameter
Boiler working pressure	215 pounds per square inch
Tractive effort	32,600 pounds
Operating weight	200.60 tons (engine plus tender)
Capacities	9100 gallons water; 9.75 tons coal
Overall length	87 feet 4 inches.

During the early 1940s the need arose in the SAR for additional passenger engines for working the Northern main lines, but also suitable for working the lighter lines laid with sixty-pound rail and for working goods trains. The engine designed to fit this need was the class 520. Later these engines received fame throughout Australia for their streamlined appearance. Engines 523 and onwards were different from the first three of the series in that they had altered front end streamlining. In service they worked most passenger trains and some goods trains to Terowie and Port Pirie. They also worked some passenger trains to Tailem Bend, worked the lines to Pinnaroo and Barmera, and were able to work to Mount Gambier after conversion of that line to 5-foot 3-inch gauge in the early 1950s. Other places commonly visited included Victor Harbour and Moonta. Even in the early 1960s it was common to see a class 520 at the front of a passenger train to Port Pirie, Terowie, or Tailem Bend, and they were the last of the big engines to be ousted by the diesels.

(Courtesy: South Australian Railways)

Illustrated is a picture of a Pacific type 4–6–2, class 600 locomotive, no. 626, pulling a Tailem Bend train, on 5-foot 3-inch tracks, into the Adelaide rail station in 1959. The front two carriages built in 1900 were of the end-loading type. The last carriage shown was originally built in 1895 for use on narrow-gauge railways. The last class 600 engine was withdrawn in 1961. Specifications were as follows:

Manufacturer:	Armstrong Whitworth (1926)
Cylinders	24 by 28 inches
Drive wheels	6-foot 3-inch diameter
Boiler working pressure	200 pounds per square inch
Tractive effort	39,300 pounds
Operating weight	197 tons
Capacities	7250 gallons water; 12 tons coal
Overall length	79 feet 3 inches.

The class 600 locomotives were of the Pacific type intended for hauling express trains and were mostly used for working passenger trains, including the "Overland," and fast goods trains between Tailem Bend and Serviceton. Their route availability was limited because of their heavy axle loading. The only other lines frequented by them were to Victor Harbour, Terowie, and Port Pirie. In later years they worked the new broad-gauge line to Mount Gambier. During the 1930s, when they were fitted with a higher pressure boiler, they also acquired smoke deflectors. Because of their restricted availability they quickly became redundant when displaced from the express runs by the diesels and were one of the first group of big engines to be scrapped.
(Courtesy: South Australian Railways)

Pictured is another class 600 Pacific type 4–6–2 tender locomotive used on the 5-foot 3-inch gauge railroads of South Australia. Here a class 600 locomotive heads the Melbourne Express in 1926. See a previous illustration for details.
(Courtesy: South Australian Railways)

The locomotive, no. 621, shown is a Pacific type 4–6–2, class 620, built over the period 1936–38 at the Islington workshops. This engine in 1981 was still being used infrequently on historical runs in South Australia. Specifications were:

Cylinders	18.5 by 28 inches
Drive wheels	5-foot 6-inch diameter
Boiler working pressure	200 pounds per square inch
Tractive effort	25,000 pounds
Operating weight	140.75 tons
Capacities	5200 gallons water; 9 tons coal
Overall length	59 feet 7 inches.

During the 1930s there was a need for light passenger engines to work the light lines laid with sixty-pound rails. The class 620 was a light Pacific engine, able to work on this light track and still work express trains at high speeds on level routes. These engines worked most Port Pirie passenger trains until the introduction of the class 520; they also worked trains to Moonta, Morgan, Balmera, and Pinnaroo. As more class 520 engines entered service, more of the class 620s were allotted to Tailem Bend and worked Murray Lands trains and services to the southeast. The Willunga passenger train was usually worked by a class 620 in the last years before its cessation. In the early 1960s the 620s still worked a few passenger trains, mainly to Port Pirie or Tailem Bend.

(Courtesy: South Australian Railways)

Pictured is a class 700 Mikado, type 2–8–2, locomotive, no. 701, on an Adelaide-Oak Bank passenger run in 1955. These engines were built by Armstrong Whitworth starting in 1926. These engines were withdrawn in 1968. Specifications were:

Cylinders	22 by 28 inches
Drive wheels	4-foot 9-inch diameter
Boiler working pressure	200 pounds per square inch
Tractive effort	40,400 pounds
Operating weight	171.3 tons (engine plus tender)
Capacities	5900 gallons water; 17 tons coal
Overall length	73 feet 1 inch.

These Mikado type engines were the third group to be introduced by Mr. Webb and were designed for working goods trains over the lighter sixty-pound track that the Mountains and the Pacifics were too heavy for. Throughout their life they worked mainly on the secondary lines such as those to Moonta, Gladstone, Morgan, Victor Harbour, Renmark, and Pinnaroo. When used on the heavy main lines it was essentially on the wayside goods trains. Although basically goods engines, they did work a number of passenger services, mainly on the Adelaide Hills line. The availability of these engines to work the lighter lines maintained a limited demand for their services after the Mountain and Pacific engines had all been scrapped, and in the mid-1960s they were still working a few trains to Willunga, Robertstown, and Tailem Bend.

(Courtesy: South Australian Railways)

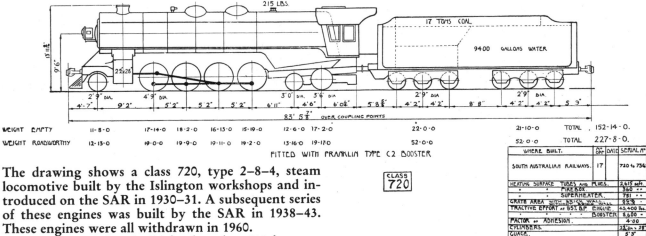

215 LBS.

17 TONS COAL

9400 GALLONS WATER

9'6"   13½"

22×28

2'9" DIA. 4'9" DIA.   3'0" DIA 3'6" DIA   2'9" DIA   2'9" DIA.
4'-7"   9'2"   5'2" 5'2" 5'2" 6'11" 4'6" 6'0¼" 5'8⅝" 4'2" 4'2" 8'8" 4'2" 4'2" 5'9"

83' 5⅞"   OVER COUPLING POINTS

WEIGHT EMPTY	11·8·0	17·14·0	18·2·0	16·13·0	15·19·0	12·6·0	17·2·0		22·0·0		21·10·0	TOTAL 152·14·0.
WEIGHT ROADWORTHY	12·13·0	19·0·0	19·9·0	19·11·0	19·2·0	13·16·0	19·17·0	52·0·0		52·0·0		TOTAL 227·8·0.

FITTED WITH FRANKLIN TYPE C2 BOOSTER

CLASS
720

WHERE BUILT.	N° OFF	DATE	SERIAL N°
SOUTH AUSTRALIAN RAILWAYS.	17		720 to 736

HEATING SURFACE TUBES AND FLUES.	2,615 sq.ft.
" " FIREBOX.	360 "
" " SUPERHEATER.	751 "
GRATE AREA WITH BRICK WALL.	46·8 "
TRACTIVE EFFORT at 85% B.P. ENGINE.	43,400 lbs.
" " " BOOSTER	8,600 "
FACTOR of ADHESION.	4·00
CYLINDERS.	21⅝" × 28"
GUAGE.	5'3"
WALSCHAERT VALVE GEAR.	

The drawing shows a class 720, type 2–8–4, steam locomotive built by the Islington workshops and introduced on the SAR in 1930–31. A subsequent series of these engines was built by the SAR in 1938–43. These engines were all withdrawn in 1960.

It was intended to build further class 710 locomotives to work the sixty-pound lines, however the failure of the class 710 machines to meet requirements caused the plans to be modified. Consequently the class 720 locomotives were introduced where the booster and firebox were supported on a four-wheel trailing truck. Technically this engine of a type 2–8–4 was a "Berkshire" class, although it was referred to in South Australia as a "Big Mikado." In their first years, the 720s worked many of the lighter lines, but it became evident that the engines were not ideally suited. Later on these class 720 engines spent the rest of their days sharing the heavy lines with the class 500 machines.

Specifications on the class 720 locomotives were as follows:

Gear	Walschaert's
Cylinders	22 by 28 inches
Drive wheels	4-foot 9-inch diameter
Boiler	
Grate area	46.8 square feet
Heating surface	
Tubes and flues	2615 square feet
Firebox	360
Superheater	751
Total	3726 square feet
Boiler working pressure	215 pounds per square inch
Tractive effort	52,000 pounds (43,400 pounds at 85 percent of boiler working pressure)
Operating weight	227 tons plus 8 hundredweights (engine plus tender)
Capacities	9400 gallons water; 17 tons coal
Overall length	83 feet 5⅞ inches.

(Courtesy: South Australian Railways)

Pictured is a class 400 Beyer Garratt locomotive built by Beyer Peacock & Company in 1953–54. No technical data was available.

During World War II there was an urgent need for additional motive power on Australia's narrow-gauge lines, and in 1942 the Land Transport Board approved the construction of sixty-five Garratt locomotives, built to untried Western Australia designs. These engines were known as Australian Standard Garratts. Twelve of these machines were built at the SAR Islington workshops although none were used in South Australia during the war. The Garratts subsequently proved to be a most unsuccessful class of locomotive. After the war the SAR acquired six such engines from the Western Australian Government Railways in 1952 for use on ore trains between Cockburn and Port Pirie, but they were only intended as a temporary measure pending the arrival of the class 400 Garratts; the latter six units were built at the Midland railway workshops of the WAGR and at Newport railway workshops in Victoria.

Introduced for hauling heavy ore trains between the locations mentioned above, the class 400 locomotives soon lived down the unfortunate Garratt reputation created with the class 300 machines. They worked the ore trains and the Broken Hill expresses, and their only relief from working the main line during these days of large scale operation was an occasional trip to Terowie. In 1963 their work was taken over by the class 830 diesels, and the class 400 engines were all placed in storage at Peterborough. Apart from an occasional run, they remained there until 1969 when a few were placed in traffic while the narrow-gauge diesels were being converted to operate the new standard-gauge line.

(Courtesy: South Australian Railways)

This illustration pictures a type 0–4–2 wood-burning tank engine which was used in the sugar cane fields of the Fairymead Sugar Company, Ltd. in Australia. The so-called "Cabbage Stacker" operated about 1925 on 2-foot gauge tracks and had these general specifications:

Cylinders	7 by 10 inches
Coupled drivers	24-inch diameter
Boiler	24⅝-inch diameter
Engine weight	18,800 pounds.

(Courtesy: Frederick Westing collection)

The Central Australian Railway, running from Port Augusta in South Australia to Alice Springs in the Northern Territory was a 650-mile line initiated early in the twentieth century. The line was not completed until 1929. The pioneer train to travel on this 3-foot 6-inch gauge railroad is now on display at a monument site at the Alice Springs railway station, and this is shown in the illustration.

(Courtesy: South Australian Railways)

Here is a 1979 picture of the Pichi Richi Railway excursion train, with engine no. W934, at Frenchman's Creek, Pichi RichiPass near Port Augusta, Flinders Ranges, originally part of the "Ghan" route to Alice Springs. This was a narrow-gauge 3-foot 6-inch railway.

(Courtesy: South Australian Railway)

1869. The original locomotives also resembled the class B locomotive in service in the Adelaide region in 1856.

The history of the railway steam engine in South Australia is set forth in the accompanying locomotive photographs and technical specification data where available. In many cases, the alphabetical class designations for various engines do not follow the order one would expect. Following the locomotives no. 1 and class B referred to above, which became operational in 1856, the succeeding railway machines introduced into South Australia were all used on 5-foot 3-inch tracks unless otherwise indicated.

The last four photographs in this section are representative of various locomotives used in South Australia: "coffee pot" steam motor coach, "cabbage stacker" wood-burning tank engine, early twentieth-century motor carriage, excursion train Pichi Richi.

TASMANIA

On Tasmania's northwest coast a forty-four mile tramway with a 3-foot gauge wooden rail and horse traction opened early in the 1840s. It ran from Burnie south to the tin mines at Waratah. Steel rails were substituted in 1844 by the Emu Bay & Mt. Bischoff Railway Company, relaid to a gauge of 3 feet 6 inches. This firm was taken over in 1895 by the Emu Bay Railway Company, owned by famous Australian entrepreneur J. S. Reid, and in 1897 the line was extended about fifty miles to the Zeehan Queenstown mining areas. The Emu Bay Railway used heavy Beyer Garratt locomotives with success on the steep grades in that part of the island and was the last railroad to utilize so-called Australian Standard Garratt locomotives, which had long been a source of many operating and maintenance headaches in Australia.

The first public railroad in Tasmania, a private endeavor on 5-foot 3-inch tracks running about twenty-five miles from Launceston to Deloraine, was known as the Launceston & Western Railway. This line went bankrupt in 1872 and was taken over by the Tasmanian government. The second public rail line in Tasmania, another private venture called the Tasmanian Main Line Railway Company, opened in 1876, operating on 3-foot 6-inch gauge tracks for about 120 miles between Launceston and Hobart. Movements on the latter line plus operations on the original Launceston & Western system were combined over a nine-mile stretch out of Launceston, by installing a third rail to permit the simultaneous use of two types of rolling stock. All tracks were converted to the common 3-foot 6-inch gauge in 1888.

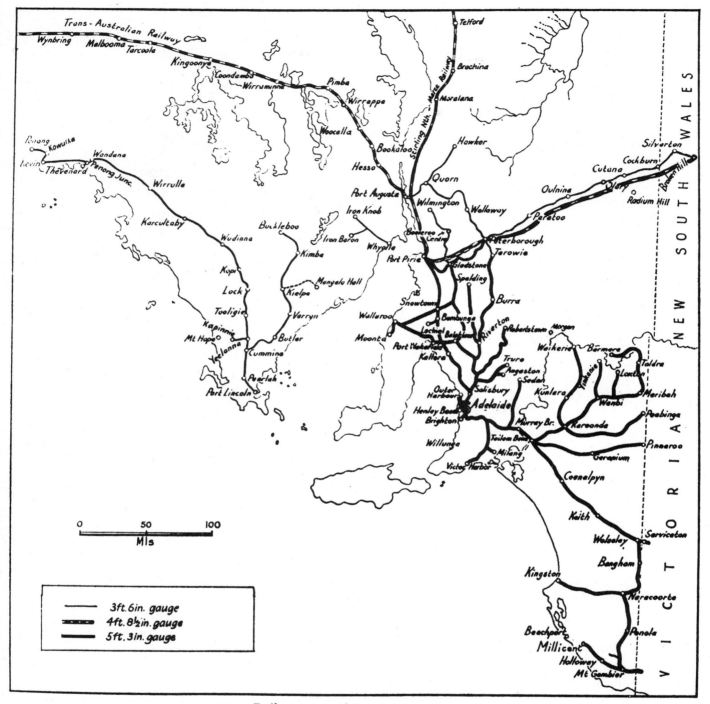

Railway map of South Australia.

It is interesting to note that one Tasmania railroad, the Mt. Lyell Mining and Railway Company, operated a spectacular twenty-one-mile rail line from Regatta Point to Queenstown that included about four miles of Abt-rack rail on a steep incline. This railroad began operations in 1899 and was abandoned in 1963.

Another famous railway in Tasmania was the scenic North-East Dundas Tramway which had 2-foot gauge tracks. In 1910 the first Beyer-Garratt locomotive, type 0–4–0 + 0–4–0, weighing about thirty tons, was placed in service on this tramway. The rail line was abandoned in 1939, and in 1947, one of the railway's small Beyer Garratt engines

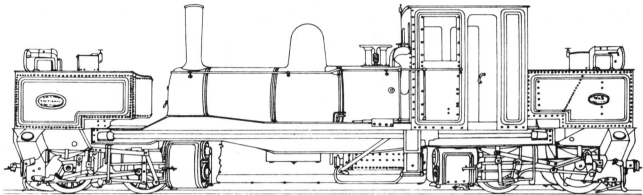

Pictured is an M class engine, the first Garratt 0–4–0 plus 0–4–0 compound locomotive built in 1909 by Beyer Peacock (no. 5292) for the 2-foot gauge North East Dundas Tramway in Tasmania. See attached drawing.

(Courtesy: Manchester Museum of Science & Technology)

was restored and returned to the Beyer Peacock works in Manchester, England, for preservation.

Following extensive correspondence with various railway entities in Tasmania, I was unable to secure any meaningful steam locomotive pictures and the required technical and specification information. The only available illustrations are a drawing and photograph of a Garratt type 0–4–0 + 0–4–0 built by Beyer Peacock in 1909.

VICTORIA

The first steam railway in Australia was the 5-foot 3-inch gauge Melbourne & Hobson's Bay Railway, running 3½ miles between Melbourne and Port Melbourne (sometimes described as from Flinders Street to Sandridge) in Victoria, which opened 12 September 1854 (see illustration). The rail line cost the construction company a prodi-

gious amount of money but it did generate Australia's first railway profits.

The next railway in Victoria involved a thirty-nine-mile line between Melbourne and Geelong, running southwest along Port Phillip Bay. This was completed in 1858 after four long years of toil and tribulation. At one time, a thousand men were employed on the project, which was kept going only by unrelenting efforts to finance the work through loans in Australia and England. It soon became clear that the railroad could not compete with intercoastal steamship shipping and it was sold in 1859 to the government of Victoria.

The railway boom in Victoria really started when the state government in 1862 pioneered inland railroads to two gold towns: northwest for about fifty miles from Geelong to Ballarat, and north by northwest about a hundred miles from Melbourne

This is a sketch of the first steam train that ran 3½ miles from Flinders Street to Sandridge on 12 September 1854 in Victoria.
(Courtesy: Victoria Railways)

to Bendigo. These first inland railroads were the most expensive ever built in Australia, since they had double tracks, easy curves, overhead road crossings, and fancy houses for railway officials. In addition, at the insistence of Victoria's chief surveyer, Andrew Clarke, the railroads used the most expensive, wide, Irish gauge of 5 feet 3 inches and at the same time rather foolishly employed relatively narrow carriages and wagons to insure stability and safety. It was subsequently demonstrated that Victoria could have saved huge sums by utilizing wider rolling stock and smaller-gauge tracks from the beginning.

A unique situation in Victoria was the presence of Australia's main river system. The Murray River, with its navigable tributaries, the Darling and the Murrumbidgee, provided four thousand miles of waterway for small steamboat traffic, all relatively close to the ocean. In order to survive economically, the railroads in the 1870s and 1880s found it feasible and profitable to connect with the various inland river ports and thereby capture the trade normally handled by river steamers. The first long railway to tap this river commerce, far up-

stream, ran 156 miles from Melbourne north to the Murray River port of Echuca. Eventually, the railroads were so successful because of their ability to move large loads of cargo that transportation on the rivers became just a secondary shuttle medium feeding traffic to the nearest railways.

In the 1880s the Victoria government, like three other states in Australia, changed to a system of commissioners to handle the details of railway administration and operation. These officials, imported at high salaries from British railway companies, held unusual power and controlled with an iron hand the destiny of thousands of employees as well as the operation of hundreds of railway steam engines. In 1884 the first chairman of commissioners in Victoria was Richard Speight from the Midland Railway in England; he had almost unlimited managerial powers. In this era of lush profits, Speight rendered many decisions merely to satisfy the whims of government politicians on whom depended his tenure in office as well as continuing funds for his railway schemes. This kind of mismanagement, of course, eventually led to a deterioration in railway efficiency. By 1894, when de-

Pictured is an R class, type 4–6–4, locomotive hauling a passenger train in Victoria, Australia. These engines were part of a group of seventy units manufactured in Victorian shops after World War II.
(Courtesy: Victoria Railways)

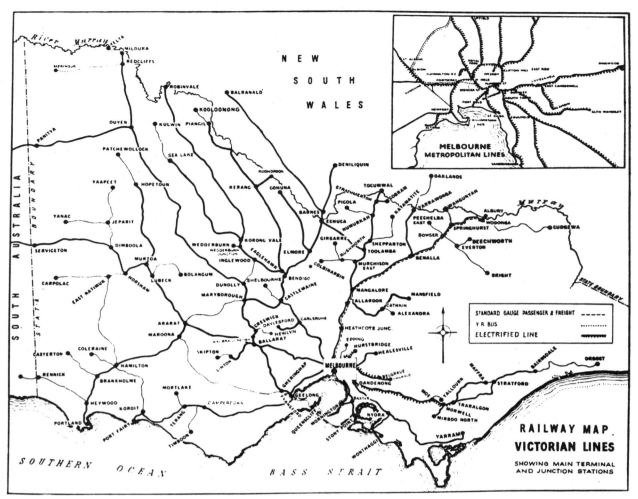

Railway map of Southern Australia, Victorian Lines.
(*Courtesy:* Janes World Railways)

Illustrated is an excursion train known as "Puffing
Billy" which, as a tourist attraction, operates on the
last narrow-gauge 3-feet 6-inch line, through the pic-
turesque Dandenong Ranges, in Victoria, Australia.
This small section of track is located between Bel-
grave, a terminal on the metropolitan electrified system, and Emerald about forty miles east of Melbourne.
(*Courtesy: Australian News & Information Bureau*)

pression hit Australia, the laxity and largess of Speight became all too apparent, and he was summarily suspended from office.

The earliest steam locomotives in Victoria, of British manufacture, were type 0–6–0 for freight handling and type 2–4–0 for passenger service. Subsequently, the Phoenix Works in Ballarat started duplicating British-designed engines in 1873, and in 1893 the Newport railway shops produced their first railroad engine. These shops after 1900 specialized in constructing heavy locomotives of the DD and A2 classes. In the early twentieth century the rail lines in Victoria used various heavy Consolidation- and Mikado-type locomotives for freight service, and later, Pacific-type engines moved the fast passenger trains. After World War II, shops in Victoria manufactured about 180 engines of various classes, including seventy units of the R class, type 4–6–4. A map of railways in Victoria is included. Also shown is an excursion train known as Puffing Billy. Steam locomotion largely terminated in Victoria in the 1960s.

WESTERN AUSTRALIA

Western Australia was the first portion of that continent to be discovered, but the last to be opened for settlement. The original settlers from England arrived at Fremantle in June 1829, and the colony of Western Australia was formed with Perth, nineteen kilometers (twelve miles) inland, as the capital. By 1868 the population had increased to fifteen thousand, and Britain granted Western Australia the right to have some say in its own government.

The first railway in Western Australia was a small private line running from Lockville, near Busselton in the far southwest, into the nearby forests. This line transported timber and timber products starting in 1871. In 1872 another small private timber line commenced operations between Rockingham, located twenty-nine miles south of Fremantle, and Jarrahdale.

The first government railway in Western Australia was constructed from Geraldton, approximately 483 kilometers (three hundred miles) north of Perth, north to Northhampton, a distance of fifty-three kilometers (thirty-three miles). Built mainly to assist the lead and copper mining industry, this railway had wrought-iron rails weighing 17.4 kilograms per meter. Many construction difficulties were encountered, aggravated by an alteration of

gauge from 913 millimeters to 1067 millimeters (3 feet to 3 feet 6 inches). Although Governor Weld turned the first sod on 22 October 1874, it was not until 26 July 1879 that the line was opened to traffic. This railroad was extended another seventy kilometers (forty-three miles) to Ajana and opened on 6 January 1913. Services were suspended on the Geraldton–Ajana section in April 1957.

The second government line was constructed from Fremantle through Perth to Guildford, a distance of 32.19 kilometers (twenty miles), and opened for traffic on 1 March 1881, forming the first section of the present Eastern Railway. A thirty-four-kilometer (twenty-one-mile) connection to Chidlow's Well, via Mahogany Creek, was completed and opened on 11 March 1884. On 29 June 1885, the line was extended a further seventy-nine kilometers (forty-nine miles) through Spencer's Brook to York, thus providing a rail link between agriculturally rich Avon Valley, on the eastern side of the Darling Range, and the coast. The line between Spencer's Brook and Northam was completed on 13 October 1886. The 1067-millimeter (3-foot 6-inch) gauge Midland–Northam railway (via Swan View) remained in full service until 13 February 1966, when the new Avon Valley railway was opened for 1067-millimeter gauge operations. Trains conveying iron ore from Koolyanobbing have continued to operate as far as Wundowie on the old route.

Great Southern Railway. The first proposal for building private railways under the land grant system was put forward in 1882. This provided for the construction of a line from the southern seaport of Albany, latitude 35° south, longitude 117°53′ east, northward to Beverley (391 kilometers; 243 miles) in return for a grant of 4,047,000 hectares of land (10,000,137 acres). The proposal did not find favor until 1884, when a London syndicate accepted the offer on the basis of a grant of three thousand hectares of land per kilometer of railway built (4603 acres per mile). The line opened between Albany and Beverley on 1 June 1889, and was worked initially by the Western Australian Land Company. On 1 December 1896, the government took over the line at a cost of $2.2 million. It is still known as the Great Southern Railway, the name originally used by the company.

Midland Railway. During the construction of the Albany–Beverley railway, another agreement was signed with John Waddington for the provision of a line between Midland and Walkaway, a dis-

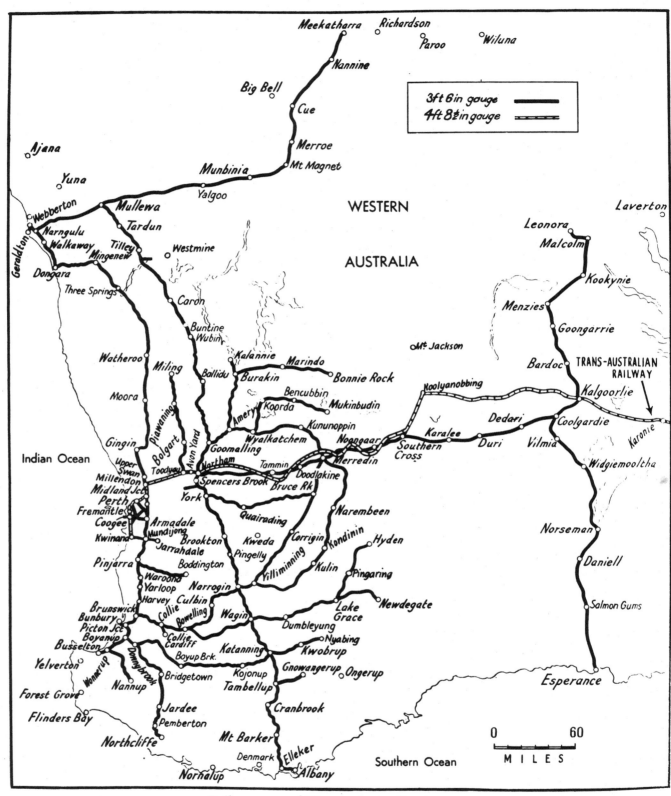

Railway map of Western Australia.
(Courtesy: Western Australia Government Railways)

tance of 446 kilometers (276 miles), connecting at each end with government lines. The agreement was based on the 1884 agreement governing the construction of the Great Southern line. Lack of capital caused a serious interruption of the project until the Midland Railway Company was organized in London to take over the concession. The rail line finally opened for traffic on 24 November 1894. The Midland Railway Company of Western Australia Ltd. continued to own and operate this line until January 1964, when negotiations were successfully completed for its takeover by the government. The integration of this line into the state railway system on 1 August 1964 enabled better coordination of services for the rapidly developing northwest areas.

Goldfields Railways. In the 1890s Western Australia was in the throes of startling gold discoveries. Southern Cross, 386 kilometers (240 miles) east of Perth, had been located by Risely and Toomey in 1887; Coolgardie, about 560 kilometers (348 miles) east of Perth, had been discovered by Bayley and Ford in 1892, to be eclipsed by Paddy Hannan's find forty kilometers further east, the following year, which culminated in the development of mines at Kalgoorlie and Boulder—the famous Golden Mines. In the northern Murchison district east of Geraldton, less sensational but extremely rich finds were reported, and thousands of people, attracted to the state by the discoveries, raised an increasing cry for adequate transportation. To meet this urgent need, a comprehensive program of railway construction was drawn up by the government, catering to the new gold mining centers in the north and east and to the expanding agricultural and timber interests in the south.

The Eastern Goldfields railway system began with the opening of the 274-kilometer (170-mile) line from Northam to Southern Cross in 1894. Heavy traffic to the goldfields necessitated easier grades over the Darling Range, and on 1 July 1896 the main eastern line was deviated from the Mahogany Creek route to run between Bellevue and Mount Helena via the 340-meter (115-foot) Swan View tunnel. On 1 January 1897, rail communication was established with Kalgoorlie, 612 kilometers (380 miles) inland. An extension northward to Menzies was then opened by the governor on 22 March 1898.

Contractors operated the Eastern Goldfields railway until 13 February 1899, when the government took control. An extension was opened to Laverton on 1 February 1905, a distance of about 966 kilometers (600 miles) from the port of Fremantle. In a like manner, the call for railway facilities for the Murchison goldfields was met by the construction of a line from Narngulu (near Geraldton) to Mullewa in 1894, followed by its extension to Cue in 1898. The railway was extended in 1903 to Nannine; in 1910, to Meekatharra, and also from Mount Magnet to Sandstone. Between 1894 and 1899, over 1600 (994 miles) kilometers of government railways were added. Wiluna, 1141 kilometers (708 miles) from Perth, following reopening of the mines, became the outpost of the northern system in 1932.

South-West Railways. On 12 March 1891, a line was opened through a rich agricultural district from Bunbury to Boyanup. The inconvenience of this isolated line soon became apparent and gave rise to the opening of a 177-kilometer (110-mile) connecting line in two sections: East Perth to Pinjarra on 2 May 1893, and from Pinjarra to Picton Junction on 22 August 1893.

As the settlement of southwest Australia increased, the original Bunbury–Boyanup line was connected to Donnybrook on 16 November 1893, and to Busselton on 26 December 1895. The extension from Donnybrook to the old established agricultural town of Bridgetown was made on 1 November 1898.

By 1914 the Government had 5,362 kilometers (3330 miles) of 1067-millimeter (3-foot-6-inch) gauge railway opened for traffic, and since that time more than 1600 kilometers (993 miles) have been constructed. The lines were built to serve agricultural and timber interests, with the exception of an isolated railway on the south coast from Hopetown to Ravensthorpe (55 kilometers; 34 miles) for mining purposes; a 183-kilometer (114-mile) link between Port Hedland and Marble Bar to serve the mining and pastoral communities north of Perth; and one of 201 kilometers (125 miles) connecting the southern port of Esperance with Norseman in the Eastern Goldfields.

In the 1960s, spectacular development of Western Australia's vast mineral resources resulted in the construction of new government and private railways throughout the state.

Owing to declining traffic, it sometimes became necessary to withdraw services or close unprofitable rail branches. The first closing occurred in the 1920s; lines from Waroona to Lake Clifton, from Bunbury to Bunbury Racecourse, from Kalgoorlie to Kanowna, and from Kamballie to White Hope were discontinued. In subsequent years, several other branch lines were closed. In 1957, services were suspended on 1320 kilometers (820 miles) of spur lines, and following the Railways Discontinuance Act of 1960, several more lines were closed. More recent closures have been the Bibra Lake–Armadale, Bellevue–Mt. Helena (via Mundaring), Bellevue–East Northam, and Clackline–Bolgart sections.

Available Western Government Railways records show that in 1879 the total number of passengers carried was 1037; goods and livestock, 1678 tons. Earnings were $3,216, and working expenses totaled $4,670. There are no details available of train-miles before 1881, but records show 108,900 kilometers (67,627 miles) for that year. Traffic multiplied gradually until 1894, then rapidly increased with the various goldfield discoveries. In the period 1965–75, expansion of Western Australia's agricultural pursuits and the spectacular development of its mineral resources have spurred a substantial increase in rail traffic. New records for tonnage of paying goods and livestock hauled have been set each year; in 1974, a record 14,839,169 tons were carried and a record 4,142,536,440 ton-kilometers achieved.

The Western Australian Government Railways system in 1974 was divided into six districts, namely, Metropolitan, Central, Eastern, Southern, Southwestern, and Northern. Each was administered by district officers. As of 30 June 1974, the railway has 9840 employees.

Steam Locomotives in Western Australia

The development of steam locomotion in Western Australia was an involved process of compromise between standardized engines built in Great Britain and America and many experimental models tried out in Australia.

Western Australia's first railway, built in 1871, was a privately owned timber line extending from Lockville, a few miles north of Busselton (latitude 33°39′ south, longitude 115°23′ east) into the adjacent forests. The first operating steam engine on this private rail line is illustrated. This engine was named "Ballarat" after the location in Victoria where it was manufactured by the Phoenix Foundry. This original locomotive in Western Australia

cost $1,600, had two cylinders measuring six by fourteen inches, and could haul 150 tons of freight at sixteen kilometers (ten miles) per hour.

In constructing the Geraldton–Northampton rail line between 1874 and 1879, the contractors used two class M, type 2-6-0 locomotives built by Kitson of Leeds, England. See illustration. The two locomotives first used on the finished railroad were class E double-ended Fairlie types, built in 1879 by the Avonside Engine Company Ltd. of Bristol, England; manufacturer's numbers 1239/40 and 1241/42. The machines were delivered by sea to Fremantle and were employed on the main Eastern Railway as no. 7 and no. 20. In 1893 no. 7 was sold and no. 20 was broken into two parts; one half was used to drive Fremantle workshop machinery and the other half, rebuilt as a 2-4-2 tank locomotive, was finally sold in June 1899. See illustration.

For subsequent use on various 3-foot 6-inch gauge lines in Western Australia, several single-boiler Fairlie type 0-6-4 tank engines were purchased from New Zealand. These machines never measured up on the various graded sections of the railroads. Accordingly, a substitute engine, a small-wheeled class K, type 2-8-4 tank machine was designed for the job (see illustration). During the same period, a variety of type 4-6-0 and 2-6-0 engines were found to perform satisfactorily for mixed freight uses.

With the opening of the Fremantle–Perth–Guildford Railway on 1 March 1881, class A, type 2-6-0 tender locomotives were put to work. Manufactured by Beyer Peacock and Dubs & Company, these had the specifications shown.

The first southwestern railways of Western Australia were opened in 1891 and used a class H, type 0-6-0 tank locomotive pictured and described.

Early in the twentieth century, a class F, type 4-8-0 shunting engine was developed and widely used in Western Australia. However, the need for a heavier, more versatile machine led to the construction of a class FS, type 4-8-0, which is pictured.

In 1902 the Baldwin Locomotive Works furnished thirty-two general-purpose locomotives, of which twenty were compound types. Details are unavailable.

About 1912 the first Garratt for 3-foot 6-inch gauge tracks, a type 2-6-0 + 0-6-2 class M locomotive, was built by Beyer Peacock, followed later in the same year by seven units of a modified version designated class MS. In 1913 several superheated types were produced. These Garratt

Western Australia's first steam locomotive, type 0–4–0, was named "Ballarat." This wood-burning engine, built in Ballart, Victoria in 1871, was used in Western Australia on a private timber line extending from Lockville, located a short distance north of Busselton in southwest Australia, into the nearby forests. The engine had cylinders 178 by 355 millimeters (7 by 14 inches), and it could haul 150-ton loads at 16 kilometers per hour (approximately 10 miles per hour). This old relic is on public display at Busselton.
(Courtesy: Western Australia Government Railways)

Here is an old 1880 photograph of a class M, type 2–6–0, tender locomotive used in constructing the Geraldton-Northampton line in Western Australia. This engine no. 2, together with engine no. 1, both built by Kitson & Company, were the first two machines used by the contractors. Engine no. 2 was subsequently renumbered no. 24 and was sold to the Whittaker's Timber Company in 1908 and named "Dandalup." In 1945 it was sold to the Bunning Brothers and renamed "Yornup"; it was retired in 1953 and later scrapped. Engine no. 2 had the following specifications:

engines performed so well that the Midland shops in 1930 manufactured ten additional units with minor modifications, designated as class MSA.

In 1924 and 1925, the use of superheaters was again explored. Various class E engines had superheaters installed and were then reclassified to Es. See illustration.

In 1924 the Western Australia Government Railways (WAGR) imported a class P, type 4–6–2 locomotive for handling freight traffic; ten such

Cylinders	12 by 20 inches
Drive wheels	3-foot 3-inch diameter
Boiler	
Grate area	10 square feet
Total heating surface	543.3 square feet
Boiler working pressure	120 pounds per square inch
Tractive effort	6920.0 pounds at 75 percent boiler working pressure
Operating weight	30 tons
Tender capacities	660 gallons water; 60 hundredweights coal
Overall height	11 feet 3 1/16 inches
Overall length	37 feet
Maximum width	Cab 7 feet 4.25 inches; footplate 9 feet.

(Courtesy: Western Australia Government Railways)

Pictured is one of two class E Fairlie double-ended locomotives first used in Western Australia on the Geraldton-Northampton rail line. These engines were built by Avonside Engine Company of Bristol, England in 1879. Specifications on the class E, type 2–4–0 plus 0–4–2, engines were as follows:

Cylinders (4)	254 by 457.2 millimeters
Coupled drive wheels	990-millimeter diameter
Boiler	
Grate area	1.21 square meters
Heat surface	77.67 square meters
Working pressure	827 kPa
Tractive force	36.95 Kn
Operating weight	33.99 tons
Overall length	11.379 meters.

(Courtesy: Western Australia Government Railways)

units were constructed by the North British Locomotive Company (see illustrations). From 1927 to 1929, the Midlands workshops produced fifteen more such machines. Based on the class P engines, a new series designated class PR were created by improving the boiler pressures and enhancing the overall adhesive weight, which increased the engine power by about 9 percent. Illustrated is a class PR engine named "Fitzroy."

In World War II, class ASG, type 4–8–2 + 2–8–4 Garratt locomotives largely supported the Austra-

In the 1880s on the 3-foot 6-inch gauge Western Australia railways, several single-boiler Fairlie, type 0–6–4, tank engines were purchased from New Zealand. These locomotives provided highly unsatisfactory service on the steep grades, and a more powerful version was designed to do the job. The latter machines, type 2–8–4, class K, were Fairlie tank engines. Engine no. 112, which was still in use as late as December 1964, had the following specifications:

Cylinders	17 by 21 inches
Drive wheels	3-foot 2-inch diameter
Leading and trailing wheels	2-foot 1-inch diameter
Boiler	
Grate area	16.7 square feet
Tubes	919.5 square feet
Firebox	93.3 square feet
Total heating surface	1012.8 square feet
Working pressure	160 pounds per square inch
Tractive effort	20,443 pounds at 80 percent boiler working pressure
Operating weight	53 tons
Capacities	2000 gallons water; 58 cubic feet coal
Overall height	11 feet 8 inches
Overall length	36 feet
Maximum width	8 feet.

These machines were built by Neilson Reid & Company of Glasgow; three different boiler pressures were tried (i.e., 120, 140, 160 pounds per square inch). Between 1915 and 1929 five class K engines were superheated but all were later reconverted to the saturated steam types.

(Courtesy: Western Australia Government Railways)

Shown is class A, type 2–6–0, locomotive used to pull the first train on the Fremantle to Perth railway in Western Australia on 1 March 1881. Twelve class A engines were used on the Western Australia Government Railways between 1881 and 1958. Of these, eleven machines were built by Beyer Peacock and the last or twelfth unit was manufactured by Dubs & Company. The Dubs's model and two Beyer Peacock engines were equipped with six-wheel tenders, in lieu of the four-wheel types in the earlier models. Originally designed for passenger service these little engines were eventually assigned to shunting duties. The last machine, no. 21, was written off the records during May 1958. These class A locomotives had the following specifications:

Cylinders (2)	304.8 by 508 millimeters
Coupled drive wheels	990-millimeter diameter
Boiler	
Grate area	0.91 square meters
Heating area	50.28 square meters
Working pressure	965 kPa
Operating weights	
Engine plus 4-wheel tender	30.94 tons
Engine plus 6-wheel tender	35.66 tons
Tractive force	36.79 kN
Overall length	10.77 meters to 11.379 meters.

(Courtesy: Western Australia Government Railways)

Shown is a class H, type 0–6–0, tank locomotive, two of which were first utilized on the Bunbury-Boyanup Railway in Western Australia in March 1891. These engines were manufactured by Neilson Reid & Company, Glasgow, in 1888 and carried the builder's shop numbers 3630 and 3631. After a somewhat varied career, no. 18 was sold to the Bunbury Public Works Department in November 1911 where it was used for another forty years; it was retained for possible preservation. In 1922 the second engine, no. 22, was shipped to Port Hedland where it was utilized on the Marble Bar Railway until November 1951. These locomotives had the following characteristics:

Cylinders (2)	228.6 by 355.6 millimeters
Coupled drive wheels	685-millimeter diameter
Boiler	
Grate area	0.49 square meter
Total heat surface	23.47 square meters
Working pressure	827 kPa
Tractive force	17.94 kN
Operating weight	14.27 tons
Overall length	6.096 meters.

(Courtesy: Western Australia Government Railways)

Pictured is a class F, type 4–8–0, tender locomotive built by the North British Locomotive Company about 1912 and used mainly with freight trains on the 3-foot 6-inch gauge tracks of Western Australia. This picture was taken before the engine was commissioned in the shops of the North British Locomotive Company. Engine nos. 366–67 arrived in 1912 fitted with "Schmidt" superheaters: nos. 398, 401, 403, and 415 had superheaters installed in 1924–25 at which time they were reclassified as FS; these machines, towards the end of their service life, were reconverted back to class F and used for shunting duties. Specifications on the class F locomotives were as follows:

Cylinders	17 by 23 inches
Coupled drive wheels	3 foot 6.5-inch diameter
Boiler	
Grate area	19 square feet
Total heating surface	1394 square feet
Boiler working pressure	180 pounds per square inch
Tractive effort	21,115 pounds at 75 percent Boiler working pressure
Operating weight	54 tons plus 2 hundredweights
Tender capacities	2200 gallons water; 250 cubic feet coal
Tender weight	30 tons and 12 hundredweights
Overall weight	12 feet 6 inches
Overall length	54 feet 4 inches
Maximum width	8 feet 2.5 inches.

(Courtesy: Western Australia Government Railways)

Still another class F, type 4–8–0, tender locomotive (no. 356) which operated on the railways of Western Australia starting about 1912 is shown. See an earlier illustration for specifications and other information.
(Courtesy: Western Australia Government Railways)

Pictured is a class F, type 4–8–0, tender locomotive built by the North British Locomotive Company in 1912 and operated on the 3-foot 6-inch gauge tracks of the Western Australia Railways. Engine no. 420 was fitted with an experimental A.F.C.I. feed water heater. Specifications and other details were the same as the class F machine shown earlier.
(Courtesy: Western Australia Government Railways)

Pictured is a class F, type 4–8–0, steam locomotive used on the Western Australia Government Railways after the turn of the twentieth century. These engines represented an improvement over the class F machines of which fifty-five units (saturated type) were imported from Dubs & Company and the North British Locomotive Company in 1902 and 1912–13, respectively. Ten others of a superheated type were also purchased. While the class F engines were used in shunting service, the class Fs engines performed mainline goods and shunting jobs. Both engines handled a maximum load of about 510 tons on a 1 in 80 grade. Specifications on the class Fs locomotives were as follows:

Cylinders	431.8 by 584.2 millimeters
Coupled drive wheels	1080-millimeter diameter
Boiler	
Grate area	1.74 square meters
Superheater	17.00 square meters
Heating surface	101.91 square meters
Working pressure	1,206 kPa
Wheel arrangement	4-8-0
Operating weight	87.08 tons
Tender capacities	10,000 liters (2642 U.S. gallons) water; 5.5 tons coal
Tractive force	103.48 kN
Overall length	16.560 meters
Number built	57.

(Courtesy: Western Australia Government Railways)

Pictured is a class Fs, type 4–8–0, steam locomotive
used on the Western Australian railways. These engines were superheated versions of the class F machines produced in 1914–25 as indicated in an earlier
illustration.
(Courtesy: Western Australia Government Railways)

Another class Fs, type 4–8–0, tender locomotive (no.
290) used in Western Australia starting about 1912 is
pictured. These engines were class F machines with
superheaters installed. The class Fs engines were bored
with three different size cylinders, namely 17-inch, 18-
inch, and 19-inch. See an earlier illustration for
specification data.
(Courtesy: Western Australia Government Railways)

In 1912 the WAGR imported seven class Ms Garratt type 2–6–0 plus 0–6–2 locomotives from Beyer Peacock of which the seventh unit, no. 389, was a superheated class M engine. Pictured is engine no. 430 which was part of another order of seven Garratts purchased from Beyer Pacock in 1913 (nos. 424–30). The latter engine was originally taken over by the Public Works Department of the Western Australia Railways but was transferred in 1914 to regular rail line work. Specifications on the class Ms engines were as follows:

Cylinders (4)	13.25 by 20 inches
Drive wheels	3-foot 3-inch diameter
Boiler	
Firegrate area	22.6 square feet
Total heating surface	1257.4 square feet
Boiler working pressure	160 pounds per square inch
Tractive Effort	24,488 pounds at 85 percent boiler working pressure
Operating weight	69 tons plus 16 hundredweights
Capacities	2000 gallons water; 60 hundredweights coal
Overall height	12 feet
Overall length	53 feet 10.5 inch
Maximum width	7 feet 6 inches.

All Garratt engines on the WAGR were written off between 1947 and 1955.

(Courtesy Western Australia Government Railways)

Shown is a class Msa, Garratt articulated locomotive which was designed by Western Australia Government Railways engineers to haul mixed and freight trains over light railroad sections, with rails 22.23 kilograms per meter, and with heavy grades and sharp curves. Ten such engines were built in the Midland workshops in 1930. These machines had about ten percent more power than class Ms articulated engines then in service. The Msa locomotives were the first Garratt type machines constructed in the southern hemisphere. Their maximum load over a 1 in 80 grade was six hundred tons. Specifications on engine no. 468 were as follows:

Cylinders (4)	336.55 by 508 millimeters
Coupled drive wheels	900-millimeter diameter
Boiler	
Grate area	2.5 square meters
Heating surface	100.93 square meters (evaporative)
Superheater	16.72 square meters
Working pressure	1,103 kPa
Wheel arrangement	2–6–0 plus 0–6–2
Operating weight	75.19 tons
Capacity	9090 liters (2401 U.S. gallons) water; 4 tons coal
Tractive force	108.93kN
Overall length	16.910 meters
Number built	10.

(Courtesy: Western Australia Government Railways)

Another class Msa articulated Garratt locomotive, type 2–6–0 plus 0–6–2, is shown. These were designed and built by the WAGR engineers in 1930 to haul mixed and goods trains over light (forty-five-pound) rail with heavy grades and sharp curves on 3-foot 6-inch gauge tracks. These units were withdrawn in 1963. Specifications on engine no. 466 were:

Cylinders	13.25 by 20 inches
Drive wheels	3-foot 3-inch diameter
Boiler	
Firegrate area	27 square feet
Total heating surface	1266.4 square feet
Working pressure	175 pounds per square inch (later reduced to 160 pounds per square inch)
Tractive effort	
26,784 pounds at 85 percent 175 pounds per square inch	
24,488 pounds at 85 percent 160 pounds per square inch	
Operating weight	74 tons plus 2 hundredweights
Capacities	2000 gallons water; 80 hundredweights coal
Overall height	12 feet 6 inches
Overall length	55 feet 5.75 inches
Maximum width	8 feet 6 inches

(Courtesy: Western Australia Government Railways)

In 1924–25 all but four class E locomotives in Western Australia had superheaters installed and were redesignated class Es. Two size cylinder bores were used on the class Es engines, namely 17-inch and 19-inch. Pictured is engine no. 326, class Es, type 4–6–2, which had the following characteristics:

Cylinders	19 by 23 inches
Drive wheels	4-foot diameter
Boiler	
Grate area	18.8 square feet
Total heating surface	1131 square feet
Boiler working pressure	160 pounds per square inch
Tractive effort	20,911 pounds at 85 percent boiler working pressure
Operating weight	84 tons plus 12 hundredweights
Overall height	12 feet 6.5 inches
Overall length	54 feet 4 inches
Maximum width	8 feet 2.5 inches
Capacities	2200 gallons water; 110 hundredweights coal.

Subsequently additional class Es locomotives were produced with standard 18 by 23 inch cylinder bores with 175 pounds per square inch boiler pressures and with tractive efforts rated at 20,527 pounds at 85 percent boiler working pressure. The latter units were used on mainline passenger trains. Earlier two types of tenders were used with class Es engines having 19-inch cylinder bores, i.e., the only difference being an increase of coal capacity from 110 hundredweights to 150 hundredweights.

In 1945 several class Es and class E engines, which had reached the end of their useful lives, were torn down to provide wheels, cylinders, and portions of the frames to fabricate eight class Dm Baltic tank engines in the Midland workshops.

(Courtesy: Western Australia Government Railways)

In 1924 the North British Locomotive Company built ten class P, Pacific type 4–6–2, tender locomotives for use on goods trains in Western Australia. These were originally numbered 441–50; in 1946–47 they were renumbered 501–10. Engines no. 443 (503 new numbering system) is shown. This had the following vital statistics:

Headlamps	Kerosene type (no. 443); electric type (No. 502)
Cylinders	19 by 26 inches
Drive wheels	4-foot 6-inch diameter
Boiler	
Grate area	35 square feet
Total heating surface	1848.5 square feet
Working pressure	160 pounds per square inch
Tractive effort	23,638 pounds at 85 percent boiler working pressure
Operating weight	102 tons plus 5 hundredweights
Capacities	2800 gallons water; 160 hundredweights coal
Overall height	12 feet 6 inches
Overall length	62 feet 2 inches
Maximum width	8 feet 3 inches.

In 1927–29 fifteen class P engines were built in the Midland workshops and numbered 451–65; the latter locomotives built by the WAGR weighed 97 tons plus 3 hundredweights, had an overall length of 57 feet 8.75 inches, and carried 2440 gallons of water and 140 hundredweights of coal, otherwise they were the same as the above North British Locomotive units. In 1941–44 eight of the class P engines were converted to Pr by increasing the boiler pressure and the adhesive weight. The last of the class P and Pr engines were written off in 1969.
(Courtesy: Western Australia Government Railways)

Illustrated is another class P tender locomotive, type 4–6–2, used to haul freight on the Western Australia Government Railways starting in 1924. See a previous illustration for detailed characteristics.
(Courtesy: Western Australia Government Railways)

Class P Pacific type locomotives were redesigned from class P types, ten of which were originally built by the North British Locomotive Company, Glasgow, and imported to Australia in 1924. Later ten models of class P were built by the Midland workshops in 1938–39. Subsequently eight of the original engines were converted to class P by increasing the boiler pressure and adhesion weight to give about a nine percent increase in power. The new engines were capable of hauling 565-ton loads over a 1 in 80 grade. These new engines carried the names of Western Australian rivers. The numbering series were 521–27, 529–38. Engine no. 141, named "Fitzroy," was later numbered 524.

Specifications on the class P locomotives were as follows:

Cylinders (2)	482.6 by 660.4 millimeters
Coupled wheels	1372-millimeter diameter
Grate area	3.25 square meters
Heating surface	
Evaporative	138.8 square meters
Superheat	32.88 square meters
Boiler pressure	1206 kPa
Tractive effort	115.01 kN
Operating weight	104.14 tons
Tender capacities	12.730 water liters; 8 tons coal
Overall length	18,754 millimeters
Number built	17
Number series	521–27, 529–38

[early numbers were 138–44 and 146(529), 147(530), 453(531), 454(532), 455(533), 456(534), 457(535), 459(536), 461(537), 464(538)].
(Courtesy: Western Australia Government Railways)

In World War II Australian transportation needs were widely supported by class Asg, 4–8–2 plus 2–8–4, Garratt type heavy goods steam engines, the most powerful then in service. These were constructed at various railway workshops throughout Australia and were under the war-time jurisdiction of the Commonwealth Land Transport Board. These engines hauled 740-ton loads over a 1 in 80 grade.

Specifications were:

Cylinders (4)	361.95 by 609.6 millimeters
Coupled wheels	1219-millimeter diameter
Grate area	3.25 square meters
Heating surface (evaporative)	157.28 square meters
Boiler pressure	1379 kPa
Tractive effort	153.55 kN
Operating weight	117.75 tons
Tender capacities	19,000 liters water; 6 tons coal
Overall length	26,162 millimeters.

Another Mountain type steam locomotive used in West Australia was the class S heavy goods engine. This motive power was designed and constructed at the Midland workshops during 1943–47; at the time these engines were the heaviest ever introduced and were intended to handle increasing freight traffic on the West Australia rail system. Class S, 4–8–2, locomotives were capable of handling 1220 tons over various sections of track. The numbering series was 541–50 and, in addition, carried the names of well-known Western Australian mountains. Specifications were as follows:

Cylinders (2)   482.6 by 609.6 millimeters

Coupled wheels	1220-millimeter diameter
Grate area	3.72 square meters
Heating surface	
Evaporative	155.43 square meters
Superheat	41.62 square meters
Boiler pressure	1379 kPa
Tractive effort	136.49 kN
Wheel arrangement	4–8–2
Operating weight	Between 121.21 tons and 128.28 tons
Large tender	22,730 liters water; 7 tons coal
Small tender	15,910 liters water; 9 tons coal
Overall length	20,205 millimeters
Number built	10.

(Courtesy: Western Australia Government Railways)

Eighteen classes DM and DD, 4–6–4 Baltic type, locomotives were built in 1946 at the WAGR Midland workshops. These were designed as suburban passenger and goods tank engines; they were essentially redesigns of the classes D and DS locomotives imported in 1912 from the North British Locomotive Company, Glasgow. The DM and DD models replaced the lesser-powdered N engines for suburban work. Their load on passenger service was 315 tons over a 1 in 80 grade—on freight service they handled a 415-ton load. Soon after building the DM engine, numbers were changed, i.e., no. 309 became no. 582. Specifications on these engines were as follows:

Classes DM and DD
Cylinders (2)   457.2-millimeter diameter by

	584.2-millimeter stroke
Coupled wheels	1372-millimeter diameter
Grate area	1.73 square meter
Heating surface	
Evaporative	106.37 square meters
Superheat	16.17 square meters
Boiler pressure	1103 kPa
Wheel arrangement	4–6–4
Tractive effort	83.43 kN
Operating weight	73.16 tons
Capacities	8270 liters water; 5 tons coal
Overall length	13,188 millimeters
Number built	8 DM; 10 DD
Number series	DM 581–88; DD 591–600.

(Courtesy: Western Australia Government Railways)

Class U, 4–6–2 type, steam locomotives were long used in Western Australia to haul passenger trains. For example, "The Australind" commenced its Perth–Bunbury service as a steam-hauled express on 24 November 1947. By July 1954 steam motive power was superceded by diesel-powered engines. Specifications on class U locomotives were not available to the author.
(Courtesy: Western Australia Government Railways)

Classes PM and PMR were Pacific type locomotives furnished by the North British Locomotive Works Company, Glasgow, to the order of the Western Australia Government Railways and introduced to service in December 1949. Based on the design of the class PR engines, built earlier in the railway workshops at Midland, improvements included roller bearings on all carrying axles, power-operated reversing gear, and mechanical lubrication to the coupled axle-box guides. The cab was large and fitted with padded seats and backrests. These engines were relegated to goods traffic, being able to handle 565-ton loads over 1 in 80 grades. Seventeen locomotives were fitted with roller bearings on the coupled axle boxes and were designated class PMR and carried the numbers 715, 720–35.

Eighteen class PM engines were built carrying the numbers 701–14, 716–19. Engine no. 730 is pictured.
Specifications were as follows:

Cylinders (2)	482.6 by 660.4 millimeters
Coupled wheels	1372-millimeter diameter
Grate area	3.25 square meters
Heating surface	
Evaporative	139.82 square meters
Superheat	33.72 square meters
Boiler pressure	1206 kPa
Tractive effort	115.03 kN
Wheel arrangement	4-6-2
Operating weight	110.75 tons
Tender capacities	18,180 liters water; 8 tons coal
Overall length	19,396 millimeters.

(Courtesy: Western Australia Government Railways)

Class W, Mountain type, goods locomotive is pictured. This 4–8–2 type engine was designed for a maximum axle load of 10.16 tons, for operations on light line (45 pounds, 22.32 kilograms per mile) sections. The engine was built by Beyer Peacock & Company, Ltd. of Manchester, England. Sixty similar locomotives were ordered and the first, no. 901, was placed in service during April 1951. Special features included the provision of roller bearings on all carrying axles, a power-operated reversing gear, and a special boiler design with a wide firebox and a large combustion chamber suitable for the efficient burning of Collie coal available in West Australia. The smokestack had a "Masters Mechanics'" type of spark arrester. The locomotive was capable of handling a 440-ton load over a 1 in 80 grade. A green and black color scheme was originally introduced with these engines. Specifications were as follows:

Cylinders (2)	406.4 by 609.6 millimeter
Coupled wheels	1220-millimeters diameter
Wheel arrangement	4–8–2
Grate area	2.51 square meters
Heating surface	
Evaporative	103.77 square meters
Superheat	28.34 square leters
Boiler pressure	1379 kPa
Operating weight	102.62 tons
40 Units	
20 units	104.65 tons
Tender capacities	
Coal	7 tons
Water	40 units 11,360 liters
Water	20 units 14,090 liters.

(Courtesy: Western Australia Government Railways)

Shown is class V steam locomotive which was introduced to the Western Australia Government Railways in April 1955. This McArthur or Mikado type 2–8–2 locomotive was designed by Beyer Peacock & Company, Ltd. of Manchester, England and was manufactured by Robert Stephenson & Hawthorns, Ltd. This was the most powerful steam engine on any government 2067-millimeter gauge railroad in Australia and was used to haul heavy freight trains. This engine was capable of handling 1625-ton loads over some sections of track in South Australia. Specifications on this locomotive were as follows:

Cylinders (2)	482.6 by 660.4 millimeters
Coupled wheels	1295-millimeters diameter
Wheel arrangement	2–8–2
Grate area	3.72 square meters
Heating surface	
Evaporative	168.8 square meters
Superheat	45.71 square meters
Boiler pressure	1482 kPa
Operating weight	136.58 tons
Capacities	24,500 liters water; 7 tons coal
Tractive effort	149.59 kN at 85 percent Boiler pressure
Overall length	21,237 millimeters
Number built	24
Number series	1201–24.

(Courtesy: Western Australia Government Railways)

lian military efforts. This engine is pictured and described.

The heaviest freight locomotives ever designed and built in Western Australia were introduced in 1943. Ten of these type 4–8–2, class S Mountain engines were constructed by 1947. This steam giant is shown with the specifications.

Heavy-duty tank locomotives, classes DM and DD, type 4–6–4, Baltics designed and built in the railroad shops of the WAGR in 1946, are pictured.

Many express trains in Western Australia were handled after 1947 by class U, type 4–6–2 steam locomotives such as those in the illustration.

In December 1949 WAGR introduced about thirty-five units of classes PM and PMR locomotives built by the North British Locomotive Company. These were Pacific-type machines for heavy duty freight operations. The two classes are pictured.

The Mountain 4–8–2 steam locomotives were again resorted to in 1951. These class W freight engines designed for operations on lighter track sections were built by Beyer Peacock. In all, sixty machines were purchased. The first unit received, engine no. 901, is shown.

Some of the last steam locomotives introduced into Australia were used on the WAGR starting in April 1955. These were class V, Mikado 2–8–2 machines designed by Beyer Peacock and constructed by Stephenson & Hawthorn in England to meet specifications set forth by the WAGR. This was the most powerful freight engine ever used in Australia on 3-foot 6-inch gauge tracks (see illustration).

The age of steam had largely been terminated in Western Australia by 1972, when total dieselization was completed.

AUSTRIA

A TRAMWAY LINE FOR GENERAL TRAFFIC WAS chartered in 1824 and opened in 1827 in Austria, but until 1838 the government positively discouraged the introduction of railways. The new policy, adopted in response to growing locomotive use in Germany, Switzerland, and France, guaranteed each railway a monopoly in its own district during the comparatively short period of its charter. At the same time, the state constructed lines of its own on a large scale. Unfortunately, the revolution of 1848 led to financial straits; in the years that followed, most of the state railways were sold to private companies for about one-half real value. The growth of the Austrian rail network was slow until after the war of 1866; then it began to develop rapidly. The subsequent railway speculation was perhaps more reckless in Austria than anywhere else in the world, resulting in severe distress when it ended during the crisis of 1873. After 1876 there were consistent efforts to increase the importance of the state railway system by purchasing old lines and constructing new ones, and by 1885 the state owned and managed two thousand miles of railroads, with approximately another six thousand miles managed by private companies.

The early railroads in Austria were built to link population centers of the existing Austro-Hungarian Empire. The earliest railway started operations in 1827 with a 3-foot 7.5-inch gauge line using wooden and iron tracks between Kerchbaum and Budweis (now in Czechoslovakia: latitude 48°58' north, and longitude 14°30' east). The system was extended to Mauthausen in 1829, and an additional fifteen miles or so to Linz in August 1832. A further extension of about forty miles from Linz to Gmunden (latitude 47°56' north; longitude 13°48' east) commenced operations on 1 May 1836. In all of the early railroads, horse traction was used until 1872 except on the Linz–Gmunden line, which initiated the use of steam traction in 1854. That pioneer railway system became part of the Kaisern Elizabeth network in 1857, by which time a gauge of 4 feet 8½ inches was finally established by the government.

The first really commercial railway, which opened 6 January 1838, was the Rothschild-financed line of Kaiser Ferdinand's Nördbahn between Vienna, Floridsdorf, and Deutchwagrum. This line later connected with Prague and Cracow, and still later was extended to Graz and to the Austrian port of Trieste. The initial locomotives, three in number, were built by the Robert Stephenson Company. Of these, two were the so-called planet-type. By 1844 Morris of Philadelphia had supplied thirty-nine engines, the first of which went into operation in 1838. An illustration shows a model of one of the Morris 4–2–0 locomotives, named "Austria." Also see another illustration.

The railways of Austria-Hungary expanded rapidly between 1848, when there were 670 miles of track, and 1862, by which time there were 3,662 miles. In 1870 the largest rail network was the Südbahn system, with 1,243 miles in operation.

World War I led to the dissolution of the Austro-Hungarian monarchy, and about 70 percent of the railroads passed to the control of Yugoslavia, Czechoslovakia, and Hungary. This marked the beginning of Austria as an autonomous entity, and

This model represents a type of locomotive introduced in 1837 by William Norris, of Philadelphia, for working on lines having steep inclines and sharp curves; such engines were used on the Austrian railways in 1838, and some were sent to England in 1840 for working the Lickey incline on the Birmingham and Gloucester Railway.

The engine had inclined outside cylinders, and a single driving axle in front of the firebox, while the forward end of the engine was carried by a four-wheeled swivelling bogie. The cylinders were 10.5-inches diameter by 21-inch stroke, and the driving wheels 46.5-inches in diameter, so that the tractive factor was fifty. The bogie wheels were 30-inches diameter, the total wheel base of the engine was 9.875 feet, while the gauge was 5 feet. The valve chests were arranged above the cylinders, and the valve rods were driven, through rocking shafts, by four eccentrics on the driving axle. There was a forward and backward eccentric to each cylinder, and each eccentric rod ended in a forked gab; the gab ends of each pair of rods faced one another and were suspended by links from a re-versing shaft, so that either the forward or the backward eccentrics could be used.

The boiler was tubulous, with a barrel 8.25 feet long by 38 inches in diameter, and it had a domed firebox of the Bury type. The heating surface was about 400 square feet and the grate area 6 square feet. Lever and direct spring-loaded safety valves were provided. The frame was of the bar construction, and the boiler was supported from it by brackets; the driving axle and those of the bogie were provided with separately adjustable plate springs. The weight of the engine in working condition was about 10 tons.

The tender was built on double frames with the springs and axle boxes between them; the water tank was of a horseshoe shape, and the central space was the fuel receptacle. It ran on four wheels 30 inches in diameter, with a wheel base of 4.875 feet. The overall length of engine and tender was 32 feet, and the total weight about 14 tons.

Scale 1:6
(Courtesy: Science Museum, London)

AUSTRIA

Illustrated is a sketch of a type 4–2–0 steam locomotive built by Morris of Philadelphia starting in 1838 for export to Austria.
(Courtesy: O. S. Nock, The Dawn of World Railways 1800–1850).

railway construction was widely pursued in all parts of the country.

To backtrack a bit, the early construction of a main line railroad from Vienna across the Alps to Trieste, and later to Belgrade and the Balkans, was a tremendous engineering task. The first section, the Vienna–Gloggnitz rail line, opened in 1841. The engineer in charge was Carlo di Ghega (see illustration) who had to contend with heavy grades and tortuous curves to penetrate the rugged terrain. From Gloggnitz, the rail line had to climb eighteen miles over a gradient of 1 in 40 to reach the 2,880-foot crest of the Semmering Pass (latitude 47°37.7′ north, longitude 15°49.7′ east), about forty-five miles southwest of Vienna. To surmount this Alpine obstacle, Ghega eventually decided on a steam locomotive, the design of which would be determined by a competition under certain prearranged conditions. Engine performance trials included hauling a 140-ton load up the 1 in 40 grade at a

Pictured is the Venetian engineer, Carlo di Ghega, who first advanced the proposition, in 1840, that the Semmering Pass in Austria could be conquered by a mountain railway. He was subsequently proved correct.
(Courtesy: Austrian Federal Railways)

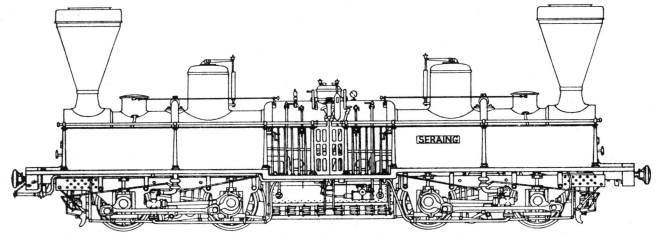

Shown is a drawing of the Belgian locomotive entry in the famous Austrian Semmering Trials in 1851. This engine, named "Seraing," was designed and built by John Cockrill. This double-ended tank engine was the forerunner of the legendary engines designed and constructed in great numbers by Robert Fairlie.
(Courtesy: Austrian Federal Railways)

Pictured is a drawing of the famous locomotive named "Bavaria," which was winner of the Semmering Trials in Austria in 1851. This engine was designed by Joseph Hall and was constructed in the Munich, Germany shops of Joseph Anton Maffei.
(Courtesy: Austrian Federal Railways)

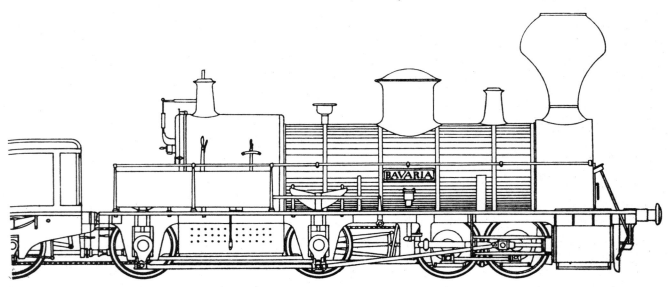

speed of no less than eight miles per hour. In the summer of 1851, competitive test demonstrations were undertaken with four different locomotive entries:

1. The Belgian firm of John Cockrill submitted a double-ended tank engine with four cylinders and two centrally fired boilers, named "Seraing." This design was later copied in somewhat modified form by Robert Fairlie, who used outside cylinders and subsequently manufactured these engines in considerable numbers. See illustration.

2. The firm of Gunther of Wiener Neustadt, Austria, entered another four-cylinder tank locomotive having but a single boiler. This was another articulated engine with two motor bogies, named "Wiener Neustadt."

3. Joseph Anton Maffei of Munich, Germany, built a type 0–8–0 tender engine designed by Joseph Hall, which had wheels spaced to permit firebox placement at a low center of gravity. The second and driving axles were chain-coupled, as were the trailing axle and the leading tender axle. Side rods coupled the leading and second axles. The engine was named "Bavaria" (see illustrations).

This is a sketch of the 0–8–0 locomotive "Bavaria," built by Maffei of Munich, Germany, which captured first prize in 1851 in trials to determine a suitable engine to surmount the difficult grades of the first Alpine railway, this across the Semmering Pass in Austria.
(Courtesy: Austrian Federal Railways)

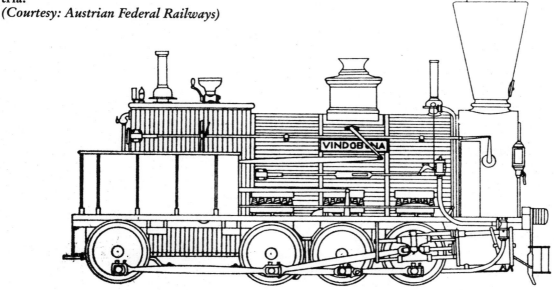

Shown is a drawing of the John Haswell designed locomotive named "Vindobona," which was one of four engines to compete in the Austrian Semmering Trials of 1851. This engine was fabricated in the shops of the Vienna Gloggnitz Railway.
(Courtesy: Austrian Federal Railways)

4. The Vienna–Gloggnitz Railway fabricated in their shops a Haswell-designed engine named "Vindobona," also with an 0–8–0 wheel arrangement. This was the first locomotive in Europe using four coupled axles, the prototype of many subsequent railroad engines. The firebox somewhat resembled that developed by Alfred Belpaire some years later. See illustration.

Actually, all four of the competing locomotives satisfied the performance requirements, producing a dilemma for the Austrian government judges. The "Bavaria," submitted by Maffei, was finally awarded first prize, 20,000 golden florins. The other three contestants received lesser awards. These trial locomotives did not produce a final engine design as a future standard, however. It was two years before the total rail system south from Vienna was constructed, by which time a new and

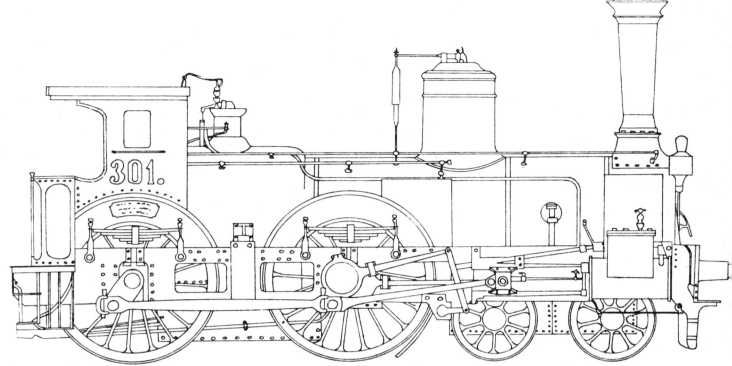

Shown is a drawing of a Sigl type 4–4–0 locomotive designed for the Austrian Semmering Railway in the 1850s. This engine resembled the Hall/Hassell machines of that era which had heavy, slotted outside frames carrying most of the machinery weight as well as absorbing the motion forces of the engine. Also shown are the eccentric sheaves and rods located between the bearings and main cranks, and the outside valve gearing.
(Courtesy: Austrian Federal Railways)

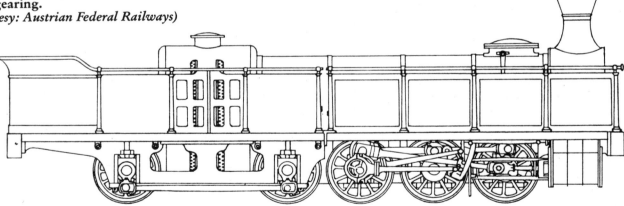

The Semmering rail line of the Austrian Southern Railway had many engine trials in 1851 before a suitable locomotive could be recommended to handle the steep grades. The problem was eventually resolved by an Austrian engineer named Wilhelm Engerth who, over a period 1847 to 1851, designed a new type of steam propulsion system for his locomotive. Illustrated is a drawing of Engerth's 1851 design for a mountain engine for the Austrian Ministry of Transport. In all, ten of these type 0–6–4–0 machines were manufactured by the Esslingen Locomotive Works. These engines had outside cylinders driving

the third pair of coupled wheels which were geared to the leading pair of trailing four-coupled wheels of the same size. Specifications were as follows:

Cylinders	18.7 by 24 inches
Drive wheels	3-foot 6.5-inches diameter
Boiler	
Grate area	13.8 square feet
Heating surface	1510 square feet
Working pressure	105 pounds per square inch
Operating weight	53.1 tons

(Courtesy: Austrian Federal Railways)

Pictured is a model of one of Engerth's type 0–6–4–0 locomotives designed in 1851 and built in 1854 for mountain and heavy freight usage. See an earlier illustration for specifications. The geared connection between the drive wheels and the trailing wheels gave a great amount of trouble and maintenance and, after about ten thousand miles, were removed, and the engines were converted to type 0–6–4 tank engines. By 1860 all were scrapped or changed to type 0–8–0 tender locomotives.
(Courtesy: Austrian Railway Museum, Vienna)

Pictured is the east end of the most important east-west Tirol Alps crossing, the Arlberg Tunnel in Austria. This double-track 6.4693-mile boring was completed on 20 September 1884.
(Courtesy: Austrian Federal Railways)

differently designed railway engine had been selected (see Sigl engine, illustration).

Late in 1851 Austrian government engineer Engerth submitted a special prototype engine to conquer the Semmering grades. This turned out to be the forerunner of the Mallet articulated locomotive. Ten such machines were eventually constructed by the Esslingen Locomotive Works. The Engerth engine successfully hauled the first train over Semmering Pass at eleven miles per hour on 12 April 1854. A model and a drawing of the Engerth locomotive are pictured.

Modified Engerth locomotives found subsequent use as mountain engines and as motive power for heavy freight service in various parts of France. They were also used on some passenger trains in Switzerland and France and on various narrow-gauge lines in Spain.

The mainline (east-west) railroad in Austria was completed in 1885. It ran from Vienna to Lake Constance at the western border of Austria and northeast corner of Switzerland. En route, in the Tirol, the famous 6.37-mile double-track Arlberg tunnel was bored during 1880–84 at a cost of $7.5 million and opened on 20 September 1884 (latitude 47°9.0′ north, longitude 10°12′ east). The Arlberg tunnel remains today the highest in Austria, at 4,309 feet above sea level. See illustration.

Another major north-south railroad that crossed the Alps in western Austria opened 7 July 1909. This route included the 5.31-mile Tauern tunnel, constructed under Bad Gastein. The tunnel was bored during 1901 to 1909 at a cost of $6,062,500 and is located at latitude 47°2.8′ north, longitude 13°7.4′ east.

Still another railroad tunnel runs north and south across the Karawanken Range between Rosenbach, Austria, and Hrusica, Yugoslavia. It is just short of five miles in length and was opened in 1906 (latitude 46°29′ north, longitude 14°01′ east).

The Brenner Pass Railway, reaching 4,496 feet above sea level, was constructed in 1867 as a north-south rail line connecting Innsbruck, Austria, with Bolzano, Italy.

An interesting bit of railroad history in Austria was the use of the rack-and-pinion arrangement on certain heavy grades where adhesion engines were impractical. In 1862 N. Riggenbach designed an improved rack-and-pinion system, which was installed in 1874 up the Kahlenberg heights near Vienna. His rack locomotive is pictured and described.

The Austrian State Railways and the Austrian Southern Railway were organized in 1880. They used a variety of locomotives, including long-boilered, type 0-8-0, eight-coupled frieght tank engines; a model is shown.

One of Austria's chief claimants to locomotive fame was Karl Golsdorf, Locomotive Superintendent of the Austrian State Railways between 1891 and 1916. See illustration. He was a very progressive engineer and was strongly international in his interests and associations. He was able to circumvent one of the serious difficulties of compound locomotives, i.e., starting the engines from a standstill. Golsdorf designed a special automatic starting arrangement that did not rely on skilled manipulation by the locomotive driver. His first two-cylinder compound locomotive in 1894, with a 4–4–0 wheel arrangement, worked successfully on various assignments and in mountain climbing service on the Arlberg route as well as on fast-running sections between Salzberg and Vienna. In 1897 he designed his so-called class 170 passenger engines, a 2–8–0 type with four cylinders, which became a classic on the Arlberg route. The latter engine types were also adapted later for freight traffic in all parts of Austria. In modifying his locomotives from two to four cylinders, Golsdorf at once secured a better-balanced machine and one more suitable for fast passenger work.

Golsdorf also developed a very successful 2–6–4 four-cylinder compound engine, a fast passenger locomotive in which he adapted the "Helmholz truck" with certain reservations. The two leading wheels and the first pair of drive wheels were carried on a bogie capable of swivelling along the right-of-way. A vertical pin joint allowed the leading drive wheels to be synchronized with those following, which were fastened to the main locomotive frame. About fifty of these machines were built between 1908 and 1916 by Steg, First Bohemian, Florisdorf, and Wiener Neustadt. Shown is a model on display in the Austrian Railway Museum in Vienna. These express locomotives were used on the Semmering, Arlberg, Brenner, and Tauern lines.

Austrian railways started electrification in 1912 on an experimental basis. A concerted program of conversion from steam to electric traction was initiated in 1920, at which time only 134 miles out of 3,728 were electrified. By 1939 there were 618 miles of electric railways, and in 1978 about 1,554 miles of Austrian railroads had been converted—

The rack and pinion as a means of locomotive haulage was patented in 1811 and used in 1812 by John Blenkinsop. After being revived in America, the system was taken up in Europe by Mr. N. Riggenbach, who patented improved appliances in 1862; in 1874 he constructed a railway up the Kahlenberg, near Vienna. This line was laid to a gauge of 4.71 feet and had a maximum gradient of 1 in 10; the ladder rack was laid midway between the rails. The model represents the framework and gearing of one of the locomotives built at the Swiss Locomotive Works, Winterthür, for this line.

The ending was carried on four wheels 26 inches in diameter, with a wheelbase of 10.17 feet. There were two horizontal outside cylinders 13 inches in diameter by 17.72 inch stroke, which drove a countershaft having a pair of pinions fixed on it; below this was a shaft carrying a toothed wheel which geared with he rack, and to each side of it was bolted a wheel gearing with the pinion above. The tractive factor was 173. The boiler was of the ordinary locomotive type with a heating surface of 582 square feet and a grate area of 10.6 square feet; the steam pressure was 132 pounds per square inch.

The engine, with its chimney at the lower end, pushed the carriages up the incline, there being no couplings. The descent was regulated by three methods of braking: (a) by a strap brake on one of the crank discs, (b) by a toothed pinion on the back axle gearing with the rack and fitted with drums and brake blocks, (c) by the compression in the cylinders of air drawn through the exhaust ports and expelled through a special regulating valve. Guards were provided to prevent derailment. The engine carried 220 gallons of water in tanks and 25 hundredweights of coal in bunkers; its weight in working order was 19.44 tons, and its ordinary load, 42 tons.

The permanent way consisted of flat-footed rails, weighing 40 pounds per yard, spiked to transverse sleepers. The rack had a pitch of 3.72 inches, the teeth being formed of wrought iron bars of trapezoidal section, with oval ends riveted into the webs of a pair of 4 by 2.4 inch channel irons, placed back to back, 5 inches apart. The rack was in lengths of about 10 feet, joined by fish plates and bolted to the sleepers; its weight was 111 pounds per yard.

Scale 1:16

(Courtesy: Science Museum, London)

about 45 percent of the entire rail system, which carried about 75 percent of all passenger and freight traffic.

In modern times, diesel locomotives have been gradually replacing steam traction on the remaining nonelectric lines, particularly on suburban routes.

Austria also has a variety of narrow-gauge rail lines operated both by private and government organizations. The Austrian Federal Railways (ÖBB), formed in 1923, has about three hundred miles of narrow track, consisting of two mountain rack meter-gauge systems and other nonrack types.

The 760-millimeter (2-foot 6-inch) gauge Steyrtalbahn line, which runs from Klaus to Garsten (latitude 48°03′ north, longitude 14°25′ east) used type 0–6–2 steam engines until it was converted to diesel power. Another line is the Waldviertalbahn Railway, also 760-millimeter gauge, located at Gmünd close to the Czech border; this line has used 0–8–4 type steam engines. The longest line operated by the ÖBB is the Mariazellerbahn, which runs southwest from St. Pölten fifty-seven miles to Gusswerk (latitude 47°45′ north, longitude 15°20′ east). It was eventually converted to electric

A model, on display in the Budapest Museum of Communications, of a class V.d 0–8–0 railroad engine built in 1881 for use on the Austrian State Railways is shown here. Cylinders were 17.7 by 23.6 inches, coupled wheels were 3 feet 8 inches in diameter, grate area was 18 square feet, heating surface was 1363 square feet, and the tractive effort was 12,900 pounds. This tank locomotive had an operational weight of 50 tons with 3 tons of coal and 1580 gallons of water. (*Courtesy: Museum of Communications, Budapest*)

Karl Gölsdorf (1861–1916) who was appointed Chief Engineer of the Imperial Royal Austrian State Railway in 1891 is pictured here. Up to 1911 Gölsdorf designed over forty-five different types of locomotives encorporating outstanding features of style and power unlike any other rail system in Europe. (*Courtesy:* La Vie du Rail, *Paris*)

traction. Several other small narrow-gauge systems run by ÖBB were converted to diesel traction about 1970.

As far as private rail lines were concerned, one of the largest was the Styrian Government Railways, which operated various narrow-gauge systems.

The oldest, the Murtalbahn dates from 1895 and uses 760-millimeter (2-foot 6-inch) gauge. It runs about forty-eight miles between Mauterndorf (latitude 47°08′ north, longitude 13°39′ east) and Unzmarkt. This system, originally operated with 0–6–2 and 0–10–0 steam engines, is now diesel-

Shown is a model of a type 2–6–4 compound super-heated express locomotive which represented the best-known design of Karl Gölsdorf, famous Chief Engineer of the Austrian State Railways. This engine first appeared in 1911, of which twenty-eight units were manufactured by four different firms in Austria. Technical characteristics were as follows:

Cylinders	
Inside Hi-pressure	15.5 by 28.5 inches
Outside Lo-pressure	26 by 28.5 inches
Coupled wheels	7-foot 1-inch diameter
Bogie wheels	Krauss-Helmholtz
Leading pair	
Four trailing	Bissel design
Boiler	49.75 square feet
Grate area	
Superheater	465 square feet (Schmidt)
Heating surface	2290 square feet
Working pressure	213 pounds per square inch
Maximum speed	100 kilometers per hour

(Courtesy: Austrian Railway Museum, Vienna)

powered. In summer, special trains operate on the 760-millimeter gauge Stainz to Predling-Wieselsdorf line using old steam engines. The Styrian Government Railways also run short rail lines between Weis (latitude 48°10′ north, longitude 14°02′ east) and Ratten of 760-millimeter gauge, and a standard gauge line, about 9.5 miles long, between Weis and Gleisdorf.

Various private firms operate other miscellaneous rail lines in Austria. In Upper Austria, Stern & Hafferl run a variety of old and modern equipment, most of which is electrified. Two of these are the standard-gauge Vorchdorf-Eggenberg to Lambach and the Haag line (Haag: latitude 48°11′ north; longitude 13°39′ east), and the Linzer–Lokalbahn line. Another Stern & Hafferl line uses one-meter gauge tracks from Vorchdorf to Gmundne (latitude 47°56′ north, longitude 13°48′ east).

Another private railway is the standard-gauge electric line between Bludenz and Scruns, called the Montafonerbahn, which opened in 1905. On occasion, they run tourist specials in the summer using an old compound 0–8–0 locomotive.

The Wiener Lokalbahn railway company uses standard-gauge tracks between Vienna and Baden.

In the early 1970s a very scenic cogwheel rack railroad, the Erzberg Railway, ran from Eisenerz (latitude 47°33′ north, longitude 14°54′ east) to Vordenberg, located between Hieflau and Leoben in east central Austria. This line operated fourteen four-cylinder, rack-type 0–6–2 tank engines built in 1890 as well as a number of large 0–12–0 tank machines built in 1912 for yard work and "pusher" duties, that is, back-up service at the tail-end of a long train. Several German 2–12–2 tank engines also were used for odd jobs.

By rough estimates, in 1973 there were approximately three hundred surviving steam locomotives in operation on the Austrian railroads. About 150 of these were various classes of Austrian steam locomotives and the balance were German classes 42 and 52, type 2–10–0 Kriegloks (war locomotives) that had outlived World War II. By the end of the 1970s it appeared that all steam locomotives on the main lines of Austria had been displaced by diesel-powered machines.

In 1978, according to *Janes World Railways,* the Austrian railways had a route length of 5,409 kilometers or 3,361 miles, all in standard-gauge track. See a map of the rail network in Austria.

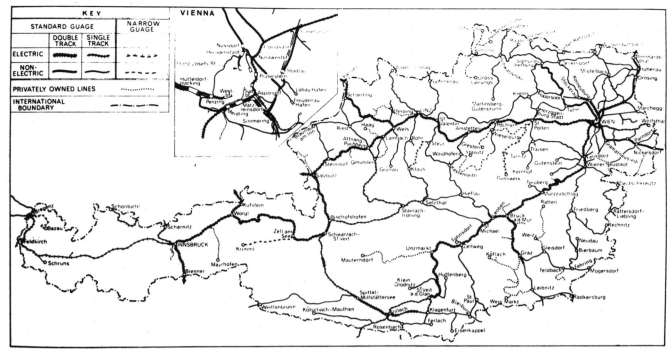

Railway map of Austria.
(*Courtesy:* Janes World Railways)

BELGIUM

SOON AFTER 1830, PLANS WERE LAID FOR A BELgian railroad system to be owned and managed by the state, and active work began in 1833. These government rail lines were arranged in the form of a cross, with the point of intersection at Malines. This railway was the world's pioneer trunk system.

On 5 May 1835, King Leopold inaugurated the first tiny stretch of railroad from Brussels to Malines. This was thus the oldest section of the planned Belgian State Railway system, which was also the first nationalized railway in Europe.

The management of the Belgian railways not only intended to develop traffic in Belgium but also to secure a large share of the transit trade between Germany and England. Keeping control of the main line rail routes, with a length of about three hundred miles, the Belgian government left the balance of railway expansion to private enterprise. Accordingly, between 1850 and 1870 private railways increased from about two hundred miles to fourteen hundred miles, and serious competition soon arose between the two systems. To avoid harmful conflicts of interest, the government decided to purchase most of the private competing lines, and by 1874 the state owned more than half the nation's railways. In 1885 it owned three-quarters, and by 1900 all rail lines in Belgium came under sovereign control.

What became the present railroad network in Belgium, more dense than in any other European country, was completed in 1875. It provided important internal trade routes as well as essential security from aggressive actions by the hostile Netherlands government, from which the Belgians had secured their independence in 1831.

The managers of Belgium's rail network had no aversions to authorizing rail connections with other countries for the purpose of promoting international communications. A link railroad with Germany was dedicated at Herbest Hal on 15 October 1843. A connection with France, the Ostend–Mons line, was opened shortly thereafter.

The Belgian rail system suffered horrendous damage by invading Germans in World War I, but in World War II the railroads remained largely intact following the rapid capture of Belgian territory by the German panzer divisions. Unfortunately, during the period 1940–45, approximately 905 locomotives and sixty-five thousand rail cars simply vanished into Germany, commandeered in support of the German war effort.

In 1976 the Société Nationale des Chemins de Fer Belges had 3,998 kilometers (2483) of standard-gauge tracks in service, of which 1,300 kilometers (807 miles) were electrified. Various light railways, which in the early days had contributed to the total Belgian transport system, had been reduced in the late 1960s to only 290 miles. The meter-gauge lines are presently operated by the Société Nationale des Chemins des Fer Vicinaux.

Steam Locomotives in Belgium

The Belgian engineers Belpaire and Walschaerts, in addition to various German and British engineers, were among the many contributors to the design of the steam locomotives used on the Belgian rail lines.

The first Belgium railway opened in 1835 between Brussels and Maline. Operating on the line were three British locomotives, one of which, named "L'Elephant," was built by Tayleur & Company, subcontractor for Stephenson; see illustration. Originally a type 0–4–2 goods engine (it was modified in 1849 to a 2–4–0 type) it had five-foot drive wheels acting off cylinders 14 by 22 inches using a boiler working pressure of 88 pounds per square inch and attaining a maximum speed of 60 kilometers per hour. A model of "L'Elephant" is housed in the Belgian Railways Museum.
(*Courtesy: O. S. Nock,* The Dawn of World Railways, 1800–1850)

Another view of Tayleur's locomotive, named "L'Elephant," used on the first Belgian railway in 1835 is shown here.
(*Courtesy: Spoorwegmuseum, Brussels*)

The first steam locomotive built in Belgium is pictured. This was named "Le Belgé" and was constructed in 1835 by Cockrill a Belgian manufacturer
using a Stephenson design.
(*Courtesy: O. S. Nock*, The Dawn of World Railways,
1800–1850)

Shown is a reproduction of the first steam locomotive
built in Belgium by the famous firm of John Cockrill
of Seraing on 30 December 1835. This was a type 2–2–2
engine named "Le Belgé" It had a 60-inch diameter
drive wheel, weighed 11.75 tons and attained a maximum speed of 60 kilometers per hour.
(*Courtesy: Spoorwegmuseum, Brussels*)

This illustration pictures an early locomotive designed by the English engineer Thomas Russell Crampton. The "Namur" was built by Tulk & Ley of the LOWCA Works of Whitehaven, England in the late 1830s for use on the Belgian rail line from Liege to Namur. The engine followed Crampton patent details and had these characteristics: Cylinders 16 by 20 inches with coupled wheels 7 feet in diameter. (*Courtesy O. S. Nock*, The Dawn of World Railways, 1800–1850)

A model of a locomotive which had become quite a success story on operations with the Belgian railways is pictured. This was a class 51 shunting engine with a 0–6–0 wheel arrangement designed by the famous Alfred Belpaire, long-time Director of Rolling Stock in the State Railways Central Offices at Brussels, Belgium. His engines were characterized by "square" fireboxes which were later employed on many other locomotives worldwide. The class 51 prototype engines were built in 1866 by Societe de Couillet and had typical "stove-pipe" smokestacks, double doors on the smoke box, oval pannier tanks, and no engineer cabs. Cylinders were 15 by 18.2 inches and driving coupled wheels 3 feet 11.2 inches in diameter. The boiler pressure was 118 pounds per square inch. Operational weights varied between 26.2 and 33.9 tons. In the period 1866–1905 the Belgian railways utilized 470 of these engines which by then were provided with cabs, rectangular pannier tanks, and less severe looking chimneys. (*Courtesy: Spoorwegmuseum, Brussels*)

Thirty-six Belpaire designed class 5, 2–4–0 tank locomotives were constructed in Belgium in the period 1880–81 by the Societe Saint Leonard of Liege. These engines performed local passenger train services on various lines of the Belgian State Railways. Cylinders were 18.75 by 17.9 inches with drive wheels 4 feet 9 inches in diameter. Boiler pressures were 118 pounds per square inch. Operational weights were 31 tons. This model is housed in the Belgian Railways Museum.
(Courtesy: Spoorwegmuseum, Brussels)

Starting in 1898 the Belgian State Railways used McIntosh type 4–4–0 locomotives which had met wide success in England. The first five engines were designated class 17. Subsequently other McIntosh designed locomotives were employed, of which class 18 machines were the most numerous, with 140 being built in the period 1902–1905. The class 18 engines, with type 4–4–0 wheel arrangements, had these characteristics:

Cylinders	19 by 26 inches
Coupled drive wheels	6.5-foot diameter
Boiler	22.3 square feet
Grate area	
Total heating surface	1373 square feet
Working pressure	175 pounds per square inch.

Illustrated is a model, displayed at the Belgian Railways Museum, of a class 20 McIntosh locomotive quite similar to the class 18 engines described above. Fifteen of the class 20 engines were built in 1908, and these had an operational weight of 56 tons with a six-wheeled tender.
(Courtesy: Spoorwegmuseum, Brussels)

A Flamme designed four-cylinder simple Pacific
locomotive introduced on the Belgian railways in 1910
is shown here.
(*Courtesy: Spoorwegmuseum, Brussels*)

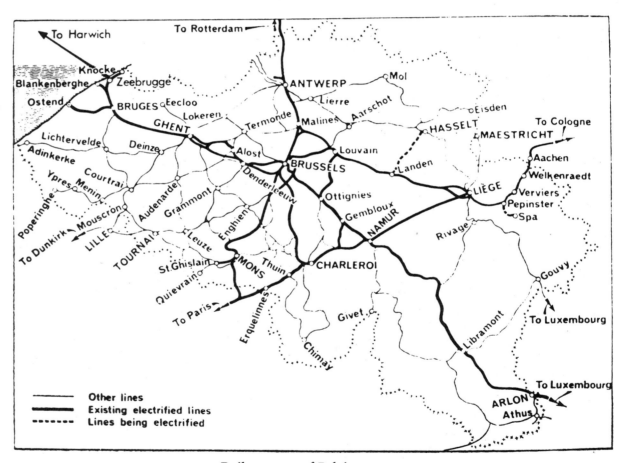

Railway map of Belgium.
(*Courtesy:* Janes World Railways)

A Belpaire designed locomotive, type 2–4–0, of which
157 units were constructed during the period 1864–83.
Operating weight was 33.25 tons with a maximum
speed of 100 kilometers per hour (62 miles per hour).
(Courtesy: Spoorwegmuseum, Brussels)

A type 0–6–0 class 51 tank engine designed by Belpaire
starting in 1866 is pictured. By 1905 about 474 units
were in operation. By 1945 106 machines had survived, and the last were seen in 1961. Operating
weight was 34 tons with a maximum speed of 45
kilometers per hour (27.9 miles per hour)
(Courtesy: Spoorwegmuseum, Brussels)

This illustration shows an articulated locomotive on the Meyer system which was first placed in service on the Grand Central Railway of Belgium in 1873. *(Courtesy: Spoorwegmuseum, Brussels)*

A Belgian tank locomotive, type 5, of which 37 machines were built in 1880–81 is shown here. Operating weight was 29.8 tons. *(Courtesy: Spoorwegmuseum, Brussels)*

Pictured is an early Belgian railway tank engine (date unknown) otherwise described as type 9. Operating weight was 35.08 tons. *(Courtesy: Spoorwegmuseum, Brussels)*

Illustrated is a Belgian tender locomotive, type 25, with a 0–6–0 wheel arrangement of which 472 units were constructed in the period 1884–94. Operating weight was 46 tons.
(Courtesy: Spoorwegmuseum, Brussels)

This shows a so-called type 12 Belgian steam locomotive, of which 115 units were built in the period 1888–97. This was a type 2–4–2 "Columbia" engine with an operating weight of 49 to 56 tons and a maximum speed of 110 kilometers per hour (68.2 miles per hour).
(Courtesy: Spoorwegmuseum, Brussels)

Illustrated is a type 96 tank locomotive which
started operations on the Belgian railways in 1903.
Originally twenty-seven such units were purchased.
Operating weight was 62.94 tons.
(Courtesy: Spoorwegmuseum, Brussels)

With the opening of Belgium's first railroad in 1835, three British-built locomotives, type 2–2–2, participated in the inaugural ceremonies: no. 1, "La Fliche"; no. 2, "L'Elephent"; and no. 3, "Stephenson." Engines 1 and 3 were constructed by Robert Stephenson & Company, and no. 2 was built by Tayleur & Company using Stephenson patents and designs. See two illustrations.

The first steam locomotive manufactured in Belgium was built in 1835 by John Cockrell of Seraing following a Stephenson design; this engine is pictured in two illustrations.

The Belgian rail line from Liege to Namur in the late 1830s, used a Crampton-designed, type 4–2–0 engine built by Tulk & Ley of Whitehaven, England (see illustration).

From 1866 to 1905, the Belgian railways utilized several hundred class 51 shunting engines, type 0–6–0, designed by Alfred Belpaire (see illustration). Belpaire also designed various type 2–4–0 locomotives between 1880 and 1881. See illustration.

With the success of the so-called Dunalastair class locomotives, designed in England by John F. McIntosh in 1896, the Belgian State Railways in 1898 ordered five units through Neilson, Reid & Company of Scotland (see illustration). While these engines performed satisfactorily, Belgian engineers influenced by the fame of de Glehn soon turned to France for many subsequent locomotives. In 1905 a number of four-cylinder compound engines were introduced. These met with success, and after World War I, seventy-five similar units with superheaters were ordered. Many of these survived into the World War II period. However, compound locomotives had various problems, and as early as 1910, when more powerful machines were required, J. B. Flamme designed the first Belgian four-cylinder, simple 4–6–2 Pacifics. These awkward looking locomotives eventually achieved great success. Their unusual appearance was due to the fact that inside cylinders used to drive the leading coupled axle were set far forward beneath a long platform ahead of the boiler, which required a leading bogie out in front of the smokebox. See illustration. A map of the Belgium railway network is provided.

Requests for photographs to various entities in Belgium brought a series of postcard pictures of several Belgian steam locomotives; however a year-long series of correspondence failed to elicit any suitable caption information or a translation of the copy on the back sides of the postcards. These pictures are nevertheless included for any value they may have.

BOLIVIA

RAILROADS IN BOLIVIA WERE SLOW-DEVELOPING, even while rail construction in adjoining Chile, Peru, and Argentina was making rapid and obvious progress. The first railway built and operated on Bolivian soil was completed in 1879: a 2-foot 6-inch gauge line running from the Pacific port of Antofagasta inland sixty miles to nitrate beds at Salinas. Following the War of the Pacific, 1879–83, when Chile defeated her Bolivian and Peruvian adversaries, Bolivia lost her Pacific coastal territory. Successive extensions of the original railroad, now in Chilean possession, were made from Salinas, with the line reaching the new Bolivian border at Ollague in 1889.

Under concessions from the Bolivian government, the Antofagasta (Chile) & Bolivia Railway Company, known as FCAB, completed a 110-mile meter-gauge extension in Bolivia, from Ollague to Uyuni, in 1889 and an additional 195 miles to Oruro in 1892.

During the era of the great rubber boom in Brazil and Bolivia, between 1860 and 1911, it became expedient to build a rail line to connect northeastern Bolivia with western Brazil, thus bypassing serious obstructions in the Madeira and Mamore Rivers. A route for the so-called Madeira & Mamora Railway was surveyed in 1872–73 under the direction of an American, Colonel George Earl Church; however, construction work did not start until 1877 due to financial and other problems. Subsequently, a Philadelphia contractor, the Phillip and Thomas Collins Company, ran into tremendous difficulties in the jungle and rain forests and, after losing an important litigation with stockholders in English courts, the project collapsed in 1880. Railroad work picked up again, this time under private Brazilian auspices, during the period 1907 to 1911, and the job was finally finished on 12 July 1912. By this time the rubber boom had subsided, and the railroad was, for all commercial purposes, largely abandoned. It was purchased by the Brazilian government in 1931, after which the tracks and rolling stock were rehabilitated. The Madiera & Mamore railroad today remains a moderately active entity providing minor transportation service in these remote parts of Bolivia and Brazil.

It is of historical interest to note that an old Baldwin locomotive named "Cornel Church," built in 1878 for the Madeira & Mamore Railway in Brazil, was recovered from the jungle in 1908. It was in relatively good shape, and after a few repairs and replacement of missing parts, it was put back in service. Although more than forty-five years old, the locomotive was still operating in 1923. The engine was subsequently retired in 1932 and placed on a monument in front of an officer's club at Porto Velho, Brazil.

A milestone in Bolivian transportation came in 1904 when rail connections from the Bolivian capital at La Paz were completed to Lake Titicaca, on which steamers joined Bolivian rail traffic with the Peruvian Mollendo–Juliaca rail system at Puno. Landlocked Bolivia, for the first time since 1879, was thus provided, through Peru, with access to a seaport on the Pacific Ocean.

During October 1908, after many years of planning and negotiating, Bolivia opened connections between Oruro and La Paz, which secured a sec-

This illustration shows an old narrow-gauge steam locomotive, type 0–4–0, introduced into Bolivia in the early twentieth century. This engine is displayed on a monument site in Cochabamba, Bolivia.
(Courtesy: Antofagasta & Bolivia Railway Company, Ltd.)

ond route, 729 miles long, to the Pacific Ocean through northern Chile and the port at Antofagasta. Unlike the Titicaca water route to Peru, this was an all-rail connection to the Pacific.

Subsequent construction projects in Bolivia produced the following important one-meter railroad systems:

Route	Miles	Year completed
Rio Mulatos–Potosi	108	1912
La Paz–Yungas	76	1914
Oruro–Cochabamba	127	1917
Villazon–Tupiza	62.1	1924
Tupiza–Atocha	62.1	1925
Potosi–Sucre	108	1929
Cochabamba–Aiguile	117	1930
Sucre–Tarabuco	50	1933
Santa Cruz–Corumba	423	1955
Santa Cruz–Yacuiba	327	1957
Santa Cruz–Santa Rosa	66	1973

Bolivian railways are covered in detail in my 1981 book, *Railways Across the Andes.*

The following eleven photographs give a very sparse view of the steam locomotives used on the railways of Bolivia.

Shown is a type 2–8–4 shunting locomotive built by Hunslet Engine Company, Ltd. for the meter-gauge FCB Railway (Ferrocarril Bolivia). This tank engine, no. 101, was placed in service during January 1913 and had these general characteristics:

Boiler pressure	180 pounds per square inch
Operating weight	85 tons
Tank capacity	2850 gallons water
Bunker capacity	4 tons coal.

(Courtesy: Antofagasta & Bolivia Railway Company, Ltd.)

In June 1914 the Bolivian meter-gauge railways placed in service several Pacific type 4–6–2 passenger locomotives built by Henschel & John. Tender engine no. 35, shown, had these general specifications: engine weight, 63 tons; operating weight (engine and tender), 114 tons; water capacity, 4500 gallons; coal capacity, 6 tons.
(Courtesy: Antofagasta & Bolivia Railway Company, Ltd.)

A Garratt type steam locomotive on the Cochabamba branch of the meter-gauge Bolivian Railways in 1920 is shown here.
(Courtesy: Antofagasta & Bolivia Railway Company, Ltd.)

Pictured is a type 2–8–2 tank locomotive operated by the FCAB (Antofagasta & Bolivia Railway Company) on the 729-mile run between La Paz, Bolivia and Antofagasta, Chile in 1922. No details available on this locomotive.
(Courtesy: Antofagasta & Bolivia Railway Company Ltd.)

A general view of the railroad station at La Paz, Bolivia, in 1930 is given. This is the highest major capital city in the world at twelve thousand feet above sea level.
(Courtesy: Antofagasta & Bolivia Railway Company, Ltd.)

Sometime before World War II Kitson & Company of Leeds, England manufactured for the meter-gauge Bolivian railways several type 2–8–2 freight locomotives. Engine no. 601 had a boiler working pressure of 180 pounds per square inch; operating weight (engine plus tender) was 72 tons; water capacity was 4500 gallons; and coal capacity was 10 tons.
(Courtesy: Antofagasta & Bolivia Railway Company, Ltd.)

Pictured is a type 4–8–2 steam locomotive, no. 341, of which sixteen machines were supplied by the Vulcan Foundry, Ltd. in 1954–55. Ten units (nos. 341–50) were put in service on the Bolivian section and six units (nos. 201–6) were used on the Chilean section of the FCAB railway system which operated between Antofagasta, north Chile to La Paz, Bolivia. Operating weights were: engine, 87 tons; tender 59 tons. See other illustrations for a head-on view of this engine and for a control-cab picture.
(Courtesy: Antofagasta & Bolivia Railway Company, Ltd.)

This shows a head-on view of engine no. 341 previously pictured and described.
(Courtesy: Antofagasta & Bolivia Railway Company, Ltd.)

The control cab of the type 4–8–2 engine no. 341 built for the Antofagasta-La Paz Railway by the Vulcan Foundry, Ltd. in 1954–55 is shown.
(*Courtesy: Antofagasta & Bolivia Railway Company, Ltd.*)

BRAZIL

INADEQUATE TRANSPORTATION BETWEEN POP-
ulated coastal areas and the interior of Brazil has
been a serious bottleneck to economic integration
since colonial times. In the 1860s, Brazilian authorities arbitrarily decided to crisscross the country with railroads to facilitate industrial and agricultural development. A few short lengths of
track were initially laid down without any kind of
master plan and, as it turned out, with inadequate
engineering and financing.

The first railway in Brazil opened on 30 April
1854. It had a 5-foot 6-inch gauge and ran ten miles
from Maná, located in the Rio de Janeiro area at the
head of the Bay of Rio, to Raiz da Serra at the foot
of Petropolis Serra mountain. This rail line was the
pioneer system on the South American continent
below the equator. It was extended later to Petropolis, necessitating a four-mile climb of Serra de
Estrella using a Riggenbach-type rack at a grade of
1 in 6.7. In 1879 this short rail line became part of
the Leopoldina Railway.

In the early 1870s an English company was organized, with Brazilian approval, to take over the
individual rail sections and combine them into a
homogeneous so-called Leopoldina system. Mr.
F. W. Barrow was general manager and Norman B.
Dickson, chief engineer. By this time, both the
physical system and the rolling equipment of the
original rail line were in terrible disrepair. The early
facilities had been built too cheaply and rapidly fell
victim to tropical insects and humidity, especially
the wooden sleepers, bridges, and culverts.

Later, trains running inland faced tremendous
odds climbing the rugged mountain ridges that
closely paralleled the coast. One railroad, passing
inland from Nictheroy on the east side of the bay
of Rio de Janeiro, had forty miles of level roadway,
then difficult 8 percent grades. In this instance the
problem was solved, uniquely, by purchasing from
Switzerland the Mont Cenis Fell rack railway,
which, with the opening of the famous Mont Cenis
tunnel in 1872, had been declared surplus. This
system was transported to Brazil and installed,
about 1874, together with its locomotives and rolling stock. The rack railway arrangement worked
well for some years until the special locomotives
gave out.

Early in 1882 the Baldwin Locomotive Works
received an inquiry from the Brazilian government
for a suitable locomotive for the Cantagallo Railway. The engine was required to haul a train of
forty gross tons up a grade of 8.3 percent (438 feet
per mile) having curves of a forty-meter radius (131
feet or 43.8 degrees). The Cantagallo Railway was
laid with heavy steel rail at a gauge of 1.1 meters, or
3 feet 7⅓ inches. This railroad also had a constant
succession of reverse curves: ninety-one curves in
two miles. The line had previously operated by the
Fell system with a central rack-rail, and in 1892 the
Cantagallo Railway proposed to introduce adhesion motive power. An initial order for three such
locomotives was entered with Baldwin. The final
engines manufactured had these specifications:

Cylinders	18 inches × 20 inches
Connected drive wheels	39-inch diameter (six in num-ber)
Drive wheel base	9 feet 6 inches
Boiler	54-inch diameter; 10 feet 9 inches length
Boiler tubes	190 with 2-inch diameter.

The locomotives and side tanks were shipped from Philadelphia in March 1883. At trials conducted on 17 October 1883 the Baldwin locomotives met all the guaranteed performance standards. One engine pulled a train of forty tons, composed of three freight cars loaded with sleepers and one passenger car the eight kilometers to Boca do Mata at twenty-four kilometers per hour. From there, it ran into the section with 8.5 percent grade with curves of forty meters in radius, meeting all tests satisfactorily. When the adhesion tests were completed to the satisfaction of all concerned, the line turned out to have the steepest adhesion traction anywhere in the world.

One problem resulting from the steep grades, which caused many rail accidents, was the inability of engineers to completely control the downgrade train speeds. Eventually, a mechanism was installed on the Baldwin engines that utilized the original rack rail as part of a braking system, thus eliminating runaways. Over the following ten years, eight more Baldwin locomotives were manufactured and adhesion power was used on this railroad from then on.

In 1889 Baldwin also built two rack-rail locomotives for the Riggenbach system. One, with a single cog wheel and four carrying wheels, weighing 32,000 pounds, was for the Corcovado Railway of Brazil; the other engine, with two cog wheels and eight carrying wheels, weighing 79,000 pounds, was for the Estra da de Ferro Principe do Grão Pará Railway of Brazil. See illustration for a picture of the engine used on the Corcovado system.

Subsequent rail extensions into the Brazilian interior had to surmount the second and third sets of ridges. In addition, there were many flooding problems in the high rainfall areas, and bridging the Parahybuna River constituted a major engineering project. Climbing the severe third series of mountain ridges was accomplished using an arrangement of switchbacks. Many spur lines were thrown out from the main track. To avoid flooding, these were kept to high ground on the sides of the hills, which led to a maze of twists and turns with no straightaway sections. In fact, these railroads possessed a fantastic assortment of S curves, horseshoe bends, and wondrous figure-eight loops.

A serious failing of early Brazilian railways, as

Illustrated is a unique Baldwin locomotive with a single cogwheel, built in 1884 to operate on a Riggenbach cog rail system on the Corcovado Railway of Brazil. This rack railroad was installed to permit trains to climb the Corcovado Mountain in Rio.
(Courtesy: FEPASA Ferrovia Paulista SA)

well as many other South American rail lines, was the propensity for using a variety of rail gauges. Originally there were five different gauges, and interconnections existed only in the vicinity of Rio de Janeiro or São Paulo. Differences in rail gauges also made traffic links with Argentina and Uruguay extremely difficult. Most Brazilian railroads were laid down to meet local requirements. Many routes spread out in a fanlike pattern to move export products such as sugar, coffee, and cacao from the interior to the coastal ports; consequently, there were all too few lateral connecting links.

In modern times, starting in 1960, the rundown condition of the Brazilian railroads led to a definite shift in transportation emphasis from railroads to highways. This fostered a government plan to consolidate the separate railroads and their organizations and provide necessary north-south rail connections. Nonetheless, between 1958 and 1971, approximately six thousand miles of track were abandoned. By 1971 extensive projects were underway to expand and modernize the existing railway system. Forty different lines were incorporated to become Rede Ferroviaria Federal SA. This system finally adopted three track gauges: 1.60-meter (5-foot 3-inch), 1-meter, and 0.762-meter (3-foot 6-inch). Total route length was 24,491 kilometers or 15,218 miles. Also, five different state-owned railroads around São Paulo were consolidated into Ferrovia Paulista SA. This system had 1,647 kilometers (1,023.4 miles) of 1.60-meter track and 3,649 kilometers (2,267.4 miles) of 1-meter track. In addition, six small railroads with nine hundred miles of track operated privately.

Railroads in Brazil, in contrast to most other enterprises there, such as utilities, highways, and mines, received annual government subsidies to meet operating costs. Despite new connections and an active modernization program, by the mid 1970s total railways in use continued to decline. In general, considering the huge size of Brazil, the country continues to be served by an abnormally small railroad network.

In 1978 *Janes World Railways* reported that Brazil had a total of 24,491 kilometers (15,218 miles) of 1.60-meter (5-foot 3-inch), 1-meter, and 0.762-meter (2-foot 6-inch) track in active service.

The world's first express Garratt locomotives were built for the São Paulo Railway in 1927; these were type 2–6–2 + 2–6–2, rebuilt in 1931–32 as 4–6–2 + 2–6–4 types.

The Central Railway of Brazil, a high-altitude line, is one of two railways in South America to employ the Gresham automatic vacuum brake system.

The worst railroad wreck in Brazil occurred near Aracaju on 20 March 1946, killing 185 people.

Steam Locomotives in Brazil

The earliest railroads in Brazil used British steam locomotives. In 1862 and 1863 Baldwin delivered several woodburning 2–6–0 freight engines shown in the first illustration. In 1871 the Dom Pedro II Railway accepted delivery of a number of Baldwin class 10-34E, type 2–8–0, Consolidation engines, which performed with great success on heavy grades of the Sierra (1 in 55 grade). See illustration. Baldwin constructed several adhesion-type engines in 1883 to replace worn-out equipment on the Fell rack railroad, as detailed above. In 1885 the Dom Pedro II Railway received several so-called Decapod (ten-wheeled) steam locomotives, which are shown. In 1889 Baldwin supplied two rack-rail engines for the Riggenbach system also discussed and described above.

Baldwin furnished various outside-frame 4–4–0, 4–6–0 and 2–8–0 engines in 1890 for the thirty-inch gauge Viacao Ferrovaria Centro Oeste line, which operated about 250 miles north of Rio de Janeiro along the Rio dos Mortes River. Many of these engines were still in service in 1973.

In 1909 Baldwin supplied several Mogul engines for use on the infamous Estrada de Ferro Madeira–Mamore Railway, which connected west Brazil and eastern Bolivia (see illustration). The Brazilian Army operated this railway after World War II, using several passenger-type Henschel engines.

J. A. Maffei constructed a number of Prairie 2–6–2 locomotives in 1913 for use on the 5-foot 3-inch gauge line of the Central Railway of Brazil. See illustration.

The American Locomotive Company in 1919 was involved in constructing various types of steam engines for the Central Railway of Brazil. One illustration shows a Pacific-type and another illustration covers a Consolidation-type engine.

In 1920 Baldwin supplied six type 2–10–2 Santa Fe locomotives for the meter-gauge Paulista Railway. Also, it built ten type 4–6–2 Pacific engines for the meter-gauge Noreste Railway in 1920, shown in the illustration. More orders were filled by Baldwin in 1921: ten Mikado 2–8–2 engines for the Sorocabana Railway, seventeen ten-wheel 4–6–

A wood-burning 2–6–0 freight locomotive built in 1862–63 by the Baldwin Locomotive Works. Specifications were:

Cylinders	18.5 by 22 inches
Drive wheels	50.5-inch diameter
Engine weight	63,000 pounds.

(Courtesy: Frederick Westing collection)

A Baldwin Consolidation, type 2–8–0, Baldwin class 10–34E, locomotive similar to that delivered to the Dom Pedro II Railway of Brazil in 1871. The firebox was adapted to burn either bituminous or anthracite coal. This type engine was built with two pairs of flanged driving wheels, either the front and rear pairs or the main and rear pairs. The other two pairs of coupled wheels had tires without flanges. The pony truck had a swinging bolster and a radius bar, the same as in the Mogul type engines. Specifications were as follows:

Cylinders	20 by 24 inches
Drive wheels	48-inch diameter
Operating weight	102,000 pounds (engine plus tender)
Tender water capacity	2600 gallons.

(Courtesy: FEPASA Ferrovia Paulista SA)

Shown is a Decapod, type 2–10–0, locomotive built by the Baldwin Locomotive Works in 1885 for use on the Dom Pedro II Segundos Railway in Brazil. These engines had five pairs of coupled drive wheels and a leading two-wheeled truck. From this arrangement has arisen the name Decapod (have ten feet). The ten drivers had a seventeen-foot wheelbase. Specifications were as follows:

Cylinders	22 by 26 inches
Drive wheels	45-inch diameter
Boiler	
Grate area	33 square feet
Total heating surface	1943 square feet
Working pressure	130 pounds per square inch
Tractive force	30,900 pounds
Operating weights	
Engine	141,000 pounds
On drivers	126,000 pounds.

(Courtesy: Rede Ferroviaria Federal SA)

In 1909 Baldwin built several Mogul type 2–6–0 tender locomotives for the Madeira–Mamore railroad which connected west Brazil with east Bolivia. These engines were similar to the one pictured. These engines, which were Baldwin class 8–26D, had the following general specifications:

Cylinders	16 by 24 inches
Drive wheels	45-inch diameter
Operating weight	71,000 pounds
Tender water capacity	2000 gallons.

(Courtesy: FEPASA Ferrovia Paulista SA)

In 1913 J. A. Maffei built several Prairie type 2–6–2 locomotives for the Central Railway of Brazil. Specifications on engine no. 463 were:

Railway gauge	5 feet 3 inches
Cylinders	23⅝ by 26 inches
Drive wheels	5-foot 1.75-inch diameter
Boiler	
Grate area	41.4 square feet
Total heating surface	2475 square feet
Boiler working pressure	180 pounds per square inch
Tractive effort	35,810 pounds
Operating weights	
Engine	105 tons
On drivers	54 tons.

(Courtesy: Rede Ferroviaria Federal SA)

Pictured is a Pacific type 4–6–2 railway engine constructed by the American Locomotive Company for use on the Central Railway of Brazil in 1919. Specifications on engine no. 378 were as follows:

Railway gauge	5 feet three inches
Cylinders	21.5 by 28 inches
Drive wheels	5 foot 8.5-inch diameter
Boiler	
Grate area	50 square feet
Total heating surface	2410 square feet
Working pressure	175 pounds per square inch
Tractive effort	28,300 pounds
Operating weights	
Engine	141,295 pounds
On drivers	54,855 pounds.

(Courtesy: Rede Ferroviaria Federal SA)

A consolidated type 2–8–0 steam locomotive used on the Central Railway of Brazil is shown here. This was an American Locomotive machine built in 1919. Specifications on engine no. 716 were:

Railway gauge	5 feet 3 inches
Cylinders	21.5 by 26 inches
Drive wheels	59.25-inch diameter
Boiler	
Grate area	40.8 square feet
Total heating surface	1855 square feet
Working pressure	180 pounds per square inch
Tractive force	43,700 pounds
Operating weights	
Engine	121,381 pounds
On drivers	67,182 pounds.

(Courtesy: Rede Ferroviaria Federal SA)

A Santa Fe type steam locomotive, with a 2–10–2 wheel arrangement, used on the meter-gauge Paulista Railway of Brazil is pictured. Engine no. 91 was part of a six-unit order from Baldwin in 1920. The locomotives were equipped with superheaters and had the following general specifications:

Cylinders	20 by 22 inches
Drive wheels	42-inch diameter
Engine weight	159,600 pounds.

(Courtesy: Frederick Westing collection)

Locomotive no. 401, a Pacific type with a 4–6–2 wheel arrangement, part of an order for ten which were purchased from Baldwin in 1920 is shown. These engines were used on the meter-gauge Noreste Railway of Brazil. General specifications were as follows:

Cylinders	15 by 20 inches
Coupled drive wheels	44-inch diameter
Engine weight	92,500 pounds.

(Courtesy: Frederick Westing collection)

Pictured is a Mikado, 2–8–2 type, locomotive, part of a ten-unit order to Baldwin in 1921. These engines were purchased for use on the Sorocabana Railway of Brazil. Specifications were:

Cylinders   19 by 20 inches
Drive wheels   41.75-inch diameter
Engine weight   127,000 pounds.

(Courtesy: Frederick Westing collection)

This is an illustration of a ten-wheeled locomotive, type 4–6–0, one of seventeen units ordered in 1921 from the Baldwin Locomotive Works. These engines were used on the Federaux de l'Est Bresilien Railway of Brazil. General specifications were as follows:

Cylinders   16 by 20 inches
Drive wheels   45-inch diameter
Engine weight   84,700 pounds.

(Courtesy: Frederick Westing collection)

A ten-wheeled steam engine, part of a four-unit order received from Baldwin in 1921 is pictured. These engines provided service on the Great Western Railway of Brazil. General specifications were:

Cylinders   16.5 by 20 inches
Drive wheels   42-inch diameter
Engine weight   82,200 pounds.

(Courtesy: Frederick Westing collection)

Shown here is a type 2–8–2 Mikado locomotive which was constructed by A.E.G. for use on the 5-foot 3-inch gauge Central Railway of Brazil in 1925. Specifications for engine no. 801 were as follows:

Cylinders	22 ¹³⁄₁₆ by 27 ¹⁵⁄₁₆ inches
Drive wheels	52.75-inch diameter
Boiler	
Grate area	66.7 square feet
Total heating surface	25.17.5 square feet
Working pressure	190 pounds per square inch
Operating weights	
Engine	149,600 pounds
On drivers	72,800 pounds
Tractive force	39,910 pounds.

(Courtesy: Rede Ferroviaria Federal SA)

In 1925 A.E.G. constructed several Mikado type 2–8–2 steam locomotives for the Central Railway of Brazil. Engine no. 402, is shown and had these specifications:

Railway gauge	39 feet ⅜ inch
Cylinders	16 by 22 inches
Drive wheels	3-foot 5.25-inch diameter
Boiler	
Grate area	47.3 square feet
Total heating surface	1134.5 square feet
Working pressure	180 pounds per square inch
Tractive force	20,790 pounds
Operating weights	
Engine	87,200 pounds
On drivers	41,400 pounds.

(Courtesy: Rede Ferroviaria Federal SA)

Pictured is another Baldwin Locomotive Works locomotive, type 2–8–2 Mikado, which was utilized on 5-foot 3-inch gauge tracks of the Central Railway of Brazil starting in 1927. Engine no. 815 had the following specifications:

Railway gauge	5 feet 3 inches
Cylinders	23 by 28 inches
Drive wheels	56.25-inch diameter
Boiler	
Grate area	79 square feet
Total heating surface	3024 square feet
Working pressure	195 pounds per square inch
Tractive force	43,100 pounds
Operating weights	
Engine	154,992 pounds
On drivers	79,152 pounds.

(Courtesy: Rede Ferroviara Federal SA)

In 1937 the Central Railway of Brazil tried out several Mallet locomotives manufactured by Henschel & Sohn. These were type 2–8–8–4. Engine no. 1307 is pictured and had the following specifications:

Railway gauge	39⅜ inches (meter)
Cylinders (4)	17 by 22 inches
Drive wheels	42-inch diameter
Boiler	
Grate area	75.6 square feet
Total heating surface	2516 square feet
Working pressure	210 pounds per square inch
Tractive force	53,970 pounds
Operating weights	
Engine	172.3 tons
On Drivers	98 tons.

(Courtesy: Rede Ferroviaria Federal SA)

Shown are two views of a type 2–10–4 steam locomotive, no. 901, constructed in 1938 by Henschel & Sohn for use on the Central Railway of Brazil. Specifications were as follows:

Cylinders	26³⁄₁₆ by 28 inches
Drive wheels	56.5-inch diameter
Boiler	
Grate area	93.6 square feet
Total heating surface	3810 square feet
Working pressure	235 pounds per square inch
Tractive force	58,080 pounds
Operating weights	
Engine	223.5 tons
On drivers	100 tons.
Railway gauge	5-foot 3-inch

(Courtesy: Rede Ferroviaria Federal SA)

A type 4–4–0 tank engine manufactured by Avonside Engine Company of Bristol, England is shown.

A type 4–6–0 ten-wheeler tender engine, no. 61, track gauge 1.6-meter, manufactured by the Baldwin Locomotive Works is illustrated.

This is a type 0–6–2 Mogul wood-burning tank engine, no. 202, track gauge 1.6-meter, manufactured by the Baldwin Locomotive Works.

Pictured is a type 4–6–0 ten-wheeler tender engine, no. 643, track gauge 1.0-meter, manufactured by the Baldwin Locomotive Works.

A type 2–8–0 tender engine, no. 700, track gauge 1.0-meter, manufactured by Beyer Peacock & Company is pictured.

A type 2–6–2 Prairie tank engine, no. 920, track gauge 0.60-meter, manufactured by Linke Hofman is shown.

This is a type 0–4–2 wood-burning engine, no. 952, track gauge 0.60-meter, manufactured by the Baldwin Locomotive Works.

Railway map of Brazil.
(*Courtesy:* Janes World Railways)

0 locomotives for Federaux de l'Est, and four ten-wheel 4–6–0 engines for Great Western. See three illustrations.

In 1925 the AEG firm supplied various Mikado-type steam locomotives for the 5-foot 3-inch gauge lines of the Central Railways of Brazil. Two machines of this type are illustrated.

Starting in 1927, Baldwin also manufactured sev-eral Mikado machines to the Central Railways of Brazil. An example is pictured. The Central Railway of Brazil also tried out a number of Mallet locomotives in 1937 and several powerful type 2–10–4 locomotives from Henschel & Sohn of Germany in 1938. See three illustrations.

In 1948 Baldwin furnished several Mikado engines and in 1950 a few 2–6–6–2 engines for use on the Teresa Cristina Railway, which served various coal mine operations along the south coast of Brazil just west of Tubarão (latitude 28°30′ south, longitude 48°19′ west).

As recently as 1970 it was discovered that a Brazil subsidiary of the Portland Cement Company operates a 2-foot gauge rail line utilizing several dozen old and modern steam engines with seven different wheel arrangements at its industrial operation near São Paulo. The official company name is Companhia Brasileira de Cimento Portland Perus.

BURMA

THE FIRST RAILWAY IN BURMA, COMPLETED IN 1876, was the meter-gauge line linking Rangoon with Prome to the north on the Irrawaddy River. This 161-mile railway served a fertile agricultural strip between the Pegu Yomas and Irrawaddy rivers and shortened the time required over the river journey from Mandalay to Rangoon by-almost one half. The second rail line opened in 1885 from Rangoon to Toungoo, a distance of about 190 miles, and extended in 1899 to Mandalay in the north, another 240 miles, serving the Sittang Valley. In 1899 the Sagaing–Myitkyina line, of about 275 miles, was constructed. Branch lines were subsequently added to all of these lines, running along historic trade routes to the east through northern Shan States, the southern Shan States, and Moulmein. The railroads normally ran through the most populous and economically significant parts of the country.

Burma's railroads have to traverse one of the world's toughest gradients; the line between Mandalay and Lashio has a steady climb of twelve miles at a slope of 1 in 25, which also includes the famous Gokteik viaduct. This bridge carries the meter-gauge Lashio line 825 feet above the river Nam Panhse. Erected in 1900 by the Pennsylvania Steel Company, the structure is supported by sixteen 40-foot spans, seven 60-foot spans, and by ten 120-foot spans. It is 2,260 feet long.

The Kalaw summit is the highest point on the Burma State Railways at 4,610 feet above sea level.

The railroads were taken over by the state government in 1929. By 1941 Burma had 2,667 miles of track; however, World War II actions resulted in much damage and track was reduced by the end of the war to 1,777 miles.

During World War II, additions to railroad facilities were, naturally, delayed. Even after the conflict, limited finances meant that the railroads must concentrate their construction resources on repairs and replacements rather than on new lines.

By 1969 the rail network in Burma was seriously overstrained. State-owned railways were then carrying three times as many passengers as they had before World War II with two-thirds the number of coaches. As many as 27 percent of the locomotives were out of order at one time and there were ten percent fewer freight cars than in 1939. In 1969 Burma railways had 373 locomotives, 9,344 freight cars, and 1,184 passenger coaches.

State-owned railways in Burma operated 1,850 miles of single track meter-gauge railways in 1970. Rail lines that were not being used were abandoned in 1970. In general, railways in this country continued to be secondary to inland waterways as a means of transportation. Spurs from the main-line north-south railway terminated at Lashio and Myingyan. The Prome–Rangoon Railway had a branch to Bassein in the Irrawaddy Delta. An important railway connected Rangoon with Moulein and ran fifty miles further south.

In 1972 work was continuing on a second track for the 386-mile Rangoon–Mandalay Railway.

According to *Janes World Railways*, in 1978 the Union of Burma railways had 3,130 kilometers (1,945 miles) of meter-gauge tracks.

The worst railroad disaster in Burma, a serious train collision, occurred near Toungoo on the Rangoon–Mandalay main trunk line on 9 December 1965, killing seventy-six people.

The accompanying fifteen illustrations show some uses of the steam locomotive on the railways of Burma between 1896 and 1922.

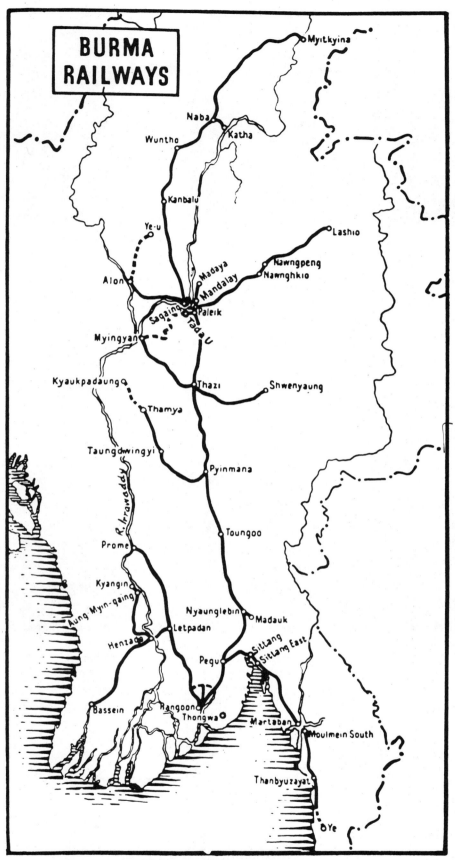

Railway map of Burma.
(*Courtesy:* Janes World Railways)

In 1896 Neilson & Company furnished two type 4–4–4 tank locomotives to the Burma State Railways (nos. 141–42). These were oil-burning models with the following specifications:

Gauge	3 feet 3 ⅜ inches
Work order no.	E 753
Cylinders	14 by 20 inches
Drive wheels	4-feet 5-inches diameter
Heating surface	650 square feet
Working steam pressure	150 pounds per square inch
Tractive force	(not stated)
Operating weight	36 tons 11 hundredweights; 200 gallons fuel oil
Capacities	960 gallons water

(Courtesy: Mitchell Library, Glasgow) N/E753

Neilson & Company in 1900 constructed a number of type 0–6–0 tender locomotives for use on the railways of Burma. These engines were class F wood-burning machines with these specifications:

Gauge	3 feet 3⅜ inches
Work order no.	E 854
Cylinders	14 by 20 inches
Driver wheels	3-foot 6½-inches diameter
Boiler heating surface	650 square feet
Working steam pressure	150 pounds per square inch
Operating weights	
Engine	23 tons 14 hundredweights
Tender	20 tons 10 hundredweights
Tender capacities	1265 gallons water; 5½ tons wood.

(Courtesy: Mitchell Library, Glasgow) N/E854

Dubs & Company in 1901 built a number of type 4–4–4 tank locomotives for use on the Burma rail lines. Specifications were as follows:

Gauge	3 feet 3 ⅜ inches
Work order no.	E 4003
Cylinders	14 by 20 inches
Drive wheels	4-foot 5-inches diameter
Boiler heating surface	650 square feet
Working steam pressure	150 pounds per square inch
Tractive force	8320 pounds
Operating weight	37 tons 18 hundredweights
Capacities	960 gallons water; 87 cubic feet fuel.

(Courtesy: Mitchell Library, Glasgow) D/E4003

In 1902 Dubs & Company supplied the Burma Railways with an unstated number of type 0–6–0 tender locomotives; these were wood-burning models with the following specifications:

Gauge	3 feet 3⅜ inches
Work order no.	E 4279
Cylinders	14 by 20 inches
Drive wheels	3-foot 6½-inches diameter
Boiler heating surface	650 square feet
Working steam pressure	150 pounds per square inch
Tractive force	10,376 pounds
Operating weights	
Engine	24 tons 13 hundredweights
Tender	18 tons 6 hundredweights
Capacities	1265 gallons water; 264 cubic feet wood.

(Courtesy: Mitchell Library, Glasgow) D/E4279

The North British Locomotive Company in 1904 constructed a number of type 4–6–0 tender engines for the Burma Railways. These machines were class J with the following characteristics:

Gauge	3 feet 3 ⅜ inches
Work order no.	L 38
Cylinders	15½ by 22 inches
Drive wheels	4-foot 9-inch diameter
Boiler heating surface	1062 square feet
Working steam pressure	180 pounds per square inch
Operating weights	
Engine	34 tons 13 hundredweights
Tender	24 tons 10 hundredweights
Tender capacities	1850 gallons water; 5 tons 10 hundredweights fuel.

(Courtesy: Mitchell Library, Glasgow) L38

This type 0–6–0 plus 0–6–0 locomotive, built by Beyer Peacock in 1905, was claimed to be the smallest Garratt ever. It was used in Burma by the Aankan Flotilla Company on the 2-foot 6-inch gauge Buthidaung Maungdon tramway. The engine weighed 23,500 pounds in operating condition.
(Courtesy: Manchester Museum of Science and Technology)

In 1909 an unstated number of type 2–6–2, class M tank locomotives were built by the North British Locomotive Company for the Burma Railways. The machines had the following specifications:

Gauge	3 feet 3⅜ inches
Work order no.	L 362
Cylinders	15 by 22 inches
Drive wheels	3-foot 7-inch diameter
Boiler heating surface	1131 square feet
Working steam pressure	180 pounds per square inch
Operating weight	43 tons 9 hundredweights
Water capacity	800 gallons.

(Courtesy: Mitchell Library, Glasgow) L362

In 1910 the North British Locomotive Company constructed an unstated number of Mallet compound tender engines, type 0–6–6–0, for use on the Burma Railways. The class N machines had the following specifications:

Gauge	3 feet 3⅜ inches
Work order no.	L 384
Cylinders	(2) 15½ by 20 inches, and (2) 24¼ by 20 inches
Drive wheels	3-foot 3-inch diameter
Boiler heating surface	1513 square feet
Working steam pressure	180 pounds per square inch
Tractive force	22,176 pounds at 50 percent boiler working pressure
Operating weights	
Engine	58 tons 4 hundredweights
Tender	31 tons 6 hundredweights
Tender capacities	200 gallons water; 6 tons fuel.

(Courtesy: Mitchell Library, Glasgow) L384

The North British Locomotive Company in 1912 furnished an unstated number of additional Mallet engines to the Burma Railways. These were class N models but somewhat modified and improved tender engines with these specifications:

Gauge	3 feet 3⅜ inches
Work order no.	L 517
Cylinders	(2) 15½ by 20 inches, and (2) 24¼ by 20 inches
Drive wheels	3-foot 3-inch diameter
Boiler heating surface	1513 square feet
Working steam pressure	180 pounds per square inch
Tractive force	22,176 pounds at 50 percent boiler working pressure
Operating weights	
Engine	58 tons 18 hundredweights
Tender	31 tons 4 hundredweights
Tender capacities	2140 gallons water; 6 tons fuel.

(Courtesy: Mitchell Library, Glasgow) L517

The Burma Railways secured from the North British Locomotive Company in 1913 an unstated number of type 4–6–0 tender locomotives. These class K engines had these specifications:

Gauge	3 feet 3⅜ inches	Boiler heating area	959 square feet
Work order no.	L 560	Working steam pressure	180 pounds per square inch
Cylinders	15 by 22 inches	Tractive force	13,920 pounds
Drive wheels	4-foot diameter	Operating weights	
		Engine	35 tons 1 hundredweight
		Tender	23 tons 11 hundredweights
		Tender capacities	1850 gallons water; 218 cubic feet fuel.

(Courtesy: Mitchell Library, Glasgow) L560

In 1914 additional Mallet, type 0–6–6–0, tender locomotives were supplied by the North British Locomotive Company to the Burma Railways. These machines were class N modified without superheaters and had the following specifications:

Gauge	3 feet 3⅜ inches	Boiler heating area	1552 square feet
Work order no.	L 631	Working steam pressure	180 pounds per square inch
Cylinders (2)	15½ by 20 inches and (2) 24¼ by 20 inches	Tractive effort	22176 pounds at 50 percent boiler working pressure
Drive wheels	3-foot 3-inch diameter	Operating weights	
		Engine	59 tons 7 hundredweights
		Tender	31 tons 3 hundredweights
		Tender capacities	2140 gallons water; 270 cubic feet fuel.

(Courtesy: Mitchell Library, Glasgow) L631

In 1915 the North British Locomotive Company supplied the Burma Mines Railway with three type 0–6–0 tender locomotives (nos. 15–17) having the following specifications:

Gauge	2 feet 0 inches	Boiler heating area	621 square feet
Work order no.	L 637	Working steam pressure	180 pounds per square inch
Cylinders	12 by 16-inches	Tractive force	10368 pounds
Drive wheels	2-foot 6-inch diameter	Operating weights	
		Engine	22 tons 16 hundredweights
		Tender	14 tons 7 hundredweights
		Tender capacities	1000 gallons water; fuel 100 cubic feet.

(Courtesy: Mitchell Library, Glasgow) L637

The Burma Railways ordered additional Mallet tender locomotives from the North British Locomotive Company in 1920. These class N, modified engines had the following characteristics:

Gauge	3 feet 3⅜ inches
Work order no.	L 743
Cylinders	(2) 15½ by 20 inches, and (2) 24¼ by 20 inches
Drive wheels	3-foot 3-inch diameter
Boiler heating surface	1442 square feet
Working steam pressure	180 pounds per square inch
Tractive force	22170 pounds at 50 percent boiler working pressure
Operating weights	
Engine	59 tons 10 hundredweights
Tender	36 tons 5 hundredweights
Tender capacities	2140 gallons water; 495 cubic feet fuel.

(Courtesy: Mitchell Library, Glasgow)

In 1922 the North British Locomotive Company constructed an unstated number of type 4–6–0 tender engines for use on the rail lines of Burma. These were class K machines modified with the following specifications:

Gauge	3 feet 3⅜ inches
Work order no.	L 771
Cylinders	16 by 22 inches
Drive wheels	4-foot diameter
Boiler heating area	895 square feet
Working steam pressure	160 pounds per square inch
Tractive force	14080 pounds
Operating weights	
Engine	35 tons 13 hundredweights
Tender	24 tons 13 hundredweights
Tender capacities	1850 gallons water; 247 cubic feet fuel.

(Courtesy: Michell Library, Glasgow)

CHILE

ONE OF THE FIRST RAIL LINES IN SOUTH AMERICA reached thirty-one miles inland from Caldera, Chile, (latitude 27'03' south, longitude 70°51' west) to the Copiapo mining center. Completed in April 1851, it was built by William Wheelwright, an American engineer and entrepreneur. From this modest beginning, a national railway system of 5,550 miles has been built, two-thirds of which is controlled by the Chilean government. The national system includes the longitudinal line from Equique in the far north (latitude 20°12' south, longitude 70°10' west) to Puerto Montt far to the south (latitude 41°29' south longitude 72°57' west)—a total distance of about fifteen hundred miles. Numerous short feeder lines connect the long north-south line with various Chilean seaports. Chile has one of the best rail networks in South America—and an exceedingly poor highway system.

The standard-gauge 114-mile railroad from Santiago to Valparaiso was constructed in 1861–63 by Henry Meiggs, the famous railroad entrepreneur whose outstanding and resourceful ability won him fame and fortune and set the stage for his later great rail achievements in Peru.

Between 1873 and 1887 (except during the 1879–83 War of the Pacific against neighboring Bolivia and Peru), a number of thirty-inch gauge rail lines were laid down in northern Chile. The new lines totaled about 276 miles and brought the railroad to the new Chilean-Bolivian border at Ollague. Most of these earlier railroads were constructed to serve the nitrate and mining interests in this part of the country. Later, between 1890 and 1910, nine branch lines from the main rail system were constructed, terminating in important mining centers. These totaled another 471 miles. The so-called nitrate railways, built between 1865 and 1890, ran from various inland mining sites to Pacific ports at such historic locations as Mejillones, Taltal, Tocopilla, Chanaral, and Iquique—a total of 377 miles.

In addition to the railroads in northern Chile, two important commercial rail systems were constructed. The meter-gauge Arica–La Paz Railway (285 miles) was finished in 1913; the Chilean section from Arica to Visviri ran 128.1 miles, including some cog sections. The meter-gauge line from Antofagasta, Chile, to Salta Argentina, (562 miles) was completed in 1948, 207.5 miles of which were in Chile.

In 1860 William Wheelwright advanced the first proposal for a railroad across the mighty Andes mountains to join Valparaiso, Chile, and Mendoza, Argentina; however, no actual work took place. The Clark brothers in 1872 pushed the same idea, but their initial success was confined to promoting a line in Argentina from Buenos Aires through Mendoza to the Chilean border, high in the Andes. The Clarks' negotiations with Chile met repeated failure and the brothers finally decided to advance their own funds to build the meter-gauge Chilean section. Work on that section began during April 1889. However, the job proved too enormous and expensive, and the Clarks were forced into bankruptcy and had to surrender all assets to their creditors. The work was resumed in 1904 by the Transandino Construction Company, and the

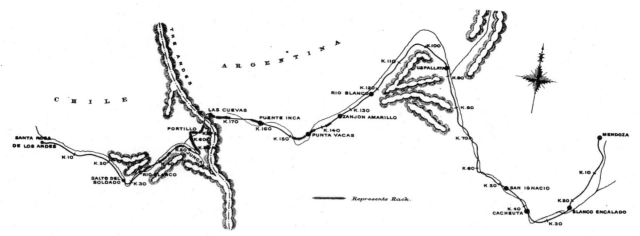

Represents Rack.

This is a sketch map showing the meter gauge Transandino Railway which crosses the Andes Mountains from Mendoza, Argentina to Los Andes, Chile. The total distance is 249.68 kilometers (155 miles). The highest point on the rail crossing is in the Summit Tunnel under Uspallata Pass, which is located on both sides of the border and has a length of 3463.5 yards, which is at an elevation of 10,521 feet above sea level. The top of the Uspallata Pass is 2000 yards above the tunnel. On the Argentine side there are nine tunnels with a total length of 575 yards. The total length of the rack sections on the Argentine side, divided into seven different lengths, is 15,381 yards. On the Chile side, divided into six different lengths, the rack totals 23,316 yards. The whole rack length, therefore, is 38,697 yards or 21.93 miles. The maximum rack gradient is eight percent with a minimum curve of two hundred meters (218.7 yards) on the rack. The radius of the minimum curve on the adhesion portion is one hundred twenty meters (131.2 yards).

(Courtesy: Sir Brodie H. Henderson, Proceedings: Institution of Civil Engineers, *vol. 195, session 1913–14, part 1)*

Cumbre tunnel at the Andes crest on the Argentine-Chilean border was finally opened on 27 November 1909. The Transandino Railway, which made possible direct and continuous rail connections between Buenos Aires and Valparaiso (893.5 miles), was finally dedicated on 5 April 1910. See map of the Transandino Railway.

Details of the Transandino Railway are contained in my book *Seven Railroads,* and the northern Chile railways are described in *Railways Across the Andes.*

Steam Locomotives in Chile

The following twenty photographs are representative of the steam locomotives used on the railways of Chile.

Of special interest are the early locomotives used on the Transandino Railway. The locomotives initially used on the Argentine side in 1893 were combined rack and adhesion types. These engines, built by Beyer Peacock, were four-coupled machines with a leading and trailing axle. Adhesion wheels were worked by outside cylinders fourteen inches in diameter, with a twenty-inch stroke. Two cogwheels engaged the rack; the hind cogwheel was worked by another pair of outside cylinders, thirteen inches by eighteen inches, while the front cogwheels ran free and were only used for braking purposes. The four-foot 2-inch by 9-foot 6-inch boiler had the following specifications:

Firebox	90.19 square feet
Tubes	1067.40 square feet
Total	1157.59 square feet
Boiler working pressure	150 pounds per square inch
Grate area	19.95 square feet.

Operating weight of the engine was forty-five tons, with a 19-foot 6½-inch wheelbase. This engine is not illustrated.

When the Transandino line operations commenced, two types of more powerful articulated engines were used. These are shown in two illustrations.

Pictured is a type 4–4–0 locomotive, of which four units were built for the Copiapo & Caldera Railway in Chile in 1858 by Kitson. Specifications were as follows:

Cylinders	16½ by 24 inches (inclined)
Drive wheels	5-foot 2-inch diameter
Bogie wheels	3-foot 6-inch diameter
Boiler	
Barrel	
Diameter	4 feet
Length	10 feet 5½ inches
Grate area	13.75 square feet
Tubes	175 2-inch outside diameter, area 991 square feet
Firebox	3 feet 4 inches by 4 feet 1½ inches, area 77 square feet.
Overall length (engine)	23 feet 2½ inches.

(Courtesy: Science Museum, London)

Pictured is an odd type 2–8–0 tender tank locomotive built by Baldwin in 1889 for the 2-foot 6-inch gauge Antofagasta Railway of Northern Chile. No specification data was available.
(Courtesy: Frederick Westing collection)

Shown is a Baldwin, type 4–4–0, steam locomotive, typical of several engines supplied to the railways in Chile in the period 1885–1900.
(Courtesy: Frederick Westing collection)

In the early part of the twentieth century the R & W Hawthorn Leslie Company, Ltd. furnished FCAB a number of type 2–8–2 freight tender locomotives for use on their railroads in northern Chile. Engine no. 169 was used on freight services on the 2-foot 6-inch gauge tracks and had these limitated specifications:

working pressure 180 pounds per square inch; water capacity 3000 gallons; coal capacity 7 tons; and operating weight 49 tons. See illustration.
(Courtesy: Antofagasta & Bolivia Railway Company, Ltd.)

In 1911 Kitson & Company of Leeds, England, built several articulated tank locomotives for the FCAB rail lines of northern Chile. This type 2–6–0 plus 0–6–2 engine followed the so-called Meyers design. The engine is pictured. Machine no. 37 had the following limited specifications:

Rail gauge	2-foot 6-inches
Boiler working pressure	180 pounds per square inch
Capacities	3100 gallons water; 4 tons coal
Operating weight	89 tons
Brake gear	Westinghouse

See also outline drawing.
(Courtesy: Antofagasta & Bolivia Railways Company, Ltd.)

This illustration shows a type 2–8–4 tank engine built by Kitson & Company, Ltd. for use on the 2-foot 6-inch gauge FCAB lines in northern Chile. Engine no. 27 was placed in service December 1911. Boiler pressure was 180 pounds per square inches. Capacities were: 2100 gallons water and 2.5 tons coal. Operating weight was 49 tons.
(Courtesy: Antofagasta & Bolivia Railway Company, Ltd.)

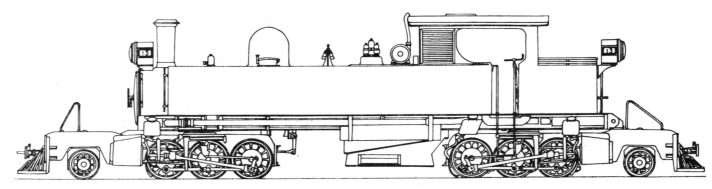

Shown is an outline drawing of a Kitson articulated tank locomotive built in 1911 and used by FCAB on 2-foot 6-inch gauge tracks in northern Chile. See also an earlier illustration.
(Courtesy: Antofagasta & Bolivia Railway Company, Ltd.)

This pictures a freight engine manufactured by Henschel & Sohn for use on the 2-foot 6-inch gauge FCAB railroads of northern Chile. This type 2–6–0 plus 2–6–0 locomotive, no. 51, was placed in service during April 1913 with the following specifications:

Cylinders	4
Working pressure	180 pounds per square inch
Water capacity	3000 gallons
Coal capacity	7 tons.

(Courtesy: Antofagasta & Bolivia Railway Company, Ltd.)

Pictured is a coal-fired steam locomotive, no. 60, built in April 1914 by Henschel & Sohn for use on the northern Chile railroads by the Antofagasta & Bolivia Railway Company, Ltd. This was a type 2–8–0 Consolidation freight engine used on the 2-foot 6-inch gauge tracks of that region. Limited available specification data were as follows:

Working pressure	160 pounds per square inch
Operating weight	99 tons (engine plus tender)
Tender capacities	4200 gallons water; 7 tons coal.

(Courtesy: Antofagasta & Bolivia Railway Company, Ltd.)

This illustration shows the front-end view of engine no. 60 pictured and described earlier. This was a type 2–8–0 locomotive built by Henschel & Sohn in 1914 for use on the 2-foot 6-inch gauge railroads of northern Chile.

(Courtesy: Antofagasta & Bolivia Railway Company, Ltd.)

Shown here is a model of a Garratt articulated steam locomotive, one of three similar machines built in 1926 for the Nitrate Railways of Chile by Beyer, Peacock & Company. This type 2–8–2 plus 2–8–2 engine was the same as that patented by H. W. Garratt in 1907, in which the boiler and the control cab were mounted on a frame slung between two self-driven bogies, which also carried the fuel and water. Each bogie had at its outer end two outside cylinders which drove the third coupled axle. The piston valves were driven by Walschaerts gear, set with a maximum cutoff of sixty percent, and controlled by a steam reversing gear. Oil was used as a fuel and a Worthington-Simpson feedwater heater and pump was installed on the side of the boiler. The front dome had a water purifying unit while from the second dome steam passed to a superheater header, thence to a regulator in the smokebox. The boiler frame was pivoted to the two bogies near their inner ends with flexible steam and exhaust pipes fitted. The engine was designed to haul loads of 350 tons over a railroad with a maximum gradient of 2.3 percent and curves of 280 foot radius. A Westinghouse brake and air sanding gear were installed. Specifications were as follows:

Cylinders	22 by 20 inches
Coupled wheels	42-inch diameter
Boiler	
Diameter	7.28-foot outside diameter
Length	13.00 feet
Tubes	299 in number, 2-inch outside diameter
Heating surface	tubes 3070 square feet
Grate area	68.8 square feet
Firebox	276.0 square feet (M & L 50 element)
Superheater	744.0 square feet
Total heating surface	4090 square feet
Working pressure	200 pounds per square inch
Tractive force	69.150 pounds at 75 percent boiler working pressure
Operating weight	
187.15 tons	
141.50 tons adhesion	
Capacities	5500 gallons water; 1410 gallons oil
Overall wheelbase length	71.75 feet.

(*Courtesy: Science Museum, London*) 3754

Shown is one of several type 2–8–4 tank locomotives, built by the North British Locomotive Company for service on the northern Chile railroads of the FCAB. This engine, no. 43, started operations during December 1927 on 2-foot 6-inch gauge tracks. Operating weight was 89 tons, the water tank held 2530 gallons, and the fuel oil capacity was 6720 liters or 1775 U.S. gallons.
(*Courtesy: Antofagasta & Bolivia Railway Company, Ltd.*)

Pictured is a type 2–8–2 mixed freight oil-burning steam locomotive manufactured by Beyer, Peacock & Company, Ltd. This engine, no. 912, was shipped to South America in April 1928 where it was used on the FCNC Railway (Ferrocarril Northern Chile Railway).
(Courtesy: Antofagasta & Bolivia Railway Company,

Pictured is another oil-burning Garratt type 4–8–2 plus 2–8–4 steam locomotive used on the northern railroads of Chile. This engine for the meter gauge FCAB lines was built by Beyer, Peacock & Company, Ltd. in 1929. The picture is dated 19 April 1929.
(Courtesy: Antofagasta & Bolivia Railway Company, Ltd.)

A type 4–8–2 passenger tank locomotive built by R & W Hawthorne Leslie Company, Ltd. in 1929 for use on the meter gauge lines of FCAB in northern Chile is shown here.
(Courtesy: Antofagasta & Bolivia Railway Company, Ltd.)

This illustration shows another Garratt type 4–8–2 plus 2–8–4 steam locomotive built by Beyer, Peacock & Company, Ltd. in 1950 for use on the meter gauge FCAB railroads of northern Chile. Operating weight was 177.5 tons; fuel oil capacity, 2200 gallons; and water capacity was 5500 gallons.
(Courtesy: Antofagasta & Bolivia Railway Company, Ltd.)

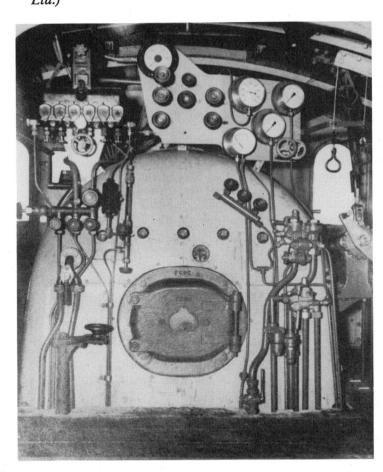

Pictured is the control cab of a type 2–8–2 locomotive built for use on the meter gauge lines of the FCNC railways of northern Chile. This engine was supplied by the Yorkshire Engine Company, Ltd. in February 1955.
(Courtesy: Antofagasta & Bolivia Railway Company, Ltd.)

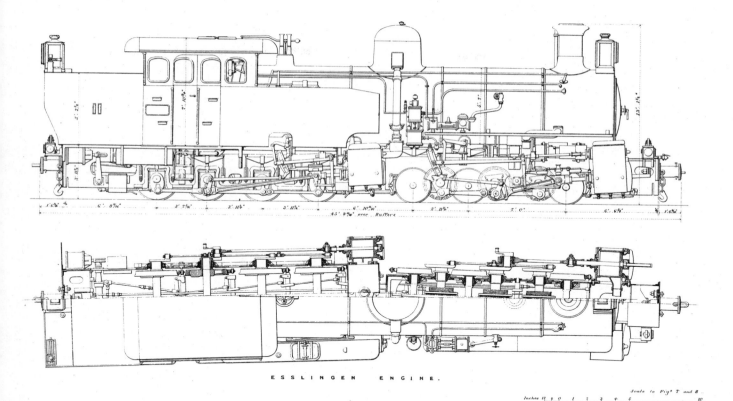

ESSLINGEN ENGINE.

Pictured is a drawing showing one of two original articulated steam engines used across the Andes Mountains on the completed Transandino Railway between Mendoza, Argentina and Los Andes, Chile, starting in 1910. This articulated engine, a modification of the Mallet type, was built by Maschinenfabrik Esslingen. It had three rack-pinions coupled together by connecting rods. The adhesion engine had eight wheels coupled, each with a diameter of thirty-six inches. These were the most powerful at the time on any rack railway; they were able to ascend an eight percent grade (1 in 12½) with a 140-ton load and non-automatic brakes and, in addition, hand brakes were applied to the driving and carrying wheels. Also, re-pression brakes were fitted for applying to both rack and adhesion cylinders, and hand brakes on all rack-pinions. Arrangements were provided for directing exhaust steam into holding tanks when working in tunnels.

Specifications on the above engines were as follows:

Adhesion cylinders	15½ by 19½ inches
Rack cylinders	21¼ by 17¾ inches
Drive wheels	36-inch diameter
Boiler	
Grate area	35 square feet
Firebox	115 square feet
Tubes	2068 square feet
Total heat surface	2183 square feet
Working pressure	215 pounds per square inch
Tractive effort	(rack mechanism)
47,000 pounds	
20,000 pounds	adhesion engine)
Operating weight	87 tons
Overall length	45 feet 9½ inches.

(Courtesy: Sir Brodie H. Henderson, Proceedings: Institution of Civil Engineers, vol. 195, session 1913–14, part 1)

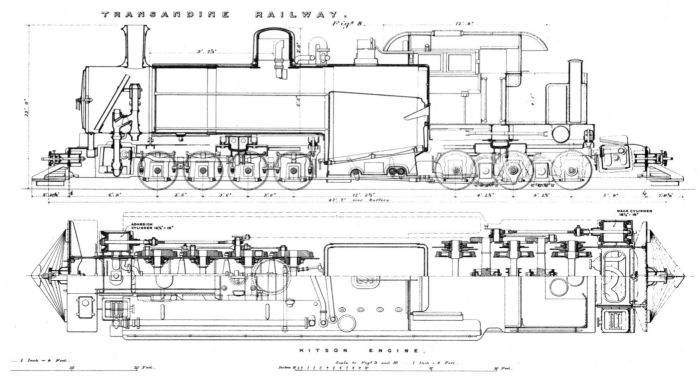

Fig⁹ 8.

KITSON ENGINE.

A drawing of the second type of articulated locomotive used on the newly opened Transandino Railway across the Andes Mountains in 1910 is shown here. This engine, built by Kitson & Company of Leeds, England, was a modification of a Meyer type machine. It consisted of two power bogies: the leading one for adhesion purposes and the trailing unit for carrying the rack-wheels. In general, power and braking characteristics were the same as indicated for the Esslingen engine. Specifications were as follows:

Adhesion cylinders	16½ by 19 inches
Rack cylinders	18½ by 19 inches
Coupled drive wheels	3-foot diameter
Boiler	
Grate area	34 square feet
Firebox	140 square feet
Tubes 292 at 1⅞-inch outside diameter	1900 square feet
Total heating surface	2040 square feet
Working pressure	200 pounds per square inch
Tractive effort	
34,600 pounds	(rack mechanism)
20,000 pounds	(adhesion engine)
Capacities	2100 gallons water; 3½ tons coal
Overall length	47 feet 7 inches.

(Courtesy: Sir Brodie H. Henderson, Proceedings: Institution of Civil Engineers, *vol. 195, session 1913–14, part 1)*

CHINA

RAILWAY CONSTRUCTION IN CHINA HAD A SLOW start, hampered principally by a religious fanaticism referred to as *Fung Shui.* This mysterious, superstitious philosophy presented unfathomable and insurmountable barriers to any kind of technological development in the "Celestial and Flowery Land."

In 1875, despite deep-rooted objections by the Chinese authorities to any intrusion by foreigners, the English initiated a valiant attempt to circumvent the influence of the *Fung Shui.* The British firm of Jardine, Matheson & Company, operating under the halfhearted approval of a local provincial governor, started on 1 January 1876 to lay down twenty miles of 2-foot 6-inch gauge rail from inland Shanghai to the terminal Yangtze River port of Woosung. The project was supported and financed mainly by Shanghai merchants. The construction presented few engineering difficulties, with only three small creeks requiring bridges and a few hollows to fill in. The first three miles of this largely forbidden railway were opened in March 1876, when a trial run, with English directors and shareholders, was carried out. The first two locomotives were tiny type 0–4–0 saddle-tank engines built by Ransome & Rapier of England. By July 1876 the whole line was completed and about four thousand Chinese, who, unlike the *Fung Shui,* had widely acclaimed the enterprise, were making daily trips; these people manifested a peculiar, satisfying delight in traveling third class on carriages drawn by the "honorable steam horse." See illustration.

When the Shanghai–Woosung line became an established reality, it was widely believed that the Chinese government's hostility would largely subside. Not so! It soon became evident that the iron horse was bitterly opposed by influential Chinese landholders and by high dignitaries in the government. Fearing the wrath of the gods, Chinese authorities forced the outright purchase of the railroad and, whipping the populace into a frenzy of rage, promoted its complete destruction. Some rolling stock and rail were salvaged by the builders and hurriedly transported to Formosa, where it eventually rusted into oblivion. Thus the first costly attempt to introduce Stephenson's railway steam engine to the Far East came to an inglorious end.

The next action to promote railways in China took place in the 1880s, when General Tong King Sing sought to exploit his interests in coal mines at Tangshan (latitude 39°39.2′ north, longitude 118°11.2′ east), thirty miles inland from the port of Pehtang in north China (latitude 39°6.2′ north, longitude 117°42.0′ east). He won government approval to connect the two locations and enlisted the technical assistance of Englishman C. W. Kinder, later known as "the father of railways in China." The first seven miles of the general's railroad were opened in October 1888, connecting the coal operations with a canal to the Gulf of Chihli. Later the line was extended to Pehtang, and another extension of twenty-nine miles was laid down in 1888 to Tientsin. From these scanty beginnings, rail systems gradually spread throughout China, including northern lines to Shenyang (Mukden), Pinkiang (Harbin), and to the Russian Trans-Siberian Railway.

Native Chinese preoccupied and fascinated with the
first railways in 1875 are shown.
(Courtesy: Illustrated London News)

The first rail operations in China were distinctly British in character, using English rail, rolling equipment, and bridge designs. The roads usually followed easy grades with wide-radius curves. Construction costs were ridiculously low due to an inexhaustible supply of cheap manpower. As in 1876, inexpensive rail travel was a source of endless amusement and satisfaction to a vast number of Chinese.

In the latter part of the nineteenth century and early in the twentieth century, railway projects were pushed forward by representatives from the United States, Belgium, France, Portugal, and Germany. Shanghai was connected with Nanking, Peking with Hankow and Nanking, and Canton with Kowloon (Hong Kong).

Jardine, Matheson & Company, notwithstanding their initial ill-fated adventure with the Shanghai–Woosung railroad, were not deterred from further efforts. In 1898 the company received an authorization to build the Peking–Nanking Railway (approximately seven hundred miles in length), which was financed by the British & Chinese Corporation. It was completed early in the 1900s and turned out to be one of the finest "fast road" European-type railways in China.

At the turn of the century, Chinese engineers finally initiated their own railway construction program. One of their first projects was the 125-mile line from Peking to Kalgan, located at latitude 40°49.6' north, longitude 114°47.7' east. Using 100 percent Chinese effort, the road required tremendous work in pushing the rails through Nankow Pass, which guarded approaches to the Great Wall. With heavy 1 in 30 grades, three Mallet-type locomotives were usually required to pull a train, in two hours at 6.5 miles per hour, to the 1,500-foot summit. The route had four tunnels, one of which was 3,850 feet long and passed two hundred feet under a portion of the Great Wall.

One of the most important Chinese rail projects was the 760-mile Peking–Hankow Line, which was started in 1900 using French and Belgian finances and know-how. In 1901 the Boxer Uprising seriously disrupted construction and inflicted approximately $5.0 million in damages; the Chinese government eventually made restitution to the syndicate as part of the so-called Boxer Indemnity of $333 million imposed by the world powers on China. The Peking–Hankow railway was ultimately finished and included a noteworthy achievement, bridging the mighty Hwang (Yellow) River with a tremendous 102-span bridge over two miles in length.

Another significant rail line, opened in 1910 with 4-foot 8½-inch gauge track, was the Canton–

Kowloon Railway, which tied China proper to British Hong Kong. This hundred-mile connection was a joint Chinese-British effort, with seventy-seven miles traversing Chinese territory. The British twenty-three-mile section had by far the most difficult construction problems: the terrain required 20.5 miles of tunnels, including the famous seven-thousand-foot Beacon Hill tunnel, the longest underground passageway in all of China.

A French railway project involving the Yunnan Railway was another superb undertaking in China. This line joined the French possession of Lao-Chay with Yunnam Sen (Kunming), capital of the province of Yunnan. This was an especially arduous job in the mountainous terrain and included the major mission of bridging Namti Gorge. Cost of this enterprise totaled $33.1 million, all before 1910.

Not a single mile of railway was in operation in China in 1877 but by 1910 there were ten thousand miles built or under construction.

Through the years, since initial construction in 1876, the Chinese railways have been the victim of invasion, civil war, and internal political and economic movements such as the Great Leap Forward and the Cultural Revolution; thus efforts to improve or modernize the railroads in China have been interrupted, from time to time, by various crises. Railroads are a natural target during civil disturbances or other upheavals. Roadbeds deteriorated, lines were severed, bridges were damaged or destroyed, and rolling stock was always left in ruin or in a state of disrepair.

During the period 1949–52, prisoners and conscripted peasant labor performed minor repair work, and a few railroads were actually extended. In the first five-year plan, 1953–57, Chou En-lai tried to enlarge and improve the transportation system in the interest of industrialization and defense. Accordingly, the railroads were given a high priority: 5.67 billion yuan (about $3 billion) were appropriated, 60 percent to be spent on the rail lines; and of this amount, 41.7 percent was allocated for new railroad construction.

Two momentous upheavals—the Great Leap Forward, which began in 1958 and lasted until 1960, and the Cultural Revolution, from 1966 to 1968—left the Chinese rail system with a great need for rehabilitation and a reorganization of basic facilities and services.

The Great Leap Forward placed a tremendous strain on transportation because of increased production in many areas. Coal production, for example, rose faster than local transportation could carry it away. Increased industrial operations required factory equipment and raw materials beyond the ability of the railroads to provide an adequate supply. To fill the need for expanding facilities, small local railroads were hastily constructed to connect mines and plants with established rail networks and navigable waterways. From 1958 to 1959 more than four hundred such temporary railroads were built. Teams of local laborers laid railroad tracks made of "backyard" steel, pig iron, or sometimes lumber, and freight and passenger cars were moved by locomotives powered with gas, diesel, electric, and steam traction. In an effort to relieve pressure on the transportation system, enterprises were expected to use all available local supplies, but the logistics were ill-planned and poorly coordinated; moreover, substitution of materials often aggravated the already overburdened transportation facilities.

Almost from the beginning of the Cultural Revolution, the transportation system, especially the railroads, suffered disorganization. Railroad rolling stock was monopolized by members of the Red Guards and by students traveling between Peking and the various provinces and municipalities. An estimated twenty million Red Guards and students, exchanging revolutionary experiences, crowded the railroads during the first year of the Cultural Revolution. The great passenger surges produced serious freight back-ups, blocking any orderly flow of supplies. Additional pressure was placed on the transportation facilities by the great number of workers, including railroad workers, who left their jobs and journeyed to Peking to present petitions. At the end of 1966, Red Guards and students were ordered to return to their homes but it was 1967 before the congestion abated.

The railroad networks also suffered from conflicts between those in government and those promoting the Cultural Revolution. In numerous cases there seemed to be a deliberate attempt by the Red Guards to paralyze the rail lines by damaging equipment and failing either to run the trains on time or to load freight cars as scheduled. A period of armed struggle ensued in which rail workers were out on strike and the system was virtually paralyzed.

In 1967 military units were assigned to take charge of the railroads. Guards were positioned on trains, and service gradually improved. The height of upheaval was followed by a period in which the various transport sectors were able to establish order and slowly rebuild services and plan their future course of action. An important step in transportation improvement was the introduction in 1969 of a plan to integrate all modes of transportation—rail, highway, and water—for greater efficiency. This integration was successfully carried out in several provinces by 1970, after which a realistic national plan seemed to take hold.

Following the government reorganization that began in 1969, a number of ministries and agencies became involved in the regulation and operation of the transportation and communications systems. The Ministry of Posts and Telecommunications and the Ministry of Railroads were the major overseers of transportation activities. The Ministry of Railroads, which was established early in the communist regime, administered the railroad system through a number of bureaus set up in 1950, and activities of the national network were coordinated within the ministry. During the upheaval of the Cultural Revolution, military control was finally established over the railways, and by 1971 the Ministry of Railroads had been absorbed into the Ministry of Communications.

Both before and after 1949, the railroads provided the backbone of China's transportation system. According to a 1959 source issued by the government, railroads accounted for 78.5 percent of the country's total freight handled during 1958. By comparison, inland water transports carried 18.6 percent, and motor vehicles 2.9 percent. Also during 1958, railroads carried 71.7 percent of all passenger traffic. During the 1960s both inland vessels and motor vehicles apparently increased their share of transportation, but the railroads remained dominant in commercial as well as military transportation.

Before the Communist takeover, the combined length of railroad trunk lines, branches, and spurs was reported to be 16,675 miles. At the end of 1949, a total of 13,750 miles were in operation. Railroads were then concentrated in the coastal provinces, which were the most highly industrialized areas. Six coastal provinces—Liaoning, Hopeh, Shantung, Kiangsu, Chekiang, and Kwangtung—accounted for 42 percent of the total length of operating trunk lines. Inland provinces accounted for 58 percent of total trackage, which was not, however, evenly distributed. The less developed provinces in the northwest and south-west—Sinkiang, Tsinghai, Kansu, and Szechwan—and the regions of Ninghsia Hui and Tibet had no railroads in operation in 1949. Fukien, though a coastal province, also lacked railroads.

In the railroad construction of post-revolutionary years, the greatest expanion took place in the strategically important northwest region, particularly in the Sinkiang Uighur Autonomous Region (Sinkiang), where a rail line was constructed to Urumchi. Lines also were built in Kansu and Tsinghai provinces and in the Ninghsia Hui Autonomous Region, and trackage added in Shensi Province. Railroads were also constructed in the southwest provinces of Szechwan, Yunnan, and Kweichow. In 1966 a railroad planned for the Tibetan Autonomous Region (Tibet) was apparently underway. Lines had been built or planned to move raw materials to the more highly industrialized areas eastward, to open up the western and northwestern part of the country, and to move troops to northern border areas in emergencies.

In railroad construction after 1949, the northwest region ranked first, followed in order by Northeast China, North China, the Inner Mongolian Autonomous Region, Southwest China, South China, Central China, and East China. In 1949 the railway system had been most highly developed in the northeastern provinces because heavy industry was concentrated there.

Information concerning the development of railroads from 1966 to 1971 is fragmentary, and no comprehensive official report is available, but in 1970 it was reported that route length was about twenty-four thousand miles.

In 1969 the Chinese railroads were classified into three major systems. The north-south trunk lines included lines from Peking to Canton, from Tientsin to Shanghai, and from Pao-chi to Chan-Chiang by way of Ch'eng-tu and Chungking. The east-west trunk lines included routes from Lan-chou to Urumchi, from Peking to Lan-chou, and from Shanghai to the border of North Vietnam. The third group of lines formed the Manchurian system of the northeast.

Mainland China in modern times is connected internationally by rail with the Soviet Union, Mongolia, the Democratic People's Republic of Korea (North Korea), the Democratic Republic of Vietnam (North Vietnam), and Hong Kong. Because of differences in gauge, however, transloading facilities are required at the Soviet and Mongolian connections.

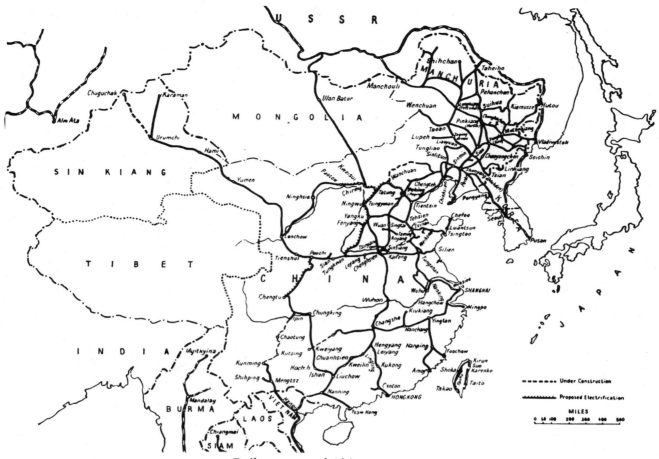

Railway map of China.
(*Courtesy:* Janes World Railways)

In 1886 Dubs & Company furnished a pair (nos. 1 and 2) of type 0–4–0 tank locomotives for use on the Chinese Railways. These engines had the following specifications:

Gauge	1 foot 11⅝ inches
Cylinders	5 by 10 inches
Coupled drivers	2-foot diameter
Boiler	

Heating surface	100.7 square feet
Working pressure	180 pounds per square inch.
Tractive force	1406 pounds
Operating weight	6 tons plus 15 hundredweights
Capacities	90 Imperial gallons water; 7 cubic feet coal.

(Courtesy: Mitchell Library, Glasgow) E2254

In 1978 China had 88,000 kilometers (54,680 miles) of standard-gauge railways. The railroads were then under a Ministry of Railways, which handled twenty railway bureaus and sixteen sub-bureaus as well as China's thirty-three locomotive and rolling-stock factories. See a map of railways in China.

The accompanying nineteen illustrations cover various steam locomotives used on the railways of China between 1886 and 1938.

In 1892 Dubs & Company of Glasgow also supplied two type 2–6–2 tank (23–24) locomotives for use on the Imperial Chinese Railway. Specifications on these engines were as follows:

Gauge	4 feet 8½ inches
Cylinders	16 by 24 inches
Coupled drivers	4-foot diameter
Boiler	
Heating surface	967 square feet
Working pressure	150 pounds per square inch
Tractive force	14,400 pounds
Operating weight	52 tons plus 11 hundredweights
Capacities	1550 gallons water; 107 cubic feet coal.

(Courtesy: Mitchell Library, Glasgow) E2900

The Imperial Chinese Railways in 1892 purchased from Dubs & Company five tender locomotives (nos. 17–22) type 2–6–0 with the following specifications:

Gauge	4 feet 8½ inches
Cylinders	17 by 24 inches
Coupled drivers	4-foot 6-inch diameter
Boiler	
Heating surface	1059.23 square feet
Working pressure	150 pounds per square inch
Tractive force	14,451 pounds
Operating weight (engine)	38 tons plus 19 hundredweights
Capacities of tender	coal and water not given.

(Courtesy: Mitchell Library, Glasgow) E2894

The China and Japan Trading Company in 1896 purchased from Dubs & Company of Glasgow several type 0–6–0 tank locomotives with the following characteristics:

Gauge	3 feet 6 inches
Cylinders	14 by 18 inches
Coupled drivers	3-foot diameter
Boiler	
Heating surface	521.4 square feet
Working pressure	150 pounds per square inch
Tractive force	11,025 pounds
Operating weight	28 tons plus 12 hundredweights
Capacities	810 gallons water; 40 cubic feet coal.

(Courtesy: Mitchell Library, Glasgow) E3420

The Imperial Railways of North China procured from Dubs & Company in 1903 a number of type 4–6–0 tender locomotives. Specifications on Dubs works order nos. 4363–66 were as follows:

Gauge	4 feet 8½ inches
Cylinders	18 by 24 inches
Coupled drivers	3-foot diameter
Boiler	
Heating surface	1407 square feet
Working pressure	180 pounds square inch
Tractive force	15,905 pounds
Operating weight (engine)	52 tons plus 11 hundredweights
Capacities	(none given).

(Courtesy: Mitchell Library, Glasgow) E4363

Pictured is a model of a massive 2–8–8–2 Mallet compound locomotive, the prototype of which was built by the American Locomotive Company in the early twentieth century for use on the Peking-Kalgan Railway in north China. These engines were employed on mountainous sections of track between Nankow and Kalgan having a maximum grade of 1 in 30 and a number of sections with a gradient of 1 in 40. Specifications were as follows:

Cylinders	
Hi pressure	20 by 26 inches (with Walschaerts gear)
Lo pressure	32 by 26 inches (with Walschaerts gear)
Coupled drive wheels	4-foot 2-inch diameter
Boiler	
Grate area	59.6 square feet
Firebox area	263 square feet
Heating surface	2353 square feet
Superheater area	565 square feet
Tractive effort	
Compound	56,500 pounds
Simple	67,800 pounds
Operating weight	185 tons (engine plus tender)
Tender capacities	6000 gallons water; 10 tons coal.

The model built by Bassett-Lowke, Ltd. England was displayed in 1915 at the Panama Pacific International Exhibition in San Francisco and later was presented to the Chinese government.

(*Courtesy: Dow*, World Locomotive Models)

In 1907 the Shanghai-Nanking Railway purchased two tender locomotives, type 4–4–0, from the North British Locomotive Company of Glasgow (nos. C21 and C22). Specifications were as follows:

Gauge	4 feet 8½ inches
Cylinders	18 by 26 inches
Coupled drivers	6-foot 7-inch diameter
Boiler	
Heating surface	1630 square feet
Working pressure	180 pounds per square inch
Operating weights	
Engine	52 tons plus 8 hundredweights
Tender	42 tons plus 13 hundredweights
Tender capacities	3630 gallons water; 315 cubic feet coal.

(*Courtesy: Mitchell Library, Glasgow*) L232

The Imperial Chinese Railways, in 1907, acquired several tank locomotives, type 2–6–2, from the North British Locomotive Company. Published specifications were as follows:

Gauge	4 feet 8½ inches
Cylinders	14 by 20 inches
Coupled drive wheels	3-foot 6-inch diameter
Boiler	
Heating area	552 square feet
Working pressure	150 pounds per square inch
Operating weight	37 tons plus 17 hundredweights
Water capacity	900 gallons.

(Courtesy: Mitchell Library, Glasgow) **L241**

In 1908 three Mallet compound locomotives (nos. 21, 22, 23), type 0–6–6–0, were constructed by the North British Locomotive Company for the Imperial Chinese Railways to be used on the Peking-Kalgan line. These engines had the following specifications:

Gauge	4 feet 8½ inches
Cylinders	18 by 20 inches and 28¾ by 28 inches
Drive wheels	4-foot 3-inch diameter
Boiler	
Heating surface	2591 square feet
Working pressure	200 pounds per square inch
Operating weight	96 tons plus 10 hundredweights
Water and coal capacities not available.	

(Courtesy: Mitchell Library, Glasgow) **L274**

The Tientsin Pukow Railway in 1910 bought from the North British Locomotive Company eight type 2–6–0 tender locomotives (nos. 7–14) with the following specifications:

Gauge	4 feet 8½ inches
Cylinders	19 by 24 inches
Coupled drive wheels	5-foot diameter
Boiler	
Heating surface	1611 square feet
Working pressure	180 pounds per square inch
Tractive force	19,490 pounds
Operating weights	
Engine	58 tons plus 13 hundredweights
Tender	46 tons plus 3 hundredweights
Tender water capacity	4000 gallons.

(Courtesy: Mitchell Library, Glasgow) L379

The Kowloon–Canton Railway, which opened to traffic in 1910, has a twenty-two-mile British section which runs from Kowloon to Lo Wu at the Chinese border. The early British railroad operators used two types of tank locomotives, 2–6–4 and 4–6–4, on their portion of the line. The accompanying photograph shows a model of a type 2–6–4 tank engine built in 1912 by Kitson & Company. The cross-head guides were of the single bar type, while the slide valves were placed on top of the cylinders and were driven by Walschaerts valve gear; reversing was done with a screw and handwheel. This engine was constructed according to the following specifications:

Cylinders	19 by 26 inches (inclined slightly)
Coupled drive wheels	5-foot 1.5-inch diameter
Bogie wheels (front and rear)	43-inch diameter
Boiler	
Grate area	32 square feet
Tubes	Iron 260 in number 2-inch out-side diameter, length 11.92 feet
Heating area	1623 square feet
Boiler length	11.5 feet
Boiler width	5-foot 4-inch diameter
Feed	Two injectors
Working pressure	180 pounds per square inch
Tractive effort	23,350 pounds at 85 percent boiler working pressure
Operating weight	
90.7 tons	
51 tons on coupled wheels	
Tank capacity	1900 gallons water
Bunker capacity	3.5 tons coal
Overall length	45.21 feet.

(Courtesy: Science Museum, London) 7802

In 1914 the Kowloon-Canton Railway procured from the North British Locomotive Company three type 2–6–0 tender locomotives (nos. A8–A10) with these specifications:

Gauge	4 feet 8½ inches
Cylinders	19 by 24 inches
Coupled drivers	5-foot diameter
Boiler	
Heating surface	1339 square feet
Working pressure	180 pounds per square inch
Tractive force	19,490 pounds
Operating weights	
Engine	59 tons plus 4 hundredweights
Tender	42 tons plus 7 hundredweights
Tender capacities	3500 gallons water; 247 cubic feet coal.

(Courtesy: Mitchell Library, Glasgow) L588

The Shanghai–Nanking Railway in 1914 purchased from the North British Locomotive Company four type 4–4–2 tender locomotives (nos. E29–E32) with these specifications:

Gauge	4 feet 8½ inches
Cylinders	20 by 26 inches
Coupled drivers	7-foot diameter
Boiler	
Heating surface	1679 square feet
Working pressure	165 pounds per square inch
Tractive force	15320 pounds
Operating weights	
Engine	66 tons plus 15 hundredweights
Tender	42 tons plus 11 hundredweights
Tender capacities	3500 gallons water; 315 cubic feet coal.

(Courtesy: Mitchell Library, Glasgow) L610

In 1921 the Peking-Mukden Railway bought from the North British Locomotive Company ten type 2–6–2 tank locomotives. Specifications were as follows:

Gauge	4 feet 8½ inches
Cylinders	17 by 24 inches
Coupled drivers	4-foot 6-inch diameter
Boiler	
Heating surface	1308 square feet
Working pressure	180 pounds per square inch
Tractive force	17340 pounds
Operating weight	64 tons
Water capacity	1100 gallons
Running numbers	240–49.

(Courtesy: Mitchell Library, Glasgow) L753

This illustration pictures a Prairie type locomotive, with a 2–6–2 wheel arrangement, which was manufactured in 1921 by the Baldwin Locomotive Works for use on the Peking-Hankow Railway in China. The original order called for thirty units of this type engine. General specifications were as follows:

Cylinders	10 by 26 inches
Drive wheels	59-inch diameter
Engine weight	154,600 pounds

(Courtesy: Frederick Westing collection)

The North British Locomotive Company in 1930 supplied the Nanking Shanghai Railway eight type 4–6–2 tender locomotives (nos. G53–G60) with the following characteristics:

Gauge	4 feet 8½ inches
Cylinders	20½ by 26 inches
Coupled drivers	5-foot 3-inch diameter
Boiler	
Heating surface	1058 square feet
Working pressure	200 pounds per square inch
Tractive force	26000 pounds
Operating weights	
Engine	90 tons plus 16 hundredweights
Tender	71 tons
Tender water capacity	6000 gallons.

(Courtesy: Mitchell Library, Glasgow) L870

In 1931 the Peking-Liaoning Railway introduced six type 2–8–2 tender locomotives (nos. 300–305). These were constructed by the North British Locomotive Company with these specifications:

Gauge	4 feet 8½ inches
Cylinders	21 by 28 inches
Coupled drivers	4-foot 6-inch diameter
Boiler	
Heating area	2726 square feet
Working pressure	180 pounds per square inch
Tractive force	30870 pounds
Operating weights	
Engine	84 tons plus 5 hundredweights
Tender	59 tons plus 19 hundredweights
Tender water capacity	5000 gallons.

(Courtesy: Mitchell Library, Glasgow) L876

In 1933 the North British Locomotive Company supplied the Tientsin-Pukow Railway with eight tender
locomotives, type 4–6–2 (nos. 413–20) with the following specifications:

Gauge	4 feet 8½ inches
Cylinders	20 by 28-inches
Coupled drivers	5-foot 9-inch diameter
Boiler	
Heating surface	2390 square feet
Working pressure	200 pounds square inch
Tractive force	24350 pounds
Operating weights	
Engine	90 tons plus 10 hundredweights
Tender	57 tons plus 8 hundredweights
Tender water capacity	5289 gallons.

(Courtesy: Mitchell Library, Glascow) **L883**

The King-Kan Railway in 1938 purchased from the
North British Locomotive Company seven type 0–8–
0 tender engines (nos. 1–6) with the following characteristics:

Gauge	4 feet 8½ inches
Cylinders	16.58 by 23.6 inches
Coupled drivers	3-foot 11¼-inch diameter
Boiler	
Heating surface	1119 square feet
Working pressure	213 pounds per square inch
Tractive force	21900 pounds
Operating weights	
Engine	52 tons by 16 hundredweights
Tender	42 tons plus 4 hundredweights

(Courtesy: Mitchell Library, Glascow) **L912**

DENMARK

THE FIRST RAILWAY IN DENMARK OPENED IN 1844 in what was then known as Holstein, a Danish monarchy, and ran south from Kiel approximately fifty-five miles to Altona near Hamburg, Germany. In Denmark proper, the first railroad was constructed about twenty miles west from Copenhagen to Roskilde and inaugurated on 26 June 1847. It used standard-gauge (4-foot 8½-inch) rail (29 kilograms per meter) on oak sleepers. In 1856 the system was extended about forty-five miles to Korsøer on the west coast of Sjaelland. Originally, the Sjaelland (Zealand) railroads were owned and operated by the Zealand Railway Company (SJS); in 1880 the Danish government took over ownership and control of the railways, with Mr. Viggo Rothe as director.

In Jutland the first railway section was opened in 1862, extending about twenty-five miles from Arhus north to Randers. In Fünen province (Fyn) a rail line running about forty-five miles between Nyborg and Middelfart was opened in 1865. The Jutland and Fünen railways were constructed by English contractors and operations were handled by the Danish Railway Operation Company, largely in the hands of an English manager. The company owned the rolling stock, but the railroads were controlled by the state government, which had little to do with the management of the enterprise. In 1867 the Danish government took over complete ownership and operation of the Jutland and Fünen rail network. In 1885 the Zealand and Jutland–Funen railways were consolidated into a single government-owned and -controlled system. At the time of this amalgamation, the Zealand lines totaled 245.44 miles and the Jutland–Funen railways totaled 702.77 miles.

In subsequent years, state railway expansion was designed mainly to strengthen and extend the main lines and fill in gaps in the secondary railway network. By 1920 Denmark railways totaled about 1,666 miles, and 4,322 miles by 1970.

For more than a hundred years, the steam locomotive was Denmark's most important source of tractive power. To be sure, some gasoline motorized rolling stock was purchased in the 1920s and 1930s, but the greater number of trains were still pulled by steam locomotives. After World War II it was obvious that a new and more economic form of rail motive power must be chosen, and the final decision favored diesel-electric power over electric traction. However, the final demise of steam locomotion was delayed by acquisitions of locomotives from Sweden, which had made an extensive conversion to electric power in 1936. Ten class E Pacifics were purchased from Sweden and twenty-five additional units were constructed in Danish shops in the mid-1940s. In 1965 Denmark had about seventy steam locomotives still on active roster, but by 1970 most mainline service had been converted to diesel-electric locomotives. The last steam locomotive was officially taken out of service in 1970. The class S 2–6–4 tank engines were some of the last to survive. The death of King Frederick IX in January 1972, and his request that a steam engine pull the royal funeral train, promoted a temporary renewal of interest in steam locomotion. The funeral train was pulled by two class E Pacifics that had been hurriedly taken out of mothballs. Subsequently, these same engines, nos. 978 and 994, have been scheduled on many excursion runs throughout Denmark.

In 1978 *Janes World Railways* reported the railroads in Denmark had a total track length (including sidings, yards, and so forth) of 4,640.4 kilometers (2,883.2 miles), all standard-gauge. Route length was 1,999.1 kilometers (1,242.2 miles).

The Danish locomotive story is outlined briefly in the succeeding series of photographs and drawings.

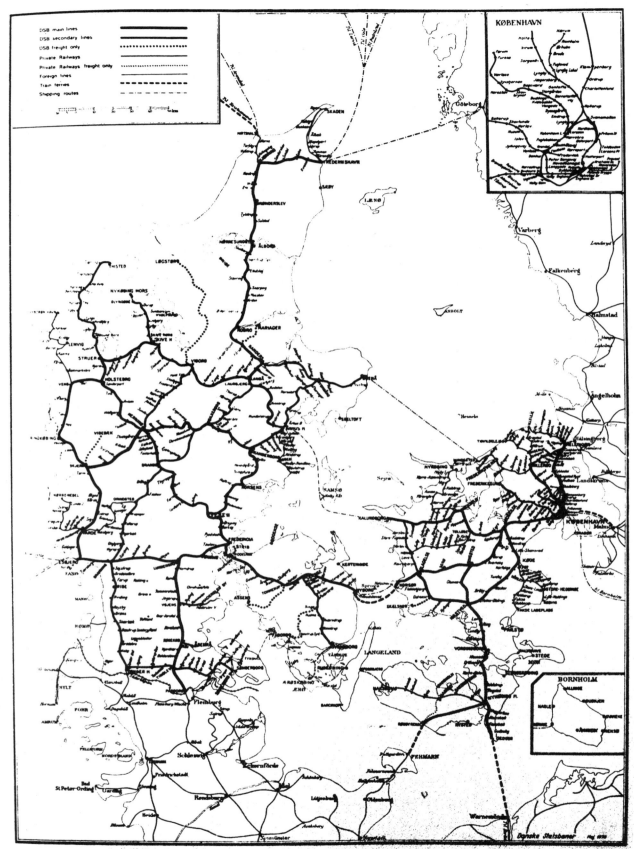

Railway map of Denmark.
(*Courtesy:* Janes World Railways)

Shown is a sketch of the first steam locomotive used
on the railways of Denmark in 1847. Data on this
British import was not available.
(Courtesy: O. S. Nock, The Dawn of World Railways
1800–1850)

This is a sketch of the Copenhagen, Denmark, railroad station as it appeared to an artist in 1849.
(Courtesy: Danish State Railways)

The now famous railway museum at Odense Banegard as it was sketched by an artist in 1865. *(Courtesy: Danish State Railways)*

Pictured is one of the first steam locomotives built in 1869 by Robert Stephenson & Company of New Castle, England, for the railways of Denmark. The Danish State took over the railways of Jutland and Funen in 1867 and ordered eleven of these class B, type 2-4-0, tender engines. These machines had a number of improvements over their predecessors including an engineer's cab and, in the overall, had a high degree of reliability. The engines were originally provided with a handwheel brake on the tender, with wooden brake blocks acting on the four wheels of the tender. See the following illustration for an outline drawing of this engine, and a subsequent illustration for an inside view of the engineer's cab. Some specifications were as follows:

Cylinders	2
Driving wheels	1534-millimeter diameter
Boiler pressure	10 kilograms per square centimeter
Operating weight	46.2 tons (engine plus tender)
Overall length	12.82 meters
Maximum speed	90 kilometers per hour.

(Courtesy: Danish State Railways)

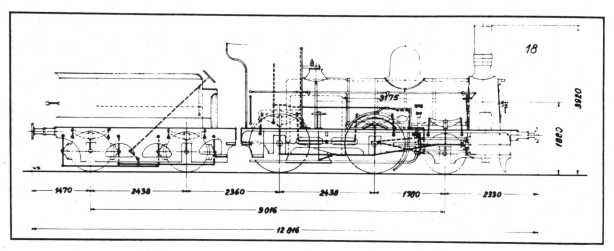

This is a drawing of the Stephenson class B, type 2–4–0, locomotive furnished to the railways of Denmark in 1869.
(*Courtesy: Danish State Railways*)

The interior of the engineer's cab of the Stephenson-built class B locomotive, type 2–4–0, furnished to the Denmark railways in 1869 is shown.
(*Courtesy: Danish State Railways*)

A typical steam locomotive used on the Danish rail-ways about 1870 is pictured. No details were available.
(Courtesy: Danish State Railways)

This illustrates a class A, type 4–4–0, tender locomotive, of which thirty-one units were manufactured by Hartmann of Germany over the period 1882–88. These engines were used on railroads in the Jutland/Funen region. The four-wheel leading bogie gave good riding stability and ensured reduced wear to wheel treads and rails. The big driving wheel diameter made possible a speed of one hundred kilometers (62 miles) per hour. The last four class A machines were finally withdrawn in 1956, of which one, engine no. 159, is on display in the Danish railway museum with an electric motor used to move the rods and wheels. See the following illustration for a drawing of this class engine. Specifications were:

Cylinders	2
Drive wheels	1730-millimeter diameter
Boiler pressure	12 kilograms per square centimeter
Operating weight	53.8 tons
Overall length	14.07 meters
Maximum speed	100 kilometers per hour.

(Courtesy: Danish State Railways)

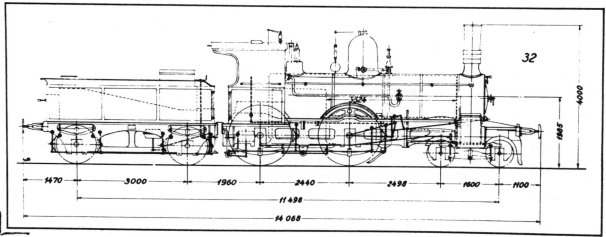

This engine drawing accompanys the photograph and description given in an earlier illustration. This was a class A, type 4–4–0, tender locomotive built by Hartmann of Germany during the period 1882–88 for operations on the Jutland–Funen railroads of Denmark. *(Courtesy: Danish State Railways)*

This shows a class P, type 0–4–4, steam locomotive built in 1882 by Hohenzollern of Germany for use on three Danish branch lines which had very light (17.5 kilograms per meter) rail. The arrangement provided a tender at the front which had a two-axled bogie (Busse's patent) thus ensuring steady movement along the tracks. This was the only DSB locomotive ever equipped with a "cowcatcher." After a few years most branch lines on the Danish roads were provided with heavier types of rail, and there were no further uses for such small locomotives; the class P engines were then sold to various private railway companies.

Engine no. 125 was retired in 1948 at which time it again reverted to DSB ownership for preservation purposes. Specifications were:

Cylinders	2
Drive wheels	1092-millimeter diameter
Boiler pressure	10 kilograms per square centimeter
Total weight	23.3 tons
Overall length	8.9 meters
Maximum speed	45 kilometers per hour.

(Courtesy: Danish State Railways)

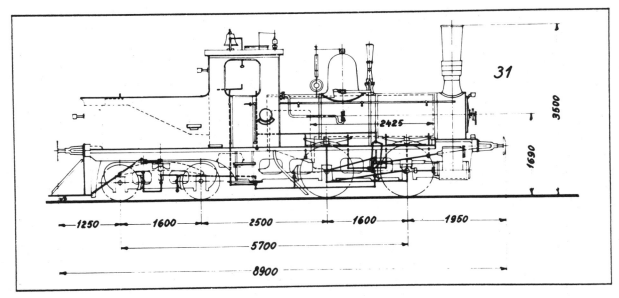

This outline drawing shows details of the class P steam locomotive built for the railroads of Denmark in 1882 by Hohenzollern of Germany. Details and a photograph are set forth in a previous illustration. *(Courtesy: Danish State Railways)*

This illustration pictures a Danish class Ks steam engine constructed in 1886 by Schwartzkopff of Germany. Six of these machines were originally ordered after the West line, from Copenhagen to Korsoer, had heavier rails installed in 1885. The class Ks engines were unique in having the cylinders placed behind the front carrying wheels with the connecting rod working the back set of wheels as drivers. These locomotives, like all early Danish locomotives, were equipped with a band of copper on the smokestacks and a two-part folding smokebox door. Engine no. 273, a similar type class Ks engine, was preserved in the railway museum in 1934. A drawing of this class engine is given in the next illustration. Specifications on engine no. 274 were as follows:

Wheel arrangement	2–4–0
Maximum speed	100 kilometers per hour
Cylinders (2)	430 by 610 millimeters
Drive wheels	1866-millimeter diameter
Boiler	
Heating surface	86.3 square meters
Working pressure	10 kilograms per square centimeter
Operating weight	
64.9 tons	
26.0 tons adhesion	
Overall length	13.85 meters.

(Courtesy: Danish State Railways)

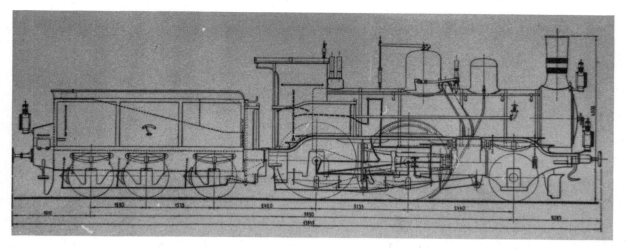

An outline drawing of the Danish class Ks steam locomotive built by Schwartzkopff of Germany starting in 1886 and used widely on the railways of Denmark is presented.
(Courtesy: Danish State Railways)

Pictured is a Danish class Hs tank locomotive of which sixty-one units were eventually built starting in 1888 by Hartmann and by Neilson. As traffic increased in Denmark in the early days, the work of expeditiously sorting and shunting cars at the larger stations became a serious problem. Accordingly, this task was solved by using special shunting engines beginning in 1874 at the Copenhagen Central marshalling yard. The class Hs engines were very successful with one engine lasting until 1956, about eighty years of service. See a subsequent illustration for a drawing of this engine. Specifications were:

Cylinders (2)	330-millimeter diameter
Drive wheels	1086-millimeter diameter
Boiler	
Heating surface	46.7 square meters
Working pressure	10 kiligrams per square meter
Operating Weight	21.1 tons
Tank capacity	2.4 tons water
Bunker capacity	0.5 tons coal
Overall length	7.48 meters
Maximum speed	25 killimeters per hour.

See a later illustration for another view of this engine.
(Courtesy: Danish State Railways)

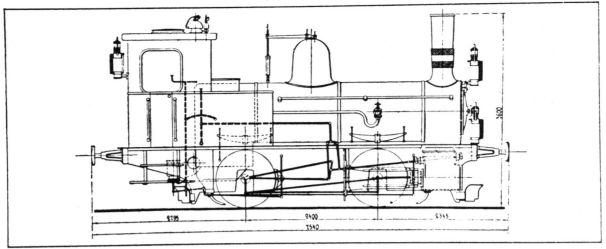

The drawing shown covers a Danish class Hs steam tank engine, built by two manufacturers Hartmann and Neilson starting in 1888 for use on the Denmark railways. See an earlier illustration for technical and other details.
(Courtesy: Danish State Railways)

This illustration shows the Danish class P, type 4–4–2, compound tender express locomotive built from 1909 by Schwartzkopff and by Linden in Germany. These engines were designed by the DSB Chief Engineer, OFA Busse, in 1907. The machine was exhibited at the Brussels World Exhibition where it was praised for its performance and harmonious styling. This class P engine was the first in Denmark with four cylinders; with its huge driving wheel of 1984-millimeter diameter it reached a top speed of 120 kilometers per hour on flat railroads. These locomotives were used until the mid-1950s at which time they were replaced by diesel-electric power. See a later illustration for an outline drawing. Specifications were as follows on engine no. 917 built by Schwartzkopff:

Cylinders (2)	
Hi pressure	340-millimeter diameter
Lo pressure	570-millimeter diameter
Drive wheels	1984-millimeter diameter
Boiler	
Heating surface	149.3 square meters
Working pressure	15 kilograms per square centimeter
Operating weight	
119.4 tons	
33.0 tons adhesion	
Tender capacities	22.0 tons water; 5.0 tons coal
Maximum speed	120 kilometers per hour
Overall length	18.52 meters.

(Courtesy: Danish State Railways)

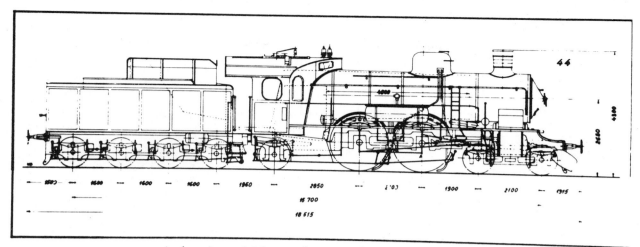

A drawing which supplements the data given in an earlier illustration is shown. This was another class P, type 4–4–2 of a more modern vintage, used on the railways of Denmark. These engines were built in 1909 by two German manufacturers, Schwartzkopff and Linden.
(Courtesy: Danish State Railways)

Pictured is a class 0, type 2–4–2, tank locomotive widely used for passenger service in Denmark. Six units were built by Borsig in 1898 for servicing local traffic in the Copenhagen area. In 1901, twenty-nine additional units were ordered from Esslingen, of which this no. 327 machine is a sample. These engines, with four-axled drivers, were able to move equally in both directions thus eliminating the time-consuming turning operations at the terminals. The bunkers and tanks were later modified to increase capacities. In all, thirty-five class 0 units were purchased, of which four operated until 1958. See a subsequent illustration for a drawing of this locomotive. Specifications were:

Cylinders (2)	340-millimeter diameter
Drive wheels	1730-millimeter diameter
Boiler	
Heating surface	72.5 square meters
Working pressure	12.0 kilograms per square centimeter
Operating weight	
52 tons	
26.5 tons adhesion	
Tank capacity	6.5 tons water
Bunker capacity	1.2 tons coal
Maximum speed	70–80 kilometers per hour.

(Courtesy: Danish State Railways)

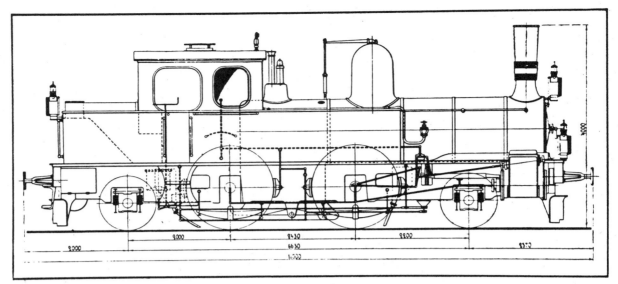

This drawing covers the Danish class 0 type 2–4–2, tank locomotive built over the period 1898–1901 by Borsig and by Esslingen for use on the railroads of Denmark. See an earlier illustration for a picture and technical details.
(Courtesy: Danish State Railways)

Another view of a class HS tank locomotive used on the Danish railways starting in 1888 is shown. See earlier illustrations for details.
(Courtesy: Danish State Railways)

ECUADOR

BY THE MID-NINETEENTH CENTURY, THE GREAT need for roads and railroads in Ecuador was clearly evident, to those who hoped for any real national development to take place. The primary difficulty in creating any kind of public works in Ecuador was the chronic shortage of capital. The first rail project was in 1874—a twenty-six mile, 3-foot 6-inch gauge line from Yaguachi to Barraganeta in the lowland vicinity of Guayaquil—was constructed using partial funds from an 1855 British loan of $8.827 million to Ecuador. An additional eighteen miles of track were laid from Barraganeta to Bucay in 1884, and in 1886 a 13.6-mile stretch joined Ya-guachi with Duran, located on the south bank of the Guayas River opposite Guayaquil.

Of course, the ideal plan, and the government's dream, in Ecuador was to connect the highland capital of Quito with Guayaquil, the second largest city and Pacific seaport. To this end, an American concern, the Ecuadorian Improvement Company, was incorporated in March 1888 to launch the really difficult task of extending the lowland rail-road along a circuitous route into the eleven-thousand-foot Andes. Financed by floating loans in Europe and the United States, the railroad work slowly dragged on and on, burdened with virtually insurmountable engineering and topographic prob-lems. In 1899 the destiny of this Ecuadorian rail-road passed into the hands of the newly incor-porated Guayaquil & Quito Railway Company. In November 1901 a twenty-two-mile section of track opened between Bucay and Quibi, which repre-sented the most troublesome part of the 288-mile railroad between Quito and Guayaquil because it involved a climb of forty-seven hundred feet in twenty-two miles. The line reached Cajabamba, eleven thousand feet above sea level and about 140 miles from Guayaquil, in February 1907. The rail-road finally arrived at Quito in June 1908, which occasioned many joyous ceremonies.

Subsequently, in 1926, the 3-foot 6-inch gauge railroad was extended north 107.6 miles from Quito to Ibarra and, in 1927, an additional 30.6 miles to Carchi. The line was ultimately pushed to completion in 1957, connecting Quito with the Pacific seaport of San Lorenzo. A French firm did a commendable job of laying down the last 93.8 miles of track. In 1959 a branch line of 90.7 miles, off the Guayaquil & Quito Railway, was con-structed from Alausi to Cuenca in the southern region of Ecuador.

Details covering railroads in Ecuador are con-tained in my 1981 book, *Railways Across the Andes*.

Steam Locomotives in Ecuador

Ecuadorian railways, from the beginning, were largely operated using various locomotives built by the Baldwin Locomotive Works. Most of these were type 2–6–0 Moguls and type 2–8–0 Consoli-dations.

Many Moguls were built in 1905, and those illus-trated are representative of these 2–6–0 engines. Between 1940 and 1960, most Mogul locomotives were rebuilt, modernized, and modified to include superheaters and use oil as fuel. By 1971 most of Ecuador's 2–6–0 engines had been downgraded to

Pictured is a Mogul, type 2–6–0, locomotive similar to those which were constructed in large numbers for the Ecuadorian railways by Baldwin starting in 1905. Many of these engines, rebuilt and modernized in the 1940s, were still rendering service in Ecuador in 1970. Some specifications were as follows:

Baldwin class 8–22D, light
    freight locomotive

Cylinders	14 by 18 inches
Drive wheels	41-inch diameter
Gauge	4 foot 8½-inch
Operating weight	48,000 pounds
Tender water capacity	1600 gallons.

Most of the above engines had superheaters installed in 1950–60 and were converted to use fuel oil in place of coal.
(Courtesy: Frederick Westing collection)

Shown is another old 1905 Mogul, type 2–6–0, Baldwin locomotive, rebuilt and modernized with superheater and oil burners in the period 1940–60. These were still in use on various Ecuadorian rail lines in 1970. See first illustration for typical specifications.
(Courtesy: State Railways of Ecuador)

The old steam locomotive pictured was photographed by the author in Quito in 1978. It is a Consolidation; type 2–8–0, engine built by Baldwin about 1930. This locomotive, no. 45, was considerably rebuilt and modernized in 1960 for use on excursion service on the Guayaquil & Quito Railroad.
(Courtesy: E. A. Haine)

yard-shunting jobs but one or two had been spruced-up to handle steam powered excursion trains.

Most of the Consolidation 2–8–0 engines were built between 1921 and 1929, but some were subcontracted by Baldwin-Lima-Hamilton from 1950 to 1952 (see illustration). The "Rushton radial driving wheel," designed by Mr. Kenneth Rushton, then vice-president in charge of engineering for Baldwin, was applied to a number of Consolidation engines built for the Guayaquil & Quito Railway in 1921. This device held the drive wheels in rigid alignment while at the same time allowing a radial deflection of the front and back pair of driving wheels so that sharp curves could be easily traversed. Consolidation locomotive no. 53 (not illustrated) represented one of the last steam locomotives constructed in American shops.

In 1972 the Ecuadorian Railways had about thirty-five steam locomotives on their roster but only twenty-five were in active service.

EGYPT

THE FIRST RAILWAY IN AFRICA, BUILT IN 1885 BY the British in Egypt, connected Alexandria and Cairo via Damanhûr, Tanta, and Bandar, a distance of 130 miles. During the reign of Ismail Pasha (1863–79), 910 miles of railroad were constructed, including connections between Port Said and Cairo, Tanta and Damietta, Cairo and Suez, and Suez and Ismailia. During World War I the British built a line from Al Qantarah to Rafah that crossed the north edge of the Sinai Desert to what is now the Israeli border, with Egyptian army reservists called up in 1916 to take part in the construction. Most rail lines were of standard gauge, although some narrow-gauge, light railroads were laid down in the delta and in the El Fayum governorate. In recent years many of the main lines were double-tracked. A program of converting steam locomotives from coal to oil was undertaken in the 1950s.

Modern railroads in Egypt continue to follow the traditional routes, i.e., seacoast and river. A standard-gauge line runs from Cairo to Alexandria and to Damietta, both on the Mediterranean coast. One line runs eastward from Cairo to·Ismalia on the Suez Canal. There are rail lines on both sides of the canal. On the west side, these run the entire length of the waterway; on the east side, they run north from the Gulf of Suez, thirty miles to Kantara, then east eighty miles to El Arish near the Mediterranean coast, then fifty miles northeast to Gaza, and on to Israel.

From Alexandria, a 160-mile railroad extends parallel to the seacoast, running west through Mersa Matrûh to Sollum at the Libyan border. A double-track rail system runs south along the Nile River from Cairo to Aswan and El Shallal; two spurs from this railroad were pushed southwest, one to El Fayum from Wasta and one to Kharga Oasis from Oasis Junction on the main line.

All public transportation of any consequence in Egypt is owned by the state and is operated either by government authorities, by companies under the control of the Ministry of Transportation, or by cooperative associations.

A substantial share of the rolling stock was obsolescent at the beginning of the 1960s. As the result of a modernization program, the main railroad lines were converted to diesel by 1964 and new, air-conditioned passenger equipment was in use. In 1969 most of the main lines were in the Nile Valley or the delta, where they approached a Western European standard in terms of mileage per unit of inhabited area. With the discovery of rich iron ore and coal deposits in the Bahariya Oasis, some two hundred miles southwest of Cairo, the government was building a 216-mile new line between Bahariya and Helwan (now completed), at an estimated cost of thirty-five million Egyptian pounds.

There is still no direct railroad link between Port Said and Alexandria or between Egypt and Sudan. At the end of 1969, however, plans were drawn to extend the railroad system by more than three hundred miles between El Shallal, south of Aswan, and Wadi Halfa, on the Egyptian-Sudanese border, to establish a direct rail line between the two countries. (The line built by the British during World War II, extending eastward from Qena, on the Nile, to Qusayr, on the Red Sea coast, had been abandoned.)

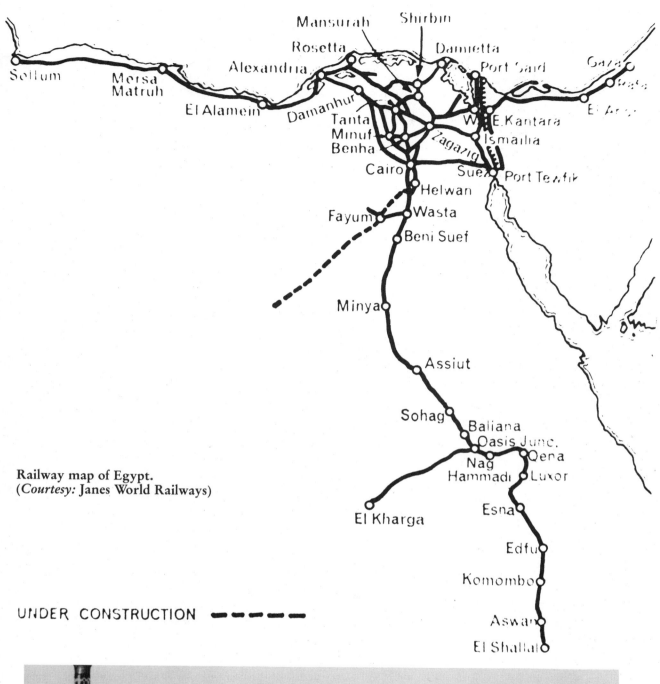

Railway map of Egypt.
(*Courtesy:* Janes World Railways)

UNDER CONSTRUCTION ━ ━ ━ ━ ━

Map labels: Sollum, Mersa Matruh, El Alamein, Alexandria, Rosetta, Mansurah, Shirbin, Damietta, Port Said, Gaza, Rafa, El Arish, Damanhur, Tanta, Minuf, Benha, Zagazig, W.E. Kantara, Ismailia, Cairo, Suez, Port Tewfik, Helwan, Fayum, Wasta, Beni Suef, Minya, Assiut, Sohag, Baliana, Oasis Junc., Qena, Nag Hammadi, Luxor, El Kharga, Esna, Edfu, Komombo, Aswan, El Shallal

The first steam locomotive used on the Egyptian Government Railways in 1856 was a 2–2–2 type express locomotive manufactured in the United States by Sharp, Stewart & Company. This had special decorations decreed by the head of state who had a strange fascination for the railroad steam engine. A drawing is shown of this first engine which carried the name "Saidia." The cylinders were 16 by 20, driving coupled wheels 6.5 feet in diameter.
(*Courtesy: O. S. Nock,* The Dawn of World Railways)

In 1979, according to *Janes World Railways*, Egypt's active railroads totaled 4,510 kilometers (2,802 miles) of 1.435-meter track and 347 kilometers (215.6 miles) of 0.750-meter track.

The railways of Egypt were mostly operated with steam locomotives manufactured in England. The early engines were sponsored by the government—more particularly, by the then ruling pashas—and these machines were usually bedecked with lavish ornaments. From 1883 to 1912, F. H. Trevithich held the chief engineer's position on the Egyptian Government Railways and was largely responsible for the basic design and procurement of early locomotives, carriages, and wagons.

The accompanying eighteen illustrations picture and describe the development and application of steam locomotion on the Egyptian railways from 1862 to 1950.

In 1862 Jeffrey Bey at Alexandria, Egypt, constructed a type 2–2–0 steam locomotive for operations between Alexandria and Suez. The water tank was built underneath the boiler which extended forward to join a section beneath the smokebox. Two small coal bunkers were installed on each side of the firebox. The valve gear was of the shifting link type, the valve boxes were inside, and two long-stroke feed pumps were fitted beneath the cylinders with the plungers being directly connected with the crossheads. Accessories included a traversing screw jack, stoking and firing irons, fire bars, lanterns, etc. A hand brake acted on the drive wheels and a miniature cab was installed over the foot plate to afford some protection from the hot sun. The gauge fittings were all fixed to a water column attached to the boiler. Limited available specification data included the following:

Cylinders	13 by 20 inches
Drive wheels	5-foot diameter.

A model is pictured.
(Courtesy: Science Museum, London) 19281

Pictured is a combined locomotive and carriage built by Robert Stephenson & Company in 1859 for Said Pasha, viceroy of Egypt. The engine was an inside cylinder, four-wheeled, single-driving machine with the framing extended rearward and carried on a four-wheeled bogie. The cylinders were 8 inches in diameter with a stroke of 14 inches. Drive wheels had a diameter of 60 inches. The leading and bogie wheels were 42 inches in diameter. The fixed wheel base was 8.58 feet, and the total wheelbase was 22.35 feet in length. The boiler had a total heating surface of 409 square feet with a grate area of 6.7 square feet. A water tank holding 400 gallons was fitted below the boiler and the fuel capacity was 4.5 hundredweights. The carriage had a coach-shaped body and was mounted on the frame extension; its roof was carried forward to cover the footplate and firebox. The vehicle was lavishly decorated, as were some other engines on the Cairo and Alexandria Railway at this time. The rails were laid on cast-iron pot sleepers.
(Courtesy: Science Museum, London) 162/55

In 1865 Neilson & Company of Glasgow provided the Egyptian Government Railways with a number of type 2–2–2 tender locomotives. These engines had the following specifications:

Gauge	4 feet 8½ inches
Cylinders	17¼ by 24 inches
Coupled drivers	8-foot 2-inch diameter (Note: this reported size is questionable. Author)
Boiler	
Heating surface	1166 square feet
Working pressure	130 pounds per square inch
Tractive force	8526 pounds at 90 percent boiler working pressure
Operating weights	
Engine	31 tons plus 18 hundredweights
Tender	22 tons plus 10 hundredweights
Tender capacities	1600 gallons water; 200 cubic feet coal.

(Courtesy: Mitchell Library, Glasgow) E290

Neilson, Reid & Company in 1898 provided the Egyptian State Railways with ten tender locomotives, type 0–6–0, nos. 354–63. These engines had the following specifications:

Gauge	4 feet 8½ inches
Cylinders	18 by 24 inches
Coupled drivers	5-foot 0¼-inch diameter
Boiler	
Heating surface	1126.2 square feet
Working pressure	140 pounds per square inch
Operating weights	
Engine	38 tons plus 5 hundredweights
Tender	26 tons plus 6 hundredweights
Tender water capacity	1800 gallons.

(Courtesy: Mitchell Library, Glasgow) E807

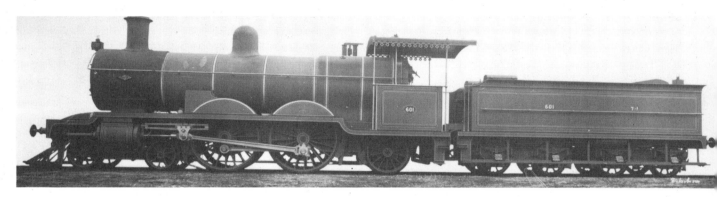

The Egyptian Government Railways in 1900 purchased from Dubs & Company a single machine, type 4–4–2. This was a tender locomotive carrying the no. 601 and having the following specifications:

Gauge	4 feet 8½ inches
Cylinders	20 by 26 inches
Drive wheels	6-foot 6-inch diameter
Boiler	
Heating surface	1996 square feet
Working pressure	180 pounds per square inch
Tractive force	18,000 pounds
Operating weights	
Engine	64 tons plus 4 hundredweights
Tender	39 tons plus 15 hundredweights.

(Courtesy: Mitchell Library, Glasgow) E3989

In 1900 Dubs & Company furnished a type 2–8–0 tender engine to the Egyptian Government Railways (no. 701) which had the following characteristics:

Gauge	4 feet 8½ inches
Cylinders	21 by 26 inches
Coupled drivers	4-foot 6-inches diameter
Boiler	
Heating surface	2200.5 square feet
Working pressure	180 pounds per square inch
Tractive force	28,665 pounds
Operating weights	
Engine	65 tons plus 2 hundredweights
Tender	39 tons plus 15 hundredweights.

(Courtesy: Mitchell Library, Glasgow) E3990

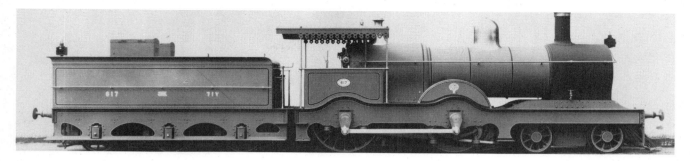

In 1901 Neilson, Reid & Company constructed ten tender locomotives (nos. 612–21) for use on the Egyptian Government Railways. These engines were used on the 4-foot 8½-inch gauge tracks and were of a type 4–4–0. Specifications were as follows:

Cylinders	18 by 24 inches
Coupled drivers	6-foot 3-inch diameter
Boiler	

Heating surface	1235 square feet
Working pressure	160 pounds per square inch
Operating weights	
Engine	45 tons plus 6 hundredweights
Tender	31 tons plus 1 hundredweight
Tender capacities	2500 gallons water; 240 cubic feet coal.

(Courtesy: Mitchell Library, Glasgow) E852

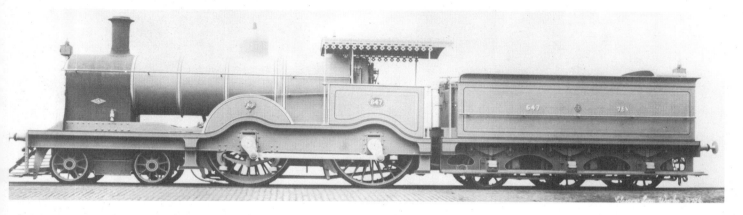

The Egyptian Government Railways in 1902 bought from Dubs & Company ten type 4–4–0 tender locomotives (nos. 647–56) with these specifications:

Gauge	4 feet 8½ inches
Cylinders	18 by 26 inches
Drive wheels	6-foot 9-inch diameter
Boiler	

Heating surface	1235.0 square feet
Working pressure	160 pounds per square inch
Tractive force	12,480 pounds
Operating weights	
Engine	48 tons plus 2 hundredweights
Tender	30 tons plus 1 hundredweight.

(Courtesy: Mitchell Library, Glasgow) E4389

The North British Locomotive Company in 1904 constructed fifteen units of a type 4–6–0 tender locomotive for use by the Egyptian War Office (nos. 69–83). These machines had the following pertinent characteristics:

Gauge	3 feet 6 inches
Cylinders	17 by 22 inches
Drive wheels	4-foot 6-inch diameter
Boiler	

Heating surface	1081.5 square feet
Working pressure	180 pounds per square inch
Operating weights	
Engine	49 tons plus 1 hundredweight
Tender	33 tons plus 17 hundredweights
Tender capacities	2600 gallons water; 260 cubic feet coal.

(Courtesy: Mitchell Library, Glasgow) L44

In 1904 the Egyptian Government Railways purchased from the North British Locomotive Company fifteen type 0–6–0 tender locomotives (nos. 419–33) having the following specifications:

Gauge	4 feet 8½ inches
Cylinders	18 by 24 inches
Drive wheels	5-feet 0¼-inch diameter
Boiler	

Heating surface	1126.2 square feet
Working pressure	160 pounds per square inch
Operating weights	
Engine	41 tons plus 1 hundredweight
Tender	35 tons plus 1 hundredweight
Tender capacities	3000 gallons water; 216 cubic feet coal.

(Courtesy: Mitchell Library, Glasgow) L75

In 1905 the North British Locomotive Company furnished the Egyptian Delta Light Railway with six type 0–6–4 tank engines (nos. 93–98). These machines had the following specifications:

Gauge	2 feet 5½ inches
Cylinders	12 by 16 inches

Coupled drivers	3-foot 0½-inch diameter
Boiler	
Heating surface	554 square feet
Working pressure	160 pounds per square inch
Operating weight	26 tons plus 6 hundredweights
Water capacity	400 gallons.

(Courtesy: Mitchell Library, Glasgow) L120

The Egyptian Government Railways in 1905 introduced a single, type 4–4–2, tender locomotive for use on its rail lines. This machine was constructed by the North British Locomotive Company and carried the identification no. 678. Specifications were as follows:

Gauge	4 feet 8½ inches
Cylinders	13¾ by 24 inches

Coupled drivers	6-foot 3-inch diameter
Boiler	
Heating surface	1671.5 square feet
Working pressure	228 pounds per square inch
Operating weights	
Engine	62 tons plus 15 hundredweights
Tender	35 tons.

(Courtesy: Mitchell Library, Glasgow) L121

Early Egyptian locomotives, wagons, and carriages were designed by Chief Engineer F. H. Trevithich, who held that post in Cairo over the period 1883–1912. A prototype design was built in 1907 by the North British Locomotive Company; this is a model on display in the Science Museum of London. The 4–6–0 locomotive had the following characteristics:

Cylinders	19 by 26 inch
Coupled wheels	6-foot 3-inch diameter
Boiler	
Firebox	172 square feet
Heating surface	2149 square feet
Steam pressure	180 pounds per square inch
Engine weight	68.6 tons, 51 tons adhesive
Tender capacity	4000 gallons water; 6 tons coal.

(Courtesy: Science Museum, London)

In 1925 the Egyptian Government Railways purchased from the North British Locomotive Company fifteen type 4–4–2 tender locomotives (nos. 780–94) with these pertinent characteristics:

Gauge	4 feet 8½ inches
Cylinders	20 by 28 inches
Coupled drivers	6-foot 6-inch diameter
Boiler	
Heating surface	2383 square feet
Working pressure	160 pounds per square inch
Tractive force	17,230 pounds
Operating weights	
Engine	76 tons plus 7 hundredweights
Tender	57 tons plus 3 hundredweights
Tender capacities	5500 gallons water; 360 cubic feet coal.

(Courtesy: Mitchell Library, Glasgow) L812

The Egyptian Government Railways added in 1928 twenty tank locomotives to their inventory (nos. 1220–39). The engines had the following wheel arrangement: 2–6–2. The North British Locomotive Company was the manufacturer and specifications were as follows:

Gauge	4 feet 8½ inches
Cylinders	21 by 26 inches
Drivers	5-feet 0¾-inch diameter
Boiler	
Heating surface	1605 square feet
Working pressure	160 pounds per square inch
Tractive force	22,640 pounds
Operating weight	84 tons
Water Capacity	1620 gallons.

(Courtesy: Mitchell Library, Glasgow) L825

In 1937 the North British Locomotive Company built four, type 2–4–2, tender locomotives for the Sentinel Wagon Works destined for use on the Egyptian Government Railways. These engines carried identification nos. 276–79. Two machines were coal-fired and two oil-fueled; all used high speed geared Sentinel engines. Specifications follow:

Gauge	4 feet 8½ inches
Cylinders	(2) Sentinel 11 by 12 inch, gear ratio 55/35
Drive wheels	3-foot 8¾-inch diameter
Boiler	
Heating surface	1480 square feet

Working pressure	200 pounds per square inch
Tractive force	15,290 pounds
Operating weights	
Engine	
Oil-burning	56 tons plus 9 hundredweights
Coal-fired	56 tons plus 13 hundredweights
Tender	
Oil	43 tons plus 10 hundredweights
Coal	44 tons plus 2 hundredweights
Tender capacities	
4½ tons oil	
(not stated) coal	
3700 gallons water.	

(Courtesy: Mitchell Library, Glasgow) L908

In 1938 the British Locomotive Company built twenty type 2–6–0 locomotives for use on the Egyptian Government Railways. These were designed for freight and passenger service on rails limited to relatively light loads. A model of this engine was displayed at the 1938 Empire Exhibition in Glasgow, Scotland. These specifications applied:

Cylinders	13.75 by 28 inches
Coupled wheels	5-foot 6.75-inch diameter
Boiler	
Grate area	25 square feet
Heating surface	1696 square feet including Melesco superheater
Boiler pressure	225 pounds per square inch
Tractive effort	25,267 pounds
Operating weight	107.75 tons (engine plus tender)
Tender capacity	3,700 gallons water; 6 tons coal.

(Courtesy: Mitchell Library, Glasgow)

In 1948 the Egyptian Government Railways bought from the North British Locomotive Company thirty-two type 4–6–0 tender engines (nos. 301–32). These were oil-fired locomotives with the following specifications:

Gauge	4 feet 8½ inches
Cylinders	21 by 28 inches
Coupled drivers	6-feet diameter
Boiler	
Heating surface	2663 square feet
Working pressure	210 pounds per square inch
Tractive force	30,610 pounds at 85 percent boiler working pressure
Operating weights	
Engine	84 tons plus 3 hundredweights
Tender	61 tons plus 13 hundredweights
Tender capacity	5500 gallons water; 9 tons oil.

(Courtesy: Mitchell Library, Glasgow) L974

In 1950 the Egyptian Government Railways purchased a second series of type 4–6–0 oil-fired tender locomotives from the North British Locomotive Company. These eighteen machines carried identification 401–18. Specifications were:

Gauge	4 feet 8½ inches
Cylinders	21 by 28 inches
Drive wheels	6-feet diameter
Boiler	
Heating area	2663 square feet
Working pressure	225 pounds per square inch
Tractive force	32,800 pounds at 85 percent boiler working pressure
Operating weights	
Engine	85 tons plus 17 hundredweights
Tender	68 tons plus 16 hundredweights
Tender capacities	5500 gallons water; 2400 gallons oil.

(Courtesy: Mitchell Library, Glasgow) L3—2d series

FINLAND

IN FINLAND, RAILWAY DEVELOPMENT LAGGED A whole generation behind steamships along the coasts and inland waterways. The Finns first realized the feasibility of steam-powered locomotives when the tall-funneled steamships *Prince Menschikoff* and *Storfursten* were observed operating between Stockholm and Helsinki and between Fallinn and St. Petersburg in 1837.

As early as 1840, the suitability of a railroad in Finland was widely debated. Opponents of such endeavors held that the enterprise was too expensive, was unnatural, and was quite unnecessary because of the widespread utilization of lakes and canals for transportation. By the mid-1850s, however, with mounting evidence of the practicability of railways in many other countries, proponents won the argument.

On 4 March 1857, the order was given for construction of the first railway. This initial rail venture consisted of a 1.524-meter (5-foot) gauge line running sixty-seven miles north and northwest between Helsinki and Hameenlina. The inaugural train passed along this route on 31 January 1862. The locomotive was a 4–4–0 type named "Lemmin Kainen," one of four built in 1860 by Peto, Brassey & Betts at Birkenhead, Canada. The other three engines were named "Ilmarinen," "Alutar," and "Suomi." The pioneer public train ran on the new railway on 17 March 1862.

By 1870 Helsinki was connected by rail with Russia by a line between Riihjmari and St. Petersburg. At this time Finland, autonomous but not sovereign, was considered a grand duchy of the Russian czarist empire. A line about seventy-five miles in length between Hanko on the Gulf of Finland and inland Hyvinge (running northeast and southwest just west of Helsinki) was opened in 1873, and this became a part of the Finland State Railways in 1875.

The early Finnish railways were all built by the government because the large amount of capital required was simply unavailable through private investors. These initial railroads stimulated the growth of outlying settlements and helped promote industry. Yields on some early capital investments amounted to 2 to 3 percent.

Railroad equipment and rolling stock for the early systems came from England, Switzerland, Germany, Austria, and the United States; however, after about 1914 locomotives and cars were mostly of domestic manufacture. Actually, the first railroad steam engine to be built in Finland was completed in 1874 at the State Railways workshops in Helsinki, but the local locomotive industry did not gain any substantial headway until just before World War I.

By 1914 Finland had twenty-six hundred miles of track. With Finland declaring its independence from Russia in 1917, the pace of rail construction increased to about sixty-two miles per year. By 1939 Finnish rail mileage had increased to fifty-four hundred miles, at which time the state owned 16 percent of all the railroads.

During World War II the Finnish State Railways were confronted with horrendous transport problems caused by the heavy movements of all kinds of freight and passengers and by a gradual reduction in the tractive power and rolling stock due to military actions. The first years after that war were devoted to repairing the wartime damage and rehabilitating the rolling stock and engines, though by this time highway transport had made terrific inroads and the fortunes of the railroads seemed doubtful. Dieselized traction was initiated in 1950, and in 1965 the first stages of electrification were begun.

Around 1970 the railways of Finland totaled only about thirty-five hundred miles since various sections had been abandoned after World War II. A break in gauge existed between Tornio in northwest Finland and Haparanda in Sweden. A connection was maintained with the Soviet rail system at Vainikkala in southeast Finland. In the north, the rail line ended at Salla on the Soviet border but no traffic passed through to the Murmansk sector.

In 1978 railways were officially listed as having a total route length of 6,010 kilometers (3,732 miles), all 1.524-meter (5-foot) gauge. At the end of 1979 the Finnish railroads had a total of 28,437 employees, making it one of the largest employers in that country; an estimated one hundred thousand Finns received their livelihood from the railways.

Steam Locomotives in Finland

Up to about 1914, most locomotives used in Finland were purchased from manufacturers in England, Switzerland, Germany, Austria, and the United States. From the beginning, the rail gauge adopted in Finland was 1.524 meters, or 5 feet. Since this gauge is the same as that used on the Russian railways, it has always facilitated an interchange of traffic between the two countries.

The first railway engine used on the pioneer Finnish railroad is described and illustrated. By 1869, Dubs & Company of Glasgow was a supplier of steam locomotives, and two are shown.

The American effort as a supplier of steam locomotives commenced in 1872 when the Baldwin Locomotive Works of Philadelphia constructed nine type 4-4-0 units for the Hanko-Hyvinge Railway. In 1900 various type 4-6-0, class Hk1 locomotives for passenger service were furnished by Baldwin and by the Richmond Locomotive Works of Virginia. These are illustrated and extensively described. Between 1862 and 1900, boiler working pressures had increased from 120 to 170 pounds per square inch.

Over the period 1892 to 1905, the railways of

Finland started using type 2-6-0, class G11 mixed-traffic locomotives built in Germany, Switzerland, Great Britain, and in various Finnish workshops. From 1901 to 1903, thirty-three compound engines of this class were built by Tampereen in Finland. A model is shown.

In 1902 the Finnish railroads received a series of steam locomotives, type 2-6-0, class Sk3, for freight service from the following manufacturers: Dubs & Company, Glasgow; Schweizerische Lok. & Maschinenfabr., Winterthur; Berliner Maschinenbau, A. G., Berlin; and Tampereen Pellava- ja Rauta-Teoll. O.Y., Tampere, Finland. Full specifications and a photograph of engine no. 376 are given.

The Finnish firm of Tampereen Pellava- ja Rauta-Teoll supplied a number of type 4-6-0, class Hk2, steam locomotives in 1904, designed for passenger service; these engines utilized a superheater for the first time. Engine no. 443, a woodburning model, is shown and described.

In 1925, class Pr1 passenger locomotives, type 2-8-2, were supplied by Hannoversche Maschinenbau A.B., Hannover, and by the two Finnish companies, Tampereen Pellava- ja Rauta-Teoll. O.Y., Lokomo O.Y. Pictured is engine no. 772 and gives all pertinent technical specifications. By this time, engine tractive force had progressed from 8,730 pounds, in 1872, to 29,700 pounds. Also in 1925, freight engines, type 2-8-0 and class Tv1, furnished by four manufacturers were added to the roster. The builders were: Tampereen Pellava- ja Rauta-Teoll. O.Y.; Lokomo O.Y.; Nydqvist & Holm, Trollhättan, Sweden; and Hannoversche Maschinenbau A.G. This class Tv1, 2-8-0 locomotive and the class Tk3 locomotive, to be described later, were Consolidation-type engines whose shape and outline have been long identified as being truly Finnish in character. These locomotives met all kinds of mixed-freight traffic requirements but were never used on heavy freight or fast passenger service. A typical engine of this class, no. 738, is shown.

In 1926 other steam locomotives designed for handling passenger trains, type 4-6-0, class Hv2, were furnished by Berliner Maschinenbau A.G. and by Lokomo O.Y. All the technical specifications are listed. Also in 1926, a type 0-10-0, class Vr3 engine was built by Hannoversche Maschinenbau A.B. and by Tampereen Pellava- ja Rauta-Teoll. The last Vr3 engine saw its final

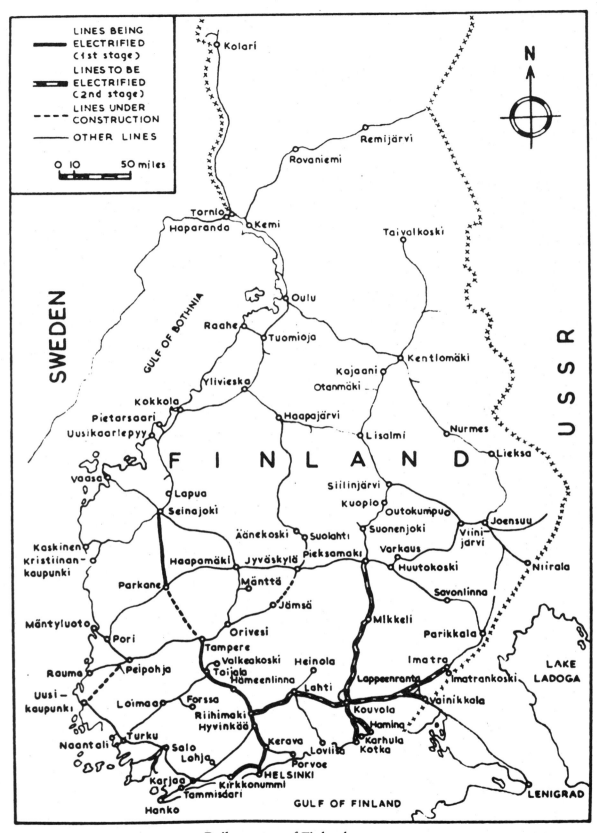

Railway map of Finland.
(*Courtesy:* Janes World Railways)

The first power-operated railway in Finland opened in 1862 running sixty-seven miles between Helsinki and Hameenlina. Rail operations started with four locomotives, type 4–4–0, built in 1860 by Peto, Brassey & Betts of Birkenhead, Canada. These engines had the following characteristics:

Gauge	1.524 meters
Cylinders	16 by 20 inches
Coupled wheels	5-foot diameter
Boiler	
Grate area	11.7 square feet
Heating surface	1044 square feet
Steam pressure	120 pounds per square inch
Tractive effort	8730 pounds at 85 percent working pressure
Locomotive speed	80 kilometers per hour
Operating weight	48 tons (engine plus tender).

A model, pictured is on display in the Railway Museum at Helsinki.
(Courtesy: Finland State Railways)

The Finland State Railways used many different steam locomotives including British 4–4–0 passenger types manufactured by Dubs & Company of Glasgow, Scotland in 1869. These had the following characteristics:

Cylinders	16 by 20 inches
Coupled drive wheels	5.5-foot diameter
Boiler	
Grate area	13.3 square feet
Heating area	954 square feet
Boiler pressure.	120 pounds per square inch
Tractive effort	7893 pounds
Operating weight	55 tons (engine plus tender).

A model engine, shown is on view at the Railway Museum in the Helsinki railroad station. A sketch of the same locomotive is also included.
(Courtesy: Finland State Railways)

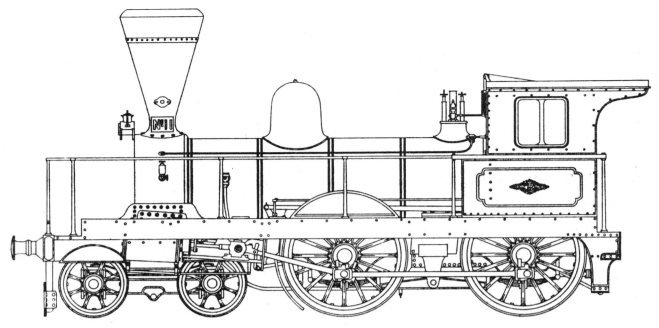

Presented is a sketch of the Dubs engine, type 4–4–0, supplied to the Finnish railways in 1869. See the previous illustration for technical details.
(Courtesy: Finland State Railways)

The Hangö–Hyvinge Railway was opened in Finland in 1873 and was absorbed by the Finland State Railways in 1875. The line started operations with nine Baldwin type 4–4–0 locomotives which were constructed in 1872. These engines had specifications as follows:

Class A4	nos. 63–71
Cylinders	15 by 20 inches
Coupled wheels	5-foot 2-inch diameter
Boiler	
Grate area	13 square feet
Heating surface	810 square feet
Boiler pressure	120 pounds per square inch
Tractive effort	7385 pounds
Operating weight	47 tons (engine plus tender)
Maximum speed	80 kilometers per hour.

A model of the original locomotive, shown is on display in the Railway Museum at the Helsinki railway station.
(Courtesy: Finland State Railways)

In 1900 the Finland State Railways placed into service a passenger steam locomotive, type 4–6–0, class Hk1. These were manufactured by Baldwin Locomotive works of Philadelphia and by the Richmond Locomotive Works of Richmond, Virginia, U.S.A. These engines, pictured in the illustration had the following specifications:

Gauge	1524 millimeters (5 feet)
Cylinders	406 by 610 millimeters
Engine wheels	
Coupled drivers	1575-millimeter diameter
Front truck	860-millimeter diameter
Total wheelbase	7124 millimeters
Boiler	
Tubes	70.87 square millimeters
Firebox	8.93 square meters
Total heating surface	79.80 square meters
Grate area	1.35 square meters
Superheater surface	21.80 square meters
Boiler working pressure	12 kilograms per square centimeter (170 pounds per square inch)
Tractive force	6510 kilograms at 85 percent boiler working pressure
Engine operating weight	44.5 tons
Weight on coupled wheels	31.5 tons
Tender	
Wheel diameter	960 millimeters
Wheelbase	2744 millimeters
Water capacity	8 cubic meters (2115 U.S. gallons)
Fuel capacity	4.5 tons
Operating weight	25 tons
Total operating weight	69.5 tons (engine plus tender).

(Courtesy: Finland State Railways)

Over the period 1892–1905 the Finland State Railways received various class G 11, type 2–6–0, mixed traffic locomotives from Great Britain, Germany, Switzerland, and Finland. A model pictured was one of a series of thirty-three compound locomotives manufactured by Tampereen Pellava- ja Rauta-Teollisuus Osake-Yhtiö of Finland in 1901–03. Specifications were as follows:

Cylinders	
Hi pressure	15.75 by 23⅝ inches
Lo pressure	22¹³⁄₁₆ by 23⅝ inches
Coupled wheels	4-foot 1³⁄₁₆-inch diameter
Boiler	
Grate area	14.9 square feet
Heating surface	824 square feet
Steam pressure	178 pounds per square inch
Tractive effort	12,700 pounds
Operating weight	58 tons (engine plus tender).

(Courtesy: Finland State Railways)

This photograph shows tender engine no. 376 introduced to the Finnish railways in 1902. This was a type 2–6–0 freight locomotive classified as Sk3. Four manufacturers were involved in the construction as follows:

Schweizerische Lok & Maschinenfabr, Winterhur
Dubs & Company, Glasgow
Berliner Maschinenbau A.G., Berlin
Tampereen Pellava, Tampere, Finland

Specifications were:

Gauge	1524 millimeters (5 feet)
Cylinders	400 by 600 millimeters and 580 by 600 millimeters
Engine wheels	
Coupled drivers	1250-millimeter diameter
Front truck	790-millimeter diameter
Total wheelbase	6380 millimeters
Boiler	
Tubes	69.5 square meters
Firebox	7.1 square meters
Total heating surface	76.6 square meters
Grate area	1.38 square meters
Boiler working pressure	12.5 kilograms per square centimeter (178 pounds per square inch)
Tractive force	5760 kilograms at 60 percent boiler working pressure
Engine operating weight	36 tons
Weight on drivers	30 tons
Tender	
Wheel diameter	960 millimeters
Wheelbase	3000 millimeters
Water capacity	8 cubic meters (9920 U.S. gallons)
Fuel capacity	4.5 tons
Operating weight	23.5 tons
Total operating weight	59.5 tons (engine plus tender).

(Courtesy: Finland State Railways)

The tender passenger locomotive, no. 443, shown in the photograph was introduced in Finland in 1904 and was manufactured by Tampereen Pellava of Tampere, Finland. This engine had a 4–6–0 wheel arrangement and was classified Hk2. Specifications were:

Cylinders	450 by 610 millimeters
Engine wheels	
Coupled drivers	1575-millimeter diameter
Front truck	860-millimeter diameter
Total wheelbase	7122 millimeters
Boiler	
Tubes	70.35 square meters
Firebox	8.35 square meters
Total heating surface	78.70 square meters
Grate area	1.45 square meters
Superheater area	21.80 square meters
Boiler working pressure	12 kilograms per square centimeter (170 pounds per square inch)
Tractive force	8000 kilograms at 85 percent boiler working pressure
Engine operating weight	45 tons
Weight on coupled wheels	30.6 tons
Tender	
Wheel diameter	960 millimeters
Wheelbase	2750 millimeters
Water capacity	9 cubic meters (2380 U.S. gallons)
Fuel capacity	5 tons
Operating weight	25.5 tons
Total operating weight	70.5 tons (engine plus tender).

(Courtesy: Finland State Railways)

Pictured is another Finnish steam locomotive used for passenger service; this was a class Hv1 engine (no. 549) with a 4–6–0 wheel arrangement. These machines were constructed by Tampereen Pellava and Lokomo O.Y. of Tamperee, Finland, starting in 1915. Specifications follow:

Gauge	1524 millimeters (5 feet)
Cylinders	510 by 600 millimeters
Engine wheels	
Coupled drivers	1750-millimeter diameter
Front truck	860-millimeter diameter
Total wheelbase	7600 millimeters
Boiler	
Tubes	98.4 square meters
Firebox	10.2 square meters
Total heat area	108.6 square meters
Grate area	1.99 square meters
Superheater	30.70 square meters (surface)
Boiler working pressure	12 kilograms per square centimeter (170 pounds per square inch)
Tractive force	9090 kilograms at 85 percent boiler working pressure
Engine operating weight	55.2 tons
Weight on coupled wheels	37.2 tons
Tender	
Wheel diameter	1050 millimeters
Wheelbase	3000 millimeters
Water capacity	14.3 cubic meters (3780 U.S. gallons)
Fuel capacity	5 tons
Operating weight	33.3 tons
Total operating weight	88.5 tons (tender plus engine).

(Courtesy: Finland State Railways)

Shown is another passenger locomotive (no. 772) used on the railways of Finland. This class Pr1 engine had a 2–8–2 wheel arrangement and was supplied by Tampereen Pellava and Lokomo O.Y. of Tampere, Finland and Hannoversche Mascheninbau A.G. of Hannover, Germany starting in 1925. Specifications were as follows:

Cylinders	570 by 650 millimeters
Engine wheels	
Coupled drivers	1600-millimeter diameter
Front truck	960-mm diameter
Trailing truck	960-millimeter diameter
Total wheelbase	10550 millimeters
Boiler	
Tubes	110.5 square meters
Firebox	11.5 square meters
Total heating surface	122.0 square meters
Grate area	2.11 square meters
Superheater	38.00 square meter area
Boiler working pressure	12 kilograms per square centimeter (170 pounds per square inch)
Tractive force	13470 kilograms at 85 percent boiler working pressure
Total operating weight	88.2 tons
Weight on coupled wheels	59.3 tons
Water capacity	7.5 cubic meters (1980 U.S. gallons)
Fuel capacity	4 tons.

(Courtesy: Finland State Railways)

Finnish tender steam locomotive no. 738 is pictured. This was constructed for freight service starting in 1925 by Tampereen Pellava, Lokomo O.Y., Nydqvist & Holm, and Hannoversche Macheninbau A.G. The engine had a 2–8–0 wheel arrangement and was designated class Tv1. Specifications follow:

Cylinders	560 by 650 millimeters
Engine wheels	
Coupled drivers	1400-millimeter diameter
Front truck	860-millimeter diameter
Coupled wheelbase	3100-millimeter
Total wheelbase	7250 millimeters
Boiler	
Tubes	112.1 square meters
Firebox	11.7 square meters
Total heat area	123.8 square meters
Superheater surface	38.6 square meters
Boiler working pressure	13 kilograms per square centimeter (185 pounds per square inch)
Tractive force	16090 kilograms at 85 percent boiler working pressure
Engine operating weight	61.5 tons
Weight on coupled wheels	32.4 tons
Tender	
Wheel diameter	1050 millimeters
Wheelbase	3300 millimeters
Water capacity	16 cubic meters (4230 U.S. gallons)
Fuel capacity	5 tons
Operating weight	36 tons
Total operating weight	97.5 tons (engine plus tender).

(Courtesy: Finland State Railways)

Pictured is a passenger type steam locomotive (no. 777) used on the Finnish railways starting in 1926. These machines were constructed by Lokomo O.Y. of Tampere, Finland and by Berliner Maschinenbau A.G. of Berlin. The engines were designated class Hv2 and had a 4–6–0 wheel arrangement. Specifications were as follows:

Cylinders	510 by 600 millimeters
Engine wheels	
Coupled drivers	1750-millimeter diameter
Front truck	860-millimeter diameter
Coupled wheelbase	4000-millimeters
Total wheelbase	7600 millimeters
Boiler	
Tubes	99.4 square meters
Firebox	10.4 square meters
Total heating area	109.8 square meters
Grate area	1.96 square meters
Superheater area	30.70 square meters
Boiler working pressure	12 kilograms per square centimeter (170 pounds per square inch)
Tractive force	9090 kilograms at 85 percent boiler working pressure
Engine operating weight	57 tons
Weight on coupled wheels	38.4 tons
Tender	
Wheel diameter	1050 millimeters
Wheelbase	3000 millimeters
Water capacity	14.3 cubic meters (3780 U.S. gallons)
Fuel capacity	5 tons
Operating weight	33.3 tons
Total operating weight	90.3 tons (engine plus tender).

(Courtesy: Finland State Railways)

Pictured is a Finland State Railways locomotive used for switching service. This was a class Vr3 engine with a 0–10–0 wheel arrangement. These machines were furnished by Hannoversche Maschinenbau A.G. of Hannover, Germany and Tampereen Pellava of Tampere, Finland starting in 1926. Specifications were as follows:

Gauge	1524 millimeters (5 feet)
Cylinders	570 by 650 millimeters
Coupled wheels	1270-millimeter diameter
Coupled wheelbase	2900 millimeters
Boiler	
Tubes	110.50 square meters
Firebox	11.50 square meters
Total heating surface	122.0 square meters
Grate area	2.11 square meters
Superheater area	38.00 square meters
Boiler working pressure	12 kilograms per square centimeter (171 pounds per square inch)
Tractive force	16,960 kilograms at 85 percent boiler working pressure
Operating weight	77.9 tons
Water capacity	6 cubic meters (1590 U.S. gallons)
Fuel capacity	4 tons.

(Courtesy: Finland State Railways)

"switching goat" service about 1971 in the rail yards at Kouvola.

In 1927 additional switching engines were furnished by Tampereen Pellava- ja Rauta-Teoll. O.Y. and by Hannoversche Maschinenbau A.G. These are the type 0–6–0, class Vr1 locomotives pictured and described.

In 1931 switching capabilities were enhanced by the addition of class Vr2, type 0–6–2 engines manufactured by Tampereen Pellava- ja Rauta-Teoll. O.Y. Engine no. 953 is featured.

Still another passenger locomotive was introduced in 1933, also built by Tampereen Pellava-ja Rauta-Teoll. O.Y. and by Lokomo O.Y. This type 4–6–0, class Hv4 woodburning engine, is pictured. In 1945, after World War II, the Finns turned to outside manufacturers to replenish their depleted and worn-out locomotives. The Vulcan Iron Works of Wilkes-Barre, Pennsylvania, supplied a number of type 0–6–2, class Vr5 engines for shunting purposes. Also in 1945, Vulcan furnished a type 0–6–0, class Vr4 tank locomotive that was later rebuilt to become class Vr5.

In 1946 Baldwin and the American Locomotive Company of Schenectady, New York, supplied a number of freight engines, type 2–10–0, Class Tr2.

Between 1936 and 1957, freight service was enhanced by the addition of sixty-seven type 2–8–2, class Tr1 Mikado locomotives (nos. 1050–1093) built by Tampereen Pellava- ja Rauta-Teoll. O.Y., Lokomo O.Y., and Arn. Jung, Lokomotivfabrik G.M.B.H., Jungenthal a.d. Sieg. This locomotive was especially reliable in the Finnish winter; while other engines gave out and were abandoned to the scrapyard, the class Tr1 engines seemed to run on forever. Two examples are shown.

In 1957 the Finnish State Railways acquired a number of class Hr1, type 4–6–2 passenger engines from Lokomo O.Y. Two views of locomotive no. 1020 are shown. Engines nos. 1020 and 1021 were the last two in regular service on the railways of Finland; they were withdrawn 22 May 1971.

The Finns have always maintained their railway locomotives and rolling stock in superb condition, as demonstrated in most of the high-quality photographs presented in this chapter.

The gradual demise of steam locomotion in Fin-

This picture shows a Finland State Railways switching engine (no. 792) of the Vr1 class. These engines were built by Tampereen Pellava of Tampere, Finland and by Hannoversche Maschinenbau A.G. of Hannover, Germany. Specifications were as follows:

Gauge	1524 millimeters (5 feet)
Wheel arrangement	0–6–0
Cylinders	430 by 550 millimeters
Coupled drive wheels	1270-millimeter diameter
Wheelbase	3400 millimeters
Boiler	
Tubes	45.6 square meters
Firebox	7.3 square meters
Total heating surface	52.9 square meters
Grate area	1.44 square meters
Superheater area	15.40 square meters
Boiler working pressure	12 kilograms per square centimeter (171 pounds per square inch)
Tractive force	8170 kilograms at 85 percent boiler working pressure
Operating weight	44.8 tons
Water capacity	4.5 cubic meters (1190 U.S. gallons)
Fuel capacity	2 tons
Introduction date	1927.

(Courtesy: Finland State Railways)

This is a photograph of a Finnish freight locomotive, class Tk3 (engine no. 895) which was constructed by Tampereen Pellava and by Lokomo O.Y. both of Tampere, Finland starting in 1930. Specifications were as follows:

Gauge	1524 millimeters (5 feet)
Wheel arrangement	2–8–0
Cylinders	460 by 630 millimeters
Engine wheels	
coupled drivers	1270-millimeter diameter
front truck	790-millimeter diameter
wheelbase coupled	4440 millimeters
wheelbase total	6980 millimeters
Boiler	
Tubes	76.2 square meters
Firebox	8.6 square meters
Total heating surface	84.8 square meters
Grate area	1.6 square meters
Superheater area	26.0 square meters
Boiler working pressure	14 kilograms per square centimeter (199.1 pounds per square inch)
Tractive force	12,490 kilograms at 85 percent boiler working pressure
Engine operating weight	51.8 tons
Weight on coupled wheels	42.8 tons
Tender	
Wheel diameter	960 millimeters
Wheelbase	2750 millimeters
Water capacity	9.5 cubic meters (2510 U.S. gallons)
Fuel capacity	4.5 tons
Operating weight	26.4 tons
Total operating weight	78.2 tons (engine plus tender)
Total wheelbase	12,660 millimeters (engine plus tender).

(Courtesy: Finland State Railways)

Pictured is a Finnish steam locomotive, type 0–6–2, class Vr2, used for switching service. The Manufacturer was Tampereen Pellava of Tampere, Finland, starting in 1931. Specifications were:

Gauge	1524 millimeters (5 feet)
Cylinders	450 by 600 millimeters
Wheels	
Coupled drivers	1270-millimeter diameter
Trailing truck	790-millimeter diameter
Wheelbase coupled	3100 millimeters
Wheelbase total	5000 millimeters
Boiler	
Tubes	58.2 square meters
Firebox	8.1 square meters
Total heating	66.3 square meters surface
Grate area	1.55 square meters
Superheater	22.6 square meter area
Boiler working pressure	12 kilograms per square centimeter (171 pounds per square inch)
Tractive force	9750 kilograms at 85 percent boiler working pressure
Operating weight	57.8 tons
Weight on coupled wheels	44.2 tons
Water capacity	5.5 cubic meters (1450 U.S. gallons)
Fuel Capacity	2.5 tons.

(Courtesy: Finland State Railways)

Pictured is a Finnish tender locomotive used on passenger service. This was a type 4–6–0 machine classed as Hv4, introduced in 1932. Manufacturers were Tampereen Pellava and Lokomo O.Y. of Tampere, Finland. Specifications follow:

Gauge	1524 millimeters (5 feet)
Cylinders	450 by 610 millimeters
Engine wheels	
Coupled drivers	1575-millimeter diameter
Front truck	860-millimeter diameter
Wheelbase coupled	3810 millimeters
Wheelbase total	7122 millimeters
Boiler	
Tubes	87.90 square meters
Firebox	8.60 square meters
Total heating surface	96.5 square meters
Grate area	1.45 square meters
Superheater area	26.0 square meters
Boiler working pressure	12 kilograms per square centimeter (170 pounds per square inch)
Tractive force	8000 kilograms at 85 percent boiler working pressure
Engine operating weight	48.1 tons
Weight on coupled wheels	32.7 tons
Tender	
Wheel diameter	960 millimeters
Wheelbase	2750 millimeters
Water capacity	9 cubic meters (2380 U.S. gallons)
Fuel capacity	5 tons
Operating weight	25.5 tons
Total wheelbase	12,204 millimeters (engine plus tender)
Total operating weight	73.6 tons.

(Courtesy: Finland State Railways)

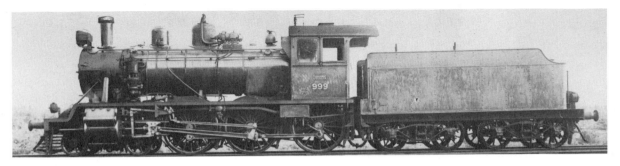

Pictured is a Finnish steam locomotive (no. 999) used on passenger service. This type 4–6–0, class Hv3, engine was introduced starting in 1939 by three different manufacturers as follows:

Berliner Maschineanbau A.G.
Tampereen Pellava
Lokomo O.Y.

Specifications were as follows:

Gauge	1524 millimeters (5 feet)
Cylinders	510 by 600 millimeters
Engine wheels	
Coupled drivers	1750-millimeter diameter
Front truck	860-millimeter diameter
Wheelbase coupled	4000 millimeters
Wheelbase total	7600 millimeters
Boiler	
Tubes	97.6 square meters
Firebox	10.4 square meters
Total heating surface	108.0 square meters
Grate area	1.96 square meters
Superheater	30.7 square meter area
Boiler working pressure	13 kilograms per square centimeter (185 pounds per square inch)
Tractive force	9850 kilograms at 85 percent boiler working pressure
Engine operating weight	57 tons
Weight on coupled wheels	38.4 tons
Tender	
Wheel diameter	1050 millimeters
Water capacity	19 cubic meters (5020 U.S. gallons)
Wheelcase	5100 millimeters
Fuel capacity	6 tons
Operating weight	44.1 tons
Total wheelbase	14,940 millimeters (engine plus tender)
Total operating weight	101.1 tons (engine plus tender).

(Courtesy: Finland State Railways)

Pictured is engine no. 1404 used for various types of service on the Finland State Railways. This was a type 0–6–0 locomotive, class Vr4, which was subsequently rebuilt to become class Vr5. These machines were supplied by the Vulcan Iron Works of Wilkes-Barre Pennsylvania, U.S.A. in 1945. Specifications were:

Gauge	1524 millimeters (5 feet)
Cylinders	457 by 609 millimeters
Wheels	
Coupled drivers	1118-millimeter diameter
Coupled wheelbase	2820 millimeters
Boiler	
Tubes	84.8 square meters
Firebox	9.2 square meters
Total heating surface	99.0 square meters
Grate area	2.79 square meters
Boiler working pressure	13.4 kilogram per square centimeters (190 pounds per square inch)
Tractice force	9900 kilograms at 65 percent boiler working pressure
Operating weight	65,770 kilograms
Water capacity	9828 liters (2600 U.S. gallons)
Fuel capacity	2720 kilograms (6000 pounds).

(Courtesy: Finland State Railways)

Engine no. 1415, type 0–6–2, class Vr5, was used for shunting purposes on the Finland Railways. These engines were supplied by Vulcan Iron Works of Wilkes-Barre, Pennsylvania, U.S.A. in 1945. The Vr5 machines were rebuilt from class Vr4 types (see illustration elsewhere). Specifications were as follows:

Gauge	1524 millimeters (5 feet)
Cylinders	457 by 609 millimeters
Wheels	
Coupled drivers	1118-millimeter diameter
Trailing truck	790-millimeter diameter
Wheelbase coupled	2820 millimeters
Total wheelbase	5420 millimeters
Boiler	
Tubes	65.8 square meters
Firebox	9.5 square meters
Total heating surface	75.3 square meters
Grate area	2.8 square meters
Superheater area	16.7 square meters
Boiler working pressure	13 kilograms per square centimeter (185 pounds per square inch)
Tractive force	12,570 kilograms at 85 percent boiler working pressure
Operating weight	63 tons
Weight on coupled wheels	48.7 tons
Water capacity	6 cubic meters (1590 U.S. gallons)
Fuel capacity	2.8 tons.

(Courtesy: Finland State Railways)

Pictured is a tender engine, no. 1307, a freight locomotive widely used on the Finland State Railway system. This machine had a 2–10–0 wheel arrangement and was classified Tr2. These locomotives were supplied by the Baldwin Locomotive Works and the American Locomotive Company starting in 1946. Specifications were as follows:

Gauge	1524 millimeters (5 feet)
Cylinders	635 by 711 millimeters
Engine wheels	
Coupled drivers	1320-millimeter diameter
Front truck	838-millimeter diameter
Coupled wheel base	5689 millimeters
Total wheel base	8484 millimeters
Boiler	
Tubes	185.8 square meters
Firebox	43.4 square meters
Total heating surface	229.2 square meters
Grate area	6.0 square meters
Superheater	63.6 square meter surface
Boiler working pressure	12.65 kilograms per square centimeter (180 pounds per square inch)
Tractive force	23,250 kilograms at 85 percent boiler working pressure
Engine operating weight	98.5 tons
Weight on coupled drivers	86.9 tons
Tender	
Wheel diameter	914 millimeters
Water capacity	28 cubic centimeters (7400 U.S. gallons)
Fuel capacity	13 tons
Operating weight	67.7 tons
Total operating weight	166.2 tons (engine plus tender).

(Courtesy: Finland State Railways)

The attached two photographs show two different class Tr1 freight locomotives: nos. 1050 and 1093. These engines had a 2–8–2 wheel arrangement; manufacturer and dates were not listed. Specifications were as follows:

Gauge	1524 millimeters (5 feet)
Cylinders	610 by 700 millimeters
Engine wheels	
Coupled drivers	1600-millimeter diameter
Front truck	960-millimeter diameter
Trailing truck	1120-millimeter diameter
Boiler	
Tubes	181.6 square meters
Firebox	13.8 square meters
Total heating surface	195.4 square meters
Grate area	3.54 square meters
Superheater	68.00 square meter area
Boiler working pressure	15 kilograms per square centimeter (213 pounds per square inch)
Tractive force	15,870 kilograms at 65 percent boiler working pressure
Engine operating weight	95 tons
Weight on coupled wheels	68 tons
Tender	
Wheel diameter	960 millimeters
Wheel base	5150 millimeters
Water capacity	27 cubic meters (7130 U.S. gallons)
Fuel capacity	9 tons
Operating weight	62 tons
Total operating weight	157 tons (engine plus tender).

(Courtesy: Finland State Railways)

land was readily apparent from the following figures for Finnish State Railways:

Year	Steam locomotives in use
1965	514
1970	262
1975	250
1978	0

The 1970s thus brought on the complete abandonment of steam traction. At the same time, a decision was made to curtail the expanding use of diesel locomotion in favor of electric traction. At the end of 1978, Finnish railways had in active service 267 diesel locomotives and 62 electric locomotives for long-haul traffic, as well as 126 diesel-operated shunting engines. They estimated that by 1985 electric traction would constitute 40 percent of the total tractive effort in Finland.

Another decision of great import, made by the

These two photographs show a passenger type locomotive, class Hr1, used widely in Finland after 1957. These 4–6–2 engines (no. 1020) were built by Lokomo O.Y. of Tampere, Finland. Specifications were:

Gauge	1524 millimeters (5 feet)
Cylinders	590 by 650 millimeters
Engine wheels	
Coupled drivers	1900-millimeter diameter
Front truck	860-millimeter diameter
Trailing truck	1120-millimeter diameter
Boiler	
Tubes	181.6 square meters
Firebox	13.8 square meters
Total heating surface	195.4 square meters
Fire grate area	3.54 square meters
Superheater area	68.00 square meters
Boiler working pressure	15 kilograms per square centimeter (213 pounds per square inch)
Tractive force	11,610 kilograms at 65 percent boiler working pressure
Engine operating weight	93 tons
Weight on coupled wheels	51 tons
Tender	
Wheel diameter	960 millimeters
Wheel base	5150 millimeters
Water capacity	27 cubic meters (7130 U.S. gallons)
Fuel capacity	9 tons
Operating weight	62 tons
Total operating weight	155 tons (engine plus tender).

(Courtesy: Finland State Railways)

Finnish military, was to retain 250 old steam locomotives in long-term storage for any future contingencies. To this end, in 1971 a program was initiated to strip the selected engines of moving elements, coat the residual engine machinery with a Cosmolene preservative, and store them in army depots. The following locomotives were selected for the storage plan:

Quantity	Class	Type
All	Vr3	0–10–OT
All	Hr1	4–6–2
All	Tr1	2–8–2
98	Tk3 and Tv1	2–8–0
14	Hv2	4–6–0
16	Vr2 and Vr1	0–6–OT
28	Vr4	0–6–OT

FRANCE

ON 7 JUNE 1826, A GOVERNMENT CONCESSION was granted for the construction of the twenty-eight-mile Saint Étienne–Lyon Railway; a small section of about eight miles, from Givors to Rive to Rive-de-Gier, was opened on 25 June 1830. On this new line, Marc Seguin, engineer and inventor, tried out the first French locomotive on 7 November 1829. The balance of the railroad opened from Lyon to Givors on 3 April 1832, and from Rive-de-Gier to Saint Étienne for freight on 18 October 1832 and for passengers on 25 February 1833.

France's first public railway opened in 1837. Named the Paris & Saint Germain Railway, it joined Paris with Pecq. Two competing railway lines were opened in 1839–40, running from Paris southwest about eight miles to Versailles. Other local lines followed, and one international trunk line from Strasbourg south to Basel, Switzerland, commenced operations in 1841. Originally railroad construction was assigned to private firms by a system of concessions, but later the state invested half the capital and also provided land, roadbeds, and bridges. In subsequent years, the government embarked on a type of cost-plus arrangement. Considerable competition arose between private firms, which was good for railway development, but the general construction suffered from a serious weakness in France's banking structure. Before 1848, of one billion francs invested in railways, only 40 percent of the building costs involved French financing; the balance came mainly from England. Nevertheless, by 1870 most major rail routes in France were laid out, and by 1880 additional seconary lines were being projected to all but the most remote sections of the country.

French laws very early stipulated that railways were to be owned by the state government, but private companies could participate through formal lease arrangements. Trunk routes were also specified by the state and these later became the main rail arteries. Subsequent concessions were as follows: Paris–Orléans Railway in 1843; Paris–Rouen line in May 1843; the Eastern Railway and the Northern Railway, both headquartered in Paris, opened in 1845; the cross-country Midi Railway system, from Bordeaux to Sète on the Mediterranean coast, organized in 1852; the Western Railway, founded in 1853. The well-known Paris, Lyon, & Mediterranean Railway (PLM) was formed in 1857 by merging a number of small rail lines.

In the mid-nineteenth century, railway expansion in France was relatively slow compared with developments in Britain, the United States, and Germany. By 1850 France's total rail length was 1,927 miles, compared to 9,092 miles in Britain, 6,658 in the United States, and 3,777 in Germany. As in many other parts of the world, rail construction in France was hampered by inadequate capital, lack of skilled workers, and little or no engineering know-how. Most early rail lines were built using British money, technology, and contractors. A good example was the eighty-two-mile Paris–Rouen Railway, which in the 1840s was three-quarters British-financed and was worked by five thousand navvies plus about five thousand laborers from other countries. The job was especially difficult, requiring four bridges across the Seine River and four tunnels in troublesome terrain. The same British contractors, Brassey & MacKenzie,

Pictured is Thomas Brassey (1805–70) the famous English railway contractor who built about seventy-five percent of the early French rail system. He also was personally involved in rail construction projects in Britain, Canada, Argentina, India, and other locations such as the Crimea.
(Courtesy: British Museum)

built the fifty-eight-mile rail extension from Rouen to Le Havre, starting construction in 1843; this route was complicated by difficult bridges and tunnels and by the famous ill-fated Barentin viaduct with its twenty-seven arches about one hundred feet above the ground. Brassey contracts were also responsible for the Amiens–Boulogne rail line in 1844 and the Rouen–Dieppe railroad in 1847. See illustration.

From 1848 to 1890 railways in France grew at a rate of about 475 miles per year. As early as 1850 an amalgamation of the seven largest private lines had taken place, and in 1878 the state government took over various other private lines in western France, which were then in serious financial straits. By 1890 the country had a total of about twenty-five thousand miles of active railroads. See illustration.

Early rivalry and suspicion about political intentions between various European nations had a harmful influence on international travel. Nevertheless, France soon had connections with Belgium through the Belgian State Railway system, and Strasbourg was linked with Basle, Switzerland, as previously stated.

In August 1857, mainly due to Italian initiatives and capital, construction commenced on the first Alpine tunnel at Mont Cenis. This 7.79-mile tun-

Shown is a model of a Fell center-rail cogwheel locomotive similar to that used on the temporary narrow-gauge railroad across Mont Cenis pass in 1870–72 while the Mont Cenis (Frejus) tunnel connecting France and Italy was being constructed.
(Courtesy: Science Museum, London)

Pictured is the north entrance to the eight mile plus 555 yard Mont Cenis tunnel which was opened on 17 September 1871; this provided a direct connection between Paris, France, and Turin, Italy.
(*Courtesy:* La Vie du Rail, *Paris*)

This illustration shows a sketch of the first train to use the new Mont Cenis (Frejus) tunnel which opened on 17 September 1871 connecting France and Italy by rail.
(*Courtesy:* Illustrated London News)

This is a contemporary engraving showing the inaugural train through the Frejus (Mont Cenis) tunnel, between France and Italy, which opened on 17 September 1871. An alignment tunnel is shown at the left. (*Courtesy:* Illustrated London News)

nel, also known as the Frejus tunnel, was located at latitude 45°08′ north, longitude 6°43′ east, and connected Modane, France, with Bordonecchia, Italy. When it was finished on 17 September 1871, it opened a direct connection between Paris and Turin, Italy. Prior to the commencement of traffic on this "under the mountain route," a temporary narrow-gauge rail line operated over the mountain pass for approximately two years. This interim system worked on the Fell principle, with a center rail interlocking with special cog wheels on the locomotive, affording positive traction when climbing and descending the steep 1 in 12.5 gradient. The trains over Col du Mont-Cenis started at St. Michel du Maurienne, France, at 2,330 feet above sea level, climbed to 6,860 feet at the top of the pass, and then descended to 1,625 feet at Susa, Italy; the trip of 48.5 miles took six hours. See illustration of a model of a steam locomotive similar to that which pulled trains over the Mont-Cenis pass in the from approximately 1870 to 1872.

In 1872 France was additionally linked with Italy at Ventimiglia by a Mediterranean route through Nice and Monte Carlo.

Many famous trains originated their international journeys from Paris. The Orient Express made its first traffic run on 5 June 1883. The illustrious Blue Train commenced service during December 1883, providing transportation from Calais through Paris to Nice and Rome. The Sud Express connected Lisbon and Madrid with Paris and Calais starting on 4 November 1887. In 1888 a new Rome Express service was initiated from Calais and Paris using the Mont-Cenis tunnel. A special, fast Paris–London service via the new Calais–Dover ferry was opened in 1889. In 1898 a Saint Petersburg–Vienna–Nice–Cannes Express was introduced on a route to the French Riviera. With the opening of the Simplon tunnel in 1906, connecting Switzerland and Italy, the French initiated the Simplon Express, which ran from Paris to Lausanne, Brig, Simplon, Milan, and later to Venice.

The busy London-Paris railroad traffic and the desire for more powerful, speedier locomotives was responsible, early in the 1890s, for the development of the famous four-cylinder compound

The monastery and seaside at Le Mont Saint Michel, on the Golfe de Saint Malo on the Normandy coast, have long been a holiday and tourist attraction for the French. Shown is a train arriving at the Saint Michel station in 1890.
(Courtesy: SNCF, Roger Viollet) L9T26

This is a photograph of Gaston du Bousquet (1840–1910), the eminent French locomotive engineer who held the position of Chief Engineer of the Northern Railway of France from 1890 to 1910. As an associate of de Glehn, he coordinated the early design and use of the latter's four-cylinder compound locomotives on the Northern Railway. Bousquet's major contributions were a successful class of 4–6–0 tender compound tank engines in 1901 for the Ceinturi Railway of Paris. He also introduced the Du Bousquet-Mallet tank engines of 0–6–2 plus 2–6–0 type for French freight traffic service.
(Courtesy: La Vie du Rail, *Paris)*

Shown is a photograph of Alfred de Glehn (1848–1936), an Englishman of German origin, who grew up in France where the name was changed from von Glehn to de Glehn. His engineering training led in 1886 to the design and construction of the first four-cylinder compound steam locomotive for the Northern Railway of France. The design had two high-pressure cylinders placed outside activating the rear drive wheels by outside cranks; also there were two low-pressure cylinders placed inside driving the first crank-axle. The drive wheels operated independently. These engine types later found wide use in France and were adapted to an assortment of locomotives in many other countries.
(Courtesy: La Vie du Rail, *Paris)*

This is a picture of the Garabit viaduct on the Béziers–
Neussargnes rail line in southwest France. The bridge
was built in 1884 by the famous builder Gustav Eiffel.
The structure is 1755 feet long, 400 feet high, and the
main arch has a 541-foot span.
(Courtesy: SNCF French Railways, Ltd.) L13N013

The following three illustrations picture the Swiss-
built Mallet type 0–6–6–0, fifty-three-ton tank locomotives used mostly with freight traffic on various
French narrow-gauge lines, principally on the
Vivarais system in the mountains of Ardeche.

This shows engine no. 403 on a meter-gauge turntable
at Tournon in September 1968.

Pictured is no. 403 Mallet locomotive on the scenic
Vivarais meter system, now a tourist railway, with a
British holiday group near Raucoules-Brosettes in
September 1968.

This is a photo of Mallet locomotive no. 41 on the
Reseau–Breton rail system at Carhaix in the middle of
the Cape Breton peninsula.
*(All three photographs courtesy: New English Library,
London)*

A Mallet type 0–6–6–0 locomotive used on the narrow-gauge railways of France is pictured. This model
engine is preserved in the Musée des Techniques, Paris.
(Courtesy: Musée des Techniques, Paris) 14.524

locomotives by Alfred de Glehn, an English engineer who had taken up residence in France, and by Gaston du Bousquet, Chief Engineer of the Northern Railway of France (see illustrations). By 1900 the northern French railways had the fastest trains in the world, using the steam compounding principle, providing passenger service from Calais to Paris, averaging fifty-six miles per hour on twenty different daily trains. A great number of the French-built de Glehn and du Bousquet engines were widely copied and utilized in many other countries.

In addition to the highly coordinated and sophisticated standard-gauge trunk line of France, operated by Société Nationale des Chemins de Fer Français, approximately thirteen thousand miles of secondary railroads were constructed between 1874 and 1914 (see illustration). These were mostly meter-gauge, rural freight systems with occasional standard-gauge or 2-foot-gauge tracks. Some additional narrow-gauge lines, scheduled for construction after 1914, were delayed by World War I actions. After the war some new narrow-gauge rail lines were added as late as 1925, after which abandonments began. Closures reached a high rate in the 1930s. During World War II, the occupying German forces reopened various narrow-gauge railways that had not been dismantled. By 1947, only seven thousand miles of such railways survived. Since then, of course, diesel and electric engines have appeared on some of these lines, but in general, by 1973 most secondary narrow-gauge railways had disappeared and the balance seemed destined for extinction.

The worst rail disaster in France, a derailment near Modane, occurred on 12 December 1917, killing 543 people; this has been recorded as the most serious railway accident in the world.

The Somport Tunnel, the longest in France at 4.89 miles, connecting Spain and France, was

The Somport tunnel which connects France and Spain is pictured here. This has a length of four miles plus 1572 yards. The tunnel was opened on 18 July 1928 and was used by the French National Railways (SNCF).
(*Courtesy:* La Vie du Rail, *Paris*)

Railway map of France.
(*Courtesy:* Janes World Railways)

opened on 18 July 1928 (latitude 42°47′ north, longitude 0°31′). See illustration.

The French Société Nationale des Chemins de Fer Français (SNCF) was formed on 31 August 1937. In December 1968 it operated 23,238 miles of standard-gauge track, of which 5,474 miles were electrified.

The last steam locomotives in France were the American class 141R, type 2–8–2 engines, a fine, rugged, and modern design by Baldwin. Imported after World War II to help rehabilitate the French railways, these were used on freight and passenger service.

A world rail-speed record of 235 miles per hour was achieved in France on 4 December 1967, between Gometz-le-Chatel and Limours by L'Aerotrain, powered by jet aero-engines. This record was broken on 28 February 1981, when a French train on a special test track attained a speed of 237 miles per hour.

The last steam train in France was a Pacific-type locomotive heading a procession of cars between

A model of Cugnot's famous steam carriage which is preserved in the Musée des Techniques in Paris is shown here. The French engineer Nicolas Cugnot in 1769 built a self-propelled steam vehicle which operated on regular roads and streets. It had a tiny boiler which supplied high pressure steam to two small cylinders whose pistons alternately applied power to a single front wheel drive. His original objective was to find a mechanical means of towing heavy artillery for the French army. Cugnot's machine travelled about two to four miles per hour and had to stop every ten or fifteen minutes to build a new fire to renew the steam pressure. Characteristics were as follows:

Cylinders	325 by 378 millimeters
Drive wheel diameter	1.30 meters
Total length	7.25 meters
Total weight	4–5 tons.

(Courtesy: Musée des Techniques, Paris)

This is a lithograph of the famous engineer and scientist Marc Seguin (1786–1875), who constructed the first steam locomotive in France which was tried out on the Saint-Etienne-Lyon Railway on 7 November 1829. This engine was the first to use a multi-tube boiler of Seguin's design. He also incorporated a draft of air from two rotary fans, driven from the tender wheels, through the firebox. The engine operating weight was 6 tons, and it could haul a 30-ton load at 4.5 miles per hour on a grade of 1 in 167.
(Courtesy: La Vie du Rail, Paris)

Calais and Amiens on 26 May 1971.

In 1978 the French National Railways had 34,717 kilometers (21,572 miles) of 1.437-meter gauge track. See map.

Steam Locomotives in France

The first steam locomotive used in France was built by Nicolas Cugnot in 1769, designed for use on streets and roads. See illustration for a discussion and details.

With the opening of the eight-mile rail line from Givors to Rive-de-Gier, Marc Seguin was able to try out his first steam locomotive on 7 November 1829. See lithographic pictures of Seguin and his engine.

Pictured is a reproduction of the first steam locomotive manufactured in France by the engineer Marc Seguin in 1829. This model is preserved in the Musée des Techniques in Paris. As can be seen, the tubular boiler was placed on top of the firebox which had an equal length. The hot gases went back and forth in the boiler, discharging finally through a smokestack at the rear of the locomotive. Note the vertical cylinder; there were two, one on each side. Some characteristics were as follows:

Drive wheels	1.15-meter diameter
Steam pressure	4 kilograms per square centimeter
Engine weight	4.5 tons
Water capacity of tender	1 cubic meter.

(Courtesy: Musée des Techniques, Paris)

Shown is a sketch of the standard 2–4–0 Stephenson locomotive which was produced for export in 1837 in Newcastle, England. Some of these engines were shipped to France where they were used on two competing Paris to Versailles rail lines and on the Paris–Saint Germain Railway. These type 2–4–0 engines had smaller leading wheels, compared with earlier models, permitting an easier placement of the cylinders. However, the larger length of the outside cranks was not considered a plus feature. The cylinders had an eighteen-inch stroke, the outside cranks were fourteen inches long, and the inside cranks on the driving axle were nine inches long.

(Courtesy: O. S. Nock, The Dawn of World Railways 1800–1850)

This picture is of a preserved Stephenson so-called "Patentee" locomotive, type 2–2–2, which was built during the period 1833–50. This had many improved features over the earlier "Rocket" model including less vibration of the internal machinery and smoother operations while travelling on the iron tracks.
(Courtesy: Science Museum, London)

MACHINE LOCOMOTIVE DE STEPHENSON.

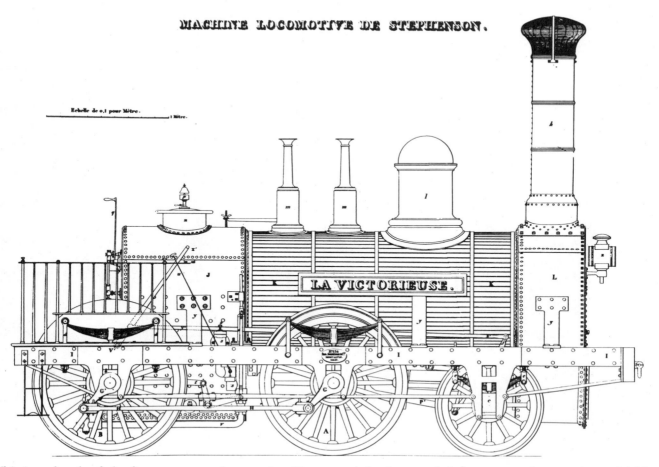

This is a sketch of the famous patent locomotive "La Victorieuse," one of the most notable engines of its day, which was supplied to France by Robert Stephenson in 1837. This machine had the least common wheel arrangement in which the trailing wheels were coupled to the driving wheels. Also in dimensions and capacity it exceeded the average locomotive available at the time. The cylinders were fifteen inches in diameter with an eighteen-inch stroke. Total heating surface was about 595 square feet with a grate area of 11¼ square feet. Operating weight was thirteen tons. *(Courtesy: Science Museum, London)* 1743

A reproduction of the old-time Buddicom type 2–2–2 engine built in France in 1843 and run on the Paris–Rouen rail line. This locomotive, no. 33, was named "Saint Pierre."
(Courtesy: SNCF, CAV) 5920-2

Pictured is an early Buddicom locomotive, type 2–2–2, used on the Paris–Rouen railways. This was named "Pierrot." No other data was available.
(Courtesy: SNCF, CAV) 8617-12

Some early English locomotives, as previously indicated, had bad swaying tendencies at higher speeds. This problem was studied in England by a Scots engineer, Alexander Allan, who was able to make substantial improvements. About the mid-1840s, W. B. Buddicom, an official of the Grand Junction Railway, took up employment in France were he instituted some of Allan's ideas. He designed a type 2–2–2 tank engine, then known as a Buddicom, which found wide application on the Western Railway of France. The design incorporated the outside cylinders into a heavy double framework. Shown is a sketch of a Buddicom 2–2–2 tank locomotive, about 1845.
(*Courtesy: O. S. Nock*, The Dawn of the World Railways 1800–1850)

FRANCE

Another 2–2–2 passenger locomotive which was used on the Northern Railway of France is pictured. This engine, built by Koechlin in 1846, had cylinders 14 by 22 inches, drive wheels 5 feet 8 inches in diameter.
(*Courtesy: O. S. Nock*, The Dawn of World Railways, 1800–1850)

In 1837 the newly constructed Paris to St. Germain Railway and two competing Paris to Versailles lines, which opened 1839–40, used locomotives built by Stephenson of Newcastle, England.

In the mid-1840s Joseph Locke of the Stephenson organization came to France to work on the Paris–He Havre rail line, bringing with him one of the Crewe-type, outside-cylinder, 2–2–2 locomotives designed by Alexander Allan. These were copied extensively in France, where they were subsequently designated as Buddicoms, and utilized on the Paris–Rouen line, which opened during May 1843. A sketch of another Buddicom locomotive, a 2–2–2 tank machine, is shown. The latter engine was used on the Western Railway of France starting about 1845.

In 1845 the Northern Railway of France opened its rail line, with headquarters in Paris. This first operated with a tender-type locomotive built by Koechlin in 1846. The Northern Railway also used several Stephenson long-boilered tender engines, type 2–2–2, in the mid-1840s. Similar locomotives

Early steam locomotives used in France on the Northern Railway were Stephenson Long-boilered 2–2–2 types; see illustration. The design for this Stephenson machine was patented in 1841. It was claimed that the long boiler was more fuel-efficient and its greater length helped to diminish sparks from the firebox escaping to the outside. Operating efficiencies were realized, but the long overhang at both ends of the engine, which had a small wheelbase, promoted a dangerous swaying action at higher speeds with a high incidence of derailments. Nevertheless, these engines met with early success in France, and when the Avignon–Marseilles Railway was opened, many were built, under license from Stephenson, by L. Benet at La Ciotat, located on the Mediterranean coast between Toulon and Marseilles.

(*Courtesy: O. S. Nock,* The Dawn of World Railways 1800–1850)

A type 2–4–0 locomotive built by Kitson for the Orleans & Bordeaux Railway is pictured. This machine, of which five were eventually delivered starting in 1846, was similar to an engine built for Leeds & Thirsk with the following characteristics:

Cylinders	14 by 22 inches
Drive wheels	5-foot 6-inch diameter
Bogie wheels	3-foot 6-inch diameter
Boiler barrel	
Diameter	3 feet 8 inches
Length	7 feet 6 inches
Grate area	11.66 square feet
Tubes	145 1¾-inch outer diameter, area 609 square feet
Fire box	
Width	3 feet 4½ inches
Length	2 feet 7 inches
Area	68 square feet
Total heating surface	677 square feet
Overall length (engine)	20 feet 2 inches.

(*Courtesy: Science Museum, London*) 72/54

Shown is a fine photograph of a reproduction of Alfred Hallette's 2–2–2 steam locomotive, engine no. 5, built at Arras, France in 1847 for use on the French railways. This engine was named "Sezanne." *(Courtesy: SNCF, CAV)*

Pictured is the preserved Crampton locomotive named "Le Continent" which was built in 1852 for service on the Paris–Strasbourg rail line. This engine had strong outside frames, the cylinders were supported between these and the inside frames, together with the driving and valve machinery. "Le Continent" of the Eastern Railway of France was built by Derosne, Cail & Company of Paris, which had first taken up the design with an order of twelve engines for the French Northern Railway in 1848–49. As a light express locomotive, this French Crampton was a fast runner. Though rough, with their low centers of gravity and relatively long wheelbase, these engines were steady runners and were widely used in France and Germany. These machines had huge driving wheels at the rear. The cylinders, connecting rods, and valve gear were outside with the platforms raised to make the machinery accessible. See other illustrations. *(Courtesy: SNCF, CAV)*

Shown is a freak type 2–4–0 French locomotive, named "L'Aigle," designed for high speed and therefore had extra large driving wheels. This engine was built at the Govin Works in Paris and was displayed at the Paris Exhibition of 1855. The locomotive was subsequently used only briefly on the Western Railway of France where it demonstrated a very poor efficiency. Specifications were:

Cylinders	Stroke 31.5 inches (normal 20 to 24 inches)
Driving wheels	9-foot 4-inch diameter
Boiler	Very complicated and placed beneath driving axles.

(Courtesy: O. S. Nock, The Dawn of World Railways 1800–1850)

Early T. R. Crampton-designed locomotives found wide use on the Eastern, Paris–Strasbourg, Northern, and PLM railways of France. The double-framed prototype, a model of which is pictured is displayed in the London Science Museum and had the following characteristics:

Cylinders	15.75 by 22 inches
Drive wheels	6-foot 10.6-inch diameter
Lead wheels	4-foot 3-inch diameter
Middle wheels	4-foot 3-inch diameter
Boiler	
Length	12 feet
Diameter	4 feet
Grate area	15.4 square feet
Heating surface	1149 square feet
Engine weight	27 tons
Overall length	45 feet including tender
Manufacturer:	Derosne et Cail, Paris, 1849.

(Courtesy: Science Museum, London)

were built by L. Benet at the La Ciotat Works, located on the Mediterranean coast between Toulon and Marseilles.

In 1846 five type 2–4–0 Kitson locomotives were delivered for use on the Orleans & Bordeaux Railway.

Thomas Russell Crampton (1816–85), an Englishman, ranks as one of the world's outstanding pioneer locomotive engineers. He is best known for his famous design for a locomotive with an oversize low boiler and a pair of extra-large driving wheels behind the firebox. Early Crampton engines tried out in England were without special distinction. The largest number of Crampton engines were used in France, starting on the Northern Railway in 1848–49. These were built by Derosene, Cail et Cie of Paris. Subsequently many others were constructed in France and Germany. Crampton locomotives were a great success for thirty years, working the fastest passenger trains between Paris and Strasbourg. One of the French Cramptons, named "Le Continent," built in 1852, is on display at the Musée des Techniques in Paris, where it is used occasionally for special purposes.

A sketch of another Thomas Russell Crampton locomotive is shown in this illustration. This engine was extensively utilized on the Paris, Lyon, Mediterranean Railway in the period around 1855. At that time it was reported that a special Imperial Train, from Marseilles to Paris, had attained an average speed of sixty-two miles per hour. Specifications are listed in an earlier illustration.
(*Courtesy: O. S. Nock,* The Dawn of World Railways 1800–1850)

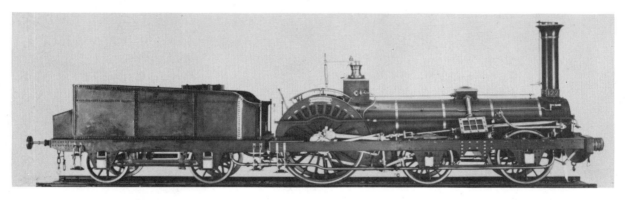

This represents an express passenger engine of the type designed and patented by Mr. Crampton in 1842–47, and built by Derosne et Cail, Paris, for the Northern Railway of France, in 1849. The arrangement shown was adopted in order to keep the center of gravity low, and at the same time to use large single driving wheels, which were placed behind the firebox.

The engine was carried on six wheels and had outside cylinders 15.75 inches in diameter by a 22-inch stroke; the driving wheels were 82.6 inches in diameter, and the tractive factor was 66. The valve chests were on the tops of the cylinders, inclined outward, and the valves were driven by eccentrics, mounted on return cranks, through Howe's link motion, so that the whole of the mechanism was easily accessible. The frames were double and tied together by transverse stays, the cylinders being bolted between the plates of each frame. The two leading axles had outside bearings, and the driving axle inside bearings only, the load being suspended by laminated springs placed above them.

The boiler barrel was 4 feet in diameter and 11.92 feet long, its center being only 4.72 feet above the rails. It contained 173 tubes of 2-inch diameter and 4 tubes of 1.75-inch diameter, these having a heating surface of 1070 square feet; the firebox had a heating surface of 79 square feet; and a grate area of 15.4 square feet. The regulator was placed in a chamber on the barrel and external steam pipes led to the cylinders. Two spring-balance safety valves were provided. The smokebox was formed as an extension of the boiler barrel, and the two exhaust pipes were led to a blast nozzle, having an orifice whose area was adjustable by means of two hinged flaps.

The rigid wheel base was 15.94 feet; the front wheels were 51 inches in diameter, and the middle wheels 48 inches in diameter. The weight of the engine in working order was 27 tons, the leading and driving axles carrying 11.5 tons each. The tender was carried on four wheels 42.2 inches in diameter, with a wheel base of 8.2 feet; it had hand brakes on the wheels and a horseshoe shaped water tank. The overall length of engine and tender was 45 feet. Scale 3 : 20.
(*Courtesy: T. R. Crampton*)

Pictured is the model of a normal Crampton type (2–2)–2–0 locomotive (double framed) after it had undergone extensive changes. The original engine was constructed in 1857 by Cail et Cie of Paris and subsequently, named "Le Belgique," operated on the PLM Railway. In 1869 it was sold to the Chemin de Fer de l'Etat where, in 1889, it was radically rebuilt with a twin-drum Flaman experimental boiler. It was displayed at the Paris Exposition of 1889 and afterwards, on the PLM line, was alleged to have set a world record of 89.9 miles per hour. The engine was finally scrapped in 1919. Specifications on the modified engine were:

Cylinders	15.75 by 23.5 inches
Drive wheels	6-foot 11-inch diameter
Working pressure	162 pounds per square inch
Tractive force	11,100 pounds
Operating weight	41.75 tons.

(Courtesy: Musée des Techniques, Paris)

In 1855 the so-called Bourbonnaise, type 0–6–0, locomotives were first manufactured for the Paris, Lyon, Mediterranean (PLM) in their work shops at Paris and Oullins. By 1882 the records indicate that 1042 machines had been constructed by PLM and other French manufacturers, most without any design changes. Specifications were as follows:

Cylinders	18 by 25.2 inches outside
Coupled drive wheels	4-foot 3.5-inch diameter
Boiler	
Grate area	14.6 square feet
Heating surface	1249 square feet
Steam pressure	143 pounds per square inch
Operating weight	35 tons (engine plus 4-wheel tender).

Two models of the above engines are on display in the Musée des Techniques.

(Courtesy: Musée des Techniques, Paris) 12857

Pictured here is a model of another Bourbonnaise type tender locomotive which operated originally on the Eastern Railway of France in the period 1850–60. This had 1.3 meter drive wheels, a boiler working pressure of 7 kilograms per square centimeter, and a total weight (engine plus tender) of 34 tons.
(Courtesy: Musée des Techniques, Paris) ·13411

A type 4–2–0 tender locomotive built by Establissement Cail in 1867 for the Northern Railway of France is pictured here. No additional information was furnished by the French Railways.
(Courtesy: SNCF) 1987b

In 1855 a very unusual steam locomotive, designed and constructed at the Govin Works in Paris, was shown at the Paris Exhibition. This was an attempt to achieve high railway speeds with exceptionally large driving wheels. The engine subsequently proved inefficient on the Western Railway of France and was discarded.

In 1855 Bourbonnais locomotives, type 0–6–0, were first constructed for the Paris, Lyon, & Mediterranean Railway (PLM) in the railroad shops at Paris and Oullins. By 1882 it was reported that 1,042 such railway steam engines had been built by PLM and other French locomotive manufacturers.

French engineer Anatole Mallet developed the compounding principles of working steam in a cylinder and then using it again, at a reduced pressure, in another cylinder. He devised the first successful compound engine to contend with the heavy grades and continuous curves of the St. Gotthard line.

The Western Railway of France introduced various four-cylinder compound locomotives in 1901. These involved the de Glehn design, modified by du Bousquet, with the construction being performed at the Batignolles Works. Many of these engines were used on the Paris–Dieppe boat train run. A model on display in the Science Museum in London is shown.

Specifications on the above type 4–6–0 engines were as follows:

Cylinders	
Hi pressure	14.75 by 25.6 inches
Lo pressure	21.6 by 25.6 inches
Coupled wheels	5-foot 6.4-inch diameter
Boiler	
Grate area	26.4 square feet
Heating surface	2.280 square feet
Working pressure	213.3 pounds per square inch
Operating weight	99 tons (engine plus tender)
Tender capacities	3300 gallons water; 5 tons coal.

(Courtesy: Science Museum, London) 27887

Shown is another example of a four-cylinder compound steam locomotive of de Glehn and du Bousquet design. This sectionalized model, in the Science Museum, London, was operated with compressed air to show all the working parts. See an earlier illustration for specifications.
(Courtesy: Science Museum, London)

Mallet locomotives for the St. Gotthard Railway had articulated connections between steam pipes and two sets of six-wheeled drive wheels in which the rear set was actuated by the high-pressure cylinders.

Alfred de Glehn collaborated with du Bousquet on a system of compound locomotives in which steam was used twice: initially it was directed into two high-pressure cylinders, usually driving the leading pair of coupled wheels, and then into two low-pressure cylinders that drove a rear pair of coupled wheels. These two engineers also developed a simple means of enhancing the engine tractive force by diverting controlled amounts of high-pressure steam into the low-pressure cylin-

ders. This kind of selective performance provided, when required, the extra power to surmount steeply graded sections of railroad. The de Glehn compound express engines, for example, were able to easily overcome the Calais–Paris gradients, thereby reducing running time from 4½ to 3½ hours before the end of the nineteenth century.

In 1899 Baldwin furnished France with its first American locomotives ever. These were express engines with a 4–4–0 wheel arrangement ordered by the State Railways. About half of the eleven-unit order were compound types and the balance two-cylinder simple types. Shown is the engine and descriptive data.

In 1909 Fives Lille manufactured a number of

One of du Bousquet's type 4–6–4 compound steam locomotives in 1911 which were widely used in the Northern Railway of France is shown here. *(Courtesy: SNCF)*

This is a picture of the first four-cylinder de Glehn compound locomotive used on the Northern Railway of France in 1886. The engine had two low-pressure cylinders inside and two high-pressure cylinders out-side. The drive wheels were not coupled. This engine, a 4–4–0 type, numbered 701, is preserved in France. *(Courtesy: SNCF, French Railways Ltd.)* L13N012

Pacific 4–6–2 locomotives for the Northern Railway of France.

From 1911 to 1917, the French built about 102 type 2–8–2 tank locomotives for use on the Eastern Railways of France. These were superheated types with specifications set forth in an illustration. Also in 1911, various Baltic locomotives were constructed for the Northern Railway of France.

In 1912 the Northern Railway started using four-cylinder de Glehn compound Pacific-type locomotives with superheaters, of which, initially, twenty were manufactured by Société Alsacienne de Belfort. In the late 1920s, those engines which had survived World War I were equipped with larger tenders, increasing the water and coal sup-ply, and we were used on three different express trains: to Brussels, to Lille, and to Calais—all originating in Paris.

With World War I underway in Europe, the hard-pressed French locomotive industry turned for help to outside sources for railway engines. In 1915 the North British Locomotive Company fur-nished about ninety four-cylinder compound locomotives, superheated, type 4–6–2, which were widely used on the French State Railways.

The demand for compound Pacific-type locomotives persisted after World War I, and in 1923 the Northern Railway of France started using still another series of type 4–6–2 Brévilles engines. These carried the prefix "Super-" to distinguish them from the Pacifics built during and before the war. The postwar Pacific engines were four-cylinder types still adhering largely to the early designs of de Glehn and du Bousquet, as shown in the illustration.

In 1940 Société Alsacienne started turning out the class U, type 4–6–4 locomotives for the Northern Railways of France.

A model of the first American railway steam engines to be brought into France is pictured. In 1899 Baldwin supplied eleven passenger type 4–4–0 engines on order by Chemin de Fer de l'Etat. These locomotives were identified as 2801–5 consisting of Vauclain compounds. A second series numbered 2851–56 were of the simple design. These engines operated initially with passenger trains on the Paris–Chartres–Thousars line, but were later downgraded to less-exacting services in Western France and in the Loire Valley. By 1932 all units had been relegated to the scrap heap. Specifications were as follows:

Cylinders
  Hi pressure   13 by 26 inches
  Lo pressure   22 by 26 inches
  Simple type   17.25 by 26 inches
Drivers   7 feet
Boiler
  Grate area   25.6 square feet
  Heating surface   1892.6 square feet
  Working pressure   215 pounds per square inch
  Boiler diameter   4 feet 10 inches
  Boiler length   12 feet 1 inch
Operating weight
  52 tons plus 13 hun-
    dredweights (engine)
  31 tons plus 3 hun-
    dredweights (adhesion).

(Courtesy: Musée des Techniques, Paris)

Pictured is a model of another example of the four-cylinder de Glehn, type 4–6–2 (Pacific) locomotive built between 1909 and 1914. These engines were designed by the Paris Orleans Railway and were constructed by Soc. Alsacienne de Constructions of Belfort. Specifications were:

Cylinders
  Hi pressure   16.5 by 25.6 inches
  Lo pressure   25.1 by 25.6 inches
Drivers   6-foot 4.75-inch diameter
Boiler
  Grate area   46.6 square feet
  Heating surface   2260.8 square feet
  Working pressure   235 pounds per square inch
Operating weight
  91 tons (engine only)
  52 tons adhesion.

(Courtesy: Musée des Techniques, Paris)

Shown is a type 4–6–2 Pacific tender locomotive built in 1909 (Fives Lille). This is Nord 231 E, no. 11. No other data was submitted by SNCF, CAV. *(Courtesy: SNCF, CAV) 19893-3*

In the period 1911–17 the French built 102 Mikado type 2–8–2 tank locomotives for use on the SNCF–Eastern Railways of France. These were equipped with Schmidt superheaters, Walschaert gear, Friedmann injectors, and carried the classification 141-TB. Pictured is a model housed in the Musée des Techniques at Paris. Specifications were as follows:

Locomotive no. 402

Cylinders	550 by 660 millimeters
Coupled drive wheels	1.570 meter
Boiler	
Grate area	2.4 square meters
Superheater area	37 square meters
Total heating surface	square meters
Working pressure	14 kilograms per square centimeter
Total weight	89 tons
Adhesion	59 tons
Water capacity	8 cubic meters
Coal capacity	3.5 tons.

(Courtesy: Musée des Techniques, Paris) 18164

The exposed interior of a type 4–6–4 Baltic class 232 locomotive, no. 31102, built for the Northern Railway of France in 1911 is shown here. No other details furnished by SNCF. *(Courtesy: SNCF, CAV) 9154-9*

In 1912 the Soc. Alsacienne de Constructions of Belfort constructed twenty type 4–6–2 locomotives for the Northern Railway of France. These were four-cylinder de Glehn compound Pacific engines carrying the identification numbers 3.1151 to 3.1170. In the period 1928–31 the same engines had special tenders attached in order to increase the water and coal capacities. In the latter period these railroad engines provided fast passenger service on runs between Paris and Brussels, Paris and Lille, and Paris and Calais. The first engine of this series is shown. Specifications were:

Cylinders
  Hi pressure   16⅜ by 26⅜ inches

Lo pressure	23⅝ by 26⅜ inches
Coupled wheels	6-foot 8.5-inch diameter
Boiler	
Grate area	33.9 square feet
Firebox	183 square feet
Superheater	521 square feet (Schmidt-Nord)
Total heating surface	1623 square feet
Boiler pressure	227 pounds per square inch
Operating weight	85 tons, 49.75 adhesion tons
Tender capacity	7709 gallons water; 9 tons coal
Tender bogie wheels	4-foot 1⅛-inch (new type) diameter.

(Courtesy Musée des Techniques, Paris) 8412-31

This is a model of a type 231 A compound locomotive, with a 4–6–2 wheel arrangement, constructed by Soc. Alsacienne de Constructions of Belfort in 1912. Specifications are the same as those given in an earlier illustration.
(Courtesy: Musée des Techniques, Paris)

Shown is the interior of a locomotive cab of a Northern Railway engine 231 A, no. 31151.
(Courtesy: SNCF, CAV) 8412-B6

During World War I, the French need for railroad locomotives and rolling stock reached massive proportions. To help provide essential war-time transportation requirements, the North British Locomotive Company built a large assortment of engines including about ninety Pacific type 4–6–2 superheated compound express machines. These followed the design of de Glehn-du Bosquet and were characterized as follows:

Cylinders
  Hi pressure   (outside) 16¹⁷/₃₂ by 25⁹/₁₆ inches
  These drove an intermediate
    pair of coupled wheels.
  Lo pressure   (inside) 25³/₁₆ by 25⁹/₁₆ inches
  These drove a leading pair of
    coupled wheels.
  Steam distribution was by
    piston valves for the out-
    side cylinders and flat bal-
    ance slide valves for the in-
    side cylinders. Walschaert
    gear on both.
Coupled drive wheels   6-foot 4.3-inch diameter
Boiler

Boiler plates	steel
Firebox plates	copper
Boiler tubes	steel
Westinghouse brake on en-
gine and tender	
Wheelbase (engine plus ten-
der)	64 feet 3⅜ inches
Grate area	45.9 square feet
Tubes	2105 square feet
Firebox	177 square feet
Superheater	683 square feet
Total heating surface	2965 square feet
Working pressure	227 pounds per square inch
Boiler diameter	5 feet 6⅛ inches (front ring)
Tractive effort	20,760 pounds at 50 percent
boiler working pressure
Operating weights	
Engine	95 tons
Tender	51 tons plus 13 hundredweights
Tender capacities	
Water	4840 gallons (British Imperial)
Coal	5.9 tons.

A model on display in the Musée des Techniques at Paris is shown in an earlier illustration.
(Courtesy: Museum of Transport, Glasgow)

The so-called Super-Pacifics of the French Northern Railway were first used in 1923. Up to 1931 fifty such locomotives were used in French service, nos. 3.1201–3.1250, especially on the Paris–Calais run where they had a high level of performance. In 1931 forty more engines were ordered from various builders, numbered 3.1251–3.1290. These were all four-cylinder compound locomotives following the design of de Glehn and du Bousquet.

Technical data on the above locomotives were as follows:

Cylinders
  Hi pressure   (inside) 17⅓ by 26 inches activating a leading pair of coupled wheels
  Lo pressure   (outside) 24.4 by 27.2 inches activating a middle pair of coupled wheels
Coupled wheels   6-foot 2.8-inch diameter
Valve gear   Walschaert
Firebox   Belpaire
Boiler
  Grate area   37.7 square feet
  Heating surface   1851 square feet including superheater
  Working pressure   227 pounds per square inch
Tractive effort
  As a compound   37,830 pounds
  As four-cylinder simple 50,771 pounds
Operating weight   175 tons (engine plus tender)
Tender capacities   9777 gallons (U.S.) water; 9 tons coal.

A model, in the possession of Mr. G. P. Keen, President of the Model Railway Club, is shown.

Pictured is a Mountain type, class 241, 4–8–2 locomotive used with heavy freight trains on the Eastern Railway of France starting in 1925.
(*Courtesy: SNCF, CAV*)

Shown is a type 4–6–4 class U locomotive built in 1940 by Societe Alsacienne for use on the French National Railways of northern France. This streamlined engine had fitted a mechanical stoker, piston valves, and Walschaert gear. See accompanying drawing.
(Courtesy: SNCF, CAV)

Pictured is a model of a class 141R, Mikado type 2–8–2, (Lima) mixed traffic locomotive used in various parts of France after World War II. About seven hundred units of this engine were constructed by American Locomotive Company, Baldwin Locomotive Works, and the Lima Locomotive Company in 1944 under contracts furnished by the then provisional French government. Specifications were:

Cylinders	23.5 by 28 inches
Drivers	5-foot 3-inch diameter
Boiler	
Grate area	55.5 square feet
Combustion chamber	231.0 square feet
Firebox syphons (2)	63 square feet
Superheater	704 square feet
Heating surface	2405 square feet
Working pressure	220 pounds per square inch
Tractive force	44,500 pounds at 85 percent pressure
Operating weight	186 tons (engine plus tender)
Tender capacities	8070 gallons water; 11.25 tons coal
Special fitting	Mechanical stoker.

(Courtesy: SNCF, CAV)

Shown is a photograph of the French class 141P, type 2–8–2 Mikado locomotive, built in 1944 by three American firms, widely used after World War II. See other illustrations for additional views and technical data.
(Courtesy: SNCF, CAV)

This is a photograph of the interior of an engineer's cab of a class 141P, type 2–8–2 Mikado mixed traffic locomotive used on the French railways after World War II.
(Courtesy: SNCF, CAV)

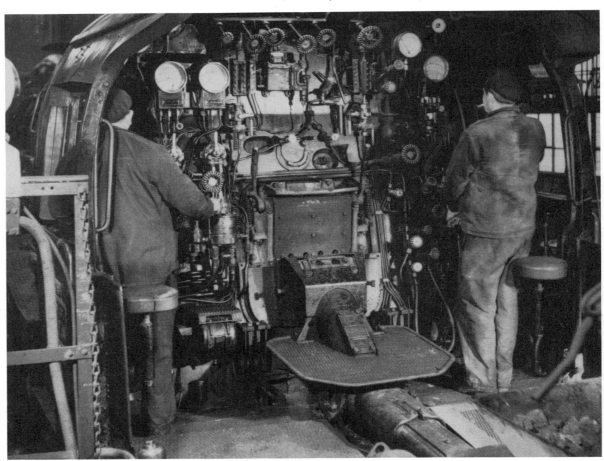

Following World War II, only about three thousand locomotives survived from seventeen thousand on active roster before the German occupation in 1940. Manufacturers in the United States and Canada from 1945 to 1947 supplied the railways of France with about thirteen hundred simple mixed-freight locomotives known as Liberation machines, class 141R. These were type 2–8–2 Mikados, which were very dependable and had relatively low maintenance requirements. By 1951, when these Liberation engines constituted only 15 percent of the active French locomotives, they still provided close to 50 percent of all tonnage traction and 35 percent of all train miles accumulated. Twenty years later, in 1971, all but 100 of the original French engines had disappeared, while about four hundred class 141Rs were still in service.

The last French passenger steam locomotives were class 241P, of which thirty-five were constructed between 1948 and 1952. These were four-cylinder compound engines with a 4–8–2 wheel arrangement; they were rigged to permit the selective admission of high pressure steam to all cylinders for maximum tractive effort on heavy grades or when moving loaded trains from a standstill. These express engines were eventually relegated to hauling freight trains.

By 1972 all steam locomotion had ceased on the main French railways. The last machines to be withdrawn were the American-built Liberation-class Mikados. Thus was closed the 144-year reign of the mighty iron horse in France.

GERMANY

GERMANY IN THE EARLY NINETEENTH CENTURY consisted of a jumble of independent autonomous states that each maintained strict control over the layout, construction, and operation of the early railroads in their jurisdictions. While most of the states were too small to have a comprehensive policy, Prussia from the very outset encouraged railway development, giving pecuniary assistance and in return reserving important rights of state control. About 1848 the government began to construct railways of its own, at the same time purchasing shares of stock in private companies. After 1870 the same policy, which had been suspended for a time, was again pushed forward in the direction of creating a German imperial railroad system, but the jealousy of the smaller states seemed fatal to its success. The Prussian government, however, began to extend its own system on a large scale.

In 1871 Bismarck succeeded in uniting Germany, and railway construction was pushed along at a high rate. By 1871 the German state controlled about five thousand miles of track, with six thousand miles in the hands of private companies. In 1887 there were 24,270 miles of German railroads and only about a thousand miles in private hands. Once the state had won the battle of unifying all the separate political units, nationalization of the railways took place quickly, and in 1903 there were 32,477 miles of railroad, with only 2,807 miles of standard-gauge track under private control. The acquisition prices paid by the government were high, as a rule (in one instance the sellers secured an income of more than 16 percent), but the lines were nevertheless managed with reasonable profit to the state. The passenger-train service was prompt and reasonably comfortable. Speeds were greater than elsewhere in continental Europe, the maximum being about forty-five miles per hour. The passenger fares were low and there were comparatively few accidents. Freight service was rather slow, however, and the charges were higher than for transporting people.

By the beginning of the twentieth century, Germany had expanded her rail lines to join the systems of all her neighboring countries, and by the start of World War I she had made many significant improvements in railroad locomotive design and had further improved train speeds and passenger comforts.

As Imperial Germany became an established reality prior to World War I, a major consideration was the strategic significance of the railways. Henceforth, there was a distinct policy that rail expansion and operations were to be based upon military motives and objectives in addition to industrial and commercial requirements. In general, mobilization plans were dependent upon the rapid deployment of forces by rail. Military plans also called for the acquisition of a vast number of locomotives and rolling stock for any war contingencies. Consequently, Germany produced a wide assortment of magnificent engines before and during the 1914–18 conflict, most of which were later divided among the victorious Allied Powers as reparations.

In 1921 a national railway company, known as the Deutsche Reichsbahn, was formed by consolidating seven state railway systems, and with hardly any railroad engines or rolling stock on hand, the enterprise set out to provide a few new and efficient standard-type engines in order to reduce unit costs, cut down on the complexities of design, and so speed up production. Contemporary German steam power dates from this time. With a serious depression hitting Germany in 1923, Deutsche Reichsbahn folded into bankruptcy and all the railways were taken over by the state, which then held sway through the Hitler era and World War II, and the system was known simply as Reichsbahn.

With the defeat of Germany in World War II, and its division into two politically different entities, German railways were divided into the Deutsche Bundesbahn (DB) in West Germany and the Deutsche Reichsbahn (DR) in East Germany. Once more the German railways were forced to start from scratch, for the original network had suffered greatly from military action and the wholesale removal of tracks and rolling stock as reparations by the victorious Allies, especially the Russians. Again the Germans initiated a railway rebuilding program, this time in two parts.

In 1970 there were forty-two thousand miles of track in West Germany, five thousand miles of which were electrified. Most of this system was owned and operated by the German Federal Railways (Deutsche Bundesbahn), but there were about 2,550 miles of track that did not belong to the federal railway system. In 1970 steam locomotives accounted for less than 10 percent of train miles, diesel-powered for engines 35 to 40 percent, and electric traction accounted for 55 percent.

In 1978 there were officially 28,686 kilometers (17,825 miles) of 1.435 meter-gauge railroads in West Germany.

In 1968 there were approximately ninety-six hundred miles of railroad lines in East Germany, of which nearly all were double-track and standard-gauge. Of this total, 750 miles were electrified. About forty-five hundred miles were main or trunk lines. The railroad density was 230 miles per thousand square miles of territory. Nearly 65 percent of all locomotives were steam types, but these were being rapidly replaced by electric and diesel engines. Since the World War II damage and reparations had severely depleted all kinds of railway equipment, locomotives and rolling stock in use in 1970 had been acquired since 1949.

Pictured is the pioneer steam locomotive, named "Der Adler," used on the first railroad in Germany, that from Nuremberg to Fürth. This was constructed by Stephenson in 1835 at his plant in Newcastle, England, and had a 2–2–2 wheel arrangement. Similar to all Robert Stephenson's early engine types, this had a simple design with outside frames and a tall, narrow smokestack.
(*Courtesy: O. S. Nock,* The Dawn of World Railways 1800–1850)

This illustration is a photograph of a reproduced steam locomotive, named "Der Adler," which duplicated Stephenson's prototype engine of 1833. (*Courtesy: Deutsche Bundesbahn archives*)

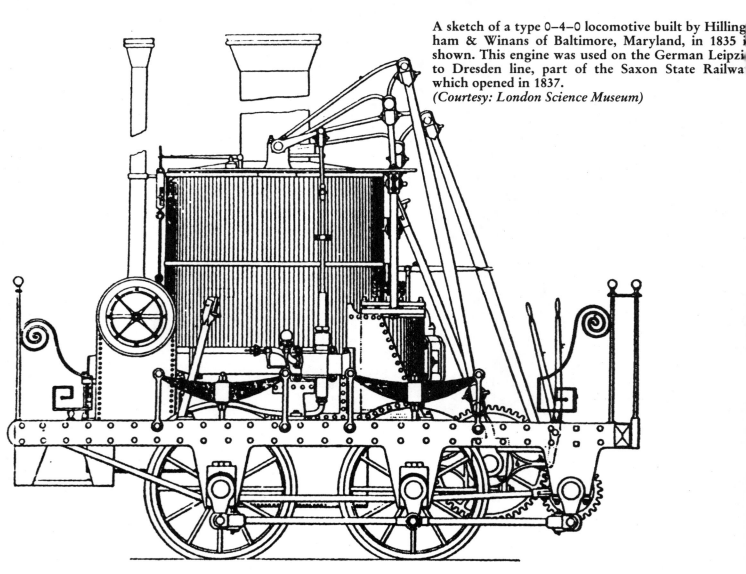

A sketch of a type 0–4–0 locomotive built by Hillingham & Winans of Baltimore, Maryland, in 1835 is shown. This engine was used on the German Leipzig to Dresden line, part of the Saxon State Railway which opened in 1837. (*Courtesy: London Science Museum*)

Steam Locomotives in Germany

The pioneer steam railway engine in Germany was a machine built by the Royal Iron Works (Königlichen Eisengiesserei) of Berlin in 1815; this was purely an experimental venture and it had no practical value in the absence of real railroad tracks.

The first railway in Germany, the Lüdwigsbahn, was a four-mile line between Nuremberg and Fürth that opened on 7 December 1835. This section of rail was equipped with a locomotive named "Der Adler," built by Stephenson in 1833 at his works in Newcastle, England. The engine had a 2–2–2 wheel arrangement to accommodate a large and heavy furnace and boiler. As one can observe, it had outside frames, a tall, narrow smokestack, and a four-wheel tender. Also included are two other pictures of this locomotive.

By 1845 Germany, not including the states of Bavaria and Baden, had 150 locomotives operating on its various rail lines, of which ninety-six had been manufactured in England, twenty in the United States, three in Belgium, and thirty-one in Germany. Locomotive construction in Germany was pioneered by August Borsig, who built a factory in Berlin and turned out his first steam railroad engine in 1841. The Borsig engine prototype was fashioned after a 4–2–0 arrangement designed by Morris in the United States.

Still another German locomotive builder destined to become famous was the firm of Henschel & Sohn of Kassel. Their first engine, a 4–4–0 type named "Drache," was built in 1848 and was utilized on a local Hessian railroad. The design here seemed to copy Stephenson's long-boiler model, although the front-wheel bogie followed a Morris plan. Even though this engine performed well on several German rail lines, Henschel only built four to eight engines per year until 1865, when production was substantially increased with improved models.

Early railroad progress in Germany also took place in Bavaria starting in 1847. Here the Royal Bavarian State Railway operated with 2–4–0 and 0–6–0 locomotives built by Maffei of Munich. An example of a 2–4–0 model, named "Donau," is

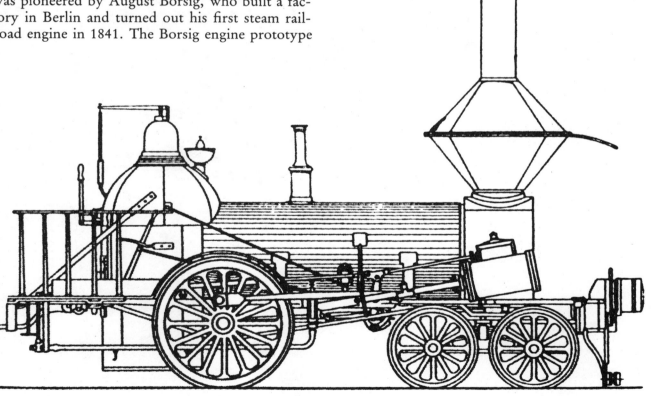

This is a drawing of a locomotive constructed by Morris of Philadelphia in 1839. This type 4–2–0 engine was used on the Berlin–Potsdam Railway in Germany.
(Courtesy: Deutsche Bundesbahn archives)

GERMANY

The first steam locomotive manufactured in Germany is pictured. This was built by A. Borsig of Berlin in 1841 for use on the Berlin–Anhalt Railway. The engine had a 4–2–2 wheel arrangement, an adaptation of a 4–2–0 design by Morris of Philadelphia.
(*Courtesy: O. S. Nock,* The Dawn of World Railways 1800–1850)

Shown is an old drawing of the famous Beuth steam locomotive constructed in the Berlin factory of Borsig in 1844 for pulling trains on the Berlin–Anhalt Railway.
(*Courtesy: Deutche Bundesbahn archives*)

Pictured here is another Borsig locomotive constructed in the hundreds during the 1840s and 1850s for use on various German railways. This engine, known as the Borsig standard, had a 2–2–2 wheel arrangement. Engineer cabs were installed from 1853 onward. General specifications were as follows:

Cylinders	15 by 22 inches
Drive wheels	5.5- to 6.5-foot diameter
Operating weight	25 to 30 tons.

(*Courtesy: O. S. Nock,* The Dawn of World Railways 1800–1850)

A drawing of the first railroad steam engine built by the famous German firm of Henschel & Sohn is shown. Their initial locomotive resembled designs by both Stephenson and Morris. This locomotive with a 4–4–0 wheel arrangement was constructed in Kassel, Germany, in 1848 and was used on a local Hessian rail line.
(*Courtesy: O. S. Nock,* The Dawn of World Railways 1800–1850)

An example is shown of still another German locomotive manufacturer, Emil Kessler of Esslingen, Germany. The "Kopernicus" was built in 1858.
(*Courtesy: Deutsche Bundesbahn archives*)

This illustration is a sketch of the Crampton type locomotive with a 4–2–0 wheel arrangement which was widely used on German railroads as early as 1853. This engine, named "Badenia," was built by Maffei of Munich, Germany, in 1863 for use on the Baden State Railway.
(*Courtesy: O. S. Nock,* The Dawn of World Railways 1800–1850)

This is a picture of Dr. Rudolf Diesel, German engineer and inventor of the famous diesel internal combustion engine. He was born at Bon Pons, France, on 18 March 1858 and died drowning in the English channel on 29 September 1913. He completed his first successful diesel engine in Augsburg, Germany in 1891; this had a single vertical cylinder with four cycles and generated a horsepower of twenty-five. The engine soon attracted world-wide attention. Diesel published two papers on the subject, one in 1894 and one in 1913.
(*Courtesy: Staatsbibliothek, Berlin*)

This is an illustration of an early prototype of a diesel engine built by the Augsburg Machine Company.
(*Courtesy: City Library of Berlin*)

A model which is exhibited in the railway museum at Nuremberg, Germany is pictured here. This was a type 2–8–0 locomotive built by Krauss & Company in 1896 for use on the Royal Bavarian State Railways. Specifications were:

Cylinders	20.2 by 22 inches
Coupled wheels	3-foot 3.6-inch diameter
Steam working pressure	176 pounds per square inch
Tractive effort	19,800 pounds
Grate area	25 square feet
Total heating surface	1720 square feet.

Class	E1

(Courtesy: Verkehrsmuseum, Nuremberg)

This illustration pictures a very unusual locomotive, manufactured by Krauss & Company, which had a 2–2–2–0–4–2 wheel arrangement and was used on the Pfalz Railway in Germany. The engine was displayed at the Paris Exposition in 1900. The locomotives were subsequently changed to type 4–4–2 and saw satisfactory service until 1920. The Pfalz rail network was absorbed by the Royal Bavarian State Railways in 1909. A model, named "Dr. Clemm," is housed in the railway museum at Nuremberg. Specifications were:

Main drive cylinders

Hi pressure	16.3 by 26 inches
Lo pressure	25.5 by 26 inches
Coupled drive wheels	5-foot 3.6-inch diameter
Bogie wheel cylinders	10.2 by 15.7 inches
Coupled wheels	3-foot 3.3-inch diameter
Bogie, center pair	flangeless
Working pressure	206 pounds per square inch
Tractive effort	11,460 pounds
Grate area	82 square feet
Operating weight	107 tons (engine plus tender).

(Courtesy: Verkehrsmuseum, Nuremberg)

now on display in the Verkehrsmuseum in Nuremberg. Also shown is the type 0–6–0 engine, named "Behaim," built by Maffei for the Royal Bavarian State Railway in 1847. Also pictured and described is a class B6, type 2–4–0, express locomotive also used on the Royal Bavarian State Railway starting in 1869.

Another German manufacturer of locomotives was Emil Kessler of Esslingen, who started production around the mid-1850s. Most of his engines were recorded in photographs, usually shown outdoors with a church steeple in the background.

The French Crampton-type locomotives were introduced into Germany in 1853 and were copied by the German firm of Maffei starting in 1863.

A radically different type of internal combustion engine, using fuel oil instead of gasoline, was introduced in Germany by Dr. Rudolf Diesel in 1891. This was destined to have far-reaching effects on the sources of power for railway locomotives, oceangoing vessels, and industrial applications.

Later, in 1896, the Royal Bavarian State Railway utilized a locomotive manufactured by still another German manufacturer, Krauss & Company of Berlin.

In 1900 Krauss & Company built a number of

Pictured is a model of a very small, one-man operated steam locomotive used on the Royal Bavarian State Railways starting in 1906. This class PtL2/2, type 0–4–0, engine was built by Krauss & Company. In 1920, when the Deutsche Reichsbahn was incorporated, these machines were identified as class 98.3. Specifications were:

Cylinders	12 by 15.7 inches
Coupled drive wheels	3-foot 3.6-inch diameter
Grate area	6.5 square feet
Heating surface	382 square feet
Working pressure	176 pounds per square inch
Tractive force	9920 pounds
Operating weight	21.7 tons.

(Courtesy: Verkehrsmuseum, Nuremberg)

A fast express locomotive (later DB class 18) built by Maffei starting in 1907 is shown here. This is a Pacific type 4–6–2 engine (no. 529) which was used on the Bayerischen Staatsbahn Railway. Specification information was not available.
(Courtesy: Verkehrsmuseum, Nuremberg)

One of about three thousand famous P8, type 4–6–0, locomotives used on the Deutsche Reichsbahn Railways, is pictured by the model shown in the illustration. These engines were built in the period 1906–23 by five different German locomotive manufacturers. They were later designated as class 38 and were used widely on mixed freight services. Many of these engines survived World Wars I and II and were used afterwards in all parts of Germany. Many others, of course, were scattered around Europe as reparations from both wars. Specifications were as follows:

Cylinders	22.6 by 24.8 inches
Coupled drive wheels	5-foot 8.9-inch diameter
Boiler	
Grate area	30 square feet
Heating surface	1620 square feet
Working pressure	176 pounds per square inch
Tractive effort	24,880 pounds
Operating weight	119 tons (engine plus tender)
Engine weight	72.5 tons.

(Courtesy: Verkehrsmuseum, Nuremberg)

Another picture of the class 28 locomotive is shown in the following illustration.
(Courtesy: Deutsche Bundesbahn archives)

Pictured is a class 38, type 4–6–0, tender locomotive no. 38–3402.
(Courtesy: Verkehrsmuseum, Nuremberg) 4207-1

unusual locomotives with a 2–2–2–0–4–2 wheel arrangement which were used on the Pfalz Railway. The engines were four-coupled, with the wheels of the leading bogie actuated from a separate set of cylinders. The main drive cylinders were compound.

In 1906 the Royal Bavarian State Railway placed in service a single-operator, driver-fireman locomotive. This 0–4–0 engine, built by Krauss & Company, is pictured. A model of this machine is on display in the Verkehrsmuseum in Nuremberg.

The North German State Railway was main-

This is another class 99, type 0–10–0, tank locomotive. These engines were introduced on narrow-gauge lines in Germany in 1923, in this case the gauge was seventy-five centimeters. Specifications were as follows:

Cylinders	430-millimeter diameter
Drive wheels	800-millimeter diameter
Boiler	
Firegrate area	1.6 square meters
Total heating surface	64.2 square meters
Working pressure	14 kilometers per square centimeter
Tractive force	10,350 kilometers
Axle loading	8 tons
Empty weight	32.5 tons
Capacities	4.5 cubic meters water; 2.5 tons coal
Overall length	8436 millimeters
Maximum speed	30 kilometers per hour.

(Courtesy: Verkehrsmuseum, Nuremberg)

The class 44, type 2–10–0, locomotive shown was introduced to German railway service in 1925. These were freight engines with the following characteristics:

Cylinders	550-millimeter diameter
Drive wheels	1400-millimeter diameter
Boiler	
Firegrate area	4.55 square meters
Total heating surface	238.0 square meters
Working pressure	16 kilograms per square centimeter
Tractive force	27,380 kilograms
Horsepower	1910 pounds per square inch
Axle loading	20 tons
Empty weight	132.5 tons (engine plus tender)
Tender capacities	34 cubic meters water; 10 tons coal
Overall length	22,620 millimeters
Maximum speed	80 kilometers per hour.

(Courtesy: Verkehrsmuseum, Nuremberg)

A Pacific, type 4–6–2, locomotive preserved in Germany is pictured. It was originally constructed by Maffei in 1912 for the Koniglich–Bayerischen Staatsbahn Railway. This engine was later classified as DB 18. Specification data was not available.
(Courtesy: Deutsche Bundesbahn archives)

tained by the Oldenburg state government in a manner quite distinct from the Prussian-Hessian system under the Hohenzollern empire. Principally used was the Oldenburg 4–4–0 locomotive, which provided efficient passenger service in the flat countryside traversed by the North German State Railway. This engine (not illustrated) was built by Von Borries and had a two-cylinder compound arrangement with a huge, oversize low-pressure cylinder on the left side.

Pacific 4–6–2 fast passenger locomotives were first built for the German railways by Maffei starting in 1907. Additional Pacific engines were supplied by Maffei and many other manufacturers in the period 1908 to 1939.

From 1910 to about 1923, German ingenuity developed a number of distinctive steam locomotives. Outstanding among these was the Prussian class P8, type 4–6–0, used on many passenger and freight service assignments. These engines were manufactured by five German firms: Henschel, Vulkan, Borsig, Schwartzkopff, and Maschinenbaugesellschaft. Also developed were the class 8–10 engines with 2–8–0, 0–8–0, and 0–10–0 wheel configurations plus their tank counterparts. In 1912, five hundred type 4–6–4T locomotives, a tank counterpart of the P8, were manufactured for

the Prussian State Railways and were classed as T18. It is interesting to note that, even as late as 1970, ten of these class T18 engines (rebuilt and modernized to some extent) were still active on the Deutsche Bundesbahn rail system. The class T18 engines were produced by the thousands before and during the first World War and were, of course, eventually dispersed over many parts of Europe as war reparations.

Following World War I, with the formation of the Deutsche Reichsbahn, the Germans produced the following steam locomotives in large numbers:

With the demise of the Deutsche Reichsbahn following the economic depression of 1923, the new Reichsbahn management set out to decide how to modify future locomotive designs. Pacific locomotives, classes 01 (simple), 02 (compound), 03 (light simple) and 04 (light compound) were produced in limited numbers in 1925 for comparison purposes. The simple-expansion class 01 engines were finally selected as the most reliable, and they were then manufactured in large numbers by Maffei, Henschel, AEG, Borsig, Krupp, Hohenzollern, and Schwartzkopff between 1925 and 1940. A model of a class 01, type 4–6–2 engine, housed in the Verkehrsmuseum at Nuremberg, is pictured.

Class	Type and Description	
S 3/6	4–6–2	Pacific-type
T3 & T9	Branch engines	
P8	4–6–0	Later designated BR38 (illustration G-406)
T18	4–6–4T	P8 counterpart
G8	0–8–0	Later designated BR55
P10	2–8–2	For fast passenger service
G12	2–10–0	Heavy freight service

Number built	Class	Type	Description
3,000–8,000	43&44	2–10–0	For freight service
3,000–8,000	24	2–6–0	Light branch work
3,000–8,000	86	2–8–2T	For mixed traffic
20 or less	62	4–6–4T	Passenger express work
520	64	2–6–2T	Light passenger service
39	80	0–6–0T	Shunting work
20 or less	81	0–8–0T	Local freight service
20 or less	85	2–10–2T	Adhesion on rack lines
20 or less	87	0–10–0T	Flexible type for curves
20 or less	99	0–10–0	For narrow-gauge
366	41	2–8–2	Fast freight service
3,000	50	2–10–0	Freight service
Limited	03	4–6–2	Light rail service
Unknown	55	0–8–0	Freight service

In addition to the above Pacific-type locomotives, the Germans manufactured several other types of engines over the period 1925 to 1939.

Other classes of locomotives looked promising, but the advent of World War II terminated their normal development:

improved Pacifics, type 4–6–2
class 06, type 4–8–4 for express service
class 45, type 2–10–2 for freight use
class 89, type 0–6–0 tank
class 23, type 2–6–2, more advanced models

The German railways during the early years of World War II, 1939 to 1942, used many different steam locomotives, including about three thousand class 50, two-cylinder, type 2–10–0 freight engines like the model displayed in the London Science Museum. The initial German military successes in the west were in sharp contrast to the severe resistance they encountered on the Russian front in 1941–42. In the winter campaign of 1941, with highway and overland transportation bogged down in mud and snow, the Germans had to resort to a wider use of rail transport than was originally anticipated. Accordingly, there were massive transfers of locomotives from western Europe, and a reconstitution of the locomotive construction industry was agreed upon. Because of limited time, and in order to shorten the design and production processes, it was decided to base any new steam engine designs on the class 43, 44, and 50, type 2–10–0 prototypes. By mid-1942 the order went out to manufacture eight thousand class 42 and seven

Pictured is a class 62, type 4–6–4, German locomotive built in the period 1925–39 for use on passenger express work. No technical data was available.
(Courtesy: Verkehrsmuseum, Nuremberg) 83658

Pictured is a class 99, type 0–10–0, tank locomotive used on various meter-gauge railroads in Germany. This was one of three designs for narrow-gauge engines built in the period 1925-39. Specifications were as follows:

Cylinders	430-millimeter diameter
Drive wheels	800-millimeter diameter
Boiler	
Firegrate area	1.6 square meter
Total heating area	64.20 square meters
Working pressure	14 kilograms per square centimeter
Tractive force	10,350 kilograms
Axle loading	9 tons
Empty weight	33.6 tons
Capacities	4.66 cubic meters water; 2.50 tons coal
Overall length	8435 millimeters
Maximum speed	30 kilometers per hour.

(Courtesy: Verkehrsmuseum, Nuremberg)

Pictured is a class 99 narrow-gauge tank locomotive, possibly a Fairlee type 0–4–4–0, using a system of compounding. No technical or other data were available.
(Courtesy: Verkehrsmuseum, Nuremberg)

This illustration shows a class 55 freight engine, type 0–8–0, placed in service in Germany in the period 1925–39. These locomotives had the following specifications:

Cylinders	600-millimeter diameter
Drive wheels	1350-millimeter diameter
Boiler	
Firegrate area	2.42 square meters
Total heating surface	137.54 square meters
Working pressure	12 kilograms per cubic meter
Tractive force	16,900 Kilograms
Horsepower	1100 pounds per square inch
Axle loading	14 tons
Empty weight	74 tons (engine plus tender)
Tender capacities	16.5 cubic meters water; 7 tons coal
Overall length	17,968 millimeters
Maximum speed	55 kilometers per hour.

(Courtesy: Verkehrsmuseum, Nuremberg)

This shows a class 24 mixed freight, type 2–6–0, tender locomotive used for light branch duties in Germany starting in 1926. Engine no. 056 had the following characteristics:

Cylinders	500-millimeter diameter
Drive wheels	1500-millimeter diameter
Boiler	
Firegrate area	2.04 square meters
Total heating surface	104.4 square meters
Working pressure	14 kilograms per square centimeter
Tractive force	12,300 kilograms
Horsepower	920 pounds per square inch
Axle loading	15 tons
Empty weight	73.3 tons (engine plus tender)
Tender capacities	16 cubic meters water; 6 tons coal
Overall length	16,995 millimeters
Maximum speed	90 kilometers per hour.

(Courtesy: Verkehrsmuseum, Nuremberg)

A class 64, type 2–6–2, tank locomotive is pictured. This engine was placed in service in Germany during 1926. Specifications were as follows:

Cylinders	500-millimeter diameter
Drive wheels	1500-millimeter diameter
Boiler	
Grate area	2.04 square meters
Total heating surface	104.4 square meters
Working pressure	14 kilograms per square centimeter
Tractive force	12,300 kilograms
Horsepower	950 pounds per square inch
Axle loading	15 tons
Empty weight	58 tons (engine)
Capacities	9 cubic meters water; 3 tons coal
Overall length	12,400 millimeters
Maximum speed	90 kilograms per hour.

(Courtesy: Verkehrsmuseum, Nuremberg)

Class 06, type 4–8–4, locomotives were streamlined express tender locomotives placed in service in Germany in 1930. These engines were built by Krupp of Essen according to the following specifications:

Cylinders	520-millimeter diameter
Drive wheels	2000-millimeter diameter
Boiler	
Firegrate area	5.04 square meters
Total heating surface	289 square meters
Working pressure	20 kilograms per square centimeter
Tractive force	23,350 kilograms
Horsepower	2350 pounds per square inch
Axle loading	18 to 20 tons
Empty weight	161.9 tons (engine plus tender)
Tender capacities	38 cubic meters water; 10 tons coal
Overall length	26,520 millimeters
Maximum speed	140 kilometers per hour.

(Courtesy: Verkehrsmuseum, Nuremberg)

Illustrated is a streamlined class 03 Pacific type 4–6–2
locomotive placed in service on the German railways
about 1936. Specification data were not available.
(Courtesy: Verkehrsmuseum, Nuremberg)

This illustration shows a type 0–6–0, class 89, tank
locomotive introduced to the German railways in
1921. Specifications were:

Cylinders	420-millimeter diameter
Drive wheels	1216-millimeter diameter
Boiler	
Firegrate area	1.62 square meters
Total heating surface	88.6 square meters
Working pressure	12 Kilograms per square centimeter
Tractive force	8500 kilograms
Horsepower	430 pounds per square inch
Axle loading	16 tons
Empty weight	37.6 tons
Capacities	5.0 cubic meters water; 1.1 tons coal
Overall length	9974 millimeters
Maximum speed	45 Kilometers per hour.

(Courtesy: Verkehrsmuseum, Nuremberg)

Another class 89, type 0–6–0 tank locomotive used on the German railways in the early 1920s is illustrated. See the previous illustration for details.
(Courtesy: Verkehrsmuseum, Nuremberg)

Pictured is a massive, type 2–10–2, class 85 tank locomotive introduced to the German railways shortly before World War II for use with freight traffic. This engine was adhesion type used on some rack railroads. Specifications were as follows:

Cylinders	600-millimeter diameter
Drive wheels	1400-millimeter diameter
Boiler	
Firegrate area	3.5 square meters
Total heating surface	195.85 square meters
Working pressure	14 kilograms per square centimeter
Tractive force	28,500 kilograms
Horsepower	1,500 pounds per square inch
Axle loading	20 tons
Empty weight	107.5 tons
Capacities	14 cubic meters water; 4.5 tons coal
Length overall	16,200 millimeters
Maximum speed	80 kilometers per hour.

(Courtesy: Verkehrsmuseum, Nuremberg)

Another class 03 Pacific type 4–6–2 express locomotive introduced to the German railway system just before World War II is illustrated. No technical or other information was available.
(Courtesy: Verkehrsmuseum, Nuremberg)

Over the period 1939–42 an assortment of German manufacturers produced about three thousand very efficient class 50, type 2–10–0, two-cylinder freight locomotives. A model shown is on display in the London Science Museum. The original engines had these specifications:

Cylinders	23.6 by 26 inches
Coupled drive wheels	4-foot 7.1-inch diameter
Boiler	
Grate area	42 square feet
Heating surface	2765 square feet
Working pressure	235 pounds per square inch
Tractive power	59,424 pounds
Operating weight	146.3 tons (engine plus tender)
Tender capacities	
26 cubic meters (6868 U.S. gallons) water	
8 tons coal.	

(Courtesy: Science Museum, London)

This illustration pictures another class 50, type 2–10–0, steam locomotive widely used on the German railways in World War II. See previous illustration for technical details.
(Courtesy: Deutsche Bundesbahn archives)

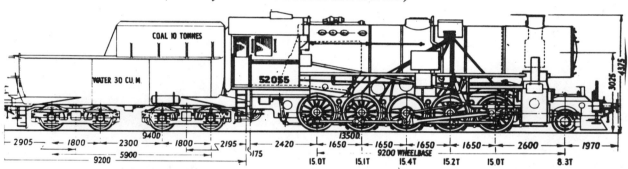

This shows a drawing of the famous World War II German class 52 "austerity" locomotive of which 6353 machines were constructed under hard-pressed conditions in Germany during that war. Specifications were as follows:

Wheel arrangement	2–10–0
Cylinders	23⅝ by 26 inches
Coupled drive wheels	4-foot 7-inch diameter
Boiler	
Grate area	42 square feet
Superheater	685 square feet
Heating surface	1908 square feet
Working pressure	227 pounds per square inch
Operating weights	
Engine	84 tons
Tender	60 tons
Tender capacities	30 cubic feet water; 10 tons coal
Horsepower	1625.

(Courtesy: Deutsche Bundesbahn archives)

thousand class 52 engines. The class 42 and class 52 locomotives, essentially modifications of the class 43–44 and class 50 types, respectively, were so-called austerity engines, designed to improve operating and maintenance reliability and to facilitate mass production in the face of serious wartime shortages of many critical metals such as copper and tin. Later in World War II, the German industrial complex produced 6,353 class 52, and 843 class 42 engines, a very substantial accomplishment

given the enormous difficulties of manpower and material shortages and Allied military actions. These locomotives were of vast importance to the German military objectives. A drawing of the class 52 steam locomotive, type 2–10–0, is provided.

After World War II, with the division of Germany into two political powers, the German railways were divided into the Deutsche Bundesbahn (DB) in West Germany and the Deutsche Reichsbahn (DR) in East Germany. The German

A class 23, type 2–6–2, tender locomotive built after World War II by Arm. Jung and Henschel. Specifications on this engine were as follows:

Wheel arrangement	2–6–2
Cylinders	550 by 660 millimeters
Drive wheels	1750-millimeter diameter
Boiler	
Firegrate area	3.11 square meters
Total heating surface	156.2 square meters
Working pressure	16 kilograms per square centimeter
Tractive force	14,600 kilograms
Axle loading	17 to 19 tons
Empty weight	98.8 tons (engine plus tender)
Tender capacities	30 cubic meters water; 8 tons coal
Overall length	21,125 millimeters
Maximum speed	110 kilometers per hour.

(Courtesy: Verkehrsmuseum, Nuremberg)

![Model of class 023 locomotive 23 001]

Pictured is a model of a class 023, type 2–6–2, locomotive which was adopted for use on the railways of West Germany after World War II. Technical details were as follows:

Cylinders	20.5 by 26 inches
Coupled wheels	5-foot 9-inch diameter
Boiler	
Grate area	33.5 square feet
Superheater	794 square feet
Evaporation surface	1681 square feet
Working pressure	200 pounds per square inch
Operating weight	145 tons (engine plus tender)
Tender capacity	6800 gallons water; 7.75 tons coal.

(Courtesy: Verkehrsmuseum, Nuremberg)

This class 42, type 2–8–2, tender locomotive, with oil burner, was introduced to West German railroad service in 1958 for heavy freight traffic. These were Mikado (class 41) engines which had survived World War II; they were rebuilt with new welded boilers and converted from coal to fuel oil. Characteristics were as follows:

Cylinders	520-millimeter diameter
Drive wheels	1600-millimeter diameter
Boiler	

Total heating surface	177.54 square meters
Working pressure	16 kilograms per square centimeter
Tractive force	15,580 kilograms
Horsepower	1975 pounds per square inch
Empty weight	124.7 tons (engine plus tender)
Tender capacities	34 cubic meters water; 12 cubic meters fuel oil
Overall length	23,905 millimeters
Maximum speed	90 kilometers per hour.

(Courtesy: Verkehrsmuseum, Nuremberg)

The last designed and constructed steam locomotive in West Germany is pictured. These engines were class 65, type 2–8–4 tank. Also in East Germany, eighty-eight units of the same locomotive were built in 1954 for the Deutsche Reichsbahn. The author was unable to readily secure any technical or specification data on the class 65 machines.
(Courtesy: Verkehrsmuseum, Nuremberg)

A large class 39, type 2–8–4, tender locomotive originally designed for mixed-traffic duties is shown. No further details were available.
(Courtesy: Verkehrsmuseum, Nuremberg)

A heavy-duty German tender locomotive (class unknown) type 2–10–0, possibly designed for freight service is pictured. No further details available on engine no. 5578.
(Courtesy: Verkehrsmuseum, Nuremberg)

rail network suffered greatly during the Allied bombing actions and after hostilities closed. Further damage followed from the wholesale removal of track and rolling stock by the victorious Russians as reparations. Again, after several years an intensive postwar railway rebuilding program was initiated in both parts of Germany.

In West Germany the first new passenger steam locomotive design was the class 023, 2–6–2 type, of which fifteen were built by Henschel and another ten by Arn. Jung, all in 1951. This locomotive was a replacement for the old-time P8 (BR 38) engine. However, after 105 machines were constructed, the Deutsche Bundesbahn management decided to

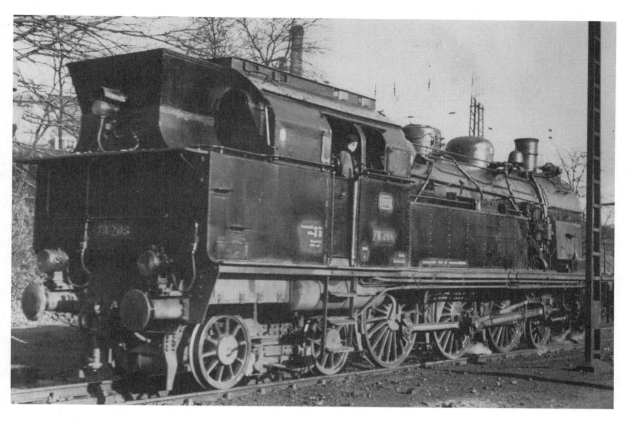

This illustration shows a heavy-duty passenger tank locomotive, class 78, type 4–6–4, used on the German railways. No additional data were available.
(Courtesy: Verkehrsmuseum, Nuremberg)

Pictured is another class 78, type 4–6–4, German locomotive. These engines were designed for passenger as well as mixed freight duties. No further data were available.
(Courtesy: Verkehrsmuseum, Nuremberg)

build no more steam engines and concentrated on using diesel and electric tractive power instead. A model of the class 023 locomotive, housed in the Verkehrsmuseum in Nuremberg, is shown.

Of course, before the authorized withdrawal of steam locomotion, much energy and money was expended recovering older pre–World War II classes of German locomotives, including the class 01 Pacifics and the class P8 (BR 38), type 4–6–0 engines. Fully twenty of the latter Prussian State Railway locomotives, built between 1906 and 1924, survived until about 1975. Type 4–6–2 Pacifics were first used to haul the fastest German express trains; however, as diesel passenger locomotives came on line, the Pacifics were the first to be displaced. Nevertheless, in 1970 four classes of Pacifics, about fifty machines, were still in service.

Much work was also done to rehabilitate some class 41, type 2–8–2 Mikados that were originally built in the period 1939–42. Those which survived were rebuilt, supplied with new welded boilers, and modified to burn oil instead of coal. These were classified as 042. (To avoid confusion, it must be pointed out that during the war "class 42" designated one of several classes of type 2–10–0 freight engines.)

The class 023 locomotives referred to above were all constructed between 1950 and 1959, and actually these were the last steam machines to be produced in West Germany. Even though class 065

engines were designed after the class 023 types, all the class 065 units were manufactured before the last class 023 locomotives were built. See illustration.

Generally, the Deutsche Bundesbahn management believed that the World War II Kriegslokomotivien steam engines would be the last to survive on the railways of West Germany. Specifically, these were the classes 042 and 052, of which a fantastic ten thousand or more were constructed from 1939 to 1945.

The Verkehrsmuseum has supplied a number of photographs of additional German steam locomotives, which are pictured. Unfortunately, accompanying technical or descriptive details were not available.

In East Germany after World War II, rail officials sought to continue using steam locomotion for as long as possible, using as many prewar and wartime engines as could be found. Much time and expense was devoted to rehabilitating such engine classes as 01, 41, 44, 50, P8 (BR 38), and G8 (BR 55), most of which were modified to burn fuel oil. Extra effort was applied to modernizing the class 01 Pacifics for express service by installing new, higher-capacity boilers and modified drive wheels, among other improvements. Of course, the *Kriegsloks* (war machines), classes 52 and 42, were also mechanically upgraded from the 1942 vintage.

Pictured is a Deutsche Reichsbahn tank locomotive class 91, type 2–6–0. These engines were originally intended for freight service. No additional data were available.
(Courtesy: Verkehrsmuseum, Nuremberg)

This illustration shows an excursion train drawn by a class 98 steam locomotive. No further information was available.
(Courtesy: Verkehrsmuseum, Nuremberg)

This is a photograph of an East German (Deutsche Reichsbahn = DR) class 52.8, type 2–10–0, locomotive which was built after World War II based on the famous and widely used class 52 wartime, so-called Kreigsloks engines.
(Courtesy: New English Library, London)

In 1954 the Deutsche Reichsbahn brought out eighty-eight units of a new class 65 engine, type 2–8–4T and twenty-seven of a new class 83, type 2–8–4T, which was a smaller class 65. These two classes were part of a production run of 322 standard locomotives that had been constructed in East Germany after World War II. Later, in early 1960, the DR introduced a class 58 engine that was a three-cylinder version of the old Prussian G12, type 2–10–0. This work was performed in the shops at Zwickau.

All production of steam-powered locomotives was terminated in 1960. From the best available evidence, it appears that the venerable steam railway engine disappeared from the East German railways about 1977.

GREECE

THE FIRST RAILWAY IN GREECE APPEARS TO HAVE been a small private line, belonging to the Laurium Company, that was used to haul lead ores from waste dumps in the vicinity of Cape Colonna, south of Athens.

In 1894 the only government railway extended 7½ miles from Athens to Piraeus. It carried passengers only. At that time, another major railway was projected from Piraeus northwest to Lamia in order to connect Greece with the general railway system of Europe. Greece was the last major country in the continent to be connected with the international system.

The north-south network was completed in 1916, but all railroads in Greece suffered severely from military actions in World War I. The mountains that cover 80 percent of Greece, as well as the low-lying peninsular topography, have made land communications difficult and time-consuming. In addition, differences in rail gauge have brought about serious deficiencies and much wasted effort in transshipping between various parts of the country.

Today, the railway main line in Greece, seventeen hundred miles long, goes north from Athens through Larissa to Thessaloníki. From there, one line goes to Sofia (in Bulgaria) and branches to Turkey, and another goes to Yugoslavia and western Europe. The railroads link all major seaports. Service is still hampered by two track gauges: the wide standard gauge is used on all the main lines and provides for a hookup to the international system; the narrow gauge is used in the Peloponnesus region.

The Greek government owns, operates, and subsidizes the deficit-ridden railroads. Much of the equipment is obsolete and thus expensive to operate and maintain. Major traffic interruptions are caused by heavy snowfalls and by summer rainstorms in the north. Steep grades and sharp curves over much of the network present problems and reduce operating efficiency. The economic importance of the railways is far below that of the roads and the coastal shipping; therefore, rail traffic continues to decline because it cannot compete effectively with the other forms of transit.

Despite these problems, an extensive rail modernization program has been in effect in recent years. The major goals are to improve the existing tracks and to double-track some, to standardize metric gauges, to forge better links with Western Europe, and to improve coordination between railway and highway traffic. The Greek topography and a late start have made this modernization effort both costly and difficult.

In 1978 *Janes World Railways* recorded that the Greek rail lines comprised 597 miles of 1-meter track, 13 miles of 0.75-meter (2-foot 5½ inch) track, and 1,596 miles of 1.435-meter (4-foot, 6½-inch) track. There were also some incidental rack and other narrow-gauge roads.

The following four illustrations briefly picture and describe the rail network and three types of steam locomotives used.

Railway map of Greece.
(*Courtesy:* Janes World Railways)

This is a photograph of a type 0–4–2 tank engine built by the Neilson Company, in 1866 (no. 1216). The locomotive was one of a batch of five identical machines originally ordered for the Northampton & Banbury Railway (U.K.). Although the engines were built, they were never delivered to the Northampton & Banbury Railway. This engine was, instead, sold to the Athens & Piraeus Railway on 24 April 1869. The other engines were disposed of, but not to Greece. Specifications follow:

Gauge	4 feet 8½ inches
Cylinders	16 by 20 inches
Drivers	5-foot 6-inch diameter
Boiler heating surface	1009.2 square feet
Operating weight	35 tons plus 5 hundredweights
Capacities	760 gallons water; 35 cubic feet coal.

(Courtesy: Mitchell Library, Glasgow) E 305

In 1892 the Piraeus Larissa Railway of Greece purchased two type 4–4–0 tank locomotives from the Neilson Company. Identification numbers were 301 and 302. Specifications were as follows:

Gauge	4 feet 8½ inches
Cylinders	15³⁄₁₆ by 22 inches
Coupled drivers	4-foot 3³⁄₁₆-inch diameter
Boiler	
Heating surface	970 square feet
Working pressure	156 pounds per square inch
Tractive force	11,598 pounds
Operating weight	38 tons plus 14 hundredweights
Water capacity	900 gallons.

(Courtesy: Mitchell Library, Glasgow) E 692

Pictured is a model of a Greek type 2–8–2 locomotive which is housed in the National Science and Technical Museum of Milan, Italy. The prototype engines, ten in number, were manufactured by Breda of Milan in 1952. These were oil-fired types originally utilized on the Piraeus–Athens–Peloponnesus Railway system in 1962. Characteristics were as follows:

Cylinders	18.5 by 22 inches
Coupled wheels	3-foot 11.4-inch diameter
Boiler	
Grate area	29.75 square feet
Superheater	376.75 square feet
Total heating area	1448.75 square feet
Working pressure	155 pounds per square inch
Operating weight	95 tons (engine plus tender)
Tender capacities	15 cubic meters water; 6 cubic meters fuel oil
Speed	60 kilometers per hour.

Comments: Could handle curves of 262 foot radius. The smoke deflectors shown in the model were later removed.

(Courtesy: Science Museum, Milan, Italy)

HAWAII

RAILROADS IN HAWAII WERE FIRST LAID DOWN following approval by King Kalakaua of legislation to "Promote the Construction of Railways" in August 1878. The chief purpose of the original rail system was to transport products from the expanding sugar industry. The first construction, in 1879, involved a three-mile section of three-foot track between the two seaports of Kahului and Wailuku on the island of Maui. The line was later known as the Kahului Railroad. Shortly thereafter, it was extended east and northeast thirteen miles to Kuiaha, and a 2½-mile branch ran south from Kahului to a sugar mill at Puunene. This first railroad in Hawaii remains active today and still contributes to the economy of that island and to the state as well.

Early records covering two original steam locomotives used on the Kahului Railroad were lost, but it is believed that the engines were built in England. Subsequent steam railroad engines, thirteen in number, all built in the United States, are listed in the first illustration.

The island of Oahu was served by narrow-gauge 36-inch railway facilities of the Oahu Railway & Land Company (OR&L). This rail line franchise was granted on 11 September 1888 by King Kalakaua. The railroad was intended to connect Honolulu with the Pearl River lagoon, a distance of about fourteen miles. The first ceremonial ride took place on 4 September 1889, using a substitute locomotive, a small Baldwin "saddle-tanker." (Identified as no. 6, it is presently preserved on a monument site at Ala Moana Center, Honolulu.) The road was officially opened on King Kalakaua's birthday, 16 November 1889, using two newly ar-

rived Baldwin steam locomotives from Philadelphia. About four thousand passengers took a free eighteen-mile round-trip ride on eleven different scheduled runs. Subsequent construction brought the tracks, in 1890, to Pearl City, an additional eleven miles, and in 1895 the line was extended to Waianae on the west coast of Oahu, about thirty-two miles from Honolulu. While some passenger transportation was provided, the railway's principal revenue was derived from service to the rapidly developing sugar plantations and, later, the pineapple plantations. Another 22½ miles of railroad were completed on 11 June 1898, along the west and north coasts from Waianae to Waialua. By 1

ROSTER OF STEAM LOCOMOTIVES—KAHULUI RAILROAD CO.

Road No.	Type	Builder	Shop No.	Yr.	Data*	Notes
1 (1st)	0-4-2T	Baldwin	4906	1879	28-8x12	A
1 (2nd)	0-4-2T	Baldwin	6102	1882	28-8x12	B
2	2-4-2T	Baldwin	6782	1883	30-9x14	
3	2-4-2T	Baldwin	8878	1887	36-9x14	
4	2-6-0	Porter	2263	1900	40-12x18-44,000	C
5	2-6-0	Baldwin	23763	1904	40-12x18	
6	2-6-2	Baldwin	31125	1907	40-12x18	
7	0-6-0	Baldwin	35982	1911	36-12x18	
8	2-6-2	Baldwin				D
9	2-6-2	Baldwin	41925	1915	40-14x20-82,900	
10	2-6-2	Baldwin	58009	1924	40-14x20-81,800	
11	2-6-2	Baldwin	60486	1928	40-14x20-81,800	
12	2-6-2	Baldwin	60690	1928	40-14x20-81,800	E

NOTE A—First Baldwin to reach Hawaii; bought new by Thomas H. Hobron for Kahului & Wailuku R.R., the Islands' first common carrier and operating since 1881 as Kahului Railroad Co. Originally named "Leslie"; preserved at Rancho Rinconada, Woodland Hills, California.

NOTE B—Preserved at Kahului roundhouse.

NOTE C—Although some Porter lists show another Porter locomotive, an 0-4-0T, shop No. 2255, as having been purchased by Kahului Railroad in 1900, there are authorities on Porter history who believe that this engine may have gone to a plantation railroad instead. Since such a locomotive does not fit into sequence in K.R.R. road numbering, and because definite identification is not yet verified, it is omitted from the above table.

NOTE D—No records survive in company files and Baldwin records fail to list No. 8 as having been sold to K.R.R. Evidence points to its having come to the company from other owners between 1912 and 1915. Mechanical department recalls it was not suitable for plantation work and used mainly in passenger service; retired 1932. Records now at Eddystone show that in April 1907 Hawaiian Commercial & Sugar Co. took delivery of Baldwin No. 30617 which became H. C. & S. No. 4. This was an 0-6-0 switcher with 4-wheel tender and Eddystone records indicate it as having been transferred to K.R.R. at an ungiven date. Again, as in the case of the Porter tank engine, it fails to find a place in K.R.R.'s numbering system and if it does provide a clue to the origin of No. 8 there remains the fact that No. 8 was a 2-6-2 and the H. C. & S. locomotive was an 0-6-0. This engine, therefore, is also omitted from the table.

NOTE E—Stored serviceable, Kahului roundhouse, 1963.

(*)—Where weights are omitted figures not available after thorough research.

(Courtesy: John Hungerford, Hawaiian Railroads)

Pictured is the first Baldwin locomotive used in Hawaii. It was built in Philadelphia in 1879 on Baldwin's shop order no. 4906. The engine was purchased new by Thomas H. Hobron for the Kahului & Wailiku Railroad, the "islands" first common carrier which, after 1891, was known as the Kahului Railroad Company. The locomotive was originally named "Leslie"; it is now preserved at Rancho Rinconada, Woodlands Hills, California. The engine with a 0–4–2 wheel arrangement had 28-inch diameter drive wheels, and cylinders were 8 inches in diameter with a 12-inch stroke.
(Courtesy: Public Archives, Honolulu, Hawaii)

The first locomotive (named "Kauila") on the Oahu Railway & Land Company railroad in Hawaii is shown. This engine was built in 1889, by Baldwin under their shop order no. 10028, for George A. Rowell of San Francisco. It was shipped to Honolulu on orders issued by the Hawaiian Ministry of the Interior dated 12 July 1889. This type 0–4–0 locomotive (later converted to a type 0–4–2) had 28-inch coupled drive wheels with cylinders 8 inches in diameter and a stroke of 12 inches. Operating weight was 24,000 pounds. This locomotive is presently preserved and displayed at Ala Moana Center, Honolulu.
(Courtesy: John Hungerford, Hawaiian Railroads)

This illustration pictures a train in Hawaii at the Oahu railway station on the Oahu Railway & Land Company railroad in 1890. This and a companion engine with 4–4–0 wheel arrangements were the first bought new on this railroad in 1889 from the Baldwin Locomotive Company. Coupled wheels had a diameter of 33 inches; cylinders were 9 inches in diameter and had a stroke of 12 inches. Operating weight with tender was 61,200 pounds.
(Courtesy: Public Archives, Honolulu, Hawaii)

This is an 1890 picture of an Oahu Railway & Land Company train approaching the Honolulu terminal. The locomotive is a Baldwin type 4–4–0 which was built for this rail system in 1889.
(Courtesy: Public Archives, Honolulu, Hawaii)

ROSTER OF STEAM LOCOMOTIVES—OAHU RAILWAY & LAND CO.

Road No.	Type	Builder	Shop No.	Yr.	Data	Notes
5	2-4-2T	Baldwin	8973	1887	41-10x16-58,000	A
6	0-4-2T	Baldwin	10028	1889	28-8x12-24,000	B
8	0-4-2T	Baldwin	4455	1878	30-9x14-35,400	C
9	0-6-0	Alco-Rogers	55826	1916	38-14x20-72,000	
10	0-6-0	Alco-Pittsburgh	46716	1910	33-12x16-47,600	
12	0-6-0	Alco-Manchester	51165	1912	38-14x20-72,000	D
15	4-4-0	Baldwin	10129	1889	33-9x12-61,200	E*
19	4-4-0	Baldwin	10131	1889	37-9x16-54,000	E
22	2-8-0	Baldwin	20324	1902	38-16½x20-92,800	
31	2-8-0	Baldwin	20325	1902	38-16½x20-92,800	
32	2-8-0	Alco-Rogers	53446	1913	38-16½x20-101,000	F
34	2-8-0	Alco-Manchester	51164	1912	38-16½x20-101,000	F
35	2-8-0	Alco-Rogers	55827	1916	38-16½x20-101,000	F
36	2-8-0	Alco-Rogers	53447	1913	38-16½x20-101,000	F
37	2-8-0	Alco-Schenectady	46170	1909	36-15x20-82,200	
39	2-8-0	Alco-Pittsburgh	46043	1909	36-15x20-82,200	
43	Shay	Lima	3165	1921	34-12x15-159,000	
44	Shay	Lima	3097	1920	34-12x15-159,000	
45	4-4-0	Baldwin	5488	1881	43-12x18-84,900	C*
57	0-6-0	Baldwin	15336	1897	33-12x16-40,500	
60	2-8-2	Alco-Schenectady	66279	1925	44-18x22-156,000	G
64	4-6-0	Baldwin	16386	1898	43-13x18-62,000	H
70	2-8-2	Alco-Schenectady	66280	1925	44-18x22-156,000	
76	2-8-0	Baldwin	15388	1897	38-14x20-68,000	
80	2-8-2	Alco-Schenectady	66685	1926	44-18x22-156,000	
83	4-6-0	Baldwin	16387	1898	43-13x18-62,000	H
85	4-6-0	Alco-Cooke	48585	1910	43-13x18-68,000	
87	4-6-0	Alco-Cooke	48586	1910	43-13x18-68,000	
88	4-6-0	Alco-Cooke	55828	1916	43-15x20-72,000	
90	2-8-2	Alco-Schenectady	66686	1926	44-18x22-156,000	
98	2-8-0	Baldwin	15567	1897	38-14x20-68,000	
111	4-6-0	Baldwin	37394	1911	44-16x20-89,200	I

NOTE A—Built for Park & Cliff House Railway, San Francisco; bought by O. R. & L., 1902/03; scrapped 1923.

NOTE B—First locomotive to operate on O. R. & L. tracks, built for George A. Rowell, San Francisco; shipped to Honolulu on order of Hawaiian Ministry of Interior, July 12, 1889; preserved and displayed at Ala Moana Center, Honolulu. Built as 0-4-0T, later converted to 0-4-2T.

NOTE C—No. 8 bought from Sonoma Valley Railroad of California where it carried name of "Sonoma." No. 45 also from Sonoma Valley; original name, "General Vallejo."

NOTE D—Preserved and displayed at Ala Moana Center, Honolulu.

NOTE E—First locomotives ordered new from builder.

NOTE F—Sold to Salvador Railway in Central America, 1950; still in operation.

NOTE G—Stored in Honolulu yards, unserviceable.

NOTE H—Weight with tender fully loaded, 110,500 lbs.

NOTE I—Built for Nevada-California-Oregon Railway as No. 11; sold 1928 to Pacific Coast Railway and redesignated No. 111.

(*)—Weight with tender.

(Courtesy: John Hungerford, Hawaiian Railroads)

Shown are two views of Baldwin engine no. 99 used on the Hawaii Consolidated Railway; before 29 February 1916 the rail system was named Hilo Railroad Company. This type 4–6–0 locomotive was built in 1899 under shop order no. 17318, but road trials in Philadelphia were delayed until about 5 January 1900. The engine had coupled drive wheels 56 inches in diameter with cylinders 16 by 24 inches.

January 1899, the tracks led to Kahuku on the north side of Oahu, then completing a total of seventy miles from Honolulu. A very important ten-mile connection from Waipahu north into the pineapple plantations in the center of Oahu was finished in 1906. Total active track length finally reached 160.19 miles.

The OR&L's peak period of freight and passenger revenues, except for World War II, was between 1920 and 1925. The Second World War, of course, brought about a tremendous workload, and the system made significant contributions to the fight against Japan. How it ever survived, using small, outmoded equipment, remains a mystery! After V-J Day, in 1946, passenger miles declined 62.5 percent and operating income fell 55 percent. With increasing inroads on short-haul business by over-the-road trucks, the OR&L was forced to abandon its entire rail system outside Honolulu, about 81.2 miles, in December 1947. Most of the

ROSTER OF STEAM LOCOMOTIVES—Hawaii Consolidated Ry., Ltd.†

Road No.	Type	Builder	Shop No.	Yr.	Data*	Notes
3	4-6-0	Baldwin	20052	1902	50-18x24	
5	2-6-2	Schenectady	5177	1899	44-16x24-106,000	A
15	4-4-0	Wm. Mason	289	1868	57-16x22-60,500	B
33	0-4-2T	Baldwin	17365	1900	37-11x18	
39	0-4-2T	Porter				C
99	4-6-0	Baldwin	17318	1900	56-16x24	D
108	4-6-0	Baldwin	32895	1908	56-17x24	
121	4-6-0	Baldwin	54897	1921	50-18x24-91,500	
191	4-6-0	Baldwin	35433	1910	56-17x24	
192	4-6-0	Baldwin	37785	1912	56-17x24	
196	2-8-0	Alco-Cooke	56163	1916	44-18x24-124,000	

NOTE A—Built for Sierra Railway of California as 0-6-0 switcher, sold to Hilo Railroad, 1903; converted to 2-6-2 at Waiakea shops.

NOTE B—Built as California Pacific No. 7, later Southern Pacific Nos. 1185, 2nd 1207 and 1485; rebuilt at Sacramento shops, brought to Hilo by D. E. Metzger, breakwater contractor.

NOTE C—Original purchaser from Porter unknown; used in construction of Hamakua Division; wrecked and scrapped about 1910.

NOTE D—Although built and completed in 1899, as indicated by road number, No. 99 was not given test trials at Philadelphia until first week in January 1900.

(*)—Where weights are omitted figures not available after thorough research. Dimensions from Baldwin records checked by Harold L. Goldsmith at Eddystone Works, May 18, 1962, and September 7, 1962.

(†)—Hilo Railroad Co. previous to February 29, 1916.

(*Courtesy: John Hungerford,* Hawaiian Railroads)

tracks were eventually lifted. In 1961 the royal charter granted in 1888 was finally terminated.

During the fifty-eight-year life of the OR&L railway system, thirty-two different steam locomotives were used. The second illustration summarizes this equipment. The numbers assigned to the rail steam engines did not follow any chronological order. The numbering system was purely arbitrary; the original developer, Dillingham, used such figures as his own age, the ages of his children, etc. Most locomotives were of Baldwin origin until 1902, after which they were secured from various American locomotive shops. The last steam locomotive (no. 111) was used equipment purchased in 1943; this was a 4–6–0 Baldwin originally built in 1911 for the Nevada-California-Oregon Railway.

The third early railroad system in the Hawaiian Islands was the Hawaii Consolidated Railway on the largest island, Hawaii. Ample supplies of water for irrigation and abundant rainfall had encouraged the cultivation of vast crops of sugarcane. Accordingly the Hilo Railroad Company, as it was known up to 29 February 1916, was authorized by the Republic of Hawaii, on 28 March 1899, to build rail facilities anywhere on the island. Tracks of standard gauge, 4 feet 8½ inches, using mostly sixty-pound rail, were laid in 1899 from Waiakea to Olaa. By 1901, trains were running twenty-five miles from Hilo west to Kapoho. Many other branches and extensions were constructed, and by 1914 there were about one hundred miles of track in use, including sidings.

As early as 1913 attempts were made to promote tourism on the island of Hawaii, but this never reached any sizable proportions in the early part of the century. Economic fortunes of the railroad were adversely influenced by volcanic eruptions in the Puna district of southwestern Hawaii in 1955 and 1960. Passenger traffic had been largely wiped out by the "great depression" in 1935. World War II naturally promoted both passenger and freight rail traffic, what with gasoline rationing and with considerable troop movement in the area.

The Hawaii Consolidated Railway suffered a mortal blow on 1 April 1946, when a tidal wave struck the south coast of the island of Hawaii. Most of the line was subsequently abandoned and the rolling stock and other operating equipment were sold. Many cars were burned for metal scrap but some key bridges were retained for use in a highway relocation plan for Route 19.

A roster of steam locomotives is shown in the third illustration. Of eleven steam engines used, seven were of Baldwin manufacture.

The following illustrations give a brief picture of the various steam locomotives used on the three rail systems of Hawaii.

Pictured is locomotive no. 12 in three different poses. This Prairie type 2–6–2 Baldwin engine was used on the Kahului Railroad. It was built in 1928 according to a Baldwin shop order of no. 60690 and constituted the last steam locomotive purchased for use in Hawaii. The engine had 40-inch coupled drive wheels; cylinders were 14 by 20 inches. Operating weight was 81,800 pounds. In 1963 the engine was stored in serviceable condition in the Kahului Roundhouse in Hawaii.

(*Courtesy: John Hungerford, Hawaiian Railraods*)

(*Courtesy: John Hungerford,* Hawaiian Railroads)

HUNGARY

IN AUSTRIA-HUNGARY, THE FIRST RAILWAY opened on 7 September 1827, from Bedweis (Budedovice, Czechoslovakia) to Trojanov. This railway used horse-drawn power, and steam locomotion was not applied until 1872. Later, the line became the first section of the Linz–Budweis Railway.

The first permanent railway in Hungary proper ran 20.5 miles from Pest to Vacz, and opened on 15 July 1846. Railway construction did not gain much real impetus until the end of the nineteenth century. In order to further the growth of Budapest, railway lines were built, almost without exception, to pass through the capital. The length of railways in operation in 1867 was about 1,375 English miles. Lines constructed between 1867 and 1876 amounted to 2,675 miles; thus, at the beginning of 1877 there were 4,050 miles of railroad in operation. By the early part of 1879, the total length was about 4,400 miles. Hungary's rail network still shows the original radially diverging pattern, centered on Budapest.

Prior to the Second World War, annual freight traffic reached 24.4 million metric tons and the number of railway passengers 103.5 million. In the period 1937 to 1962 the volume of goods transported by railway quadrupled, with the number of passengers was about five times the prewar figure.

After the war the rolling stock had to be completely restored; the retreating fascist armies had destroyed every important railway, river, and highway bridge in the country, and hauled away or destroyed 85 percent of all rolling stock. War damage, however, was liquidated within a relatively short time, and in 1949 there were already as many railway carriages and locomotives on the lines as there were before the war.

Among the main Hungarian railways, starting from Budapest, are several international lines: a route to the USSR through Budapest, Debrecen, Nyíregyháza, and Záhony; the Budapest–Hegyesshalom–Vienna line; the line connecting Czechoslovakia with Rumania through Szob, Budapest, and Békéscsaba; the line to Yugoslavia from Budapest through Kelibia; the Budapest–Miskolc–Sátoraljaújhely line; and the Budapest–Nagykanizsa–Triester main line, the latter touching Lake Balaton.

In modern times, the Hungarian railway system has been updated, and in the course of this procedure obsolete steam locomotives were gradually replaced by diesel traction. The railway line connecting Budapest to Miskolc, the chief industrial center of the north, had already been electrified in 1970. With new, fast trains being put in service, transport on lines leading to main railway junctions and to spots attracting foreign tourists will be better than ever before.

The worst railroad accident in Hungary, a collision at or near Budapest on 22 December 1968, killed forty-three people.

According to Janes, in 1978 the Hungarian State Railways had a route length of 7,550 kilometers (4,691 miles) and a track length (including sidings, shops, and yards) of 12,523 kilometers (7,782) miles, all in 1.435-meter (4-foot 6½ inch) gauge.

The following six illustrations include a map of the railroad network of Hungary and five photographs of various Hungarian steam locomotives.

The Hungarian State Railways had built in 1896, at the Floridsdorf shops, a combination rack and adhesion locomotive known as class T IVb. A model engine, no. 4281, is pictured. These four-cylinder locomotives had the following characteristics:

Cylinders	
Outside, normal use	19.6 by 19.6 inches
Rack use	15.5 by 17.7 inches
Coupled wheels	3-foot 5.3-inch diamter
Grate area	25 square feet
Total heating surface	1785 square feet
Tractive effort	30,800 pounds
Operational weight	70.5 tons
Capacities	1900 gallons water; 4 tons coal.

(Courtesy: Hungarian State Railways)

A model on display in Budapest is shown here. This is a class 2, type 4–4–2, steam locomotive used widely on the Hungarian State Railways starting in 1901. Specifications on the original engine were as follows:

Cylinders	20 by 26.7 inches
Coupled wheels	6-foot 10.6-inch diameter
Boiler	
Grate area	32.25 square feet
Heating surface	1547 square feet
Boiler pressure	
Tractive effort	14.450 pounds
Operational weight	102.75 tons (engine plus tender)
Tender capacities	4675 gallons water; 7 tons coal.

(Courtesy: Hungarian State Railways)

The Hungarian State Railways, after World War I, used a number of massive type 4–6–0 express locomotives of series 328. Fifty-eight were constructed in the Budapest shops in 1919, and Henschel & Sohn in Germany built one hundred additional engines about this same time. Characteristics were as follows:

Cylinders	22.4 by 25.5 inches
Coupled wheels	6-foot diameter
Brotan boiler	
Grate area	35 square feet
Superheater	486.3 square feet (Schmidt)
Heating area	1598.4 square feet total
Boiler pressure	176 pounds per square inch
Tractive effort	17,592 pounds at 60 percent boiler pressure
Operating weight	110.4 tons (engine plus tender), adhesion 42.7 tons.

Pictured is a model of the above locomotive which is exhibited in the personal collection of Dr. Alexander Varga.
(Courtesy: Hungarian State Railways)

Pictured is a model of a series 424, type 4–8–0 steam locomotive. The original tender engines, built in Hungarian shops, were placed in service in 1924. Up to 1947 about 145 units were manufactured. Specifications were:

Cylinders	23.6 by 26 inches
Coupled drive wheels	3.5-foot diameter
Boiler	
Grate area	47.8 square feet
Superheater	624.3 square feet (Schmidt)
Total heating surface	1740.2 square feet
Working pressure	190 pounds per square inch
Tractive force	22,848 pounds at 60 percent boiler working pressure
Operating weight	146 tons (engine plus tender).

(Courtesy: Dr. Alexander Varga)

A model locomotive in the personal collection of Dr. Alex. Varga of Budapest, Hungary is shown. The prototype engine was the largest nonarticulated type used in Hungary starting in 1950. These type 4–6–4 locomotives, originally manufactured in Hungary, had the following specifications:

Cylinders	21.6 by 26 inches
Coupled wheels	6-foot 6.75-inch diameter
Boiler	
Grate area	59.2 square feet (mechanical stoker)
Heating surface	2583 square feet total
Steam pressure	256 pounds per square inch
Tractive effort	25,760 pounds
Operational weight	107.7 tons (engine)
Tender capacities	5500 gallons water; 12.7 tons coal
Locomotive height	15 feet 3 inches.

(Courtesy: Hungarian State Railways)

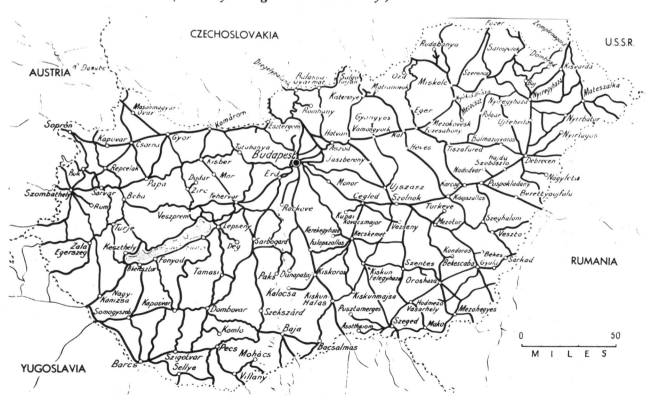

Railway map of Hungary.
(*Courtesy:* Janes World Railways)

INDIA

RAILROADS IN INDIA, ORIGINALLY SUGGESTED in 1843, were slow to materialize due to deep doubts as to their feasibility, commercial value, and profitability. Eventually their merits became evident and there also arose a realization that the presence of the railroad itself could stimulate development of greater traffic. In 1845 the East Indian and the Great Indian Peninsular Railway companies—both private organizations—were formed, and four years later the government arranged for these two companies to construct railways in the presidencies of Bengal and Bombay. Several railway systems, essentially prototype lines, were initiated about 1850. One ran from Howrah, opposite Calcutta on the right bank of the Hooghly River, to the coalfields of Raniganj, 150 miles inland; a second line ran from Bombay east to Thana, twenty-one miles inland. The latter route became part of the Great Indian Peninsular Railway, which opened for public service on 18 April 1853. A third prototype railway, extending from Madras for sixty-five miles, was finished in 1856. The first of the imperial state railways, which opened near Bombay in 1873, soon had 114 miles of track.

Thus was inaugurated a new era of rapid economic development and social change in India. Railroads were normally financed by loans where the British-controlled Indian government gave a ninety-nine-year guarantee of 4½ to 5 percent interest on all capital invested. By and large, railway construction in India was carried out in an enormously wasteful manner. The first lines in India were all "gold plated" and inefficient. The railroads were early perceived as a means of facilitating the distribution and sale of British-made products to India's still unopened interior as well as transporting Indian cotton and coal to world markets. The rail lines were also strategically recognized as rapid means to move troops to trouble spots, and it was believed that thus a substantial reduction in British Indian garrisons could eventually be achieved. Railroads also provided a means of combating the famine conditions that were all too common in various sections of India.

Visionary officials in the Indian government were able to propose a broad scheme for railway construction, designed to link Bombay, Madras and Calcutta, including a trunk line up the Ganges River from Calcutta to Delhi and Lahore. British private development was favored under the government's guaranteed interest agreements. David Jones (1834–1906), the well-known English locomotive designer and engineer, was an important consultant on the Indian railways in the early 1880s. Many in Britain believed the overall railway program would "confer on India the greatest boon she would ever derive from the power of England."

From the beginning, the Indian population developed a fondness for railroad travel that almost reached a national passion among the lower castes. They took to the railroads with eager interest and persistent delight. Railroad ticket offices were always besieged by more riders than there were railway carriage seats to accommodate them. Indians often engaged in heated discourse with ticket clerks in an unlawful attempt to bargain down the cost of the fares. Most natives traveled third-class, which

The early 5.5-foot gauge Bombay, Baroda & Central India Railway, incorporated in 1855, first used a British 2–4–0 locomotive built by E. B. Wilson & Company at their Leeds railway foundry. The design was almost identical with Alexander Allan's "Crew" class of goods engines built at the Crewe Works between 1843 and 1857. This locomotive had outside inclined cylinders 14 by 24 inches with Howe's link motion. The coupled wheels were 5 feet in diameter. The lead-ing pair of 3-foot 4-inch wheels were fastened to axle boxes on the outside frames. Two spring-balance lever safety valves were fitted to the boiler, one on a dome over the firebox and the other on the barrel. Operational weight of the engine was 22.4 tons. A model of the above locomotive is on display in the Science Museum of London and is pictured.
(Courtesy: Science Museum, London) 2069

left first- and second-class facilities virtually abandoned. For each person embarking on a train trip, there were dozens of relatives and other well-wishers on hand at the crowded station to see him off.

One of the oldest Indian railroads was the 5-foot 6-inch gauge line constructed by the Bombay, Baroda, and Central India Railway, which was incorporated in 1855. The first section of eighty miles was opened between Surat and Baroda, on the west coast, in 1856. A 2–4–0 locomotive built by E. B. Wilson & Company of Leeds, England, was the first engine used on that line (see illustration). Additional railways were constructed rapidly, and by 1859 there were 432 miles of rail in active operation. All tracks, cars, and locomotives were produced by private British midland steel companies, where the market was one of constant expansion and profit.

By 1862 Calcutta was linked by rail with Allahabad in northeast India, about 450 miles distant, and Bombay became the center of a rail network in the central and southern part of the country. By 1869 there were five thousand miles of railway track laid in India. With a host of coal mines operating at Ranaganj, coal became the official fuel for all Indian locomotives.

In 1870 a rail line of about 1,200 miles officially linked Calcutta with Bombay through Allahabad. The railway from Bombay to Madras, about 650 miles, was completed in October 1873. By 1880 there were a total of 9,000 miles of railroad track in active use in India, and at the end of 1882 there were 10,250 miles, with 2,332 more under construction. In 1888 the broad-gauge Bengal–Nagpur Railway was opened between Calcutta and Bombay, which followed a shorter course (approximately 975 miles) across central India, greatly diminishing the route mileage compared to the earlier path through Allahabad.

Railroad construction was reaching mania proportions by 1884, when India had the following active railways: East Indian Railway (1,509 miles), guaranteed railways (4,641 miles), assisted companies (256 miles). Bombay merchants, through the Chamber of Commerce, were exerting powerful pressures on the government to build an additional two to three thousand miles of track each year for at least the next ten years, at an estimated cost of $100 million per year. In 1883 profits from rail operations amounted to 5.07 percent on capital costs; in 1885–86 the figure was 5.84 percent, and in 1886–87 a return on investment came to 5.90 percent. The best profits were seen on the Great Indian Peninsular and the Rajputana–Molwa Railways.

India, like so many other countries, had many controversies over what gauge or gauges should be used on the railways. An early English recommendation was for the standard 4-foot 8½-inch gauge. After many arguments, in 1849 a gauge of 5 feet 6 inches was finally settled on. Then, in 1869 the government, under the rule of Lord Laurence, decided to change the original rail gauge to 1 meter, or 3 feet 3⅜ inches, using the lightest rails and rolling stock compatible with the requirements of Indian traffic. Nonetheless, by 1884 there were still five different railroad gauges in India: 5½ feet, 1 meter, 4 feet, 2½ feet, and 2 feet. In 1884, with continuing disputes, it took a select committee of the British House of Commons to decide on a 5-foot 6-inch gauge for leading trunk lines and a meter gauge for secondary, lighter traffic lines.

Through the years, the railways continued to grow under the auspices of major British investors. By 1920 the government owned about 70 percent of the railroads, but operations were controlled by private firms with headquarters in London. In 1922, following recommendations of the Acworth Committee (a British advisory committee formed in 1921 to improve the profits of Indian Railways) management of the rail network reverted directly to the Indian government. Some electric traction was introduced in 1925. The fortunes of the railways deteriorated considerably starting in the depression years of the 1930s, accelerated later by extensive military demands during World War II.

With another expansion of the railroads after World War II, and an accompanying increase in passenger and freight traffic, significant shortages of rolling stock and locomotives developed. To establish a degree of self-sufficiency and to cut down on import dependence, India in 1950, three years after gaining its independence, embarked on a program of domestic production. The Chittaranjan Locomotive Works was the first of several production facilities to build Indian railway engines. Up to 1972, three thousand steam locomotives and three hundred electric engines had been produced. In addition, three hundred diesel locomotives had been manufactured since 1963 at the Varanasi plant. Passenger coaches have been produced since 1955 at the Integral Coach Factory in Perambur, Madras. Freight car construction has been handled mostly by fifteen private manufacturers and, to a limited extent, by government-owned workshops.

Next to Russia, India has the longest rail system in the world under the control of a single administration. In 1972 there were about thirty-six thousand miles of active track, carrying close to eleven thousand trains daily, making stops at seven thousand stations, with a daily travel distance of about eight hundred thousand miles. In the process, they moved about a half million tons of freight and over 6.5 million passengers per day. In 1972 there were about 1.3 million employees directly involved in the operation of the Indian railways. It has been estimated by the Indian Railways administration in 1972 that 5 percent of the population of India directly or indirectly received a daily stipend from the railroad industry. Commodities transported consisted mainly of food grain, coal, ore, cement, fertilizer, and petroleum products. Rail operations in 1972 were carried out with 9,500 steam, 1,250 diesel, and 620 electric locomotives, utilizing 387,000 freight cars, 24,500 passenger coaches, and 1,830 electric multiple-unit rail cars.

The highest summit in India is traversed by the North Eastern (formerly Darjeeling) Himalayan Railway. The 2-foot-gauge line reaches its highest altitude at Ghoom, 7,407 feet above sea level.

The longest railway bridge in Asia is in India—the Upper Sone bridge on the Grand Chord route between Delhi and Calcutta. This was completed on 27 February 1900, and stretches 1.9 miles. Other long railroad bridges in India are as follows:

The Godavari Bridge over the River Godavari between Madras and Calcutta. This was opened on 6 August 1900, and has a length of 1.72 miles.
The Mahanadi Bridge on the South Eastern Railway, opened 11 March 1900, and is 1.30 miles long.
The Izat Bridge over the Ganges River at Allerhabad on the North Eastern Railway has a length of 1.20 miles.
The Hardinge Bridge over the Ganges River north of Calcutta has a length of 1.11 miles and carries the main trunk line between Calcutta and Siliguri at the foot of the Himalaya mountains. This was opened 4 March 1915.

India's worst railway disaster occurred 23 November 1956, at Marudaiyar River, with a loss of 143 lives—a derailment accident.

In 1978 according to *Janes World Railways*, India had the following rail gauges and route and track lengths:

Gauge	Route Length	Track Length
1.676 meter	18,667 miles	26,532 miles
1.0 meter	15,876 miles	21,690 miles
0.762 meter and		
0.610 meter	2,781 miles	3,125 miles
Totals	37,324 miles	51,347 miles

Steam Locomotives of India

British locomotives were naturally favored in India for about a century, and many of the English railway engine traditions continued until India became an independent nation in 1947. Standardization of steam locomotives was widely practiced over a large part of the Indian broad-gauge rail lines, and by the early twentieth century two popular British designs were being used in great numbers: type 4–4–0 for express purposes and type 0–6–0 for freight services. This process of establishing standard types of engines for different purposes continued after India attained her independence. Most engines were traditionally British in character, being mostly two-cylinder simples with outside Walschaerts gear. Passenger locomotives consisted of three types of Pacifics: class XA for light branch work, class XB for medium traffic service, and class XC for heavy express routes. The corresponding freight types had 2–8–2 wheel arrangements: class XD was used for medium freight service (illustration ID-14), and class XE for the heaviest freight duties.

Before World War I, the Bengal–Nagpur Railway purchased a few four-cylinder de Glehn compound engines, type 4–4–2, from the North British Locomotive Company. These worked so well that after that war additional compound machines, called Super-Pacifics, were purchased. These were similar to the Brévilles, type 4–6–2, used so successfully on the Northern Railway of France. The Super-Pacifics had standard class XC boilers that readily handled Bengal bituminous coal. Boiler pressures were unusually high, at 250 pounds per square inch. Tractive force was about 40,500 pounds at 85 percent boiler working pressure. Operating weights were 170.5 tons, engine and tender.

Even though engine standardization was widely established, the major railways of India, including the North Western, the Great Indian Peninsular, and the Bengal Nagpur, which independent man-

agements and engineering philosophies, inevitably sought variations from standard designs. Such modifications included thermic siphons in the fireboxes, Caprotti valve gear, roller bearings, balanced slide valves with low-pressure cylinders, and the use of de Glehn four-cylinder Pacific locomotives.

The worldwide depression of the early 1930s played havoc in India, especially with the program of replacing worn-out locomotives. This situation continued for about ten years. In 1942 Baldwin received an order for a simple two-cylinder Pacific engine of Indian design based on long experience with the class XB and XC machines. In the latter days of steam in India, only two types of 4–6–2 and 2–8–2 engines were continued on the broad-gauge lines. These newly designed passenger locomotives were supplied by Baldwin, by the Canadian & Montreal firms in North America, and by shops in Poland, India, and Austria. The freight engines, type 2–8–2, were constructed in Great Britain. A type 4–6–2 Pacific class WP engine is shown.

In the era of British control of India, significant numbers of meter-gauge railroads and locomotive styles were also in use, providing an interesting array of engines for the "Railroad Buffs," consisting of various 2–6–0, 0–6–0, and 4–4–0 types. After independence, the meter-gauge railways continued to comprise a major part of the Indian transportation network. Consistent with broad-gauge locomotive development, two types of 4–6–2 and 2–8–2 engines were widely utilized on these narrow-gauge lines, for passenger and for mixed traffic and freight respectively. These engines were supplied locally as well as by overseas manufacturers.

British firms provided the pioneer Indian railways not only with the steam locomotives but also with the iron rail and the cars. This was true of the Bombay, Baroda and Central India Railway in 1855.

A series of type 2–2–2 passenger tank engines were built in 1856–57 by Kitson & Company and by Stothel & Slaughter of Bristol, England, for suburban service between Raniganj and Howrah, just west of Calcutta.

In 1860 various Indian colliery donkey locomotives were provided by E. B. Wilson and Manning Wardle of Leeds. In 1862 Sharp, Stewart & Company built several large 4–6–0 engines, the first of this type ever, for work on the Ghat inclines of the

In 1865 Neilson & Company furnished the Bombay, Baroda & Central India Railway with five type 2–4–0 tender locomotives (running numbers 45–49). Specifications follow:

Gauge	5 feet 6 inches
Cylinders	16 by 22 inches
Coupled drivers	5-foot diameter
Boiler	

Heating surface	1107.3 square feet
Working pressure	(not available)
Operating weights	
Engine	31 tons plus 12 hundredweights
Tender	(not available)
Tender capacities	1850 gallons water; 200 cubic feet coal.

Photograph shows only the engine.
(Courtesy: Mitchell Library, Glasgow) E 284

The East Indian Railway in 1867 purchased a number of type 0–6–0 tender locomotives from Dubs & Company with the following specifications:

Gauge	5 feet 6 inches
Cylinders	17 by 24 inches
Drive wheels	5-foot diameter
Boiler	
Heating surface	1178.4 square feet

Working pressure	(not available)
Operating weights	
Engine	35 tons plus 16 hundredweights
Tender	26 tons
Tender capacities	1700 gallons water; 150 cubic feet coal.

(Courtesy: Mitchell Library, Glasgow) D/E 137

Great Indian Peninsular Railway. These engines were unique in using outside skid brakes for downgrade travel on mountain service.

In the period 1865 to 1900, the various Indian railways were supplied by steam locomotives constructed by Neilson & Company, Dubs and Company, and Sharp, Stewart & Company. These various tank and tender machines had several wheel arrangements: 2–4–0, 4–4–0, 0–6–0, and 0–6–4. See six illustrations.

From about 1902, various intercity broad-gauge passenger railways adopted as standard a two-cylinder, type 4–6–0 engine of British manufacture. Deliveries of such machines continued until 1908,

301

In 1873 the Indian State Railway placed in service an indeterminate number of type 0–4–4, class B tank locomotives purchased from Dubs & Company. Specifications follow:

Gauge	3 feet 3⅜ inches
Cylinders	11 by 18 inches
Coupled drive wheels	3-foot 6-inch diameter
Boiler	
Heating surface	427 square feet
Working pressure	140 pounds per square inch
Tractive force	5445 pounds
Operating weight	21 tons plus 5 hundredweights
Capacities	650 gallons water; 46 cubic feet coal.

(Courtesy: Mitchell Library, Glasgow) E 736

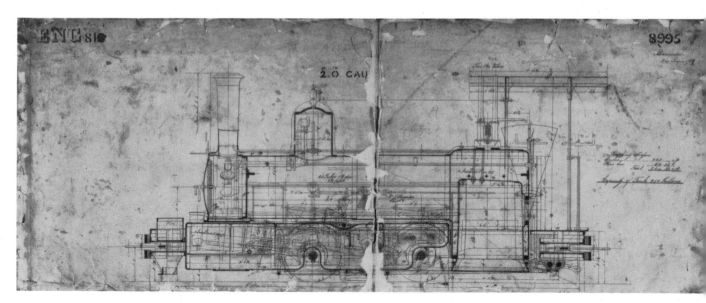

An old drawing of a 2-foot gauge, type 0–4–0 tank locomotive built by Sharp Stewart of Manchester, England in 1888 for the Darjeeling & Himalayan Railway. The only data visible on this drawing were as follows:

Cylinders	10-inch diameter by 14-inch stroke (inclined 1 in 10)
Drive wheels	2-foot 2-inch diameter
Boiler tubes	65 1⅝-inch diameter, area 228 square feet
Firebox	36.33 square feet
Total heating surface	264.33 square feet
Tank capacity	250 gallons water
Operating weight	15½ tons.

(Courtesy: Science Museum, London)

The above saddle tank engines were used in very difficult mountain terrain where the major ascent included a sixteen-mile section with an average grade of 1 in 29, having curves of seventy-foot radius. The last of this type was constructed by the North British Locomotive Company in 1927 making a total then in service of thirty-two; of these twenty-seven were on active status in 1976.

The Great India Peninsula Railway in 1893 received from Neilson & Company several type 4–4–0 tender locomotives with the following specifications:

Gauge	5 feet 6 inches
Cylinders	17¼ by 26 inches
Drivers	5-foot 6-inch diameter
Boiler	
Heating surface	1111 square feet
Working pressure	150 pounds per square inch
Operating weights	
Engine	43 tons plus 12 hundredweights
Tender	29 tons plus 1 hundredweight
Tender capacities	2000 gallons water; 200 cubic feet coal
Locomotive class	A/2.

(Courtesy: Mitchell Library, Glasgow) E 699

Sharp, Stewart & Company in 1893 constructed several type 0–6–0 compound tender engines for the Bombay, Baroda & Central India Railway. Only a few specifications were available:

Gauge	5 feet 6 inches
Cylinders	19 by 26 inches and 27 by 26 inches
Coupled drive wheels	4-foot 7½-inch diameter
Equipped with Worsdell compound engines	
Water capacity	2000 gallons.

(Courtesy: Mitchell Library, Glasgow) E 1017

by which time superheaters were added and various front-end modifications were made. Many of these locomotives survived until about 1950. The same type locomotives were used on the Bengal Nagpur Railway, where they were designated class G. Later, type 4–4–2 Atlantic express engines were used. Big 2–8–0 locomotives handled long-haul and heavy freight trains while 4–4–0 and 0–6–0 locomotives were employed with lighter passenger and freight traffic. On the Ghat grades, large tank locomotives of the 2–8–4 type were utilized along with 2–8–2 and 0–8–4 types. Still heavier engines operated on the GIPR (Great Indian Peninsular Railway), such as 2–10–0 tender locomotives.

In 1912 several type 4–6–0 standard passenger locomotives for the Madras & Southern Mahratta Railway were furnished by Kitson & Company.

In the early 1920s a heavy freight engine of the XD class was widely used. The Bengal Nagpur Railway purchased from the North British Locomotive Company a number of heavy-duty 2–8–2 tank locomotives.

Starting in 1923, the Baldwin Locomotive Works built various steam locomotives for the Indian railways. Pictured is a type 0–6–4 engine designed for industrial service with the Punjab Public Works Department. A type 4–6–2 Pacific locomotive was also purchased in 1924 for use on the 5-foot 6-inch gauge Madras & Southern Mahratta Railway. In the same year, Baldwin also shipped to India a number of type 2–6–6–2 Mallett locomotives designed to handle the heavy grades on parts of the North

Neilson & Company in 1902 constructed several type 0–6–0, class F tender locomotives for His Royal Highness The Nizam's Guaranteed State Railway. These steam engines had the following specifications:

Gauge	3 feet 3⅜ inches
Cylinders	14 by 20 inches
Coupled drive wheels	3-foot 6½-inch diameter
Boiler	
Heating surface	645.6 square feet
Working pressure	160 pounds per square inch
Operating weights	
Engine	23 tons plus 12 hundredweights
Tender	18 tons plus 13 hundredweights
Tender capacities	1500 gallons water; 140 cubic feet coal.

(Courtesy: Mitchell Library, Glasgow) E 876

The Great India Peninsula Railway in 1903 purchased fifteen type 2–6–0 tender engines from Sharp, Stewart & Company. These machines bore identification numbers 217–31 and had the following characteristics:

Gauge	3 feet 3⅜ inches
Cylinders	18½ by 26 inches
Drive wheels	4-foot 6½-inch diameter
Tender water capacity	3000 gallons.

(Courtesy: Mitchell Library, Glasgow) L1200

In 1904 the Indian State Railways procured for the Eastern Bengal Railway a number of type 4–6–0 tender locomotives from the North British Locomotive Company; these were the first standard meter gauge engines used in India. Specifications follow:

Gauge	3 feet 3⅜ inches
Cylinders	15½ by 22 inches
Drive wheels	4-foot 9-inch diameter
Boiler	
Heating area	1062 square feet
Working pressure	180 pounds per square inch
Operating weights	
Engine	33 tons plus 12 hundredweights
Tender	22 tons plus 19 hundredweights
Tender water capacity	2000 gallons.

(Courtesy: Mitchell Library, Glasgow) L 1

The North British Locomotive Company in 1908 supplied the East Indian Railways with ten type 4–4–2 tender engines (running numbers 1173–82. Specifications are listed as follows:

Gauge	5 feet 6 inches
Cylinders	19 by 26 inches
Drive wheels	6-foot 6½-inch diameter
Boiler	
Heating surface	1615 square feet
Working pressure	180 pounds per square inch
Operating weights	
Engine	60 tons plus 13 hundredweights
Tender	37 tons plus 11 hundredweights
Tender capacities	3150 gallons water; 250 cubic feet coal.

(Courtesy: Mitchell Library, Glasgow) L 258

In 1909 the North British Locomotive Company constructed five class P, type 0–8–2, tank engines for the South Indian Railways. These machines were identified as P1 to P4 and were actually Abt rack and adhesion locomotives combined. Specifications follow:

Gauge	3 feet 3⅜ inches
Cylinders	16½ by 16 inches and 16½ by 14¼ inches
Drive wheels	2-foot 8-inch diameter
Boiler	
Heating surface	1100 square feet
Working pressure	180 pounds per square inch
Tractive force	18,370 pounds
Operating weight	49 tons plus 12 hundredweights
Water capacity	1000 gallons.

(Courtesy: Mitchell Library, Glasgow) L 371

Pictured is a model of a type 4–6–0 steam locomotive originally constructed by Kitson & Company in 1912 for passenber service on the 5.5-foot gauge Madras & Southern Mahratta Railway of India. This was one of four similar engines built by Kitson at the same time. Howe's link motion was fitted, controlled by a screw and hand wheel. The connecting rods drove the second coupled axle, the eccentric rods being bent to clear the first coupled axle. The boiler had a conical barrel with its center 8.75 feet above the tracks. It contained 173 steel tubes with a 2½-inch outside diameter. The fire box was 8 feet long. A double Ramsbottom safety valve was installed to regulate the steam pressure. Feed water was supplied to the boiler by two injectors placed below the foot plate. Specifications were:

Cylinders	20 by 26 inches
Coupled drive wheels	6-foot 2-inch diameter
boiler	
Dimensions	5 by 15.6 feet
Grate area	32 square feet
Firebox	158 square feet
Heating area	1617 square feet
Working pressure	180 pounds per square inch
Tractive force	22,767 pounds at 90 percent steam pressure
Operating weight	112.85 tons (engine plus tender)
Tender capacities	4000 gallons water; 7.5 tons coal
Overall length	61.56 feet.

This model was built in India in 1920–22 and is now on display in London.
(Courtesy: London Science Museum) 2400

Shown is one of two standard heavy freight engines, type 2–8–2, used on the various railways of India in the 1920s. This class XD locomotive operated on the majority of broad-gauge Indian rail lines.
(Courtesy: O. S. Nock; Great Steam Locomotives of All Time)

The Bengal Nagpur Railway in 1920 purchased from the North British Locomotive Company fourteen class L, type 2–8–2, tank locomotives (nos. 450–63) with these specifications:

Gauge	5 feet 6 inches
Cylinders	20 by 26 inches
Drive wheels	4-foot 3-inch diameter
Boiler	

Heating surface	1450 square feet
Working pressure	180 pounds per square inch
Tractive force	27,530 pounds
Operating weight	78 tons plus 16 hundredweights
Capacities	1400 gallons water; 135 cubic feet coal.

(Courtesy: Mitchell Library, Glasgow) L738

This illustration shows a model of a locomotive built in 1923 by the North British Locomotive Company, one of twenty-five type 2–8–0 freight engines, for the 5.5-foot gauge East Indian Railways. Piston valves above the cylinders were driven by Walschaert valve gear, controlled by a screw and hand wheel. The connecting rods drove the third coupled axle and underhung plate springs were fitted. The front end had a Bissel truck with 43-inch wheels. The boiler barrel stood 8.79 feet above the rails. Water was supplied through a top feed valve by a Weir pump mounted beside the firebox. The model was built by Jamalpur, India in 1924 and is presently housed in the London Science Museum.

Specifications were as follows:

Cylinders	22 by 26 inches
8 coupled drive wheels	56.5-inch diameter
Boiler	

Dimensions	68.5 inches by 12.5 feet
Grate area	32 square feet
Firebox	172 square feet (Belpaire)
Superheater	390 square feet (Marine & Loco.)
Number tubes	
134 2¼-inch outside diameter type	
28 5¼-inch outside diameter	
Total heating surface	2082 square feet
Working pressure	160 pounds per square inch
Tractive force	32,070 pounds at 90 percent boiler pressure
Operating weight	138.03 tons (engine plus tender)
Tender capacities	4500 gallons water; 10 tons coal
Overall length	64.06 feet.

(Courtesy: London Science Museum,) 2397

This is a Baldwin type 4–6–2 locomotive built in 1924 for the 5-foot 6-inch gauge Madras & Southern Mahratta Railway in India. This engine, no. 900, a clean-cut Pacific type, had movable window shutters on the engine cab and front part of a roofed over tender to shield the work crew from monsoon rains. General specifications were as follows:

Cylinders	22 by 28 inches
Coupled drive wheels	74-inch diameter
Engine weight	184,000 pounds.

(Courtesy: Frederick Westing collection)

In 1925 the Darjeeling Himalayan Railway procured from the North British Locomotive Company three class B, type 0–4–0, tank engines with the following characteristics:

Gauge	2 feet
Cylinders	11 by 14 inches
Drive wheels	2-foot 2-inch diameter
Boiler	
Heating surface	316 square feet
Working pressure	140 pounds per square inch
Tractive force	6840 pounds
Operating weight	15 tons plus 22 hundredweights
Running numbers	45B–47B
Capacities	380 gallons water; 34 cubic feet coal.

(Courtesy: Mitchell Library, Glasgow) L 806

Western Railway, where rail weight limitations were eighteen gross tons per axle. These engines had four cylinders of 19 by 30 inches and 29.5 by 30 inches. Drive wheels had a diameter of 52 inches, and operating engine weight was 274,000 pounds.

A handsome locomotive, of which 154 were built between 1924 and 1950, was the British class HPS, type 4–6–0. These engines were widely used in India and they turned in a commendable performance.

From 1925 to 1929 the North British Locomotive Company supplied India with various type 0–4–0T, 4–6–2, and 2–8–2 engines.

Pictured too is a Beyer Garratt type 4–8–2 + 2–8–4 Beyer Garrett steam locomotive built in 1940 for the Bengal Nagpur Railway.

A small superheated engine built in 1942 by Baldwin for the 2-foot-gauge Mysore Iron & Steel Works is shown. In 1950 Baldwin supplied one of its last steam locomotives, a type 2–8–2 Mikado, for the meter-gauge government railways.

One of the most outstanding locomotives used in India in modern times was the streamlined class WP Pacific, over two thousand of which were still active in 1972. These engines were built between 1947 and 1967, mostly by firms in Austria, India, and Poland, and by Baldwin and the Canadian & Montreal firms in North America. The Pacifics at that time took on all heavy express duties on the Indian railways even though their operating speeds averaged only about forty miles per hour. These locomotives normally were built without such modern aids as mechanical stokers, and consequently two firemen were always required. Other Pacific-type engines used in India were class YP, type 4–6–2, 100 of which were furnished by the North British Locomotive Company in 1952–53.

A large number of steam locomotives were built by the Chittaranjan Locomotive Works, starting in 1950 with class WG heavy freight engines for broad-gauge tracks. In 1950 production amounted to eight WG units per month, which was increased to fourteen units per month by 1956. The 1959 production run included class WP Pacifics for express service on the main lines, class YT, type 2–6–2 tank engines for shunting and suburban duties, and class WL engines for light passenger service on branch lines. One of the last locomotive classes constructed was class YG, type 2–8–2; these were

The North British Locomotive Company in 1928 supplied the Bengal-Nagpur Railway with eighteen class M, type 4–6–2, de Glehn four-cylinder compound tender locomotives (nos. 792–809). Specifications follow:

Gauge	5 feet 6 inches
Cylinders	
Inside	16½ by 26 inches
Outside	25 by 26 inches
Coupled drivers	6-foot 2-inch diameter
Boiler	
Heating area	3076 square feet
Operating pressure	250 pounds per square inch
Tractive force	28700 pounds at 60 percent boiler weight pressure
Operating weghts	
Engine	105 tons
Tender	65 tons plus 12 hundredweights
Tender capacities	4750 gallons water; 10 tons coal.

(Courtesy: Mitchell Library, Glasgow) L 854

In 1929 the North British Locomotive Company supplied His Royal Highness The Nizam's Guaranteed State Railway with a number of class XD, type 2–8–2, tender locomotives. These engines had the following specifications:

Gauge	5 feet 6 inches
Cylinders	22½ by 28 inches
Drive wheels	5-foot 1½-inch diameter
Boiler	
Heating surface	2716 square feet
Working pressure	180 pounds per square inch
Tractive force	31,100 pounds
Operating weights	
Engine	96 tons plus 15 hundredweights
Tender	64 tons plus 16 hundredweights
Tender capacities	4500 gallons water; (not available) coal.

(Courtesy: Mitchell Library, Glasgow) L 862

Pictured is a model of a Beyer Garratt locomotive used on the 5-foot 6-inch gauge Bengal-Nagpur Railway of India (now named South Eastern Railway). Four such engines were built by this manufacturer in 1940 for a steeply graded and curved fifty-four mile rail section of the above railway leading to the Anuppur-Chirmiri coal fields (approximate latitude 23° 10′ north, longitude 82° east). Specifications on these huge Beyer Garratt locomotives were as follows:

Cylinders (four)	20.5 by 26 inches
Coupled wheels	4 feet 8 inches
Wheel arrangement	4–8–2 plus 2–8–4
Boiler	
Diameter	7 feet
Grate area	70 square feet
Total heating area	4114 square feet
Working pressure	210 pounds per square inch
Tractive effort	68,660 pounds
Operating weight	230 tons
Dimensions	101.5 feet overall.

(Courtesy: Bassett-Lowke, Ltd.)

Shown here is a tiny "Mike" superheated locomotive
built by Baldwin in September 1942 for the 2 foot-
gauge Mysore Iron & Steel Works of India. Note outside frames and counterbalanced cranks extending beyond the drive wheels. Cylinders were 12 by 18 inches,
boiler diameter was 48 inches, drive wheels 33-inch
diameter, engine weight 66,800 pounds.
(Courtesy: Frederick Westing collection)

One of the standard streamlined heavy express passenger locomotiyes, class WP Pacific type 4–6–2,
widely used in India beginning in 1947 is pictured.
These engines, of which two thousand were reported
to be in sevice in the early 1970s, were built by Baldwin and Canadian & Montreal in North America and
by manufacturers in Austria, Poland, and India. This
is a photograph of the famous Himalayan Express.
(Courtesy: India Ministry of Railways)

Over the period 1952–53 the Indian Government Railways purchased from the North British Locomotive Company, one hundred class YP, type 4–6–2 tender locomotives. Specifications were as follows:

Gauge	3 feet 3⅜ inches
Running numbers	1921–2020
Cylinders	15¼ by 24 inches
Drive wheels	4-foot 6-inch diameter
Boiler	
Heating area	1442 square feet
Working pressure	210 pounds per square inch
Tractive force	18,450 pounds at 85 percent boiler weight pressure
Operating weights	
Engine	57 tons plus 3 hundredweights
Tender	41 tons plus 1 hundredweight
Tender water capacity	3000 gallons.

(Courtesy: Mitchell Library, Glasgow) L21 2d series

built in India up to the very end of steam production in 1972. Another late class of steam locomotives built at the Chittaranjan Locomotive Works were the class WL, type 2–6–2 locomotives.

In the early 1970s India still had an estimated nine thousand steam locomotives handling about 50 percent of all rail traffic. Included in this total were about a thousand type 4–6–2 Pacific engines on broad-gauge lines and another thousand on meter-gauge lines.

India in 1978 still had a huge network of narrow-gauge railways: 21,690 miles of meter-gauge tracks, and 3,125 miles of a combination of 0.762-meter (2-foot 6-inch) and 0.610-meter (2-foot) gauge tracks. In 1972 an estimated five hundred steam locomotives of a great variety were still in opera-

tion on the Indian narrow-gauge lines. Concurrently, highway truck transportation was providing serious competition, and some narrow-gauge railways were abandoned. Also, the introduction of diesel traction was making inroads on the old-time narrow-gauge rail lines. Several Indian railways had a gauge of 2 feet 6 inches:

1. Eastern regions—the Nabadwip Ghat & Shantipur Railway used many 2–4–0 tank locomotives.

2. Western regions—various systems used many 0–6–2 engines.

3. Operations out of Delhi used 2–6–2 tank engines. Shahdara Saharahpur Railway.

4. Darjeeling Himalaya Railway.

This illustration shows a 1970 picture of a class YG, type 2–8–2, locomotive, one of the last steam engines built anywhere for a major railroad. This locomotive was constructed by the Chittaranjan Locomotive Works in India.
(Courtesy: India Ministry of Railways)

This is a picture of a class CS, type 2–4–0, tank engine used on the 2-foot 6-inch gauge Shantipur–Nabadwip Ghat line of India in the 1960s.
(Courtesy: India Ministry of Railways)

Shown is a work engine used on the Delhi Pacific Railway in India. No specification data were available.
(Courtesy: La Vie du Rail, Paris)

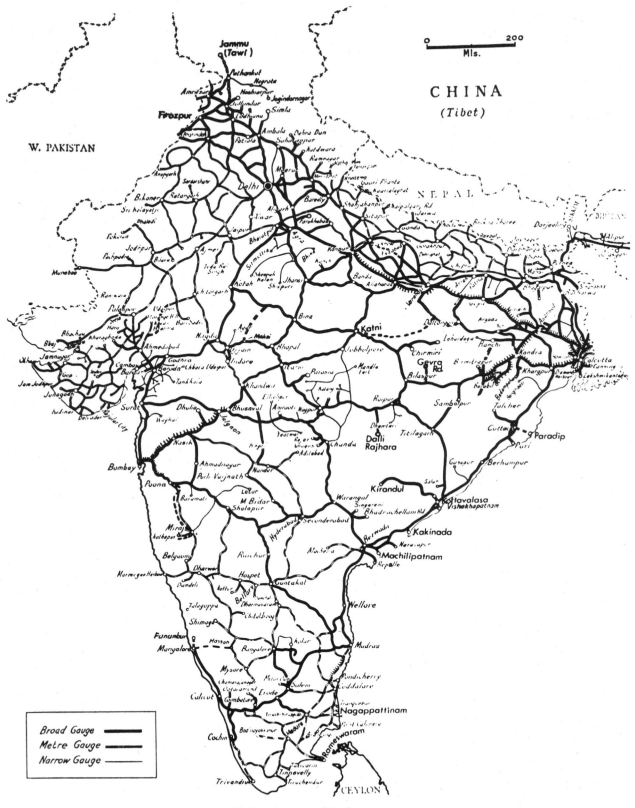

Railway map of India.
(*Courtesy:* Janes World Railways)

INDONESIA

INDONESIA IS THE WORLD'S LARGEST ARCHIPE-lago, comprising about three thousand islands, with a land area of 1.9 million square kilometers, lying along the earth's equator. The railway network is confined to the islands of Java, including Madura, with a route length of about forty-nine hundred kilometers (3042.9 miles), and Sumatra, with about two thousand kilometers (1242 miles). The system was built to its present size during a seventy-year period prior to World War II; 40 percent of it was privately owned and operated.

The railways in Indonesia date back to the nineteenth century when, on 17 June 1864, the section from Semarang to Tanggung in Central Java, a distance of twenty-six kilometers, was opened to traffic. Additional rail lines were successively built in Java and Sumatra. Prior to World War II there were eleven private railway companies in Java and one in North Sumatra, in addition to one owned and operated by the Dutch East Indies Company. When Japan occupied Indonesia during 1942–45, the railways in Java were placed under military control of the army, and those in Sumatra under the navy. A considerable amount of railway material, including rails, locomotives, and other rolling stock was transferred by the Japanese to other countries for war purposes.

After Indonesia's Independence Proclamation in August 1945, the railway service was managed by the State Railway of the Republic of Indonesia. In 1950, all but one private rail line, that in North Sumatra, were merged with the government network. The last private railway, the so-called DSM line, was absorbed by the state system in 1957.

The present system is a government-owned enterprise called Perusahaan Jawatan Kereta Api (PJKA) of the Indonesian State Railways. Management of the Indonesian railways is in the hands of a president director, assisted by a board of five directors and four chiefs of centre, and a corporate secretary at the head office in Bandung. There are six regional managers under the guidance and supervision of the director general of land transport of the department of communications. Organizationally, the railways are divided into six regions—three in Java and three in Sumatra—and there are sixteen inspections—eleven in Java and five in Sumatra. The chiefs of regions reports directly to the president director, while the chiefs of inspection are responsible to the appropriate chief of region.

The Indonesian State Railways in 1978 operated a system of 5,881 route kilometers (163 kilometers double-track, of which 58 kilometers were electrified), distributed in the three main islands as follows:

Location	Gauge (millimeters)	Route Length (kilometers)
Java and Madura	1.067	4,113
South Sumatra	1.067	639
West Sumatra	1.067	251
North Sumatra	1.067	485
Other	.750	393
	Total	5,881

Sleepers were mostly hardwood, and ballast was broken stone on gravel. Track lengths were as follows:

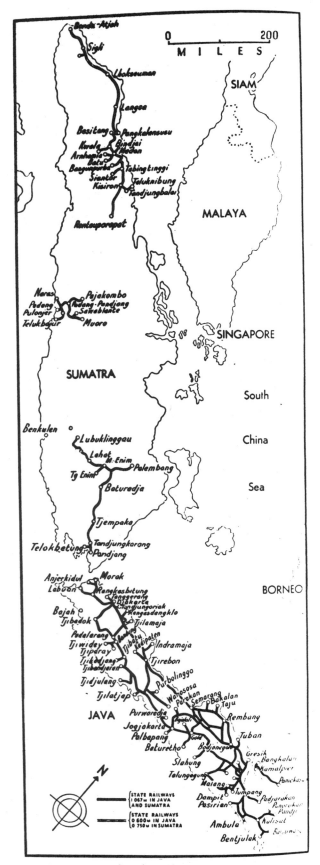

Railway map of Indonesia.
(*Courtesy:* Janes World Railways)

	Main Line (km)	Side Line (km)	Total (km)	(Miles)
Java	2,790	1,322	4,113	2,556
Sumatra	1,594	174	1,768	1,099
Totals	4,384	1,496	5,881	3,655

In 1978, the PJKA system had 8,015 bridges, aggregating 90,862 meters. There were sixty-seven viaducts, totaling 425.5 meters in length. The whole network had nineteen tunnels totaling 8,277 meters.

MOTIVE POWER AND ROLLING STOCK

	Java	Sumatra
Registered freight cars	11,674	3,821
Registered passenger cars	1,749	268
Registered Diesel locomotives	306	73

Steam locomotives—a total of 367, of which 161 were in service.

Railroad employees in 1978 were broken down as follows:

Head Office	1,767	South Sumatra	4,268
West Java Region	13,866	West Sumatra	1,256
		North Sumatra	4,115
Central Java Region	12,123	Workshops	6,002
		Stores	1,028
East Java Region	12,347	Total	56,772

The most southerly point in Asia reached by rail is Bentjulak, on the island of Java. This is a 3-foot 6-inch line at latitude 8.0 degrees south.

The worst railroad disaster in Indonesia occurred in Java on 28 May 1959, a derailment killing ninety-two people.

Steam Locomotives in Indonesia

Steam traction in Indonesia was characterized by a vast assortment of engine makes, types, sizes, and wheel arrangements. The well-recognized emphasis on engine appearance was somewhat negated by a general inefficiency in overall operations.

Some early locomotives, built in 1880 and used in Indonesia, are shown. Between 1880 and 1891, Indonesia purchased about fifty type 2–6–0 tank locomotives, class C11, which were used on all kinds of railroad service up until the end of the steam era, a period of eighty to ninety years. Also

Illustrated is an old steam engine, no. B 5002, built in 1880 in Manchester for use on the Indonesian railroads. This was a type 2–4–0 engine having a horse-power of 330. It was widely used on passenger service in Java on the Madiun–Ponorogo run. (*Courtesy: Indonesian State Railways*)

An old tank steam locomotive, no. C 10.04, preserved in Indonesia is shown here. This was built in Manchester in 1880; it was a type 0–4–0 engine with a horse-power of 215. It was used on two sections of Java: Klakah–Jember–Banyuwangi and Jember–Panarukan. (*Courtesy: Indonesian State Railways*)

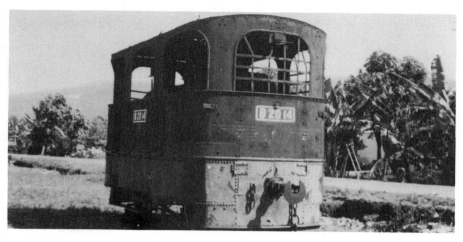

Pictured is a one-man enclosed utility steam tram, no. B 2014, built by Beyer Peacock of Manchester, England in 1899. This engine had a horsepower of two hundred. These engines, known as "dwarf lokies," saw street and other service before the advent of electric tramways on the following sections of track in Java: Telgal–Semarang–Demak and Semarang–Kedungjati. (*Courtesy: Indonesian State Railways*)

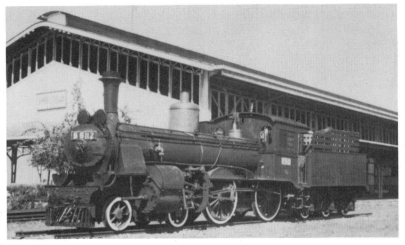

Another preserved locomotive in Indonesia is pictured. This engine, no. B 5112, type 4–4–0, was manufactured in 1900 by Werk Spoor with a horsepower of 415. It was utilized in Java on runs between these locations: Gambringan–Cepu–Bojonegoro–Cepu–Rembang.
(Courtesy: Indonesian State Railways)

Pictured is another preserved steam locomotive in Indonesia. This no. C 2728, type 4–6–4, engine was built by Werk Spoor in 1919 and was used in Java on two sections of track: Kroya–Yogyakarta and Kroya–Cilacap. Horsepower was listed at 650.
(Courtesy: Indonesian State Railways)

Illustrated is a preserved Indonesian tank steam locomotive, no. BB 1012, type 0–4–4–2, built by Hartman Chennitz in 1900. This compound engine had a horsepower of 465 and was used in Java on runs between Kedungjati, Ambarawa, and Secang.
(Courtesy: Indonesian State Railways)

in the 1880s, Sharp, Stewart & Company furnished about fifteen type 2–4–0, class B50 locomotives, many of which are still operating.

A one-man utility steam car, built in 1899 by Beyer Peacock, is shown. Many of these tram locomotives, used on city streets, were constructed classes B-12, B-17, and B-20.

The Dutch supplied various excellent steam locomotives for their overseas possessions, including Indonesia, in the nineteenth century. One of these was a type 4–4–0 machine built in 1900; it is pictured in an illustration. The Dutch East Indies Company furnished a number of type 4–6–4 tank locomotives in 1919. The Dutch also supplied a number of type 4–6–2, class C53 Pacific locomotives in 1921, some of which were still operating until they were displaced by diesels in the early 1970s.

Indonesia's first compound locomotive, type 0–4–4–2, class BB10, was built by Hartmann in 1900 and is shown in an illustration. Also at the turn of the century, a variety of class B22, type 0–4–2 tank tram engines were used that had remarkable longevity up to the early 1970s.

Other steam locomotives included type 0–6–2 machines built by Hartmann in 1903 and type 0–4–2 engines furnished by Esslingen in 1904. Various type 4–4–0 class, B53 engines were supplied by Hartmann in 1912, and type 4–6–0, class C51 engines by Beyer Peacock in 1913. Some of these locomotives survived the age of steam to the mid-1970s.

In 1928, Swiss Winterthur constructed several compound locomotives, type 2–6–6–0, class CC50, one of which is pictured.

Through the years in Indonesia, a variety of lightly powered locomotives were used, such as the type 4–6–4, class C27 tanks and type 4–4–0, class B51 tender engines. As many as sixty type 4–6–4 tank engines, class C28, used on passenger service, also survived until the early 1970s. Locomotives used for heavier service were type 2–12–2 tank engines, class F10 and heavy-duty Mallet locomotives such as class CC10, type 2–6–6–0 tanks, and classes DD50 and CC50, type 2–8–8–0 tender models.

A powerful locomotive, class D52, type 2–8–2, was built in 1951 by Friedkrupp for the Indonesian railways.

Shown here is a preserved tank steam locomotive, no. C 2001, type 0–6–2, built by Hartman & Chennitz in 1903 for use on the Indonesian railways section between Solo and Baturetno in Java. Horsepower was 380.
(Courtesy: Indonesian State Railways)

Shown is a locomotive built by Esslingen in 1904 for use on the Kedungjati–Ambarawa–Secang section of the Indonesian railways in Java. This was a type 0–4–2 engine, number B 2505, possessing a horsepower of 420. No other specification data was available. *(Courtesy: Indonesian State Railways)*

Pictured is an old steam locomotive preserved in Indonesia. This, no. CC 5025, type 2–6–6–0, unit was a compound engine built by Winterthur Schweiz in 1928 for service on the Cirebon–Kroya and Banjar–Kroya–Yogyakarta sections of the Indonesian railways in Java. Horsepower was listed at 1190. *(Courtesy: Indonesian State Railways)*

A picture of a large steam locomotive built in 1951 by Friedkrupp for the Indonesian railways. This engine, no. D 52080, had a 2–8–2 wheel arrangement and a horsepower of 1600. It was used on the following sections of railroad in Java: Bandung–Banjar–Kroya–Yogyakarta and Kroya–Purwokerto. *(Courtesy: Indonesian State Railways)*

ITALY

THE ITALIAN STEAM LOCOMOTIVE STORY IS largely outlined in the accompanying pictorial presentation (sixty-seven photographs), which is divided into three major parts.

Part 1 is a series of thirty-one photographs of Italian locomotives, arranged chronologically from 1839 to 1928. These have individual captions that, unfortunately, show a general lack of technical specification information.

Part 2 consists of two tables outlining detailed specification data on twenty-eight locomotives, with appropriate photographs. Despite repeated requests to the Italian State Railways, I was not able to extract the names of manufacturers or dates of construction for these engines.

Part 3 includes eight pictures on which it was impossible to secure any data whatsoever.

The first railway in Italy, from Naples to Portici, a distance of about five miles, was built by a French company and opened to traffic on 4 October 1839; this small line connected King Ferdinand's palace with Italian troops and barracks based at Portici. It was extended to Nocera in 1884.

As in other European countries, growth of the railroads was hindered by a variety of political contentions. Italy, at that time, was divided into various small kingdoms and duchies provided numerous frontiers, watched by suspicious sovereigns who had real fears about their security, which negated any means of rapid communication. Nevertheless, some progress was made with rail construction. The Milan–Monza rail line in the north, then under Austrian jurisdiction, was opened in 1840. In 1842 a railroad linked Padua with Mestre, and in 1844 a connection between Leghorn (Livorno) and Pisa was consummated. The Turin–Moncalieri line was completed in 1848. The Papal States finally finished a railway between Rome and Frascati in 1856.

Beginning in 1856, railways in Italy pushed forward at a more rapid pace. Many rail lines were laid down, using English capital and the experienced stewardship of British contractor Thomas Brassey. As previously described in the chapter on French railroads, Italian finances and initiative fostered construction of the first Alpine tunnel, Mont Cenis (Frejus), which opened in December 1870. With the military defeat of Austria in 1861 by Napoleon II, Italy was finally unified and, had 1,330 miles of railroad in active use, with 1,200 miles under construction, and another 835 miles on the drawing board.

The new sovereign Italian government actively promoted railway building, and a great number of contractors were involved, all interested in the generous government subsidies. In this period, 1861 to 1867, many new rail projects were initiated and completed. The Naples–Rome connection was opened in 1863. In Sicily, an eight mile line from Palermo to Bagheria was completed on 28 April 1863. The Milan–Venice line was extended to include Florence in 1864. The Florence–Rome rail line was completed in 1866, and in 1867 a Brenner Pass railroad, crossing the Alps at a height of 4,496 feet above sea level, provided an international link between Innsbruck, Austria, and Balzano and Verona in Italy.

Railway map of Italy.
(*Courtesy:* Janes World Railways)

The first rail line in Italy ran five miles from Naples to Portici in 1839 and was serviced by a locomotive named "Bavard" built by Stephenson of Newcastle, England. This engine plus its tender weighed 20 tons, boiler pressure was 3.5 kilograms per square centimeter, horsepower was 65, and maximum speed was 50 kilometers per hour.
(Courtesy: Italian State Railways)

The restored version of the first locomotive used in Italy on the pioneer tracks between Naples and Portici is shown.
(Courtesy: National Museum of Science, Milan)

Pictured is a type 2–2–2 locomotive built in Pietrarsa following Stephenson patents in 1845. This engine had a horsepower of 100 and attained a speed of 60 kilometers per hour.
(Courtesy: Italian State Railways)

The first locomotive constructed in Italy by Cantieri Ansaldo in 1854 is pictured. This was a 0–4–2 type engine with a horsepower of 417 and a maximum speed of 65 kilometers per hour.
(Courtesy: Italian State Railways)

An early rail line from Rome terminated at nearby Frascati where a special station was constructed in 1856. This station was unique in that it was placed far above the tracks to permit the trains to follow an easy gradient underneath. Of course, the passengers had a long climb up the steps from the loading-unloading platform to reach the station proper.
(Courtesy: Italian State Railways)

Shown is a class 42 S.F.M. (120 F.S.) Italian locomotive, type 2–4–0, built about 1864 for use on the Strade-Ferrate Meridioali-line. This engine developed 380 horsepower and attained a maximum speed of 65 kilometers per hour.
(Courtesy: Italian State Railways)

This is a picture of an 1864 Italian locomotive, type 0–8–0, which was imported from France for use on mountainous terrain in the areas near the French-Italian border. Horsepower was 660 with a maximum speed of 35 kilometers per hour.
(Courtesy: Italian State Railways)

In the early 1860s the Italian railways resorted to imported steam locomotives to enhance their available motive power. This is a picture of a French Bourbonnaise steam engine, type 0–6–0, which was used on the Italian railroads near the French-Italian border. These were built by the PLM workshops in Paris and Oullins and by other large French locomotive manufacturers. These engines were often used in double-heading fashion to push-pull heavy freights over the mountains on the Giovi lines. Specifications were as follows:

Cylinders	18 by 25.5 inches
Coupled drive wheels	4-foot 3.5-inch diameter
Boiler	
Grate area	14.6 square feet
Total heating surface	1249 square feet
Working pressure	143 pounds per square inch
Operating weight	35 tons (engine plus tender)
Horsepower	325
Maximum speed	50 kilometers per hour.

(Courtesy: Italian State Railways)

This French Bourbonnaise type 4–4–0 locomotive (engine no. 530) was purchased by the Italian railways in 1871 to compliment their own engines for heavy freight service in mountainous terrain. The engine was used in northern Italy at the time of the opening of the Mont Cenis (Frejus) tunnel with France in December 1871. Horsepower was 490, and it attained a maximum speed of 35 kilometers per hour.
(Courtesy: Italian State Railways)

In 1873 the Italians introduced, on the Northern Railways of Italy, the locomotive (no. 687) pictured. This class 660 S.F.A.I. (150 R.M.) engine named "Ariosto" was used on fast passenger service. Horsepower was 450, and the maximum speed was 80 kilometers per hour. The wheel arrangement was 2–4–0.
(Courtesy: Italian State Railways)

This pictures an 1884 Italian, type 4–6–0, steam locomotive class 650 F.S. It was designed by railway engineers at Torino. The engine was the first with three coupled drive wheels and was used with heavy passenger trains. Horsepower was 650 with a maximum speed of 80 kilometers per hour. *(Courtesy: Italian State Railways)*

This Italian class 180 R.A. (545 F.S.) locomotive, type 4–4–0, was designed at Florence for high-speed passenger service in 1885. Horsepower was 530 and maximum speed 100 kilometers per hour. *(Courtesy: Italian State Railways)*

This is a picture of an 1888 Italian steam locomotive, class 51–100 R.S. (500 F.S.), single expansion type with a 4–4–0 wheel arrangement. Horsepower was 520 and maximum speed 85 kilometers per hour. *(Courtesy: Italian State Railways)*

This Italian class 170 R.M. (560 F.S.), type 4–4–0, steam locomotive, named "Giuditta," was designed in the Torino engineering offices in 1889. Horsepower was 560 and maximum speed 100 kilometers per hour. *(Courtesy: Italian State Railways)*

This Italian steam locomotive was named "Vittorio Emanuele" when it was constructed in 1894. It was a type 4–6–0, class 650 F.S. engine designed for use in mountainous terrain to haul heavy passenger trains. With this engine the Italian engineers started using drive wheels with larger diameters and American-type bogie wheels in the front. This locomotive was used on the rail lines between Torino and Genoa. Horsepower was 650 and maximum speed 80 kilometers per hour. *(Courtesy: Italian State Railways)*

In 1894 the Torino office engineers designed a higher power locomotive by elevating the steam pressure and using double-expansion cylinders. The boilers were all steel which helped to boost the boiler working pressure from around 9 kilograms per square centimeter to 12–14 kilograms per square centimeter. The first locomotive so designed was type 0–6–0, class 380 R.M. (310 F.S.) which had a horsepower of 550 and attained a maximum speed of 60 kilometers per hour. This first double-expansion engine, no. 3804, is pictured. *(Courtesy: Italian State Railways)*

Italian no. 1896, class 550 F.S. steam locomotive designed by engineers at Florence with a 4–4–0 wheel arrangement and single-expansion type cylinders is pictured. Horsepower was 540 with a maximum speed of 100 kilometers per hour.
(Courtesy: Italian State Railways)

The Italian State Railways had built fourteen 4–4–0 type locomotives in 1896–98 by Ernesto Breda of Milan and another four more by Costruzioni Meccamiche Saronno in 1898. The engines had cylinders 18.1 by 23.6 inches with coupled wheels 5 feet 5.5 inches in diameter. The grate area was 21.8 square feet, heating surface 1157 square feet which developed a boiler pressure of 170 pounds per squre inch. Engine and tender under working conditions weighed 70 tons. These locomotives were used up to 1930 on the Milan-Bologna and Milan-Venice runs. A model picturing the Breda series of locomotives is located in the Museo Nazionale della Scienza e della Technica, Milan. Wheel arrangement was 4–4–0.
(Courtesy: National Museum of Science, Milan)

This class Gr 180 bis R.A. (552 F.S.), 1899 locomotive type 4–4–0; for the Italian railways was an improved design by Florence engineers in 1884 to provide high-speed passenger train service. The engine, when displayed at the 1900 Paris exposition, created quite a sensation in railroading circles. Later this machine achieved highly satisfactory operating service, both technical and economical.
(Courtesy: Italian State Railways)

Pictured is a model of an experimental four-cylinder, type 4-6-0, locomotive designed for the Italian Southern Railway. This full-sized engine was displayed at the 1900 Paris Exposition. The design was unique in that the front of the engine contained the cab and firebox and water was carried in a separate trailing six-wheeled tender. Eventually a series of like-designed engines were constructed by Borsig of Berlin. The above locomotive had the following characteristics:

Cylinders
  Lo pressure   23⅛ by 25.5 inches
  Hi pressure   15⅛ by 25.5 inches
Coupled wheels
Tractive effort   14,450 pounds
Boiler
  Grate area   32.25 square feet
  Heating area   1547 square feet
  Boiler pressure
Operational weights
  Engine   62.5 tons
  Tender   4675 gallons water only
  Coal bunker on engine   7 tons.

(Courtesy: Museum of Communications, Budapest, Hungary)

The steam locomotive in the foreground is preserved in the National Museum of Science in Milan. This was a class 685 F.S., type 2-6-2, engine built in the early twentieth century with the specifications listed in Table no. I-   . The engine in the background is an 1899, class 552 F.S., type 4-4-2, previously described in a separate photograph.
(Courtesy: National Museum of Science, Milan)

This is a 1903 class Gr. 280 R.A. (870 F.S.) Italian steam
locomotive, type 0–6–0, which used single-expansion
cylinders. Horsepower was 360 and maximum speed
sixty-five kilometers per hour.
(Courtesy: Italian State Railways)

This Italian class Gr 380 R.A. (600 F.S.), type 2–6–0,
tender locomotive, of the double-expansion type, was
used on passenger and freight service starting in 1904;
it achieved a good ratio between cylinder and drive
wheel sizes. Special bogie wheels improved the stability of the running engine. With this engine there
ended an era of private ownership of the railroads in
Italy. Horsepower was 660 and maximum speed was
eighty kilometers per hour.
(Courtesy: Italian State Railways)

Steam locomotive class 730 F.S. was used mainly on
freight service on Italian flatlands starting in 1907.
Cylinders were the double-expansion type with a
wheel arrangement of 2–8–0. Horsepower was 900
and maximum speed 60 kilometers per hour.
(Courtesy: Italian State Railways)

This class 800 F.S. engine called a locomotive tender was a steam-powered motor car as used on the Italian railways in 1907. Horsepower was 260 with a maximum speed of 45 kilometers per hour.
(Courtesy: Italian State Railways)

This class 690 F.S., type 4–6–2, locomotive was used on the Italian railroads starting in 1911. It was an important engine on the Italian lines. It first used the Caproti system of steam distribution which enhanced operating efficiencies. Horsepower was 1400 with a maximum speed of 130 kilometers per hour.
(Courtesy: Italian State Railways)

This Italian, type 2–6–0 locomotive, class 645 F.S., was designed by engineers at Florence for use on the Rumanian Railways in 1917. Four hundred units ordered by Rumania were eventually constructed by a private Italian firm but were retained for use in Italy during World War I. Horsepower was 870 and maximum speed 65 kilometers per hour.
(Courtesy: Italian State Railways)

This type 2–6–0, class 302 F.S., 1922 steam engine was designed for small, secondary railroads on the hills of Sicily. Horsepower was 420 and maximum speed was __ kilometers per hour.
(Courtesy: Italian State Railways)

This Italian type 2–8–0, Class 743 F.S. tender locomotive built in 1924, first incorporated Franco-Crosti's system of preheating boiler water. Horsepower was 1100 and maximum speed was 65 kilometers per hour. (Courtesy: Italian State Railways)

A model of an Italian locomotive on display in the Leonardo da Vinci Technical Museum in Milan is pictured here. The prototype engine was class 691 with a 4–6–2 wheel arrangement. The later class engines were built in the Florence workshops in 1928. Specifications were as follows:

Cylinders	17.75 by 26.75 inches
Drive wheels	6-foot 7⅞-inch diameter
Boiler	
Grate area	46.2 square feet
Superheater	721.2 square feet
Total heating surface	2551 square feet
Working pressure	199 pounds per square inch.

(Courtesy: National Museum of Science, Milan)

ITALIAN LOCOMOTIVES
DATA AND PHOTOGRAPHS COURTESY ITALIAN STATE RAILWAYS
(Note: Manufacturer and year not given)
All with superheaters but classes 630-680-747-835-850-940

Class F.S.	460	471	480	623	625	630	640	680	683	691	685
Wheel Arrangement	0–8–0	0–10–0	2–10–0	2–6–0	2–6–0	2–6–0	2–6–0	2–6–2	2–6–2	4–6–2	2–6–2
Cylinders	2	4	2	2	2	2	2	4	4	4	4
Drive Wheel Diameter—mm	1350	1370	1370	1530	1850	1850	1850	1850	1850	2030	1850
Grate Area—Meters^2	2.65	3.50	4.30	2.38			2.42		3.50	4.30	3.50
Boiler Pressure—Kg/Cm^2	14	16	12	16	16	16	12	16	12	16	12
Tractive Effort—Kg	9700	10540	10700				6290			7700	6430
Axle Loading—Kg	17100	15500	1500	15900	14400		14700		17000	20000	15100
Maximum Speed—Km/Hr	55	50	60	80	80	100	100	110	120	130	120
Horsepower	960	1170	1500	920	800	700	800	1100	1450	1750	1250
Final ID. No.	I-532	I-533	I-534 I-535	I-536	I-537	I-538	I-539	I-540	I-541	I-544	I-542 I-543

I-532

I-533

I-534

I-535

I-536

I-537

I-538

I-539

I-540

I-541

I-542

I-543

I-544

In 1865 the destiny of the Italian railways was committed to the hands of four private operating companies: the Upper Italy railroads in the north; the Roman Railroad, controlling the central Florence–Rome–Naples operations; the Calabrian–Sicilian Railroads, managing operations in the south; and the Southern Railroad, organized to build an Adriatic coastal line. The latter system was actually completed in the 1860s, running from Bologna to Lecce, far to the south.

Although the British contractor Brassey, with English engineers but using local labor, built many of the early Italian railways, Italy later provided a substantial number of its own builders. One such contractor was Count Giacomo Ceconi, who in the 1870s carried out a great proportion of the construction work on the Udine–Pontebba rail connection with Austria, which was finished in 1879. Subsequently, Ceconi handled many other tough building assignments such as drilling tunnels in Austria and Yugoslavia.

By 1869 the Upper Italy, the Roman, and the Calabria-Sicilian rail companies were all largely in a state of bankruptcy, whereas the Southern Railway, running parallel to the Adriatic coast, was providing a fair return to its stockholders. It was therefore erroneously theorized that north-south transportation routes held greater financial promise. Accordingly, in 1885 two new north-south rail systems were proposed, one on each side of the Apennine Mountains, and operations on the rail lines in Sicily were reorganized. However, it was subsequently proved that organizational and operational success or failure had little or nothing to do with the geographical location of the railways, or the direction of their movements.

The most serious obstacle to railroad expansion in many parts of Italy was the difficult mountain topography. Early on, attention had to be focused on mountain-climbing problems, and a special type of locomotive had to be designed and built. One particularly successful locomotive was a type 0–8–0, manufactured for the Upper Italy Railways in 1873 by Wiener Neustadt of Austria. Between 1885 and 1905, about 105 similar machines were constructed and utilized in Italy. Some of these engines actually provided satisfactory service until they were retired in 1950.

A special assortment of problems was posed by the steep hills surrounding the port of Genoa. Eventually two so-called Giovi inclines were constructed to permit railway access to the sea. The first, 4.5 miles long, had a one in 28.5 gradient; the second, finished in 1885, was 14.5 miles long with a gradient of one in 62, which allowed an easier approach to Genoa. Transportation over these inclines was first furnished by a 4–6–0 locomotive named "Vittorio Emanuele II," followed in 1902 by the first 4–8–0 type. Both engines were designed in the Turin office of the Mediterranean Railways.

ITALIAN LOCOMOTIVES
DATA AND PHOTOGRAPHS COURTESY ITALIAN STATE RAILWAYS
(Note: Manufacturer and year not given)
All with superheaters but classes 630-680-747-835-850-940

Class F.S.	735	736	740	741	744	745	746	747	835	851	940
Wheel Arrangement	2–8–0	2–8–0	2–8–0	2–8–0	2–8–0	2–8–0	2–8–2	2–8–2	0–6–0	0–6–0	2–8–2
Cylinders	2	2	2	2	2	2	4	2	2	2	2
Drive Wheel Diameter—mm	1370	1478	1370	1370	1630	1630	1880	1880	1310	1510	1370
Grate Area—Meters^2	3.17	3.81	2.80	2.80	3.50	3.50	4.30		1.48	1.53	2.80
Boiler Pressure—Kg/Cm^2	12	15.8	12	12	12	12	14		12	12	12
Tractive Effort—Kg	8500	8950	8000	8000	8340	8160	9260	13960	5750	5540	7600
Axle Loading—Kg	15000	15900	14000	14800	14800	14400	16200		15100	14700	15400
Maximum Speed—Km/Hr	65	70	65	65	80	75	100	110	55	65	65
Horsepower	1080	1250	980	1100	1250	1250	1600		370	400	980
Final ID No.	I-546	I-547	I-548	I-549	I-550 I-551	I-552 I-553	I-554 I-555	I-556	I-557 I-558	I-559	I-560

I-546

I-547

I-548

I-549

I-550

I-551

I-552

I-553

I-554

I-555

I-556

I-557

I-558

I-559

I-560

The type 4–8–0 engines, two-cylinder compound, were found to be generally unsatisfactory, having insufficient power on the inclines, and were soon transferred to less demanding tasks in other parts of Italy.

Starting in 1872, the Mediterranean Railways system (RM) had established an engineering office at Turin whose chief purpose was to study, research, and design superior steam locomotives to surmount the difficult Italian mountain terrain and give better performance at the higher elevations. Likewise, at Florence the Adriatic Railways system (RA) created a special organization for studying ways of achieving higher locomotive speeds on level terrain. These offices were both successful in solving many locomotive problems, which led to higher operating speeds and technical improvements, as exemplified in six locomotives pictured.

By 1880 the Italian railways were composed of three basic systems: the Mediterranean (RM), the Adriatic (RA), and the Sicilian (RS), all operating privately under twenty-year concessions from the central Italian government. Then followed a decade and a half of attempts to improve railroad operations, provide better and faster service, expand the rail networks, build modern railway stations and other facilities, and construct new shops for carriage and locomotive repairs. Naturally, many of Italy's rail problems were attributable to the difficult Alpine and Apennine topography, which engendered steep gradients, endless curves, and necessitated construction of close to two thousand railroad tunnels. Despite heroic efforts on the part of various rail company managements, by 1905 persistent financial crises made nationalization of the Italian railways mandatory, creating the present Italian State Railways system.

On 1 July 1905 the Mediterranean, Adriatic, and Sicilian railways were unified to become the Italian State Railways administration. At that time, Italy had 10,557 kilometers (6,560 miles) of railroad and 2,678 locomotives, which were representative of Italian technical developments from 1872 to 1905. The new rail administration also unified all the former study and development organizations into a central technical institution located in Florence. This engineering entity, togther with a well-developed construction organization, permitted the Italian State Railways to compete successfully with the best railways in the world. In time, the Italian shops made considerable progress in achieving greater locomotive power, higher speeds, and better overall performance, as well as enhanced economic efficiency.

By 1965 the Italian State Railways (Ferrovie dello Stato F.S.) had about one thousand steam locomotives on active roster, of which about five hundred were normally out of commission for maintenance or other reasons. By 1975, about eight hundred engines were still carried on an active status, with about three hundred machines on daily freight, passenger, or shunting service. The Italian repair people have been quite adept at extending the life of their steam locomotives, since no new engines were introduced after 1930. However, in 1955, Italian locomotive manufacturers did construct twenty large type 2–10–2 locomotives for the Hellenic State Railways of Greece. In the last years of steam traction in Italy, surviving machines have been mostly light Consolidation 2–8–0 type machines.

The following eight steam locomotive pictures were received from the Italian State Railways, but vital technical/specification information was not included nor was it obtainable after much correspondence (Class Locomotive: 370, 666, 670–1900, 675, 743, 806, 816, 822.)

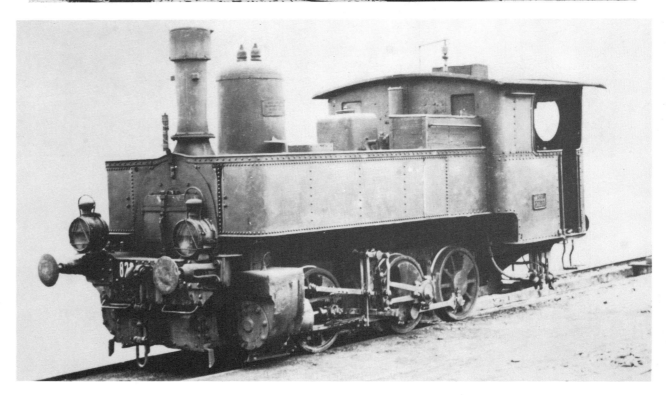

JAMAICA

CONSTRUCTION OF RAILWAYS IN JAMAICA, THE first anywhere under English auspices outside the British Isles, was commenced in 1844 by two English brothers, David and William Smith. The first line, fourteen miles in length, using standard-gauge track, ran west from the capital city of Kingston to Angels Station, just beyond Spanish Town. This first railroad in the British colonies was officially opened to traffic on 22 November 1845. Early motive power for the railway consisted of two small steam locomotives fabricated in 1844 by Sharp Brothers of Manchester, England. The first two engines were named "Projector" and "Patriot." In 1850 four more engines were added to the line: "Emancipation," "Enterprise," "Perseverance," and "Success."

In July 1869 an eleven-mile extension was constructed west from Angels Station to Old Harbour. At this point, Sharp Brothers supplied two additional engines, "Extension" and "New Era."

By 1879 the rail enterprise ran into serious financial difficulties, and the Smith brothers were forced to turn over the line to the Jamaican government. On 26 February 1885, the railroad was extended twenty-four miles west to Porous, about halfway across the island. Then, on 13 August 1885, another twenty-four-mile line was begun north from Spanish Town to Ewarton. This extension, running through Rio Cobre gorge, required considerable engineering expertise as it included four tunnels; the longest one, named Gibraltar, was about 723 yards, near Bog Walk. Between 1879 and 1885, the government rail administration added twelve more engines, numbered 1 through 12,

manufactured by Kitson-on-Leeds, in England.

On 1 January 1890 the destiny of the Jamaica Railway passed by sale to an American firm, the West Indies Improvement Company, which proceeded to extend the trackage and add to the rolling stock. Twelve modern steam locomotives were purchased, eight from Rogers and four from a Rhode Island works. An intricate rail extension of sixty-six miles, over the mountains to Montego Bay, was completed in 1894. This had some gradients as steep as 1 in 30 and countless curves, some with a radius of 320 feet. In 1896 a fifty-four-mile extension north from Bog Walk to Port Antonio was completed, including twenty-five tunnels and a number of difficult bridges.

By 1898 the West Indies Improvement Company found itself in serious financial difficulties and, defaulting on its interest commitments, was forced to sell out to the Jamaican government at a tremendous loss. From 1900 on, affairs of the Jamaica railway system remained in the hands of government administrators.

Along with revising the rail organization, management, and operating procedures, the government also purchased additional locomotives from the Kitson-Mayer firm in England. In 1907 tender-type engines were procured for the first time from the Baldwin Locomotive Works in the United States. At this time, railroad mileage in Jamaica totaled 194 miles. In 1913 two spur lines were added: Bog Walk to Linstead, four miles; May Pen to Chapelton, thirteen miles.

Over the years, despite enhanced utilization of rail facilities and heroic efforts to improve operat-

Pictured is the first mountain type 4–8–2 locomotive ever built by the Baldwin Locomotive Works of Philadelphia. This engine was constructed in July 1916 for the standard-gauge rail system on the Jamaica Government Railways. Specifications follow:

Cylinders	19 by 26 inches
Coupled drive wheels	46-inch diameter
Engine weight	157,400 pounds.

(Courtesy: Frederick Westing collection)

ing efficiency, deficits were perpetual. Finally a program of subsidization was initiated that has remained in effect to this day. Between 1920 and 1924, the Jamaica Railway Company added twenty-four steam locomotives manufactured by the Canadian Locomotive Company of Kingston, Ontario. Just before World War II, with the establishment of several U. S. military bases in Jamaica, various small rail branches were built, which brought the overall trackage to 224 miles. A gradual changeover to modern diesel-electric

locomotives was initiated in 1955.

By 1980 the Jamaica Railway Company was supplying important rail service that contributed substantially to that nation's economic and social progress.

The most serious railway accident in Jamaica, a derailment into a ravine near Kendal on 1 September 1957, killed 178 persons.

For further information, reference to my earlier book, *Seven Railroads,* which covers the Jamaica railroads in detail.

JAPAN

IN 1869 THE BRITISH MINISTER TO JAPAN, SIR Harry Smith Parkes, recommended that an era of railroad construction be initiated in that country. At first, neither the government nor Japanese capitalists were willing or able to furnish the required financing, but about this time another Englishman, Horatio Nelson Lay, offered to float a million-pound loan on the London market to cover the cost of the railway. The proposal was to first connect Tokyo with Yokohama, and next, Osaka with the adjacent port of Kobe. The general plan was most bitterly opposed by some Japanese nationalists, who feared the loss of independence because foreign capital was involved. However, farsighted officials in the government were able to put forth superior arguments, and the plan was approved.

The first rail line, the sixteen-mile section from Tokyo to Yokohama, of 3-foot 6-inch gauge, was opened on 14 October 1872 after two years of work. The British supplied most of the materials, equipment, and engineering know-how, under the supervision of E. Morell. Inaugural festivities were attended by Emperor Meiji, whose presence gave the railway scheme top-level credence and silenced forever all internal opposition. The second line, running about forty miles between Osaka and Koba, was finished in 1874, and another line of about twenty-five miles from Osaka to Kyoto, was completed in 1877.

Walter Mackersie Smith (1842–1906), a British locomotive engineer, was the first Locomotive Superintendent of the Imperial Japanese Government Railways from 1874 to 1883. In all the preliminary rail construction projects, British engineers had surveyed the routes, designed the bridges and tunnels, and supervised the work, but the Japanese proved to be apt pupils and were soon able to dispense with most foreign assistance. The first all-Japanese railroad construction effort involved the Kyoto–Otsu line of about six miles, which opened in 1880. Throughout all the rail-building programs up to about 1877–80, the government exercised a close, parental role over the activities.

By the 1880s, with the advantages of railways becoming more and more apparent, commercial investors began their financial involvement. Private companies organized the Nippon Railway Company and projected a vast network of railroads in Japan. This work later resulted in a line running northwest from Tokyo to Takasaki for about sixty-five miles, another line from Tokyo north about 190 miles to Sendai on the Pacific coast, and the Tohoku line (Ueno–Aomori), which on 1 September 1891 connected northern and central Japan. By 1885 private companies had constructed 130 miles of track, and the total was 1,500 miles by 1895. During the same period, government projects had increased railway mileage from 220 miles to 580 miles. By 1884 the central Japanese government revitalized its interest in railway construction and passed the Railway Construction Act of 1892, which evolved basic railway policy for the future and included a recommendation to consolidate all existing rail lines into a single unified system.

In due course, the main trunk lines had been extended along the Pacific coast from Aomori, in northern Honshu, to Kobe in the south. A branch line of about ninety miles was also built across the mountains west from Takasaki to the seaport of Naoetsu (latitude 37° 9.9′ north, longitude 138° 14.2′ east) on the Sea of Japan. The latter construction involved crossing the extremely difficult Usui Pass, which work was delayed to the end of the project. The pass was ultimately approached from both sides and included surmounting many heavy grades, using the Abt-rack system, plus boring twenty-six tunnels over a distance of seven miles. The connection between Tokyo and Naoetsu finally was completed in 1893. Since freight traffic and resulting profits were quite high on this line, former samurai and feudal lords who had invested in the venture were well rewarded.

Eventually, late in the nineteenth century, the main backbone trunk line from Aomori to Kobe, was extended to the south end of Honshu at Shimonoseki, thus completing a linkage of over 1,153 miles. On 11 June 1942 this line was connected with railways on the island of Kyushu by the undersea Kammon tunnel beneath the Strait of Shimonoseki. Early in the twentieth century, two principal rail lines were laid down: from Moji south 232.5 miles to Kagoshima, and from Moji to Nagasaki, on the southwest coast, 163.5 miles distant. Additional eastward lines were also installed in Honshu, which tied the east-coast rail network to the major west-coast seaports of Niigata (latitude 37°55′ north, longitude 139°03′ east), and Tsuruga (latitude 35°39′ north, longitude 136°04′ east).

The war with Russia in 1904–05 revealed tremendous weaknesses in Japan's ability to properly coordinate transportation among thirty-five private railway companies. One result was enactment of the Railway Nationalization Law of 31 March 1906, which was designed to ensure proper railroad operations and development in consonance with strategic military plans. Further justification for nationalization was based on allegations that private ownership had placed too much emphasis on immediate profits, to the detriment of long-range planning, and that there had been little, if any, effort devoted to standardizing rail equipment and operating procedures. Thus, military considerations became primary factors not only on the railroads but in all other phases of Japanese industrial life.

In 1907 only the islands of Hokkaido and Shikoku were without a rail line; elsewhere in Japan, railways carried about 140 million people and 24 million tons of goods annually. About 1910, the first rail line finally was laid in the northern island of Hokkaido. A forty-five-mile line from some coal mines to a seaport. This project was supervised by a railroad engineer from the Pennsylvania Railroad in the United States and the engines were imported from the Baldwin Locomotive works in Philadelphia.

Starting in 1908, the destiny of the railroads in Japan was placed in the hands of a special Railway board responsible to a member of the cabinet. By 1913, technological progress, along with heavy engineering and construction, had advanced so well that facilities in Japan were able to manufacture railway locomotives and rolling stock. About 1918, for strategic reasons, the Japanese started to push for the conversion of all trunk lines from narrow to standard gauge. In 1920 the Railway board became part of the cabinet, with a minister for railways, and in 1943 all forms of transportation were placed under the control of the new Ministry of Transportation and Communications. In 1945 these two functions were separated into two distinct ministries, and in 1948 the minister of transportation took control of all national and private railways. The government railways were reorganized in 1949 to become the Japanese National Railways (JNR), a separate and semiautonomous corporation subject to the control of the ministry of transportation.

In general, throughout the twentieth century, Japanese railroads on or near the coasts played a secondary role to coastal shipping, with rail carriers handling only about one-third of the nation's domestic trade. As a consequence, railways emphasized passenger traffic, from which they developed most of their income.

In World War II the Japanese railroads experienced every conceivable type of problem, aggravated greatly by allied bombing, which destroyed many locomotives, cars, and rail shops. This in turn put an additional load on marine facilities. After the war, with U.S. aid, a tremendous railway rehabilitation and improvement program was undertaken.

On 20 April 1959, a new standard-gauge Tokaido line was initiated, which was the start of the famed supertrains in Japan. The first regular, over 100-miles-per-hour rail service was introduced on 1 November 1965, on the standard-gauge system between Tokyo and Osaka. Even in 1960 Japan ran thirty-two daily trains at an average speed of just over 100 miles per hour.

Considerable double-tracking took place in the 1960s, and the diesel locomotive was introduced during this period. Also in the sixties, the Tokyo–Haneda Monorail connecting Tokyo with the International Airport at Haneda opened during October 1964.

By 1972, Japan had seventeen thousand miles of mainline railroads, of which 12,500 miles were government owned. At this point, 18 percent of the JNR system was electrified, as were 80 percent of the 4,500 miles of private lines. Japan had in service about 5,000 locomotives in 1972, including 800 electric types and 120,000 freight cars. Some key statistics on the Japanese Railways, as of 1978, are set forth in an illustration.

What will be the longest sea railway tunnel, thirty to thirty-five miles in length, was under construction in 1980. The Seikan Tunnel will pass 330 feet below the water, in badly faulted granite with water-filled rock seams, connecting Yoshioka on the island of Hokkaido with Miumaya on Honshu. Work began in 1964 on shafts and pilot tunnels. Rails at the center of the proposed rail tunnel will be 788 feet below sea level.

Japan has the most easterly railroad in Asia, the 3-foot 6-inch gauge line at Nemuro on the island of Hokkaido (longitude 145.34° east). An illustration shows the rail network throughout Japan.

The most serious rail disaster in Japan, a collision near Osaka, occurred on 29 January 1940, killing two hundred people.

Steam Locomotives in Japan

The first steam locomotives to be used in Japan were twelve imported a year before the Japanese railway service was inaugurated in 1872. Ten were tank engines and two were of the tender type. The locomotive given the distinction as unit no. 1 is now preserved in Tokyo's Transportation Museum. Built by Vulcan Foundry, it weighed 23.5 tons and had an overall length of 7.43 meters. The first tender engine, type 2–6–0, was delivered in 1880 and was named "Benkei." All early locomotives were made in Britain by such manufacturers as Sharp, Stewart & Company, and the Yorkshire Engine Company. Later, of course, many other manufacturers were involved. Among American products imported were various Baldwin and Porter engines. The Schnectady machines were considered grace-

fully designed tender types, as were those supplied by Beyer Peacock and by Neilson. Also popular were the small engines of America's Pittsburgh and Nasmyth Wilson, and Germany's Koppel and Krauss. A few locomotives came from Switzerland, France, and Belgium. Among the special engines introduced in 1912 were superheated Mallets and Abt-system engines. In Japan there were no rack railways for tourists, such as those on Mount Washington in the United States and the Brienz-Rothorn-Bahn of Switzerland.

In 1885 Dubs furnished a number of type 0–6–0 tank locomotives to the Imperial Railways of Japan (see details in an illustration). In June 1887 two six-wheeled engines for 3-foot 6-inch gauge tracks in the Mie Kie mines were the first locomotives ever shipped by the Baldwin Locomotive Works to Ja-

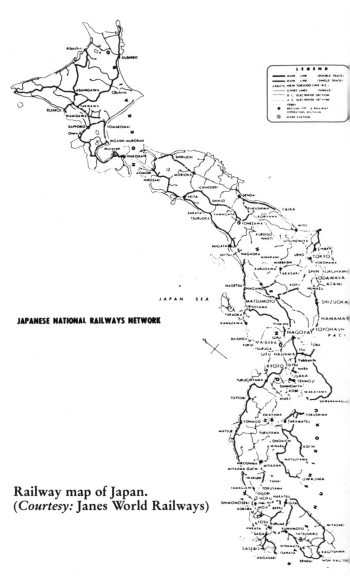

JAPANESE NATIONAL RAILWAYS NETWORK

Railway map of Japan.
(*Courtesy:* **Janes World Railways**)

Pictured is part of the Japanese Tokyo–Haneda mono-rail system which started operations in October 1964. *(Courtesy: Japanese Ministry of Foreign Affairs)*

KEY STATISTICS

	1978
Railway Route Length (km)	21,307
Double- and Multi-tracked Sections	5,530
	(26.0%)
Electrified Sections	8,157
	(38.3%)
Conventional Lines, Narrow Gauge (1,067 mm)	
D.C.	4,822
A.C.	3,335
Shinkansen, Standard Gauge (1,435 mm)	
A.C.	1,177
Railway Stations	5,294
Passenger and Freight	1,294
Passenger	3,888
Freight	112
Length of Bridges (km)	2,280
Length of Tunnels (km)	1,840
Train-km (thousands)	678,099
Railway Traffic Volume (millions)	
Passengers Carried	6,997
Tons Carried	133
Passenger-km	195,844
Ton-km	40,413
Number of Employees	426,697
Revenues & Expenses (million yen)	
Revenues	2,588,800
Expenses	3,475,500

Key statistics for Japanese Railways.

pan. In 1890, 1891, 1893 and 1896, the Neilson and Dubs companies shipped a variety of tender and tank locomotives. See Five illustrations.

Early in 1897, a group of locomotives designed to burn an inferior grade of soft coal, thus requiring a large grate area and a firebox with extra depth and volume, were shipped to Japan by Baldwin—Atlantic-type engines for passenger service and a modified Consolidation type for freight service. Later engines made by Baldwin had a wide, deep firebox placed entirely back of the driving wheels and over a rear truck. Cylinders were 18.5 by 24 inches, drive wheels had a forty-four-inch diameter, and the engine weighed 119,600 pounds. Freight locomotives of a design somewhat similar to those built for the Nippon Railways were subsequently introduced into the United States, and

were appropriately designated the Mikado type. Also in 1897, Nielson supplied a number of type 4–4–0 tender engines to the Imperial Railways of Japan. In 1898 additional type 4–4–0 tender locomotives were furnished by Sharp, Stewart and by Dubs.

In 1904 Baldwin exported sixteen tank engines to the Imperial Government Railways of Japan. These type 0–6–2 machines has three pairs of driving wheels and a two-wheeled rear truck and were constructed with plate frames in accordance with Japanese design specifications. Another 150 locomotives with the same specifications followed in 1905. Also in 1905 the North British Locomotive Company constructed seventeen type 0–6–2 tank engines for use in Japan. These were followed in 1908, 1911, 1912 by various locomotives built by Bald-

The Imperial Railways of Japan in 1885 purchased from Dubs & Company an unstated number of type 0–6–0 tank locomotives. Specifications follow:

Gauge	3 feet 6 inches
Work order	E2123
Cylinders	15 by 22 inches
Drive wheels	4-foot diameter
Boiler heating area	827 square feet
Working steam pressure	140 pounds per square inch
Tractive force	10,828 pounds
Operating weight	36 tons plus 5 hundredweights
Capacities	970 gallons water; 70 cubic feet fuel.

(Courtesy: Mitchell Library, Glasgow) D/E2123

In 1890, under work order no. E 666, the Sanyo Railway Company of Japan ordered from Neilson & Company an unstated number of type 4–4–0 tender locomotives. Pertinent specifications were as follows:

Gauge	3 feet 6 inches
Cylinders	15½ by 22 inches
Drive wheels	4-foot 6-inch diameter
Boiler heating surface	861.11 square feet
Working steam pressure	150 pounds per square inch
Operating weights	
Engine	28 tons plus 12 hundredweights
Tender	22 tons plus 10 hundredweights
Tender capacities	2000 gallons water; 135 cubic feet coal.

(Courtesy: Mitchell Library, Glasgow) N/E666

The Osaka Railway in 1891 bought from Dubs &
Company a number of type 2–4–2 tank locomotives
with the following specifications:

Gauge	3 feet 6 inches
Work order	E 2765
Cylinders	13 by 18 inches
Drive wheels	4-foot diameter
Boiler heating area	501 square feet
Working steam pressure	140 pounds per square inch
Tractive force	6654 pounds
Operating weight	29 tons plus 7 hundredweights
Capacities	700 gallons water; 60 cubic feet fuel.

(Courtesy: Mitchell Library, Glasgow) D/E 2765

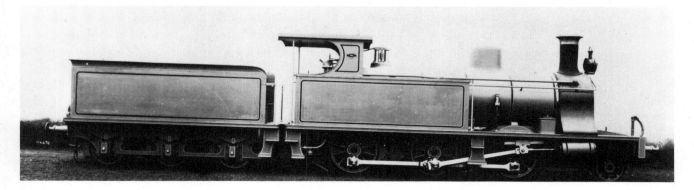

According to Neilson & Company work order no.
E714 of 1893, the Nippon Railway Company of Japan
purchased an unstated number of type 2–6–0 tank
locomotives with attached tenders. These engines had
the following specifications:

Gauge	3 feet 6 inches
Cylinders	17 by 22 inches
Drivers	4-foot diameter
Boiler heating area	989.4 square feet
Working steam pressure	160 pounds per square inch
Operating weights	
Engine	40 tons plus 16 hundredweights
Tender	23 tons plus 1 hundredweight
Engine tank water capacity	700 gallons
Tender capacities	2000 gallons water; 135 cubic feet coal.

(Courtesy: Mitchell Library, Glasgow) N/E 714

Dubs & Company in 1896 supplied the Nishinari Railway of Japan with an unstated number of type 0–6–0 tank locomotives. Specifications follow:

Gauge	3 feet 6 inches
Work order	E 3409
Cylinders	13 by 18 inches
Drivers	3-foot diameter
Boiler heating surface	498 square feet
Working steam pressure	140 pounds per square inch
Tractive force	8872 pounds
Operating weight	24 tons plus 6 hundredweights
Capacities	450 gallons water; 35 cubic feet fuel.

(Courtesy: Mitchell Library, Glasgow) D/E 3409

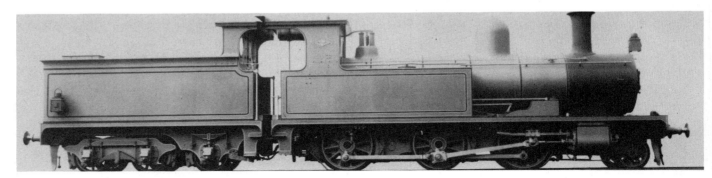

The Kansei Railway of Japan in 1896 purchased an unstated number of type 2–6–0 tank locomotives (with tender attached) from Dubs & Company. Specifications were as follows:

Gauge	3 feet 6 inches
Work order	E 3598
Cylinders	17 by 22 inches
Drive wheels	4-foot diameter
Boiler heating area	999.9 square feet
Working steam pressure	140 pounds per square inch
Tractive force	13,908 pounds
Operating weghts	
Tank engine	40 tons plus 3 hundredweights
Tender	21 tons plus 12 hundredweights
Capacities	
Tank engine	not stated water
Tender	2000 gallons water; 135 cubic feet fuel.

(Courtesy: Mitchell Library, Glasgow) D/E 3598

In 1896 Dubs & Company furnished a number of tank engines to the Imperial Railways of Japan; these machines were type 0–6–2 with the following specifications:

Gauge	3 feet 6 inches
Work order	E 3623
Cylinders	16 by 24 inches

Drive wheels	4-foot 1 inch diameter
Boiler heating surface	1007.07 square feet
Working steam pressure	150 pounds per square inch
Tractive force	14,106 pounds
Operating weight	48 tons plus 9 hundredweights
Capacities	1716 gallons water; 76 cubic feet fuel.

(Courtesy: Mitchell Library, Glasgow) D/E 3623

The first Baldwin locomotive built with a 2–8–2 wheel setup and with an accompanying tender. This engine was constructed in 1897 for the government of Japan and was assigned the name "Mikado" in honor of the Japanese sovereign.
(Courtesy: Frederick Westing collection)

In 1897 the Imperial Railways of Japan purchased from Neilson & Company (order no. E 780) a number of type 4–4–0 tender locomotives. Specification data follows:

Gauge	3 feet 6 inches
Cylinders	16 by 24 inches
Drivers	4-foot diameter
Boiler heating surface	827 square feet

Working steam pressure	140 pounds per square inch
Operating weights	
Engine	30 tons plus 9 hundredweights
Tender	23 tons plus 5 hundredweights
Tender capacities	700 gallons water; 135 cubic feet fuel.

(Courtesy: Mitchell Library, Glasgow) N/E 780

Sharp, Stewart & Company furnished the Nippon Railway in 1898 with a number of type 4–4–0 tender locomotives. Specification information follows:

Gauge	3 feet 6 inches
Work order	E 1114
Cylinders	16 by 22 inches
Drivers	4-foot 6-inch diameter
Tender water capacity	2000 gallons.

(Courtesy: Mitchell Library, Glasgow) SS/E 1114

In 1898 Dubs & Company sold to the Nippon Railway Company of Japan an unstated number of type 4–4–0 tender locomotives. Specifications were as follows:

Gauge	3 feet 6 inches
Work order	E 3657
Cylinders	17 by 23 inches
Drive wheels	4-foot 6-inch diameter
Boiler heating surface	996 square feet
Working steam pressure	160 pounds per square inch
Tractive force	14,771 pounds
Operating weights	
Engine	39 tons plus 1 hundredweight
Tender	30 tons plus 10 hundredweights
Tender capacities	3000 gallons water; 288 cubic feet fuel.

(Courtesy: Mitchell Library, Glasgow) D/E 3657

The Nippon Railway Company of Japan in 1902 purchased from Dubs & Company several type 0–6–2 tender locomotives with the following specifications:

Gauge	3 feet 6 inches
Work order	E 4304
Cylinders	18½ by 24 inches
Drivers	4-foot 7-inch diameter
Boiler heating area	1500 square feet
Working steam pressure	160 pounds per square inch
Tractive force	17,921 pounds
Operating weights	
Engine	43 tons plus 11 hundredweights
Tender	21 tons plus 6 hundredweights
Tender capacities	2000 gallons water; 135 cubic feet fuel

(Courtesy: Mitchell Library, Glasgow) D/E 4304

The Kansei Railway of Japan in 1903 purchased an unstated number of type 0–6–2 tank engines from the North British Locomotive Company with the following characteristics:

Gauge	3 feet 6 inches
Work order	L 2
Cylinders	16 by 24 inches

Drivers	4-foot diameter
Boiler heating surface	998.5 square feet
Working steam pressure	140 pounds per square inch
Operating weight	48 tons plus 10 hundredweights
Capacities	1700 gallons water; 65 cubic feet fuel.

(Courtesy: Mitchell Library, Glasgow) L 2

The Imperial Railway Company of Japan in 1905 purchased seventeen type 0–6–2 tank locomotives from the North British Locomotive Company (nos. 466–83). Specifications follow:

Gauge	3 feet 6 inches
Work order	L 108
Cylinders	16 by 24 inches

Drivers	4-foot 1-inch diameter
Boiler heating surface	999.8 square feet
Working pressure	160 pounds per square inch
Operating weight	49 tons plus 10 hundredweights
Capacities	1716 gallons water; 76 cubic feet fuel.

(Courtesy: Mitchell Library, Glasgow) L 108

win and the North British Locomotive Company.

As in many other locations, the famous type 4–6–2 Pacific locomotives were widely used on passenger express service. These had been introduced into Japan in 1911 by the American Locomotive Company. About 1913 Japan started mass production of steam locomotives, designed in styles peculiar to that country. A large number of Consolidation 2–8–0 engines were built in that first year, and a few of these lasted to the end of the steam era in the 1970s. Typical of the high performance engines

made later in Japan were the C51s, the C53s, and the C57s, all of which helped create Japan's golden age of steam engines.

In 1935 the Japanese railroads purchased sixty-two additional Pacific-type units, then designated as class C55; by 1972 only three engines of this series remained active. Also in 1972, 67 engines survived out of 201 class C57, type 4–6–2 machines. Of 380 tank locomotives, class C11, type 2–6–4, only 80 were still in operation in 1972. Only 150 of the newer tank engines, class 12, type

The North British Locomotive Company in 1908 supplied an unstated number of type 2–4–2 tank engines to the Imperial Taiwan Railway. Limited specification information is listed as follows:

Gauge	3 feet 6 inches
Work Order	L 284
Cylinders	14 by 20 inches
Drivers	4-foot 1-inch diameter.

(Courtesy: Mitchell Library, Glasgow) L 284

In 1908 the Imperial Taiwan Railway purchased from the North British Locomotive Company a number of type 4–4–0 tender locomotives with the following specifications:

Gauge	3 feet 6 inches
Work order	L 285
Cylinders	16 by 22 inches
Drivers	4-foot 6-inch diameter

Boiler heating surface	997.27 square feet
Working steam pressure	169 pounds per square inch
Operating weights	
Engine	33 tons plus 10 hundredweights
Tender	25 tons plus 10 hundredweights
Tender capacities:	2300 gallons water; 110 cubic feet fuel.

(Courtesy: Mitchell Library, Glasgow) L 285

2–6–2, survived into the later stages of steam locomotion, though 780 had been built originally.

In 1946 the Japanese National Railways had 5,958 steam locomotives—the maximum at any given time. By 1969, that number had dropped to 2,266. Classes 8620 and 9600 were the first locomotives to be produced on a large scale in Japan. While class 51 was the most popular engine for freight service, class 62 (see two illustrations), with 1,750-millimeters driving wheels, was Japan's largest and most powerful engine for passenger service.

Japanese railroads in 1948 converted fifty class 52 Mikado locomotives to class 62 Hudsons, type 4–

6–4. These, together with forty-seven class 60, and thirty-three class 61 Hudsons, made a total of 130 of this classic design, shown in two illustrations. Only a few of these carried on until diesel traction took over. Built in 1959 were six class 61 machines, Japan's final venture into the realm of steam.

In 1969 the JNR designated the class of its steam locomotives by a letter (B, C, or D) followed by a two-digit numeral; the letter indicated the number of axles (respectively, 2, 3 or 4), while the numerals 10 through 48 designated a tank locomotive, and 50 to 99, a tender locomotive. This designation did not apply to classes made before 1928.

Steam locomotives moved only 8 percent of total

In 1911 the Imperial Railway Company of Japan purchased a single type 4–6–0 tender locomotive from the North British Locomotive Company. Specifications are listed as follows: (tender not pictured)

Gauge	3 feet 6 inches
Work Order	L 446
Engine no.	8700–11
Cylinders	17½ by 24 inches
Drivers	5-foot 3-inch diameter
Boiler heating surface	1427 square feet
Working steam pressure	180 pounds per square inch
Tractive force	15,750 pounds
Operating weights	
Engine	48 tons plus 6 hundredweights
Tender	(not stated).

(Courtesy: Mitchell Library, Glasgow) L 446

Shown are two views of the famous Consolidation class 51, type 2–8–0, locomotives built by the Japanese starting in 1913; these machines found most useful application in freight services.
(Courtesy: Japanese National Railways)

Two illustrations picture the class C57, type 4–6–2,
Pacific locomotives of Japanese manufacture which
were widely used throughout that country.
(Courtesy: Japanese National Railways)

own is a class 60, type 4–6–4, Hudson locomotive.
ourtesy: Japanese National Railways)

A class 61, type 4–6–4, Hudson locomotive is pictured here; this was a classic design widely manufactured and used in Japan. The last steam locomotives constructed in Japan in 1959 were six of these class 61 engines.
(Courtesy: Japanese National Railways)

Shown are the class 62 Hudson locomotives, type 4–6–4, which were class 52 Mikado engines converted in 1948. These machines had large 1.75-meter drive wheels and were the largest and most powerful locomotives ever used in passenger service in Japan.
(Courtesy: Japanese National Railways)

passenger rail travel in 1969. The figure for freight locomotives was 41 percent of total traffic, as against 80 percent ten years earlier. In 1969 it was estimated all steam engines would disappear by 1974. Actually, by 1973 the Japanese National Railways calculated that only nine hundred locomotives had survived the steam age, and all had gone from the scene by 1977. As in several other countries, the Japanese initiated a realistic preservation program for all major classes of railway steam engines. The Umekoji Museum in Kyota has a full complement of them. Predominant among pre-

served locomotives is the type 2-8-2, named Mikado; these were class D51s, of which about four hundred held out almost to the end, along with ten larger class D52 Mikados, 275 of which were originally constructed in 1943.

The following nine steam locomotive photographs were received from the Japanese National Railways, but without caption information. Two of these pictures show class 39 engines that appear to be type 0-8-0, and another shows a class 58 locomotive.

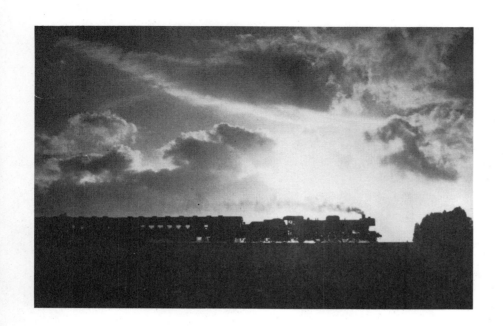

KENYA

THE 1-METER GAUGE UGANDA RAILWAY FROM Mombasa on the Indian Ocean to Lake Victoria in Kenya-Uganda was constructed by the British between 1895 and 1901. The line terminated at Kisumu, on the eastern shores of Lake Victoria, 582 miles from the coast. This first railway in East Africa was a tremendous, adventure-filled engineering achievement won against widespread tropical disease, horrendous topographic obstacles—including the Taru Desert, the Rift Valley, and the Mau escarpment—attacks by poisonous insects as well as wild animals, and the boundless opposition and fury of native tribesmen. The railroad opened up the unproductive, primitive heartland of central Africa, brought modern developments to the area, and delivered a mortal blow to the shameful traffic in Negro slaves. Final cost to the British government was 5.5 million pounds sterling.

In all, thirty-two thousand laborers had been recruited and transported from India, sixty-five hundred of whom succumbed to sickness and disease and had to be shipped back home. About twenty-five hundred Asians and an untold number of Africans perished building the Uganda railroad. Approximately sixty-seven hundred Indians decided to remain in Africa after the railroad was completed. Since its construction, the railroad has been a vital lifeline from north central Africa to the Indian Ocean; it facilitated commerce, colonization, and development, and brought into being the great state of Kenya.

A detailed history of the Uganda Railroad is included my book *Seven Railroads,* which is listed in the bibliography section.

The following seventeen illustrations set forth some historical data on the railroads and to steam locomotives used in East Africa on the Kenya Railways and on earlier rail lines.

Pictured is a multiple incline into the Rift Valley temporarily used during the construction of the Uganda Railway in East Africa between 1895 and 1901.
(Courtesy: Kenya Railways)

Shown is a freight train on high wooden trestle of the meter-gauge Uganda Railway under construction in East Africa in the period 1895 to 1901.
(Courtesy: Kenya Railways)

This illustration shows Indian workers on the Uganda Railway sometime during the early twentieth century in East Africa.
(Courtesy: Kenya Railways)

This is a wood-burning steam locomotive used during the construction of the Uganda Railway in East Africa during the early twentieth century.
(Courtesy: Kenya Railways)

This 1902 picture is of the first train to leave Kilindini, East Africa, on the newly completed Uganda Railway. The 582-mile rail line, from Mombasa on the Indian Ocean to Lake Victoria in interior Africa was constructed between 1895 and 1901 by the British.
(Courtesy: Kenya Railways)

A coal-fired steam locomotive is shown hauling water tanks on the Uganda Railway of East Africa about 1905.
(Courtesy: Kenya Railways)

The train at Samburu Station in East Africa in 1905 is pictured. This was an early coal-fired British-built steam engine used on the Uganda Railway in its early days.
(Courtesy: Kenya Railways)

Pictured is a meter-gauge Uganda Railway work train with a wood-burning steam engine in East Africa, about 1905. Note handcar removed from the tracks just in time to avoid a serious accident.
(Courtesy: Kenya Railways)

This illustration shows a mail train on the Uganda Railway with a wood-burning steam locomotive at Athi River Station in East Africa in 1907.
(Courtesy: Kenya Railways)

This 1909 picture was taken of an ancient steam
locomotive on the Uganda Railway near Limuru,
East Africa.
(Courtesy: Kenya Railways)

This pictures a steam locomotive and train on the
Uganda Railway in East Africa in 1910.
(Courtesy: Kenya Railways)

Pictured is the model of a class 57 Beyer Garratt, type 4–8–4 plus 4–8–4, locomotive used on the meter-gauge East African Railways. The prototype engine was one of six built for passenger and freight service on this railway in 1939. Specifications were as follows:

Cylinders	16 by 26 inches
Coupled drive wheels	4.5-foot diameter
Boiler	
Diameter	6-foot 4¼-inch diameter
Grate area	48.5 square feet
Total heating surface	2750 square feet (includes superheater)
Steam pressure	220 pounds per square inch
Tractive effort	46,090 pounds
Operating weight	186 tons plus 6 hundredweights
Water capacity	6000 gallons
Coal capacity	12 tons
Miscellaneous	Thermic syphons (Nicholson) provided.

(Courtesy: Bassett-Lowke, Ltd.)

This is a photograph of repair work underway in the locomotive shops of the Kenya Railways at Nairobi.
(Courtesy: Kenya Railways)

This 1950 picture shows the locomotive shed of the Kenya Railways at Nairobi. Note lineup of various Garratt type steam locomotives.
(Courtesy: Kenya Railways)

This is a class 29 oil-fired tender locomotive built by the North British Locomotive Company starting in 1949 for use on the Kenya Railways. See table for technical data.
(Courtesy: Kenya Railways)

Pictured is a model of a class 59 Beyer Peacock locomotive, the prototype of which was built for the East African Railways in 1955. This engine, oil-fired, type 4–8–2 plus 2–8–4, was at the time the most powerful meter-gauge locomotive ever constructed. Specifications were as follows:

Cylinders	20.5 by 28 inches
Coupled drive wheels	4.5-foot diameter
Boiler	
Diameter	7.5 feet
Grate area	72 square feet
Heating surface	4308 square feet (Superheater included)
Steam pressure	225 pounds per square inch
Tractive effort	83,350 pounds (85 percent boiler pressure)
Operating weight	252 tons
Fuel oil capacity	2700 gallons
Water capacity	8600 gallons
Overall length	104 feet 2 inches.

(Courtesy: Bassett-Lowke, Ltd.)

Pictured is Beyer Garratt steam locomotive on the
May Escarpment in Kenya, East Africa (about 1965).
This scene is near the Equator at an elevation of 9136
feet above sea level.
(Courtesy: Kenya Railways)

KENYA RAILWAYS STEAM LOCOMOTIVES - METRE GAUGE

CLASS	11	22	24	28	29	53	55	56	58	59
YEAR	1930	1919	1930	1926	1949	1931	1951	1949	1947	1950
MANUFACTURER	HUNSLET	NORTH BRITISH	VALCAN	Robert STEPHENSON	NORTH BRITISH	BEYER PEACOCK	BEYER PEACOCK	BEYER PEACOCK	BEYER PEACOCK	BEYER PEACOCK
WHEEL ARRANGEMENT	2-6-2	4-8-0	4-8-0	2-8-2	2-8-2	4-8-2+2-8-4	4-8-2+ 2-8-4	4-8-2+ 2-8-4	4-8-4+ 4-8-4	4-8-2+ 2-8-4
CYLINDERS - INCHES	15x22	16x22	18x22	21½ x 28	18x26	16½ x 22	16x24	16x24	16½ x 26	20½ x 28
DRIVERS - DIAMETER	3ft 7in	3ft 7in	3ft 7in	4ft 3in	4ft	3ft 7in	4ft	4ft	4ft 6in	4ft 6in
HEAT AREA SQ FT	1000	1173	1184	2851	2272	2430	2382	2287	2561	4284
FIRE GRATE SQ FT	12.75	17.5	19.1	40.5	38.0	49.6	48.75	48.75	48.5	72.0
STEAM PRESS. LBS Sq. In	165	180	165	180	200	180	200	200	225	225
TRACTIVE FORCE POUNDS @ 85% BWP	16150	20040	23249	37938	29835	42600	43520	43520	50200	83350
OPERATING WT - TONS	53.9	75.35	86.05	155.4	126.8	138.3	133.4	146.75	186.25	251.66
WATER -GALLONS	1200	2500	3500	5000	4800	4925	4590	4200	6000	8600
OIL CAPACITY-GALS	1033	1900	1900	3275	2056	2455	1200	2382	2375	2700
ADHESION WT -TONS	34.45	32.85	40.05	69.55	52.00	83.75	83.7	88.0	94.0	159.52
TYPE	TANK	TENDER	TENDER	TENDER	TENDER	GARRATT	GARRATT	GARRATT	GARRATT	GARRATT

**Partial summary of Kenya Railways locomotives and
data covering engines built between 1919 and 1951 is
presented.**
(Courtesy: Kenya Railways)

MALAYSIA

UNTIL ABOUT 1880, RIVERS WERE THE ONLY means of transport in West Malaysia (Malaya). Early rail lines, built by the British, were fairly short, running east-west from the tin mines to the west coast. Various railroads were constructed as follows: a meter-gauge line from Taiping 7.5 miles to Port Weld on the Larut River (1885); from Kuala Lumpur to Bukit Kuda (1886); from Bukit Kuda to Klang via the Connaught Bridge (1890), and later to Port Swettenham (1899); from Seremban to Port Dickson (1891); from Tapah Road to Telok Anson in Perak (1893); and to Prai-Bukit Mertajam, in 1899. These railroads speeded two-way traffic between the tin mines and the straits, and also stimulated the production of this metal. There were also short lines from Kuala Lumpur to other mining locations at Rawang and Kuala Kubu to the north and at Sungei Besi to the south, constructed between 1888 and 1895. The rails to Port Weld were lifted for use on the Burma–Siam Railway during World War II when Japanese occupied Malaya; these were replaced after the war. Port Weld is now served by a freight line only.

All except the Seremben–Port Dickson line were government railways from the start. Finances came from state revenues, aided sometimes by loans from the British Straits Settlement. British engineers were recruited from the Ceylon Public Works Department for planning and construction and skilled labor was introduced from Ceylon and Bengal. Local Chinese and Malays made up the balance of the work force.

After federation of the four central states in 1963, the western railroads were linked together in the Federated Malay States Railway (KTM) by a north-south line that joined the existing railheads and ran northward to Prai, opposite Pinang, and southward as far as the borders of Johore at Gemas. This work, planned in cooperation with the Straits Settlement for the Province Wellesley sector, was completed in 1908. In the meantime, in 1903 a new branch line ran to Malacca from the north-south line between Seremban and Gemas. The Seremban–Port Dickson line was taken over by the Federated Malay States Railway from the Sungei Ujong Company in 1908.

The next stage was to extend the line southward from Gemas and northward from Prai, done with cooperation from the state governments of Johore and Kedah. Johore Bahru was reached in 1909, and a ferry service linked with Singapore's island railway, which had been constructed in 1903. In 1924 a railway was opened across the causeway between Johore and Singapore Island to complete this connection. The Johore-Singapore causeway was officially opened on 28 June 1924 by the governor of the Straits Settlement, though the first freight train had crossed the causeway on 17 September 1923, and the first passenger train went through on 1 October 1923. The length of the causeway is 3,465 feet, and 1½ million cubic yards of granite fill were used in its construction. In 1923 the terminus at Singapore was only a tin shed, which remained for nine years. In 1932 the Singapore Deviation, as the causeway was called, was opened to traffic. The terminus since 1932 has been the

The magnificent railroad station in Singapore is pictured. This was built in 1932 and remains one of the outstanding architectural sights in that city.
(Courtesy: Keretapi Tanah Melayu, Malaysian Railways)

magnificent station building near the dockyard, which remains one of the imposing edifices in Singapore.

The railroad development had many significant consequences. Villages and areas of cultivation followed along the tracks; new settlements were created, and land in many areas appreciated in value. Telegraph and postal services also developed in conjunction with the roads and railroads.

Meanwhile, the west-coast rail line was continued north and linked with the Thai railroad in 1918. By 1923, however, plans were pressing ahead for a line through central Malaya, begun in 1907 and intended to terminate at Kota Bharu, at the top of the east coast. This line, known today as the East Coast Line, (though Tumpat, its actual terminus, is the only part of the coast it touches) was completed in 1931 from Gemas, in Negri Sembilan, to Tumpat in Kelantan—a distance of 327.75 miles. It was officially opened on 9 May 1931. In many respects, the East Coast Line is the most interesting of the whole system, with some really wild and rugged scenery. It is the sole means of communication between Kuala Lipis and Kuala Kerai, since there are no roads in this part of Malaya. The branch (for it is not classified as a main line), boasts the longest tunnel on the railway (780 yards) and the longest bridge, the Guillemard Bridge, which spans the Kelantan River. The bridge is a most impressive piece of engineering, consisting of five 250-foot spans and five 150-foot spans, covering a distance of nearly half a mile. The bridge is shared with a road, and the rails are laid in the center of the narrow single carriageway. Level crossing gates at each

Railway map of the Malay Peninsula.
(Courtesy: Malayan Railways)

end deny road and foot passage while a train crosses the bridge. About 157 miles of the East Coast Line (between Jerantut and Manek Urai) were lifted by Japanese in World War II, for use on the Burma–Siam Railway. These rails were replaced after the war and the line was operational again by the mid-1950s.

Since 1931 only three significant alterations to the railway have been made. First, the twenty-one-mile Malacca branch, removed as material for the Burma–Siam Railway, was not reinstated though the track bed remains. There has been talk of rein-

stating the line, on a different alignment, in connection with plans for a deep-water harbor at Malacca. Second, in 1966 a new branch about six miles long was constructed on Singapore Island between Bukit Timah and Jurong, Singapore's new industrial complex on the west side of the island. Last, is the extension of the northern terminus from Prai to Butterworth, involving a new swing bridge, completed in 1967.

In 1963 Malaysia was created out of a group of former British dependencies, with the States of the Federation of Malaysia, which had become inde-

Class	Year	No. Built	Cylinders	Cpld Wh	Wt in Wo	Wh Arr	Fuel Cap*	Water	T.E.	Working Press.	Heating Surface	Grate Area	Remarks
A	1885	18	10"×16"	3'3"	20t 5c	4-4-0T				120 lb			
B	1890	7	12"×18"	3'3"	24t 16c	4-4-0T				120 lb			
										160 lb			
C	1893	7	Specifications as for 'B' Class, except that tender now added										
D	1894–5	4	14"×20"	3'3"	42t 0c	4-6-0				140 lb			
E	1897	2	14½"×20"	4'3"	43t 0c	4-6-0				150 lb			
G	1899	34	14½"×20"	4'3"	51t 15c	4-6-0			10,390 lb	160 lb			
†J	1899	3	10¼"×18"	2'9"	23t 12c	0-6-2T‡				130 lb			Taken over by F.M.S.R. in 1908
†K		1	12"×18"	3'6"	42t 0c	4-4-2T				130 lb			
H	1907	60	15½"×24"	4'6"	75t 6c§	4-6-2	315 cu ft	2,000 gal	16,293 lb	180 lb	1,235 sq ft	18·5 sq ft	
I(1)	1908	35	14½"×20"	4'4"	41t 15c	0-6-4T	90 cu ft	800 gal	12,370 lb	180 lb			
I(2)	1913	As for (1)						1,200 gal	As for (1)				
Burma E	1912 to	20			15t 12½c	0-4-2				120 lb			
Burma O	1914				23t 15c	4-4-0				140 lb			
P	1914–20	20	17"×24"	4'6"	78t 11c	4-6-2	315 cu ft	2,000 gal	19,645 lb	160 lb/||	1,000 sq ft	18·5 sq ft	Bogie wh 2'6" Pony wh 2'9½"
Q	1919	12	17"×24"	4'6"	79t 0c	4-6-2	5t	2,056 gal	18,553 lb	170 lb	1,403 sq ft	24·9 sq ft	From U.S.A.
R	1920	10	16"×20"	3'6"	38t 6c	0-6-0T	2t	1000 gal	17,554 lb	160 lb	504 sq ft	12 sq ft	From U.S.A.
~~M~~	~~1920~~	~~10~~	~~14"×18"~~	~~3'1"~~	~~53t 8c~~	~~2-6-0~~	~~6t~~	~~1830 gal~~	~~12,257 lb~~	~~160 lb~~	~~761 sq ft~~	~~13·1 sq ft~~	~~From U.S.A.~~
L	1920	20	17"×24"	4'6"	86t 10c	4-6-2	6t 100	2,500 gal	19,645 lb	180 lb	1,485 sq ft	24·3 sq ft	Bogie wh 2'6"
T	1926	5	13"×20"	3'3"	31t 0c	0-6-2T	1t 100	750 gal	11,787 lb	160 lb	422 sq ft	9·6 sq ft	
K¶	1927	7	17"×24"	4'6"	91t 5c	4-6-2	7t	2,500 gal	19,645 lb	180 lb	1,445 sq ft	24·6 sq ft	Bogie wh 2'6" Pony wh 3'0"
S¹ (3 cyl)	1928–30	11	17"×24"	4'6"	108t 9c	4-6-2	7t	3,000 gal	29,480 lb	180 lb	2,335 sq ft	35·0 sq ft	Bogie wh 2'6" Pony wh 3'0"

Class	Year	No. Built	Cylinders	Cpld Wh	Wt in Wo	Wh Arr	Fuel Cap*	Water	T.E.	Working Press	Heating Surface	Grate Area	Remarks
C²	1929	5	14½"×22"	4'6"	73t 0c	4-6-4T	158 cu ft	2,000 gal	19,272 lb	250 lb	1,026 sq ft	23·6 sq ft	Bogie wh 2'6"
O³ (3 cyl)	1938–40	28	13"×24"	4'6"	103t 16c	4-6-2	11·25 tons	3,530 gal	23,940 lb	250 lb	1,109 sq ft	31 sq ft	
WD	1944				52t 9c	2-8-2	8 tons	4,168 gal	20,100 lb	185 lb	1,001 sq ft	27·6 sq ft	From U.S.A. 28 sent to Malaya
Mallets	c1918		HP13"×22" LP19"×22"	3'8"	71t 17c	0-6-0/ 0-6-0	256 cu ft	2,122 gal	18,250 lb	180 lb	1,308 sq ft	19·3 sq ft	From U.S.A. 2 sent to Malaya

Notes: * Denotes *solid fuel* capacity as originally built.
 † Taken over from the Sungei Ujong Railway.
 ‡ Later converted to a 4-4-2.
 § Later increased to 78t.
 ¶ Four more delivered in 1931 with HS of 1,316 sq ft.
 || Later increased to 180 lb per sq in.

S¹ A third batch of 5 introduced in 1932. Differs only in fuel and water capacity (10t and 4,000 gal respectively) and in having Rotary Cam Poppet Valve Gear.
C² Caprotti Valve Gear. 2 batches of improved 'C' Class introduced in 1939-40 with Rotary Cam Poppet Valve Gear.
O³ 40 more introduced between 1946 and 1948 with minor modifications. Little difference, externally, between these and original 'O' Class.

Class	Builder	Last of Class Withdrawn
A	Hunslet	Not known
B	Hunslet	Not known
C	Hawthorn, Leslie; Kitson	Not known
D	Kitson; Dübs	1928
E	Kitson	1930
G	Kitson; Hunslet; Neilson, Reid; R. Stephenson	1947
H	Kitson; Nasmyth, Wilson	1958
I	Kitson	1949
J	Dübs	1924
K	Dübs	1926
Burma E	Vulcan	1922
Burma O	Neilson	1928
P	Kitson; North British	1958
Q	Baldwin	1959
M	Baldwin	1958
R	Baldwin	1964
L	Kitson	531.01 to National Museum 1971
T	Bagnall	1966
K	Beyer, Peacock; R. Stephenson	c. 1970
S	North British	1959
C	North British	c. 1971
O	North British	33 in service late 1972
WD	Baldwin/Davenport/Alco	One still in service late 1972
Mallets	Baldwin	1930

NOTE: Many sources consulted differ: even dimensions supplied by the Railway Administration varied on occasions.

Steam Locomotives—Malayan Railway and Constituents.

pendent in 1957, as its nucleus. In the mid-1970s, the railway network in peninsular Malaysia totaled about thirteen hundred miles of meter-gauge, single track. It consisted of a 488-mile west-coast line, a 327-mile mid-interior line, and many branch lines serving port and urban areas. Both of the main lines connected with the Thailand State Railway, at two different points on the northern border, and merged at Gemas with a joint line to Singapore in the south. The railroad system was considered the most economical form of transport over medium- and long-range distances as of 1963, and the government regarded its efficient operation as essential for the movement of agricultural, forestry, and mining products, and in the execution of many new development schemes then under consideration.

In 1972 the railways were carrying six million passengers per year and nearly four million tons of freight. Steam traction in 1972 had largely given way to diesel locomotives. In 1978 the meter-gauge railroads of Malaysia had a route length of 1,665 kilometers, or 1,035 miles.

Steam Locomotives in Malaysia

Steam locomotives used in Malaysia were furnished by a wide assortment of manufacturers, including Neilson; Dubs; Sharp, Stewart; North British Locomotive; Hunslet; Hawthorn, Leslie; Kitson; Stephenson; Nasmyth, Wilson; Vulcan; Baldwin; and Beyer Peacock. The tabulation outlines the steam locomotives in use on the Malayan Railroad and constituents from 1885 to 1944.

In 1970, before extensive substitution of diesel power, KTM (Keretapi Tanah Melayu), had a roster of two hundred steam engines, including two classes of 4-6-4 tank machines, and a few U.S. Army 2-8-2 MacArthurs from World War II. They also had at that time a large number of 4-6-2 Pacifics, including sixty-seven with three cylinders, complicated poppet valves, and center headlights. All Pacifics had names inscribed on the boiler sides—Roman on the left and Malayan on the right.

By December 1972 diesel traction had largely displaced steam locomotives, and only twenty active Pacifics remained.

The accompanying fourteen illustrations picture, outline, and describe some of the steam locomotives used in Malaysia from 1888 to 1946.

In 1888 Neilson & Company constructed a single type 4-4-0 tank locomotive (no. 4) for the Selangor Railways of the Malaya States. This engine had the following specifications:

Gauge	3 feet 3⅜ inches
Work order no.	E 642
Cylinders	10 by 18 inches
Drive wheels	3-foot 3-inch diameter
Boiler heating surface	370 square feet
Working steam pressure	130 pounds per square inch
Tractive force	4000 pounds at 75 percent boiler working pressure
Operating weight	20 tons plus 8 hundredweights
Capacities	400 gallons water; 100 cubic feet fuel.

(Courtesy: Mitchell Library, Glasgow) N/E 642

The Neilson Company in 1893 supplied the Perak State Railway of Malaya two type 4–4–0 tender locomotives (nos. 8, 9). Specifications were as follows:

Gauge	3 feet 3⅜ inches
Work order no.	E 708
Cylinders	12 by 18 inches
Drive wheels	3-foot 3-inch diameter

Boiler heating area	503.3 square feet
Working steam pressure	140 pounds per square inch
Operating weights	
Engine	22 tons plus 11 hundredweights
Tender	12 tons plus 13 hundredweights
Tender water capacity	1000 gallons.

(Courtesy: Mitchell Library, Glasgow) N/E 708

In 1894 Dubs & Company supplied the Selangor Railways of Malaya with two (nos. 7, 8) type 4–6–0 tender locomotives. These engines had the following characteristics:

Gauge	3 feet 3⅜ inches
Work order no.	E 3220
Cylinders	14 by 20 inches
Drive wheels	3-foot 3-inch diameter

Boiler heating area	689.88 square feet
Working steam pressure	140 pounds per square inch
Tractive force	10,554 pounds
Operating weights	
Engine	26 tons plus 6 hundredweights
Tender	11 tons plus 19 hundredweights
Tender capacities	1000 gallons water; 250 cubic feet fuel.

(Courtesy: Mitchell Library, Glasgow) D/E 3220

In 1897 Sharp, Stewart & Company furnished two type 4–4–0 tender locomotives (nos. 9, 10) for use on the Selangor Railways of Malaya. Specifications follow:

Gauge	3 feet 3⅜ inches
Work order	E 1095
Cylinders	16 by 20 inches
Drive wheels	4-foot 3-inch diameter
Boiler details	(not stated)
Tender water capacity	1000 gallons.

(Courtesy: Mitchell Library, Glasgow) SS/E 1095

Dubs & Company in 1898 constructed one type 4–4–2 (no. 4) tank locomotive for the Sungei, Ujong Railway of Malaya. Specifications were as follows:

Gauge	3 feet 3⅜ inches
Work order no.	E 3621
Cylinders	12 by 18 inches
Drive wheel	3-foot 6-inch diameter
Boiler heating surface	573 square feet
Working steam pressure	130 pounds per square inch
Tractive force	6017 pounds
Operating weight	27 tons
Capacities	500 gallons water; 120 cubic feet fuel.

(Courtesy: Mitchell Library, Glasgow) D/E 3621

In 1901 the Perak State Railway purchased from Neilson & Company six type 4–6–0 tender locomotives (nos. 28–33) with the following specifications:

Gauge	3 feet 3⅜ inches
Work order no.	E 871
Cylinders	14½ by 20 inches
Drive wheels	4-foot 3½-inch diameter
Boiler heating surface	732 square feet
Working steam pressure	150 pounds per square inch
Operating weights	
Engine	29 tons plus 19 hundredweights
Tender	20 tons plus 3 hundredweights
Tender capacities	1770 gallons water; 240 cubic feet fuel.

(Courtesy: Mitchell Library, Glasgow) N/E 871

The Federated Malay States Railways in 1912 purchased three type 0–6–4 tank engines from the North British Locomotive Company (nos. 120, 123, 124). Specifications follow:

Gauge	3 feet 3⅜ inch
Work order no.	E 497
Cylinders	14½ by 20 inches
Drive wheels	4-foot 4-inch diameter
Boiler heating surface	806 square feet
Working steam pressure	180 pounds per square inch
Tractive force	10,900 pounds
Operating weight	41 tons plus 17 hundredweights
Capacities	800 gallons water; 90 cubic feet fuel.

(Courtesy: Mitchell Library, Glasgow) L 497

Shown is a class M Mogul type locomotive, with a 2–6–0 wheel arrangement, ten of which were furnished in 1920 by Baldwin for use on the meter-gauge Federated Malay States Railways. Specifications were as follows:

Cylinders	14 by 18 inches
Coupled drive wheels	37-inch diameter
Boiler	
Grate area	13.1 square feet
Heating surface	761 square feet
Working pressure	160 pounds per square inch
Tractive force	12,257 pounds
Operating weight	53 tons plus 8 hundredweights (engine plus tender)
Tender capacities	1830 gallons water; 6 tons coal.

(Courtesy: Keretapi Tanah Melayu, Malaysian Railways)

This illustration shows a class R six-wheeled tank locomotive, one of ten furnished by Baldwin in 1920 for use on the meter-gauge Malaysian Railways; this was a type 0–6–0 engine having these specifications:

Cylinders	16 by 20 inches
Coupled drive wheels	42-inch diameter
Boiler	
Grate area	12 square feet
Heating surface	504 square feet
Working pressure	170 pounds per square inch
Tractive effort	17,554 pounds
Operating weight	38 tons plus 6 hundredweights
Capacities	1000 gallons water; 2 tons coal.

(Courtesy: Keretapi Tanah Melayu, Malaysian Railways)

The Federated Malay States Railways procured from the North British Locomotive Company in 1928 an unstated number of type 4–6–2, class S Pacific tender locomotives with these specifications:

Gauge	3 feet 3⅜ inches
Work order no.	L 840
Cylinders	17 by 24 inches
Drive wheels	4-foot 6-inch diameter
Boiler heating area	2335 square feet
Working steam pressure	180 pounds per square inch
Tractive force	26,000 pounds
Operating weights	
Engine	69 tons plus 3 hundredweights
Tender	39 tons plus 6 hundredweights
Tender capacities	3000 gallons water; 7 tons fuel.

(Courtesy: Mitchell Library, Glasgow) L 840

In 1929 the North British Locomotive Company furnished an unstated number of additional Pacific type 4–6–2 tender engines for use on the Federated Malay States Railways. Specifications follow:

Gauge	3 feet 3⅜ inches
Work order no.	L 860
Cylinders	17 by 24 inches
Drive wheels	4-foot 6-inch diameter
Boiler heating surface	2335 square feet
Working steam pressure	180 pounds per square inch
Tractive force	26,000 pounds
Operating weights	
Engine	70 tons plus 3 hundredweights
Tender	39 tons plus 6 hundredweights
Tender capacities	3000 gallons water; 7 tons fuel
Class	S with modifications.

(Courtesy: Mitchell Library, Glasgow) L 860

In 1938 the North British Locomotive Company supplied the Federated Malay States Railways with eleven type 4–6–2, class 0.1 tender locomotives (nos. 60–70) having the following specifications:

Gauge	3 feet 3⅜ inches
Work order no.	L 911
Cylinders	12½ by 24 inches
Drive wheels	4-foot 6-inch diameter
Boiler heating surface	1327 square feet
Working steam pressure	250 pounds per square inch
Tractive force	22,130 pounds at 85 percent boiler working pressure
Operating weights	
Engine	58 tons
Tender	42 tons plus 18 hundredweights
Tender capacity	3500 gallons water; 10 tons fuel.

(Courtesy: Mitchell Library, Glasgow) L 911

The Federated Malay States Railways introduced in 1939 six type 4–6–4 tank locomotives (nos. 23–28). These engines, constructed by the North British Locomotive Company had the following characteristics:

Gauge	3 feet 3⅜ inches
Work order no.	L 920
Cylinders	14½ by 22 inches
Drive wheels	4-foot 6-inch diameter
Boiler heating surface	1033.5 square feet
Working steam pressure	250 pounds per square inch
Tractive force	18,202 pounds at 85 percent boiler working pressure
Operating weight	74 tons plus 1 hundredweight
Capacities	2000 gallons water; (not stated) fuel.

(Courtesy: Mitchell Library, Glasgow) L 920

In 1946 the Malayan Railway purchased a series of type 4–6–2 tender locomotives from the North British Locomotive Company (nos. 564.01–564.40). These Pacific type engines had the following specifications:

Gauge	3 feet 3⅜ inches
Work order no.	957
Cylinders	13 by 24 inches
Drive wheels	4-foot 6-inch diameter
Boiler heating surface	1361 square feet
Working steam pressure	250 pounds per square inch
Tractive force	21,120 pounds
Operating weights	
Engine	59 tons plus 10 hundredweights
Tender	44 tons plus 6 hundredweights
Tender capacities	3430 gallons water; 10 tons fuel
Class	564.

(Courtesy: Mitchell Library, Glasgow) L 957

MEXICO

IN THE FIRST THIRD OF THE NINETEENTH CENtury, railroad construction should have provided the answer to Mexico's grievous transportation problems, but the required finances were unavailable and political turmoil discouraged foreign investors. Nevertheless, in 1837, with great enthusiasm and glowing oratory, the government let the first concession for a railroad to connect Mexico City with Vera Cruz, a distance of 264 miles. Three years later the contract was cancelled since nothing had been accomplished. In 1842, President Santa Ana granted another concession, and the contractor actually initiated construction on a right-of-way; however, this was also cancelled in 1849 by the Herrera government since only three miles of track had been laid. Subsequently, the state of Vera Cruz took over the project and constructed another eight miles of rail by 1850, though by 1854 only a total of fifteen miles of 4-foot 8½-inch gauge track had been set down. New revolutions and turmoil then interrupted construction work, and after twenty-three years of intermittent effort, there were still only fifteen miles of railroad in service in 1860.

In general, construction in the rugged mountainous terrain between Mexico City and the gulf port of Vera Cruz was an engineering nightmare. The roadbed had to rise from sea level on the gulf to over eight-thousand feet, crossing numerous canyons and precipices. Initially the major concessions were held by the Imperial Railway Company, a corporation registered in London. British engineers, working for archduke Maximilian, made good progress, opening the section from Vera Cruz to Paso del Macho (about forty miles) in 1865, but by 1866 the company was virtually bankrupt and all work was suspended. After Maximilian's demise in 1867, the new Mexican leader, Benito Juárez, indicating a great need to complete the line, agreed to subsidize the bankrupt company with an annual grant of 560,000 pesos for twenty-five years. Shortly thereafter, the railway firm was renamed Ferrocarril Mexicano (Mexican Railroad Company), to soothe the feelings of various antagonistic members of the Mexican congress.

The British engineers subsequently did a fantastic job of construction, digging endless tunnels, and breaching the Barranca de Metlac, a chasm 900 feet across and 375 feet deep. The rails ascended fifty-five hundred feet in the first ninety-five miles from Vera Cruz and then gained an additional twenty-five hundred feet in twelve miles to the edge of the central tableland, all the while presenting tremendous engineering difficulties. After crossing the Infernillo viaduct, six miles north of Nogales, the route passed through a series of sharp curves, giving the duplex double-boiler Fairlie engines great climbing problems. The line reached a maximum elevation of 8,323 feet in two places before descending into the Valley of Mexico at an altitude of 7,348 feet. All of the gaps were eventually closed, the rails were joined, and the job was finished on 20 December 1872. It was officially inaugurated on 1 January 1873. The construction of this rail line was considered to be one of the most important economic achievements in Mexican history. When the Vera Cruz–Mexico City railroad was completed, with a few short feeder lines, Mexico had a total of four hundred miles of railway in service, compared to thirty thousand miles in the United States.

The next president of Mexico, Sebastian Lerdo de Tejada, in 1873 let several contracts for construction of a new line north from Mexico City to the United States border. Accordingly, an American-British concessionaire founded the Mexican Central Railroad and proceeded to lay out the project. The Mexican Central Railway was planned to run 1,224 miles from Mexico City to the northern frontier of Cuidad Juárez (El Paso). As it turned out, this project had none of the horrendous engineering difficulties encountered on the Mexico City–Vera Cruz line. The Mexican Central Railway Company was incorporated in Massachusetts in 1880 and started construction almost immediately. The line was opened to Tula in 1881, to Queretaro in 1882, and was completed 8 March 1884. In spite of many sharp curves and some bridges in the southern section, its building was attended by no special technical problems.

The Sonora Railroad Company in 1884 made a rail connection between Guaymas, on the Mexican west coast, and Nogales, on the border, a distance of approximately three hundred rail miles.

Operating difficulties on the Mexico City–Vera Cruz line led London, a British entrepreneur, to form a rival company called the Inter-Oceanic Railway in 1888. The plan was to amalgamate existing narrow-gauge facilities into a single system, which produced another Mexico City–Vera Cruz connection with easier grades and a safer ride. The company also merged various other narrow-gauge lines, resulting in a railroad from Laredo on the United States border, to Mexico City. This route was reconstructed and modified as a standard-gauge system in 1903.

In 1903 the first line south from Mexico City was built, reaching to Oaxaca. One section of this line, the 228 miles from Puebla to Oaxaca, required boring many tunnels and erecting a variety of bridges to conquer the intervening mountain ranges. The winding route ran through countless gorges, where tracks had to be placed at a high level to prevent flooding. In one place, a river had to be diverted from its course to make room for the right-of-way.

By the turn of the century Mexico City was linked reasonably with all parts of the country except Yucatán. In 1896, a contract to cross the isthmus of Tehuantepec (185 miles) was awarded, and the line was completed in 1907. This was linked with Guatemala by the so-called Pan American Railway in 1913. The Mexican government carried out a vast merger in 1907, which placed the National Railways under state control. Yucatán was finally connected with Mexico City in the 1950s.

In 1927 the old Southern Pacific Railway link down the west coast of Mexico was finally completed as far as Guadalajara, where it was joined with the lines of the National Railway.

The Chihuahua Pacific railroad of 418 miles, starting at Chihuahua, extended the rail line from Presidio-Ojinaga, on the border, to the Pacific Ocean at Topolobampo Bay (Ojinaga to Chihuahua, 167 miles). This was originally envisioned as a short-cut from Kansas City to San Francisco, with rail to the Pacific and a steamer north to California. Robert Kinsey Owen first planned the route in 1873, and Arthur Stilwell & Associates began construction in 1885. However, two factors that cost many thousands of lives and several fortunes delayed the job for ninety years: the almost insurmountable Sierra Madre Mountains and the Mexican political shenanigans. The most serious delay was in 1912, due to the raging revolution, by which time rails had been laid 184 miles from Chihuahua to Creel. Conquering the Sierras, the line climbed to over eight thousand feet and then dropped seven thousand feet in ninety-four miles, looping its way down the western side of the mountains, through eighty-six tunnels (one over a mile long), and across thirty-seven trestles bridging streams and chasms hundreds of feet below, dropping, curving, but never exceeding a grade of 2.5 percent. The railroad, which included the so-called Copper Canyon route, was finally completed in 1961, after an investment of a hundred million dollars and countless lives.

During the last five years of steam power on the standard-gauge National Railways of Mexico, engines were dispatched from a roundhouse in the northern suburbs of Mexico City. In 1964 one hundred steam engines of five different wheel arrangements still in service. Of these, only one was being used on passenger service; the others handled about 60 percent of the freight traffic. At this time, Mexico had the last 4–8–2 Mountain-type locomotives in service in North America. Most steam locomotives were of United States manufacture and consisted of second-hand engines from many famous

U.S. railways. All European engines were obsolete or had been reduced to scrap. Conversion to diesel traction was largely complete by 1968, in the last days of steam power on the Mexican railways.

Mexico has always been aware of the important role that railroads played in its development. The widespread rebellion of 1910 saw adversaries on both sides using the railways for military purposes. Murals depicting popular uprisings show the steam engine as part of the scene. Railroad travel has always been, and continues to be, a favorite Mexican pastime.

Janes World Railways in 1980 indicated that Mexican railroads had a total route length of 13,807 kilometers (8580 miles) of 1.435-meter track and 401.8 kilometers (250 miles) of 0.914-meter track.

Steam Locomotives in Mexico

The map shows the railroad network in Mexico, and fourteen illustrations picture and describe some steam locomotives used from 1879 to 1945.

In 1921 the National Railways of Mexico ordered eighty-three Baldwin locomotives consisting of twenty Pacific-type engines for passenger service, twenty-three Mikado-type for heavy freight service, and forty Consolidation-type engines for general freight use, of which twenty were standard-gauge and twenty narrow-gauge. The Pacific engines (not illustrated) had cylinders 25 by 28 inches, drive wheels 67 inches in diameter, with engine weights of 250,870 pounds.

Railway map of Mexico.
(*Courtesy:* Janes World Railways)

In 1879 Dubs & Company constructed two, type 4–4–0, tender locomotives for the ICM of Mexico. These engines had the following identifications: no. 2, named "Benito Juarez," and no. 3, named "Porfino Diaz." Specifications follow:

Gauge	3 feet
Cylinders	10 by 18 inches
Coupled drivers	3-foot 6-inch diameter
Boiler	
Heating area	388.76 square feet
Working pressure	130 pounds per square inch
Tractive force	4178 pounds
Operating weights	
Engine	15 tons plus 7 hundredweights
Tender	8 tons plus 14 hundredweights
Tender capacities	500 gallons water; 85 cubic feet coal.

(Courtesy: Mitchell Library, Glasgow) E 1329

In 1882 Neilson & Company constructed several type 4–6–0 tank locomotives for the Mexican Railway Company. These engines had the following specifications:

Gauge	4 feet 8½ inches
Cylinders	17 by 22 inches
Coupled drivers	3-foot 9-inch diameter
Boiler	
Heating surface	1100 square feet
Working pressure	140 pounds per square inch
Operating weight	47 tons plus 5 hundredweights
Capacities	1200 gallons water; 1½ tons coal.

(Courtesy: Mitchell Library, Glasgow) E-544

Neilson & Company in 1883 furnished several Fairlie, type 0–6–6–0, locomotives for use on the lines of the Mexican Railway Company. These engines had the following characteristics:

Gauge	4 feet 8½ inches
Cylinders	16 by 22 inches
Drivers	3-foot 9-inch diameter
Boiler	
Heating surface	1813 square feet
Working pressure	140 pounds per square inch
Operating weight	73 tons
Capacities	2000 gallons water; 90 cubic feet coal.

(Courtesy: Mitchell Library, Glasgow) E 545

A model of a Fairlie locomotive on display in the Science Museum of London is pictured here. This represents an engine which was used on standard gauge railroads in Mexico. The prototype, type 0–6–6–0 locomotive, was built in 1889 by Neilson & Company. Each six-wheel power bogie had two 16 by 22 inch cylinders with driving wheels 3.5 feet in diameter. Steam pressure was 180 pounds per square inch in each of the two boilers. Tractive effort at 90 percent steam pressure was 39,800 pounds. Tanks had a total of 2850 gallons of water. Spark arresters were fitted due to the use of wood as the boiler fuel. Operating weight was 98 tons.
(Courtesy: Science Museum, London)

The Interoceanic Railway of Mexico in 1890 procured from Dubs & Company several type 4–6–0 tender engines of which one was identified as no. 35. Specifications were as follows:

Gauge	3 feet
Cylinders	16 by 22 inches
Coupled drivers	4-foot diameter
Boiler	
Heating surface	796 square feet
Working pressure	150 pounds per square inch
Tractive force	13,200 pounds
Operating weights	
Engine	35 tons plus 7 hundredweights
Tender	23 tons plus 12 hundredweights
Tender capacities	2000 gallons water; 300 cubic feet coal.

(Courtesy: Mitchell Library, Glasgow) E 2571

In 1894 Neilson & Company built three additional Fairlie, type 0–6–6–0, engines for the Mexican Railway Company. These carried the identification numbers 21, 27, and 32 with the following specifications:

Gauge	4 feet 8½ inches
Cylinders	16 by 22 inches
Coupled drivers	3-foot 6-inch diameter
Boiler	
Heating surface	1712 square feet
Working pressure	165 pounds per square inch
Tractive force	33,188 pounds
Operating weight	98 tons plus 8 hundredweights
Capacities	2850 gallons water; 300 cubic feet coal.

(Courtesy: Mitchell Library, Glasgow) E 717

The Mexican Railway Company in 1894 purchased from Neilson & Company four tender steam locomotives type 4–6–0 which carried the running numbers: 3, 5, 6, 20. Pertinent characteristics were as follows:

Gauge	4 feet 8½ inch
Cylinders	18½ by 26 inches
Coupled drivers	5-foot diameter
Boiler	

Heating surface	1328 square feet
Working pressure	175 pounds per square inch
Tractive force	19,465 pounds
Operating weights	
Engine	56 tons plus 3 hundredweights
Tender	43 tons plus 8 hundredweights
Tender capacities	3500 gallons water; 270 cubic feet coal.

(Courtesy: Mitchell Library, Glasgow) E 720

In 1894 the Mexican Railway Company introduced four type 0–8–0 tender engines (nos. 1, 10, 14, 62). These were built by Neilson & Company and had the following specifications:

Gauge	4 feet 8½ inches
Cylinders	18½ by 26 inches
Coupled drivers	4-foot diameter
Boiler	

Heating surface	1811 square feet
Working pressure	175 pounds per square inch
Tractive force	24,331 pounds
Operating weights	
Engine	55 tons plus 16 hundredweights
Tender	43 tons plus 8 hundredweights
Tender capacities	3500 gallons water; 270 cubic feet coal.

(Courtesy: Mitchell Library, Glasgow) E 727

This camelback 0–8–0 type engine was built for the Conquista Coal Company of Mexico by Baldwin in 1901.
(Courtesy: C. A. Brown collection)

In 1901 Neilson furnished additional Fairlie, type 0–6–6–0, locomotives to the Mexican Railway Company. These machines had the following specifications:

Gauge	4 feet 8½ inches
Cylinders	16 by 22 inches
Drivers	3-foot 6-inch diameter
Boiler	
Heating Area	1712 square feet
Working pressure	165 pounds per square inch
Tractive force	33,188 pounds
Operating weight	98 tons plus 7 hundredweights
Capacities	2850 gallons water; 300 cubic feet coal.

(Courtesy: Mitchell Library, Glasgow) E-846

In 1903 the Mexican Railway Company bought four Fairlie, type 0–6–6–0, locomotives from the North British Locomotive Company. These engines bore the identification numbers 171–74 and had specifications as follows:

Gauge	4 feet 8½ inches
Cylinders	16 by 22 inches
Drivers	3-foot 6-inch diameter
Boiler	
Heating surface	1712 square feet
Working pressure	165 pounds per square inch
Tractive force	33,188 pounds
Operating weight	97 tons plus 5 hundredweights
Capacities	2850 gallons water; 300 cubic feet coal.

(Courtesy: Mitchell Library, Glasgow) L 6

The Mexican Railway Company in 1908 purchased two more Fairlie locomotives, type 0–6–6–0; the identification numbers were 181, 182 with the following specifications:

Gauge	4 feet 8½ inches
Cylinders	17 by 25 inches
Drivers	4-foot diameter
Boiler	
Heating area	2376 square feet
Working pressure	200 pounds per square inch
Operating weight	120 tons plus 2 hundredweights
Capacities	3500 gallons water; 315 cubic feet coal.

(Courtesy: Mitchell Library, Glasgow) L 273

A Baldwin, type 4–4–0, locomotive built September 1945 for use on the 3-foot gauge Ferrocarriles Unidos de Yucatan Railway. This engine had 13 by 28 inch cylinders, a boiler diameter of 44 inches; drive wheels had a diameter of 46 inches, and the engine weighed 65,500 pounds.
(Courtesy: Frederick Westing collection)

The Netherlands

THE FIRST RAIL LINES IN HOLLAND WERE CON-structed by private companies between 1839 and 1856. In 1860 a state system was begun that included, at one time, nearly two-thirds of the total mileage of the kingdom. It was not managed by the state directly, being instead leased to a private concern, but the financial results were not satisfactory to either party, and a commission in 1881–82 strongly recommended against the arrangement.

The first two railways in the Netherlands were: (1) The Holland, which ran about fifteen miles from Amsterdam west to Haarlem, and was opened on 24 September 1839, and (2) the Rhenish, which started commercial service in 1843, running about twenty-five miles from Amsterdam south to Utrecht. The track gauge at that time was 6 feet 4⅜ inches. Operations on both lines started with 2–2–2 locomotives manufactured by Sharp, Roberts & Company of Manchester, England.

Early in the twentieth century, the North Brabant Railway was constructed to run from Boxtel in the southern Netherlands 62.75 miles almost due east to Wesel, Germany. This line used the first six-coupled express locomotives in the Netherlands, which were built by Beyer Peacock & Company in 1908.

Early Dutch railways produced severe competition between British and German builders, although German locomotives were heavily favored.

During the period 1900–14, when compound locomotives were being extensively introduced into Continental Europe, the Dutch railroads did not adopt this means of improving thermal efficiency.

The Netherlands had a major problem, unique to these lowlands: the soft, water-soaked soil limited the size and weight of locomotives. Engineering restrictions had to be imposed on the axle loading of all locomotives. These restraints, of course, had a direct bearing on the long-term design and utilization of steam locomotives.

Since before World War II, operation of the Dutch railways has been in the hands of one company, NV Nederlandsche Spoorwegen in which the government is the sole shareholder. Of the total network of 1,968 miles in 1969, about one thousand miles were electrified. Dutch trains were not only fast and comfortable, they were also punctual, well-heated, and sanitary.

In 1969 passenger transport accounted for approximately 54 percent of railway revenue, and an average of five-hundred thousand travelers were carried each day. As was the case in most other countries, as more people acquired private automobiles, regular railway passenger traffic slowly declined. Freight in the same year provided 40.1 percent of the income for the railways. Keen competition from highway and inland waterway transport meant that Nederlandsche Spoorwegen did not show a profit from 1964 to 1970. The poorest year on record was 1967, when the deficit amounted to 94 million guilders ($25.92 million); this was reduced to about 80 million guilders in 1968. International car-sleeper trains (about ten thousand were carried by the Dutch railways in 1969), and special holiday trains—similar to the Bergland Express of Austria, Switzerland, and

Italy, and the Zonespres in the south of France, Italy, and Spain—helped offset rail losses. A new service in 1969 was the growing interest in so-called mini-trips during off-peak seasons. On the freight side, the subsidiary company Van Gend en Loos handled collection and delivery of goods by road, in conjunction with the railways. Passenger luggage and mail made up the balance of the Nederlandsche Spoorwegen income.

In 1968 the Dutch railways adopted a new color scheme for their rolling stock—bright yellow paint and a new logo. Express services were improved. There were then four trains per hour between Amsterdam and Utrecht; three between Rotterdam and the Hague and Utrecht, and between Utrecht and Arnhem; and from seven to nine trains per day between Amsterdam and Groningen or Leeuwarden. In 1969 rolling stock consisted of 523 locomotives, 1,914 passenger coaches, and 21,291 freight cars. Railway staff then totaled some twenty-eight thousand people.

Janes World Railways reported that railways in the Netherlands totaled 2,825 kilometers (1,755 miles) of 1.435-meter (4-foot 6½-inch) track in 1978.

The worst accident in Dutch railway history was a collision at Woerdon on 8 January 1962, in which ninety-one people lost their lives.

Steam Locomotives in the Netherlands

The first railroads in the Netherlands, which opened in 1839 and 1843, used a gauge of 6 feet 4⅜ inches and started traffic operations with type 2–2–2 locomotives built by Sharp, Roberts & Company of Manchester, England. See illustration.

By 1864, as steam traction engines were gradu-

Early Dutch railways consisted of two systems: the Rhenish running from Amsterdam to Utrecht which opened in 1843, and the Holland from Amsterdam to Haarlem which commenced operations in 1839. Both lines used tracks at a gauge of 6 feet 4⅜ inches and 2–2–2 engines manufactured in Manchester, England by Sharp, Roberts & Company. These locomotives had 14- by 18-inch cylinders with 6.5-foot drive wheels and 59 pounds per square inch working steam pressures. One of the first Rhenish steam engines is pictured. It is a model on display in the Railway Museum at Utrecht.
(Courtesy: Railway Museum, Utrecht, Holland)

ally improved, express trains on the Dutch railways used type 2–4–0 machines built by Beyer Peacock & Company of Manchester.

German manufacturers were beginning to meet Dutch locomotive requirements by 1880. An illustration pictures and describes a Borsig-built type 2–4–0 express engine.

In 1881 Beyer Peacock & Company furnished a number of type 2–4–0 express locomotives, one of which is illustrated. Also in 1881, a single-operator utility engine was built by Merryweather & Sons of London, for street use in various Dutch cities.

In 1889 more modern railway steam engines entered the picture with a type 4–4–0 locomotive supplied by Sharp, Stewart & Company of Glasgow, Scotland. Engine no. 107 is featured. Similar types were built in 1899 by Richard Hartmann of Germany, and from 1901 to 1903 by Hartmann and Hohenzollern.

An advanced type of street engine was built in 1904 by Henschel and Sohn of Kassel, Germany.

In 1908 Beyer Peacock supplied a number of six-coupled, type 4–6–0 locomotives for passenger use on the North Brabant Railway.

Dutch manufacture of steam locomotives started in the early twentieth century. An type 4–6–0 express engine was built in 1911 by the Nederlandsche Fabriek van Werktuigen en Spoorwegmaterieel of Amsterdam for use on Dutch railways. This engine is pictured and described.

Many successful express locomotives were built in 1914 for operations on the various Dutch railways. A model of a type 4–6–0 locomotive manufactured by J. A. Maffei of Munich is shown. Other engines were supplied by Maschinenbau A. G. of Berlin and by Schwartzkopff of Berlin. Still another steam utility engine appears in an illustration built in 1920 by Orenstein & Koppel of Berlin for use on the Dutch city streets.

An illustration characterizes a powerful type 4–8–2 freight engine built by Schwartzkopff and Maschinenbau A.G. of Berlin in 1931 for the Netherlands railroads.

In 1945, at the close of World War II, various British military locomotives were delivered to the Netherland to bolster their war-depleted rolling stock. A typical war department British engine, type 2–10–0, is shown.

This express train locomotive was built in 1864 by Beyer, Peacock & Company Ltd., Manchester (GB) for the "Maatschappij tot Exploitatie van Staatsspoorwegen." Specifications for locomotive SS13 were:

Wheel arrangement	2–4–0
Cylinders (2)	406 by 508 millimeters
Drive wheels	1700-millimeter diameter
Boiler	
Grate area	1.38 square meters
Heating surface	85 square meters
Steam pressure	8.3 kilograms per square centimeter
Operating weight	49,300 kilograms
Tank capacity water	6.6 cubic meters
Bunker coal capacity	3500 kilograms.

(Courtesy: Netherlands Railway Museum)

In 1880 A. Borsig, Berlin, built this express train locomotive for the "Hollandsche Ijzeren Spoorweg–Maatschappij." Specifications for locomotive Nestor HSM 89 were:

Wheel arrangement	2–4–0
Cylinders (2)	406 by 558 millimeters
Drive wheels	1869-millimeters diameter
Boiler	
Grate area	1.82 square meters
Heating surface	93.5 square meters
Steam pressure	10.3 kilograms per square centimeter
Operating weight	63,900 kilograms
Tender water capacity	9 cubic meters
Tender coal capacity	3600 kilograms.

(Courtesy: Netherlands Railway Museum)

Beyer, Peacock & Company Ltd., Manchester (GB) built this express train locomotive in 1881 for the "Maatschappij tot Exploitatie van Staatsspoorwegen." Following are the specifications for locomotive SS 326:

Wheel arrangement	2–4–0
Cylinders (2)	457 by 660 millimeter
Drive wheels	2150-millimeter diameter
Boiler	
Grate area	2.10 square meters
Heating surface	103 square meters
Boiler pressure	10.3 kilograms per square centimeter
Operating weight	75,800 kilograms
Tender water capacity	13 cubic meters
Tender coal capacity	4000 kilograms.

(Courtesy: Netherlands Railway Museum)

Shown is a street engine built in 1881 by Messrs Merryweather & Sons, London, for the "Rhijnlandsche–Stroomtramweg–Maatschappij." Specifications for the locomotive RSTM 2 follow:

Cylinders	178 by 279.5 millimeters
Drive wheels	739-millimeter diameter
Boiler	
Grate area	0.4092 square meters
Heating surface	13.95 square meters
Boiler pressure	10.33 kilograms per square centimeter
Operating weight	8730 kilograms
Water capacity	1.65 cubic meters
Coal capacity	320 kilograms.

(Courtesy: Netherlands Railway Museum)

In 1889 Sharp, Stewart & Company, Ltd., Atlas Works, Glasgow, Scotland, built this express train locomotive for the "Nederlandsche Rhijnspoorweg–Maatschappij." The specifications for locomotive NRS 107 were:

Wheel arrangement	4–4–0
Cylinders (2)	457 by 660 millimeters
Drive wheels	2016-millimeters diameter
Boiler	
Grate area	2.15 square meters
Heating surface	113 square meters
Steam pressure	10.3 kilograms per square centimeter
Operating weight	80,500 kilograms
Tender water capacity	10.2 cubic meters
Tender coal capacity	2800 kilograms.

(Courtesy: Netherlands Railway Museum)

The 4–4–0 tank locomotives, described below, were built for the Netherlands Central Railway by Richard Hartmann of Chemnitz in 1899. Later in the 1901–03 period additional units with only slight variations were manufactured by Hartmann and by the Hohenzollern Works of Düsseldorf. The prototype, a model of which is housed in the Railway Museum at Utrecht, is pictured and had these characteristics:

Cylinders	14.75 by 19.75 inches
Coupled wheels	4-foot 5⅛-inch diameter
Boiler	
Grate area	11 square feet
Heating surface	698 square feet
Boiler pressure	175 pounds per square inch
Operating weight	37,100 kilograms
Tank water capacity	3.5 cubic meters
Bunker coal capacity	1000 kilograms.

(Courtesy Railway Museum, Utrecht, Holland)

Pictured is a street engine built in 1904 by Henschel and Sohn, Kassel, for the "Tramweg–Maatschappij Zutphen–Emmerik." Specifications for locomotive ZE 7 were:

Cylinders	260 by 320 millimeters
Drive wheels	750-millimeters diameter
Boiler	
Grate area	0.64 square meter
Heating surface	21.58 square meters
Boiler pressure	14 kilograms per square centimeter
Operating weight	16,000 kilograms
Water capacity	1.8 cubic meters
Capacity	500 kilograms.

(Courtesy: Netherlands Railway Museum)

The first six-coupled locomotives used in the Netherlands were built by Beyer, Peacock & Company in 1908. These engines were used on the North Brabant Railway which ran about sixty-two miles between Boxtel, Holland and Wesel, Germany. These 4–6–0 engines had the following characteristics:

Cylinders	19 by 26 inches (inside and inclined 1 in 24)
Coupled wheels	6.5-foot diameter
Boiler	

Grate area	28 square feet
Total heating surface	1536 square feet
Working pressure	200 pounds per square inch
Operating weight	98 tons (engine plus tender)
Engines numbered 30–31–31 were fitted with superheaters in 1917.	

Pictured is a model on display in the Railway Museum at Utrecht.
(Courtesy: Railway Museum, Utrecht, Holland)

This express engine was built in 1911 by the Nederlandsche Fabriek van Werktuigen en Spoorwegmaterieel (Werkspoor), Amsterdam, for the "Maatschappij tot Exploitatie van Staatsspoorwegen." Locomotive NS 3737 had the following specifications:

Wheel arrangement	4–6–0
Cylinders (4)	400 by 660 millimeters
Drive wheels	1850-millimeter diameter
Boiler	

Grate area	2.84 square meters
Heating surface	145.5 square meters
Boiler pressure	12 kilograms per square centimeter
Operating weight	115,000 kilograms
Tender capacities	18 cubic meters water; 6000 kilograms coal.

(Courtesy: Netherlands Railway Museum)

Express engine built in 1914 by J. A. Maffei Lokomotiv-und Maschinenfabrik, Munich, for the "Nederlandsche–Centraal–Spoorweg–Maatschappij." Model no. NCS 78 had the following specifications:

Wheel arrangement	4–6–0
Cylinders (4)	400 by 640 millimeter
Drive wheels	1900-millimeter diameter
Boiler	
Grate area	3.44 square meters
Heating surface	159 square meters
Steam pressure	12.25 kilograms per square centimeter
Operating weight	120,000 kilograms
Tender capacities	20 cubic meters water; 5000 kilograms coal.

(Courtesy: Netherlands Railway Museum)

Express train locomotive built in 1914 by the "Berliner Machinenbau A. G., vormals L. Schwartzkopff, Berlin, for the "Hollandsche Ijzeren Spoorweg–Maatschappij." Specifications for locomotive NS 2104 were:

Wheel arrangement	4–4–0
Cylinders (2)	530 by 660 millimeters
Drive wheels	2100-millimeter diameter
Boiler	
Grate area	2.4 square meters
Heating surface	120 square meters
Boiler pressure	12.4 kilograms per square centimeter
Operating weight	105,000 kilograms
Tender capacity	19 cubic meters water; 6000 kilograms coal.

(Courtesy: Netherlands Railway Museum)

Street engine, built in 1920 by Orenstein & Koppel A.G., Berlin, for the "Rotterdamsche–Tramweg–Maatschappij." Specifications for locomotive RTM 57 follow:

Cylinders	330 by 400 millimeters
Drive wheels	885-millimeter diameter
Boiler	

Grate area	0.8 square meters
Heating area	27 square meters
Boiler pressure	14 kilograms per square centimeter
Operating weight	23,000 kilograms
Water capacity	2.5 cubic meters
Coal capacity	900 kilograms.

(Courtesy: Netherlands Railway Museum)

The Berliner Maschinenbau A.G., vormals L. Schwartzkopff, Berlin, built this goods engine in 1931 for the "Nederlandsche Spporwegen. Specifications follow for locomotive 6317 NS:

Wheel arrangement	4-8-2
Cylinders(4)	420 by 660 millimeters
Drive wheels	1550-millimeter diameter
Boiler	

Grate area	3.16 square meters
Heating surface	167 square meters
Steam pressure	14 kilograms per square centimeter
Operating weight	127,000 kilograms
Water capacity	14 cubic meters
Coal capacity	4500 kilograms.

(Courtesy: Netherlands Railway Museum)

Goods engine built in 1945 by North British Locomotive Company, Ltd., Glasgow, Scotland, for the British War Department. The locomotive became no. 5085 at the "Nederlandsche Spoorwegen. Specifications for locomotive W.D. 73755 follow:

Wheel arrangement	2–10–0
Cylinders (2)	483 by 711 millimeters
Drive wheels	1435-millimeter diameter
Boiler	
Grate area	3.72 square meters
Heating surface	165.1 square meters
Boiler pressure	12 kilograms per square centimeter
Operating weight	136,100 kilogram
Tender capacities	22.7 cubic meters water; 9100 kilograms coal.

(Courtesy: Netherlands Railway Museum)

NEW ZEALAND

NEW ZEALAND, A BRITISH DOMINION, CONSISTS of two large islands and a number of smaller islands that lie at some distance from the main group. Situated in the south Pacific Ocean about twelve hundred miles east of Australia, it lies seven thousand miles almost due south of Alaska and four thousand miles west of the coast of Chile. It is fifty-four hundred miles by direct route from San Francisco. The two large islands are North Island and South Island, separated by Cook Strait, which varies in width from sixteen to ninety miles. The two main islands lie entirely in the south temperate zone and form a line stretching about one thousand miles in a northeast-southwest direction, with a maximum width of 180 miles. Total area of the dominion is 103,575 square miles.

The first railroad in New Zealand, the Dun Mountain Railway, ran a few miles inland from Nelson on the far northern coast of South Island in 1862. This rail line, on 3-foot-gauge tracks with horse traction, facilitated transportation of minerals and timber from the hills to the port at Nelson. The line lasted only ten years.

The first locomotive-powered rail system, also on South Island, was the Canterbury Railway, which ran 4.35 miles from Christchurch to temporary docks at Ferrymead. This 1.600-millimeters (5-foot 3-inch) gauge rail line opened 1 December 1863. The railway formed part of a rail line from Christchurch to Lyttelton, which was finished in November 1867, including a 2.595-kilometer (1.61-mile) tunnel through the Port Hills. Another line from Invercargill, at the south end of South Island, to the fine deep-water port of Bluff was opened in December 1886; this used British stan-dard-gauge tracks, i.e., 4 feet 8½ inches.

Most railroads in New Zealand were state-owned from the beginning. A fundamental aim, accepted by all political parties and economic entities, was that the railroads had to meet two basic criteria: they had to be self-supporting and they had to contribute to the improvement and development of New Zealand.

Although installation of the original railways progressed slowly, after 1920 the rate of construction, funded by British capital, was greater than in the United States, Canada, or Great Britain. The railways eventually permeated every aspect of New Zealand life, becoming the largest enterprise in that country and the largest employer. Unlike the United States railways, those in New Zealand did not foster the growth of a great number of new communities wherever the rails were extended. Rail systems in New Zealand were primarily concerned with moving mining products, coal, timber, and pastoral produce from the back country to the seaports, then carrying foodstuffs, farm equipment, lumbering machinery, textiles, fertilizers, and cement on the return trip.

The rough topography of New Zealand, involving countless lofty and broken ridges, always necessitated a great number of expensive bridges. Early chasm crossings were timber trestles, all of which had to be eventually replaced with steel structures.

In 1870 the state wisely mandated, at the insistence of a visionary named Julius Vogel, that all future New Zealand railways should be of a common 3-foot 6-inch gauge (1.067-millimeter). As a consequence, most early locomotives and rolling stock were sold off to South Australia, which had embarked on Irish 5-foot 3-inch gauge systems. Once the matter of rail gauge was finally settled, several rail lines in New Zealand were pushed inland along the river valleys. A main line was also built parallel to the east coast of South Island from Invercargill to Dunedin and later on to Christchurch, the distance from Invercargill to Christchurch being 549 kilometers, or 341 miles. In time, the main line was extended north to the Blenheim and Picton areas in the northeast. By 1880 there were about 3,300 kilometers (2,050.5 miles) of government-owned railways.

With development of the valuable coal deposits along the northwest coast of South Island, a network of rail lines grew up to transport this product from the Reefton region to the ports of Westport and Greymouth.

While most of the railway development in New Zealand was undertaken by the state, in 1880 some private lines began to appear. Two of these, the Wellington & Manawau Railway Company and the New Zealand & Midland Railway Company, were the most important.

Many rail construction projects on South Island turned out to be virtual railroad engineering nightmares. The 140-mile line from the east coast at Christchurch, through Arthur's Pass to west coast Greymouth, was an example. The line had to cross the Southern Alps, which had many high peaks (Mt. Cook, at 12,349 feet above sea level, is the highest). The Otira Tunnel, opened 14 August 1923, and was 1.32 miles long. It passed under a gorge of the same name and had 1 in 50 (2 percent) grades. Here, steam locomotion was used from either end of the tunnel, with small electric engines taking over in the tunnel itself to exclude smoke and cinders. Along this same route were four high steel viaducts and seventeen smaller tunnels. All in all, the grades were extremely severe and put steam locomotion to the test!

Another outstanding job in New Zealand involved construction of the Central Otago Railway in the southern part of South Island from 1889 to 1921. This ran from Dunedin, on the east coast, inland to Cromwell, and turned out to be one of the most scenic of all railways in New Zealand, with 146 miles of wild, magnificent terrain. Near Dunedin the railway had to plunge twenty miles through the Taieri River gorges, which made numerous tunnels and viaducts necessary. Still

another section ran south from the interior through the mountainous Otago basin along the Oreti River to various locations on the south shore opposite Foveaux Strait and Stewart island. Other sections of the line covered the central and northeastern part of Otago province. This rail system needed such a large number of connecting bridges that it eventually became known as The Bridge Line.

NORTH ISLAND

Blood, sweat, and tears epitomize the building of the North Island Main Trunk Railway. The construction of this steel highway is a saga of faith and courage. It tells of the determination, perseverance, and optimism of men in an often cataclysmic era.

The pioneers were presented with more than just formidable terrain in the seemingly bucolic country through which the railway was to run as a link between two important cities. Behind the tranquil facade lurked a real hornet's nest, for this countryside was also the home of the defiant Maoris, who were further thorns in the path of progress.

Early settlers of Auckland depended largely on small coastal vessels and riverboats for transport, but as far back as 1863, the more sagacious of these men had begun to visualize a line linking Auckland and Wellington with branches to Hawke Bay and Taranaki. The Auckland Provincial Council actually took up the gauntlet that very year and began preliminary work on a railway to Drury, thirty-two kilometers south of Auckland. Plans and estimates were readied while materials for the line were ordered from England; however, work on the proposed railway appeared fated to be delayed as the tentacles of war extended over the North Island. The Waikato region was a gory battlefield for the next nine months while the henchmen of Maori King Tawhiao fought in bush and mud to resist the *pakeha* invaders.

The Waikato war ended in April 1864 and the following year saw work on the railway resumed, but progress was laboriously slow. By 1866 the railway commission had squandered most of the hundred thousand pounds allocated for the project, with only a few kilometers of track to show for it. Protracted disputes between engineers of the provincial council and the contractors further delayed progress in the following six years. In 1872 the government decided to take over and contracted the English firm of Brogden & Sons to finish the project. The line was then built as far as Mercer, at which point the government decided to let soldiers build the rest of the railway because of fears of renewed hostilities with the Maoris.

Beyond Mercer was the wilderness of swampland inhabited by a Maori population still harboring bitter memories of the Waikato war. Relentlessly, though, the soldiers toiled to lay tracks over old battlefields and quaking swamps.

Southward the railway crept; it skirted the Waikato River at Mercer in 1875, snaked past Taupiri—site of a pioneer mission station—to enter the old Maori capital of Ngaruawahia in August 1877. Hamilton was reached before Christmas 1877, and by July 1880 trains were running between Auckland and Te Awamutu.

For a few years this remained the end of the railroad, as few white men dared venture beyond this point. A few miles away was the frontier, the Punia River, beyond which the Maori king and his fighting men had retreated after their last glorious stand at Orakau. This was Tawhiao's territory, where the law of the tomahawk and the long-barreled Enfield rifle reigned.

Meanwhile, farther south, a line between Longburn and Palmerston North was opened for traffic in April 1876. This was extended to Wanganui in 1878 and to New Plymouth in 1885. On the eastern side, Napier was linked with Palmerston North in 1891. In 1878 construction of a government railway from Wellington to Foxton was authorized and work began the following year. However, in 1880 the Royal Commission on Railways, set up to reduce public expenditure, recommended against continuation of the railway, and plans were shelved indefinitely. The merchants of Wellington, though, were quick to take up the cudgels. Deciding the railway was essential to further their business interests, they formed the Wellington and Manawatu Railway Company in 1881 to carry on where the government had left off.

Progress was swift on the railway, which was resurveyed to connect with the government system at Longburn instead of Foxton. The twenty-six-kilometer (16.1-mile) section between Wellington and Paremata was opened in September 1885 and, in August 1886 the sixty-kilometer (37.2-mile) section from Longburn to Otaki was completed. Three months later, the first trains were running from Longburn to Wellington.

Up north, the government passed the Railway Loan Act in 1882, authorizing the raising of one million pounds to push the line south from Te Awamutu. The railroad could take one of three routes: a central line from Te Awamutu to Marton, a westerly line to Taranaki, or an easterly line to Hawke Bay via Taupo. The first two routes required the railway to pass through the King Country, still dominated by Tawhiao.

Surveyors were appointed to traverse the three routes. The most notable of these was John Rochfort, a courageous and tenacious individual, who began his survey at Marton in 1883. His initial "intrusion" into the King Country saw him captured by hostile Maoris and threatened with death; however, diplomatic overtures by the government obtained the support of Wahanui, Rewi, and Taonui, chiefs of the Ngatimaniapoto tribe, and Rochfort was able to carry on without fear of being scalped or of becoming the main dish on King Tawhiao's menu.

Fifteen months later Rochfort completed his survey, and the 337-kilometer (209.3-mile) route from Te Awamutu to Marton (already on the Wellington–New Plymouth line) was accepted by the government in 1884. Work began the following year, and by 1889 the railway had gone past Te Kuiti to the Mokau Valley below Te Awamutu. Farther south at Poroolarao, a long tunnel was driven through a saddle between the Mokau and Wanganui watersheds. At the Marton end, the railway extended to Rangatira, and the short Mangaonoho section was completed before lack of money brought work to a standstill.

The success of the Liberal Party in the 1891 elections saw Minister of Public Works Richard J. Seddon, dispense with private contracts and let the work out to cooperative groups under supervision of government engineers.

Work was slow but steady, and Taumarunui was linked with Auckland in 1903. In 1904 trains ran northward from Marton to Taihape, and by 1906 the railroads were only ninety-eight kilometers apart, separated by mountainous, forest-clad plateaus. By March 1908 the railheads had reached Makatote and Ohakune, and the gap was down to seventeen kilometers. On 3 August 1908 the rails were linked on the Manganui-o-te-Ao viaduct to serve as a temporary line for the first train, a parliamentary special, to travel from Wellington to Auckland.

The official last spike was driven on 6 November 1908, between the Manganui-o-te-Ao and Makatote viaducts, exactly halfway between Wellington and Auckland, and trains began running between the two cities three days later.

The last act of Joseph Ward's government in the saga of the North Island Main Trunk Railway was the acquisition of the privately owned Wellington & Manawatu Railway and their line from Wellington to Longburn. In September 1908 the Wellington & Manawatu Railway Purchase Act was passed, allowing the government to buy the railroad for 933,000 pounds. The North Island Main Trunk 450-mile railway was now a reality.

The central section of that railway, especially, had presented horrendous engineering problems, with steep grades and the need for many costly viaducts. However, with the exception of the peculiar, meandering, so-called Raurimu Spiral, there were no insurmountable obstacles, no zigzags, and only a few short tunnels. The Raurimu Spiral occupied a portion of the line (about latitude 39°10' south, longitude 175°25' east) that ran from a deep valley near Raurimu to a much higher elevation on a volcanic plateau at National Park. The spiral followed a long, twisting path, after which it made a complete 360-degree circle, including two short tunnels, all on an approximate grade of 1 in 50.

The lines out of Wellington normally involved greater construction difficulties. The first railroad, running north and east, had to surmount the tremendous Rimutaka ranges. A Fell system on the 3½-mile Rimutaka incline allowed rail cars to be lowered down the precipitous escarpment to a lower level at Cross Creek. This incline, with a grade of 1 in 14, was closed on 3 November 1955 after completion of the single-track 5.5-mile Rimutaka tunnel, the longest in the southern hemisphere.

The most energetic early railroad building program in New Zealand occurred during the period 1870–80. By 1921 there were 3,147 miles of railway, of which 3,009 miles were owned and operated by the state government. The New Zealand Railways reached their maximum extent of 3,536 route miles in 1953. By 1970 there were 3,259 miles of track controlled, with minor exceptions, by the state. Traffic volumes were heavier on North Island, particularly on the main trunk line between Auckland and Wellington. The most frequented short-distance hauls were between Wellington and Frankton, Wellington and Parkakariki, Wellington and Upper Hutt, and (on South Island) between Christchurch and Lyttleton. In 1972 a new 5.5-mile tunnel through the Kaimai Hills in North Island was being constructed on a new line running from Tauranga on the northeast coast to inland Rotura; this was expected to be compled in 1977.

The highest railway bridge in New Zealand is a steel trestle, named Mohaka Viaduct, on the Napier–Gisborne extension in North Island. It is 908 feet long, with a height of 318 feet, and was built in the between 1936 and 1942.

The two highest railway summits in New Zealand are: Pokaka, gauge 3 feet 6 inches, 2,671 feet above sea level; Waiouri, gauge 3 feet 6 inches, 2,670 feet above sea level.

The worst rail accident in New Zealand was a bridge collapse near Waiouru on 24 December 1953, in which 155 people were killed.

In 1978 *Janes World Railways* reported a route length of 4,716 kilometers (2,930 miles) of 1.067-meter (3-foot 6-inch) track.

Steam Locomotives in New Zealand

In 1863, when New Zealand's first railway locomotive was delivered in what was then a colony, railways were spreading rapidly in North America and Europe. Early settlers, having experienced the value of this new, cheap form of transport in their homelands, knew they needed railways if the country was to be opened up. They also knew that transport by other means was often prohibitively expensive.

New Zealand's first locomotives were British, and more suited to the heavily constructed railways that served the denser population and the developing industries of the homeland. So New Zealand engineers were soon seeking lighter, more suitable locomotives for the lightly laid, developmental railways in their young colony. They turned to America and American locomotives, developed for the rough-and-ready conditions faced by railroads pushing westward across the prairies; these American engines were brought to New Zealand from 1877 onward. Ultimately, from an amalgam of British and American designs, the typical New Zealand locomotives of the early twentieth century evolved.

The first locomotives to arrive in New Zealand was for the 1.6-meter (5-foot 3-inch) gauge Canterbury Railways. It was landed in May 1863 at Ferrymead, a temporary port at the mouth of the Heathcote River between Christchurch and Lyttelton. Built in Bristol, England, in 1862 for the Melbourne and Essendon Railway in Victoria, it was never used on that railway. Typically British, Canterbury Railways locomotive no. 1 weighed thirty-two tons, ready for service. It had six wheels in a rigid frame and "inside" cylinders under the smokebox. No. 1 was heavy for its period, and evidence suggests that she and her three sisters proved too heavy for some of the light iron rails laid in Canterbury in the 1860s.

Narrow-gauge locomotives during the period of the Vogel government (the 1870s), mostly weighed between ten and twenty tons, more in keeping with the light traffic and light trains of early colonial days. The Canterbury Railway broad-gauge locomotive No. 1 could run at eighty kilometers (49.6 miles) per hour with substantial loads (although that would have been unwise on the light iron rails), but locomotives imported for the 1.067-meter (3-foot 6-inch) gauge railways laid in the 1870s were built for speeds of twenty-four to forty-eight kilometers (fifteen to thirty miles) per hour.

Among the locomotives built for the early 1.067-meter gauge railways in New Zealand were several of the distinctive double-ended Fairlie type. Named after inventor Robert Fairlie, a noted engineer of the day, these locomotives were designed for colonial railways where light rails, sharp curves, and steep gradients were the rule. They looked like two locomotives in one, with a central cab and a funnel at each end. The driver stood on one side of the boiler and the fireman on the other.

The first two Double Fairlie locomotives for New Zealand were built in 1872 by the Vulcan Foundry in England, for the thirteen-kilometer Dunedin and Port Chalmers Railway. Named "Rose" and "Josephine," each weighed twenty-six tons and had 1.142-meter (44.9-inch) diameter wheels. "Josephine" survived to be placed on display in 1926 near the Dunedin railway station. She is still there.

Eight larger Double Fairlie locomotives of two different classes were built in 1874 and 1875. Most of these were used in the Wanganui district. Two classes (R and S) of a modified design known as the Single Fairlie were introduced in 1878 and 1880. Twenty-five were built by Avonside Engine Company, and were mainly used in the Wellington and

The New Zealand Railways, which opened in 1863, used a number of Fairlie articulated engines. These were 0-4-4-0 types with double-ended boiler and a firebox in the middle. The Fairlie machines were quite powerful and easily negotiated the heavy grades and tight curves in mountainous New Zealand. The last double Fairlies were built in 1875 by Avonside Engine Company of Bristol, England. They were used on 3-foot 6-inch gauge tracks in various parts of New Zealand until 1919, by which time all had been scrapped.

The prototype of the model shown, a class E engine, had these specifications:

Cylinders	10 by 18 inches
Coupled drive wheels	3-foot 3.75-inch diameter
Boiler	
Grate area	1 5⅔ square feet
Heating surface	847 square feet
Working pressure	130 pounds per square inch.

(Courtesy: New Zealand Railways, Publicity & Advertising Department)

Shown is a Robert Fairlie type locomotive built for the
New Zealand railways in 1874. This was a double-
ended patent locomotive somewhat similar to the En-
gerth engine finally approved in 1854 for use on the
Semmering Pass in Austria.
(Courtesy: New Zealand Railways)

This pictures a single-boiler Fairlie locomotive, of
which twenty-five units were built in 1875–80 by the
Avonside Engine Company. Cylinders varied between
12¼ inches and 13 inches with a 16-inch stroke. All
had 3½-foot coupled drive wheels. The grate area was
11⅔ square feet with total heating surfaces of 556
square feet developing steam pressures up to 130
pounds per square inch. A model of no. 273 is preserved in New Zealand.
(Courtesy: New Zealand Railways)

This class F, type 0–6–0, tank locomotive was one of the most outstanding railway steam machines ever to be used in New Zealand. Eighty-eight of these versatile engines were built by seven different British manufacturers in the period 1872 to 1888. Pictured is engine no. 163 which was constructed by Dubs & Company of Glasgow, Scotland in 1872. Specifications were:

Cylinders	10.5 by 18 inches
Coupled drive wheels	3-foot 1.5-inch diameter
Tractive force	6960 pounds
Operating weight	20 tons.

(Courtesy: New Zealand Railways, Publicity & Advertising Department)

Wanganui districts. See illustration.

Among the many other classes of locomotives that gave valuable service in New Zealand's early railway years was the twenty-ton F class, of which eighty-eight were built by seven different British makers between 1872 and 1888. Devised primarily for the Dunedin and Clutha Railway, the little class F proved one of the most useful engines that New Zealand Railways ever possessed. It could haul prodigious loads and, to quote a contemporary writer, it could "climb like a cat." See illustration.

Various other classes and types of valuable New Zealand steam locomotives in the early period (1870–90) were as follows:

One class A, type 0–4–0 tank engine, built by Dubs & Company in 1873

one class C, type 0–4–0 tank engine, built in 1873 by Neilson & Company of Glasgow (illustration NZ-13).

A class G, type 4–4–0 tank locomotive, built by "Bl. Hthan," also in 1873.

The first American locomotives were the racy type 2–4–2 engines bought for the Christchurch–Dunedin express trains in 1878. These ornate and speedy little locomotives, the first class K, and provided a marked contrast to the big 145-ton Ka class used on heavy North Island express trains toward the end of the steam era.

Two Rogers locomotives were built in 1878 for use on the private Rakaia & Ashburton Forks line in South Island. These were 2–4–4 tank engines.

The class K locomotives of 1878 were followed in 1880 by six forty-two-ton 2–8–0 freight engines built by the Baldwin Locomotive Works of Philadelphia. These were officially limited to twenty-nine kilometers (eighteen miles) per hour and could drag loads of five hundred tons on level track at low speed. They were the first eight-coupled locomotives—with four driving wheels on each side coupled together—used on New Zealand Railways.

As traffic developed, and as track and bridges were made stronger or replaced to carry heavier loads, larger and more powerful locomotives were introduced. Developments in workshop techniques and advances in metallurgy also led to improvements in locomotive design. Higher steam pressures were made possible in the boilers, and various refinements in design from time to time enabled the steam to be used more efficiently.

Shown is a class A, type 0–4–0, tank locomotive, no. 62, built by Dubs & Company at the Glasgow Locomotive Works in 1873. Specifications were:

Cylinders	8 by 15 inches
Coupled drive wheels	2-foot 6-inch diameter
Working pressure	120 pounds per square inch
Operating weight	tons.

(Courtesy: New Zealand Railways)

Pictured is a class C locomotive, type 0–4–0, no. 1772 built by Neilson & Company of Glasgow, Scotland, in 1873 for use on the New Zealand railways.
(Courtesy: New Zealand Railways)

This class G, type 4–4–0 tank locomotive, no. 57, was built by "Bl. Hthn" in 1873. Specifications were:

Cylinders	10.5 by 18 inches
Drive wheels	3-foot diameter
Working pressure	130 pounds per square inch
Operating weight	20.5 tons.

(Courtesy: New Zealand Railways)

The first American locomotives used on the New Zealand Railways were class K, type 2–4–2, built by the Rogers Locomotive Works of Paterson, New Jersey. These engines hauled express trains on the South Island Main line starting about 1877. Specifications were:

Cylinders	12 by 20 inches
Coupled drive wheels	4-foot diameter
Working pressure	130 pounds per square inch
Operating weight	23.2 tons
Engine number	96.

(Courtesy: New Zealand Railways)

A private railroad on the South Island of New Zealand, the Rakaia & Asburton Forks Railway, imported a couple of American 2–4–4 tank locomotives built by Rogers Locomotive Works of Paterson, New Jersey in 1878. These engines had 11- by 18-inch cylinders, 4-foot coupled drive wheels, and an operational weight of 29 tons. Service results indicated a lack of required power and they were withdrawn from service in 1900. See picture of a model.

(Courtesy: New Zealand Railways, Publicity & Advertising Department)

Six Consolidation type 2–8–0 locomotives for the 3-foot 6-inch New Zealand Government Railways were built by the Baldwin Locomotive Works starting in 1879. One of these engines, no. 99, a class O machine, had these specifications:

Cylinders	15 by 18 inches
Drive wheels	3-foot diameter
Working pressure	130 pounds per square inch
Operating weight	29.2 tons.

(Courtesy: New Zealand Railways, Publicity & Advertising Department)

Part of the six-unit order starting in 1879 from the Baldwin Locomotive Works was this Consolidation type 2–8–0 machine, no. 106 which had the following specifications:

Cylinders	15 by 20 inches
Drive wheels	3-foot diameter
Working pressure	139 pounds per square inch
Operating weight	28.2 tons
Class	T.

(Courtesy: New Zealand Railways, Publicity & Advertising Department)

Until 1889 most locomotives for New Zealand Railways were imported from Britain or North America, but in that year, the railways' own workshops produced their first engine. Thereafter, locomotives were imported only when workshops in New Zealand could not cope with the demand. The last American-built steam locomotives for New Zealand Railways were imported in 1914.

From the thirty-seven-ton class W tank locomotive, built at the Addington Workshops in 1889, there developed a notable series of engines. These included the Wa class, built between 1892 and 1903; the Wd, built in 1901; the Wf, built from 1904 to 1909; the Wg, from 1910 to 1912, and the Ww, from 1913 to 1919. The original class W en-

gine has been kept for display. See three illustrations.

The first New Zealand–built tender locomotive was the class U, of which nine were produced between 1893 and 1903. Several variations of this class were built overseas around the turn of the century.

The most notable innovation at this time was the world's first Pacific-type locomotive, the New Zealand railway's Q class, of which thirteen were constructed by the Baldwin Locomotive Works in 1901. The Pacific type embodied the 4–6–2 wheel arrangement, with a wide firebox carried behind the driving wheels and over the trailing truck.

The famous Rimutaka Incline and the accompanying Fell traction system, one of New Zealand's

A class Wa, type 2–6–2, tank locomotive, one of the very first built in the New Zealand Railways Addington shops starting in 1889 is pictured here. This was one of a series of W class engines built to develop New Zealand's own steam locomotive industry. Engine no. 67, constructed in 1892, had these specifications:

Cylinders	14 by 20 inches
Drive wheels	3-foot 3.75-inch diameter
Working pressure	170 pounds per square inch
Operating weight	37.2 tons.

(Courtesy: New Zealand Railways, Publicity & Advertising Department)

Another tank locomotive used in New Zealand was class Wd, type 2–6–4. Engine no. 325 built by Baldwin in 1901 is shown. This engine had the following specifications:

Cylinders	14 by 20 inches
Drive wheels	3-foot 3.75-inch diameter
Working pressure	200 pounds per square inch
Operating weight	43.7 tons.

(Courtesy: New Zealand Railways, Publicity & Advertising Department)

Still another tank engine widely used in New Zealand was class Wf, type 2–6–4. Locomotive no. 467 constructed by A & G Price (New Zealand) in 1904 is pictured with these specifications:

Cylinders	14 by 22 inches
Drive wheels	3-foot 9-inch diameter
Tractive force	15,330 pounds
Operating weight	43 tons plus 14 hundredweight.

(Courtesy: New Zealand Railways, Publicity & Advertising Department)

New Zealand-produced tender locomotives were first issued in 1893 and carried a U classification. Of nine such machines built between 1893 and 1903, class U engine no. 274, type 4–6–0, had these specifications:

Cylinders	16 by 20 inches
Drive wheels	4-foot 6-inch diameter
Tractive force	13,650 pounds
Operating weight	63 tons
Year built	1894.

(Courtesy: New Zealand Railways, Publicity & Advertising Department)

Another type 4–6–0, class Ub tender locomotive is shown; this was built by Baldwin in 1898 for use on the New Zealand Railways. Specifications were as follows:

Cylinders	16 by 20 inches
Drive wheels	4-foot 1⅛-inch diameter
Tractive force	16,670 pounds
Operating weight	58 tons plus 7 hundredweights.

(Courtesy: New Zealand Railways, Publicity & Advertising Department

Another U class tender locomotive with the 4–6–0 wheel arrangement was built in 1901 by Sharp Stewart. Pictured is engine no. 368, class Uc which had the following general specifications:

Cylinders	16 by 22 inches
Drive wheels	4-foot 1-inch diameter
Working pressure	200 pounds per square inch
Operating weight	38.1 tons.

(Courtesy: New Zealand Railways, Publicity & Advertising Department)

Still another tender engine, built in New Zealand at the end of the nineteenth century, this type 4–8–0, class B, is pictured. Locomotive no. 909 was built in 1899 and had these characteristics:

Cylinders	16 by 22 inches
Drive wheels	3-foot 3.5-inch diameter
Tractive force	18,500 pounds
Operating weight	68 tons plus 10 hundredweights.

(Courtesy: New Zealand Railways, Publicity & Advertising Department)

The first mainline Pacific-type locomotives for the New Zealand Railways were built by Baldwin in 1901. These were characterized by wide fireboxes, piston valves, and Walschaert's gear. These engines could handle 600-ton freight loads on the level or 170-ton loads on 1 in 35 grades. Passenger trains attained speeds of about 50 miles per hour.

Specifications were as follows:

Cylinders	16 by 22 inches
Coupled wheels	4-foot 1⅛-inch diameter
Grate area	40 square feet
Heating surface	1673 square feet
Boiler pressure	200 pounds per square inch
Operational weight	72 tons (engine plus tender).

Shown is a model which is on display in New Zealand.
(Courtesy: New Zealand Railways)

New Zealand's first big-engine policy emerged after the major rail lines were laid and after there had been an opportunity to observe the fine characteristics and operating values of the American-type locomotives. The famous Q class, type 4–6–2, engines were the first mainline Pacifics ever built anywhere. These were furnished by Baldwin who built thirteen units in 1901.

Engine no. 344 had these specifications:

Cylinders	16 by 22 inches
Drive wheels	4-foot 1-inch diameter
Working pressure	200 pounds per square inch
Engine weight	48 tons.

(Courtesy: New Zealand Railways, Publicity & Advertising Department)

In North Island, New Zealand, the railroad north out of Wellington always faced tremendous obstacles clearing parts of the Rimutaka mountain ranges. The so-called Rimutaka Incline, with a gradient of 1 in 14 for 3½ miles, was surmounted using the historic Fell system; this employed a double-head rail raised horizontally between two normal rails. The Fell-type locomotive had an extra set of driving wheels or gears which locked into the raised center rail thus affording positive traction. A number of these Fell locomotives (at least four) were built by Neilson & Company in the early twentieth century. Tank engine no. 204, one of the Fell type had these specifications:

Class   H

Type	0–4–2 tank locomotive
Gauge	3 feet 6 inches
Outside cylinders	12 by 16 inches
Inside cylinders	12 by 14 inches
Drive wheels	2-foot 8-inch diameter
Rear bogie wheels	2-foot 6-inch diameter
Boiler	
Firebox	Copper
Tubes	Brass
Total heating surface	974 square feet
Engine weight	
Empty	30 tons plus 19 hundredweights
Operating	38 tons plus 18 hundredweights
Tank capacity	660 gallons water;
Bunker capacity	36 cubic feet coal.

(Courtesy: New Zealand Railways Publicity & Advertising Department)

The New Zealand Railways utilized another notable series of type 4–6–2 (Pacific) locomotives in the period 1914–27. In all, 141 engines were purchased from various manufacturers incuding Baldwin and the North British Locomotive Company. Pictured is a class Aa type 4–6–2 engine, no. 654, built by Baldwin in 1914. Specifications were:

Cylinders	18 by 24 inches
Drive wheels	4-foot 1-inch diameter
Tractive force	21,580 pounds
Operating weight	90 tons plus 14 hundredweights.

(Courtesy: New Zealand Railways, Publicity & Advertising Department)

Another type 4–6–2 locomotive, no. 738, class Ab was built in 1915 by the North British Locomotive Company. This engine had the following specifications:

Cylinders	17 by 26 inches
Drive wheels	4-foot 6-inch diameter
Tractive force	20,000 pounds
Operating weight	84 tons plus 15 hundredweights.

(Courtesy: New Zealand Railways Publicity & Advertising Department)

The New Zealand Railways in the period 1913–27 built and used various medium-heavy type 4–6–4 tank locomotives which are illustrated and described in three different photographs. Pictured is a class Ww, type 4–6–4, tank engine, no. 492, with the following specifications:

Cylinders	15.5 by 22 inches
Drive wheels	3-foot 9-inch diameter
Tractive force	16,900 pounds
Operating weight	51 tons plus 10 hundredweights
Year built	1913.

(Courtesy: New Zealand Railways, Publicity & Advertising Department)

A class Wab, type 4–6–4, tank engine, no. 764, built by NZR in 1917 is shown. Specifications were:

Cylinders	17 by 26 inches
Drive wheels	4-foot 6-inch diameter
Tractive force	22,250 pounds
Operating weight	71 tons plus 10 hundredweights
Year built	1917.

(Courtesy: New Zealand Railways, Publicity & Advertising Department)

Many 4–6–4 tank engines, designed by H. H. Jackson, Chief Mechanical Engineer, were used on the New Zealand Railways. The model pictured is a representation of a series of thirty manufactured in the government factory at Addington in the period 1917–27. Specifications on these engines were as follows:

Cylinders	17 by 26 inches
Coupled wheels	4.5-foot diameter
Boiler	
Grate area	33 square feet
Heating surface	772 square feet
Superheater	250 square feet
Fire box	123 square feet

Steam pressure	200 pounds per square inch
Tractive effort	22,250 pounds
Operational weight	70.7 tons, 37.5 tons adhesion
Tank capacity	1700 gallons water
Bunker capacity	3 tons coal.

These locomotives were mainly used on suburban trains around Auckland and Wellington. Most were withdrawn from service by 1965 of which two were retained for monument display.

(Courtesy: New Zealand Railways Publicity & Advertising Department)

Shown is a class K, type 4–8–4, locomotive no. 905, built by the NZR shops in 1932. This engine was used on the heaviest possible jobs on the New Zealand Railways. Specifications were:

Cylinders	20 by 26 inches
Drive wheels	4-foot 6-inch diameter
Tractive force	30,815 pounds
Operating weight	134 tons plus 16 hundredweights.

(Courtesy: New Zealand Railways, Publicity & Advertising Department)

On the New Zealand Railways on North Island a very effective locomotive carrying out mainline services was class Ka, 145-ton, 4–8–4 type, of which thirty-five were constructed in the Hutt workshops near Wellington during the period 1939–50. These were huge engines standing 11.5 feet above the tracks with a maximum width of 8.5 feet and barely meeting the maximum axle load limits of 14 tons.

Specifications were as follows:

Cylinders	20 by 26 inches
Drive wheels	4.5-foot diameter
Boiler	
Grate area	47.7 square feet
Heating surface	
Steam pressure	200 pounds per square inch
Roller bearings	used on all axles including the tender
Tractive force	30,815 pounds
Operating weight	142 tons

Ka engines could haul 1000-ton freight loads on the level and could speed a 400-ton train at 60–65 miles per hour. In 1946 these locomotives were changed from coal to fuel oil. Two of these 145-ton monsters were saved for possible restoration and preservation. All were replaced in 1967 by diesel-electric types. Shown is a model displayed in New Zealand.

(Courtesy: New Zealand Railways, Publicity & Advertising Department)

A modern photograph of the New Zealand Railways class Ka, type 4–8–4, locomotive, no. 954 is shown.
(Courtesy: New Zealand Railways, Publicity & Advertising Department)

The J series of Mountain type locomotives (4–8–2), of which forty streamlined units were constructed in 1939 by the North British Locomotive Company, were designed for a wide range of lighter services on the New Zealand Railroads including express duties. The NZR Hillside Works at Dunedin also built thirty-five units after World War II. In 1951 the North British Locomotive Company built an additional sixteen machines. Pictured is class J engine, no. 1224, which had the following specifications:

Cylinders	18 by 26 inches
Drive wheels	4-foot 6-inch diameter
Tractive force	24,960 pounds
Operating weight	108 tons.

(Courtesy: New Zealand Railways, Publicity & Advertising Department)

Another class Ja, type 4–8–2, locomotive quite similar to the machine described earlier is pictured. Engine no. 1275, built in the shops of the NZR, had these specifications:

Cylinders	18 by 26 inches
Drive wheels	4-foot 6-inch diameter
Tractive force	24,955 pounds
Operating weight	109 tons plus 9 hundredweights
Year built	1939.

(Courtesy: New Zealand Railways, Publicity & Advertising Department)

former railway attractions, is briefly discussed.

A French system of compound working, whereby steam was used twice before being exhausted to the atmosphere, was incorporated in the numerous A and X class locomotives built between 1906 and 1914 for mainline duties, chiefly in the North Island. The ponderous ninety-five-ton class X machines were assigned specifically to the central mountain section of the North Island main trunk railway, completed in 1908, and were the first locomotives in the world to have a wheel arrangement of 4–8–2, later designated the Mountain type in America.

The New Zealand Railways introduced another useful series of type 4–6–2 Pacific locomotives between 1914 and 1927. Other notable steam locomotives on the New Zealand railways were the 4–6–2 class Ab, of which 141 were built between 1915 and 1927; the 4–6–4 class Wab, for heavy suburban duties at Auckland and Wellington as well as some mainline service; the 4–8–4 K, Ka, and Kb classes, built between 1932 and 1950 for the heaviest mainline duties; and the J, Ja, and Jb classes, lighter 4–8–2 type engines suited for a wide range of duties in many parts of the country.

The progress made by New Zealand Railways is nowhere more clearly demonstrated than in the loads that latter-day steam locomotives could pull. For example, whereas the Double Fairlie locomotives could haul only 75 tons of train up the steep grade north from Wanganui, a latter-day class K locomotive could take 210 tons. On level track, where the class T could drag about five hundred tons at some sixteen kilometers (ten miles) per hour, a K or Ka could move a thousand tons at about fifty kilometers (thirty-one miles) per hour.

The little class K of 1878 could move a train of not much more than one hundred tons at eighty or ninety kilometers (forty-nine to fifty-five miles) per hour, where the grade was favorable. The big oil-fired class Ka of 1950 was capable of maintaining a mile a minute on level track with a four hundred-ton train.

By about 1974, diesel traction had supplanted all steam locomotives on the North Island and only about twenty class J and Ja engines were still performing South Island express services. With the final demise of the steam locomotives in about the mid-1970s, one class Ja, two class K machines, and three Pacifics, plus some other smaller engines, were preserved for posterity.

NORWAY

INITIALLY IT WAS REGARDED AS INCONCEIVABLE that railways would ever be built in a country as small and mountainous as Norway. It was felt that canals would have to answer the domestic transportation requirements. However, in the years just before 1850, more and more people came to realize that a railway was the potential solution to serious transportation problems that had developed between Norway's capital of Christiana (renamed Oslo in 1925) and Lake Øyern, just to the east. These difficulties were caused by the large amounts of lumber moved annually by horse-cart or sledge from sawmills twenty-five miles east, at Illestrøm, to the port of Christiana. In 1848 a railway bill was enacted, and in 1851 the building of the Norwegian Trunk Railway commenced. The line was planned to connect Christiana not only with Lake Øyern but also with the more northerly Lake Mjøsa (latitude 60°40′ north, longitude 11°20′ east) and its steamer service.

The first railroad, a short forty-two-mile narrow-gauge line northeast from Oslo to Eidsvoll, was begun in 1851, financed by Norwegian and British capital. It was finished on 1 September 1854, and operated as a privately owned enterprise up to 1926. The initial job was supervised by Robert Stephenson, son of the famous locomotive inventor. Two illustrations picture the first locomotive used in Norway, a type 2–4–0 engine, numbered 1, manufactured at Stephenson's engineering works in Newcastle, England. This engine is now displayed in the Railway Museum at Hamar, Norway.

The original small set of tracks seemed unimpor-tant at first, but the rail system soon carried a heavy traffic load and the iron horse quickly proved its inherent value. Unfortunately, due to a shortage of finances, additional railroad construction came slowly. Nonetheless, Norwegian authorities were able to extend the rail facilities from Oslo east toward the Swedish border during the 1860s, and in the latter part of that decade, 225 miles of track were laid to link the capital with marine facilities operating on the five principal lakes in southeastern Norway.

In the 1870s the state government, again supported by loans from England, was able to construct some additional rail lines; the national debt was naturally increased but the venture actually enhanced credit abroad. By this time it became clear that narrow-gauge tracks had many shortcomings and, starting in 1876, all new rail lines were of standard gauge.

A leading stimulus in the 1870s was the necessity to provide transportation for the huge, long-established copper mining industry located at Røros, about latitude 62° 34′ north, longitude 11° 22′ east. These ancient mines stagnated until the coming of the railroads. The first main route called the Røros line, which connected Christiana with Trondheim (with a break in the gauge at Hamar), was completed in the 1870s. (Trondheim is located at latitude 63° 40′ north, longitude 10° 24′ east.)

Also finished were two international connections with Sweden: the Meraeker line and the Østfold line. A line from Oslo running southwest about twenty miles to Drammen, was also completed, and the latter location became the narrow-gauge

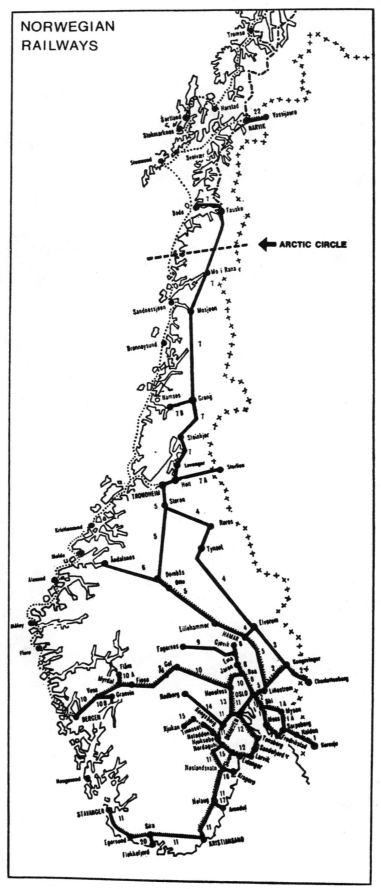

Railway map of Norway.
(*Courtesy:* Janes World Railways)

The first steam locomotive delivered by Robert Stephenson & Company of Newcastle, England, for use on the pioneer railway of Norway is shown here.

This was built in 1854 and is preserved at the Railway Museum in Hamar, Norway.
(Courtesy: Norwegian State Railways)

Here is another picture of the original steam locomotive used in Norway. This was manufactured by the Stephenson engineering works at Newcastle, England in 1854. This oldest preserved steam locomotive named "Caroline" is shown at the Railway Museum in Hamar, Norway. Also pictured outside the Hamar station is the famous "Dovregubben" locomotive, the largest ever designed and built in Norway.
(Courtesy: Norwegian State Railways)

network center in southeastern Norway. The Randsfjord line, with branches to Kongsberg and Lake Krøderen, and the Vestfold line were also constructed. The Jaeren railway from Stavanger to Egersund, a line about thirty-five miles long, was built on the southwest coast, and in 1883 the Bergen–Voss Railway was opened. Actually, after 1875, due to the effects of the economic depression, no new rail authorization was provided until about 1890, at which time there were about eleven hundred miles of railroad throughout Norway.

On 1 March 1894, a rail line from Oslo to the

Pictured is a type 4–4–0 steam locomotive, number 63, named "Nidaros," which operated on standard-gauge tracks of the Norwegian State Railways during the period 1877 and 1953. A total of twenty-four units of this class were manufactured in Norway. Principal specifications were as follows:

Cylinders
  381-mm diameter
  508-mm stroke
Coupled wheels   1448-mm diameter
Running wheels   711-mm diameter
Tender wheels   965-mm diameter
Boiler

Grate area	1.3 square meters
Heating surface	73 square meters
Boiler pressure	9.85 kilograms per square centimeter
Operating weight	31.3 tons (engine and tender)
Empty weights	
Engine	28.5 tons
Tender	9.1 tons
Adhesive weight	19.7 tons
Tender capacities	5.3 tons water; 2.5 tons coal
Maximum speeds	
Forward	60–65 kilometers per hour
Backward	40 kilometers per hour.

(Courtesy: Norwegian State Railways)

Dubs & Company in 1881 constructed four type 4–4–0 tender locomotives for the Norwegian Government Railways (nos. 51–54). These engines had the following specifications:

Gauge   3 feet 6 inches
Cylinders   12 by 18 inches
Drive wheels   4-foot 8-inch diameter
Boiler

Heating surface	518.57 square feet
Working pressure	140 pounds per square inch
Tractive force	4860 pounds
Operating weights	
Engine	20 tons plus 6 hundredweights
Tender	9 tons plus 4 hundredweights
Tender capacities	500 gallons water; 85 cubic feet coal.

(Courtesy: Mitchell Library, Glasgow) E1508

In 1891 Dubs & Company furnished three type 2–6–0 tender engines (now. 64–66) for use on the Norwegian State Railways. Characteristics were as follows:

Gauge	4 feet 8½ inches
Cylinders	16 by 24 inches
Drivers	4-foot 8½-inch diameter
Boiler	
Heating surface	1006 square feet
Working pressure	142 pounds per square inch
Tractive force	11558 pounds
Operating weights	
Engine	33 tons plus 11 hundredweights
Tender	16 tons plus 18 hundredweights
Tender capacities	1550 gallons water; 144 cubic feet coal.

(Courtesy: Mitchell Library) E2843

Dubs & Company in 1891 also supplied the Norwegian State Railways with one type 2–6–2 tank locomotive (no. 67) with the following specifications:

Gauge	4 feet 8½ inches
Cylinders	16 by 24 inches
Drivers	4-foot 8⅛-inch diameter
Boiler	
Heating surface	1006 square feet
Working pressure	142 pounds per square inch
Tractive force	11,558 pounds
Operating weight	44 tons plus 4 hundredweights
Capacities	750 gallons water; 55 cubic feet coal.

(Courtesy: Mitchell Library, Glasgow) E2846

The Norwegian State Railways in 1891 purchased from Dubs & Company two type 4–4–0 tender locomotives (nos. 68–69). These were Worsdell-Von Borries three-cylinder compound engines. Specifications were:

Gauge	4 feet 8½ inches
Cylinders	15¾ by 24 inches, and 23 by 24 inches
Drive wheels	5-foot 8⅛-inch diameter
Boiler	
Heating area	1006 square feet
Working pressure	170 pounds per square inch
Tractive force	6348 pounds
Operating weights	
Engine	34 tons plus 18 hundredweights
Tender	16 tons plus 18 hundredweights
Tender capacities	1550 gallons water; 144 cubic feet coal.

(Courtesy: Mitchell Library, Glasgow) E2841

The Norwegian State Railways purchased from Dubs & Company in 1893 two type 4–4–0 tender engines (nos. 30, 31). These machines were of the Worsdell-Von Borries three-cylinder compound type. Specifications were:

Gauge	3 feet 6 inches
Cylinders	12⅝ by 18 inches, and 18⅛ by 18 inches
Drive wheels	4-foot 7-inch diameter
Boiler	
Heating surface	516.54 square feet
Working pressure	171 pounds per square inch
Tractive force	3964 pounds at 40 percent boiler working pressure
Operating weights	
Engine	20 tons plus 15 hundredweights
Tender	8 tons plus 18 hundredweights
Tender capacities	700 gallons water; 70 cubic feet coal.

(Courtesy: Mitchell Library, Glasgow) E3074

In 1893 Dubs & Company constructed a single type 2–6–0 tender locomotive (no. 32) for use on the Norwegian State Railways. The following specifications applied:

Gauge	3 feet 6 inches
Cylinders	13⅞ by 18⅛ inches
Coupled drivers	3-foot 5¹¹⁄₃₂-inch diameter
Boiler	
Heating surface	620.11 square feet
Working pressure	150 pounds per square inch
Tractive force	9497 pounds
Operating weights	
Engine	23 tons plus 10 hundredweights
Tender	10 tons plus 19 hundredweights
Tender capacities	880 gallons water; 120 cubic feet coal.

(Courtesy: Mitchell Library, Glasgow) E3049

The Norwegian State Railways procured from Dubs & Company in 1894 two type 2–6–2 tank engines (nos 1 and 2) with these specifications:

Gauge	3 feet 6 inches
Cylinders	11 by 18 inches
Drivers	3-foot diameter
Boiler	
Heating surface	458.75 square feet
Working pressure	142 pounds per square inch
Tractive force	6443 pounds
Operating weight	22 tons plus 4 hundredweights
Capacities	450 gallons water; 35 cubic feet coal.

(Courtesy: Mitchell Library, Glasgow) E3172

In 1894 the Norwegian State Railways purchased two additional tank locomotives from Dubs & Company. These engines were type 2–4–2 T (nos 3, 4) with the following characteristics:

Gauge	3 feet 6 inches
Cylinders	11 by 18 inches
Drive wheels	3-foot 9⅛-inch diameter
Boiler	
Heating surface	406.9 square feet
Working pressure	142 pounds per square inch
Tractive force	5154 pounds
Operating weight	20 tons plus 14 hundredweights
Capacities	400 gallons water; 35 cubic feet coal.

(Courtesy: Mitchell Library, Glasgow) E3174

In 1895 Dubs & Company supplied the Norwegian State Railways with a single type 2–6–0 tender locomotive (no. 60). This engine was equipped with Worsdell-Von Borries three-cylinder compound power units. Specifications follow:

Gauge	4 feet 8½ inches
Cylinders	16¾ by 24 inches and 25 by 24 inches
Drivers	4-foot 8⅛-inch diameter
Boiler	
Heating area	1006 square feet
Working pressure	170 pounds per square inch
Tractive force	9107 pounds at 40 percent boiler working pressure
Operating weights	
Engine	35 tons plus 14 hundredweights
Tender	19 tons plus 6 hundredweights
Tender capacities	1700 gallons water; 150 cubic feet coal.

(Courtesy: Mitchell Library, Glasgow) E3348

This photograph was taken at Otta rail station, Norway on 6 June 1906, when King Haakon VII arrived there on his journey to his coronation in Trondheim. The engine is a class 9a (by the 1918–71 designation system), type 4–4–0, which was introduced into the Norwegian railroads in 1877.
(*Courtesy: Norwegian State Railways*)

In 1895 Neilson & Company furnished the Norwegian State Railways with two type 2–6–0 tender locomotives. These machines had the running numbers 34 and 35. Specifications were:

Gauge	3 feet 6 inches
Cylinders	13⅞ by 18⅛ inches
Drive wheels	3-foot 5⁵⁄₁₆-inch diameter
Boiler	
Heating surface	620 square feet
Working pressure	142 pounds per square inch
Operating weights	
Engine	22 tons plus 11 hundredweights
Tender	13 tons plus 9 hundredweights
Tender capacities	990 gallons water; 120 cubic feet coal.

(*Courtesy: Mitchell Library, Glasgow*) E744

Pictured are two views of the steam locomotive named "Dovregubben," the largest ever designed and manufactured in Norway. This engine was introduced in 1935 as class 49 (a, b, c), type 2–8–4, with a horsepower of 2600. Specifications were as follows:

Cylinders
49a   465/720-millimeter diameter; 650/700-millimeter stroke
49b   465/720-millimeter diameter; 650/900-millimeter stroke
49c   440/650-millimeter diameter; 650/700-millimeter stroke

Coupled drive wheels   1530-millimeter diameter
Boiler
Grate area   5.0 square meters
Heating surface

Evaporative   2560 square meters
Superheater   1020 square meters
Boiler pressure   17 kilograms per square centimeter

Operating weight
49a   98.5 tons
49b   103.9 tons
49c   99.0 tons

Empty weights
49a   87.2 tons engine; 17.4 tons tender
49b   92.7 tons engine; 17.4 tons tender
49c   88.6 tons engine; 18.4 tons tender

Tender capacities   27.2 tons water; 8.4 tons coal.

(Courtesy: Norwegian State Railways)

west-coast seaport of Bergen was approved, and survey work commenced early in 1895. In October 1895 the navvies set to work on the mountainous bedrock with hammers, drills, and dynamite. Work on the great 3.3-mile Gravahals tunnel was begun in 1894 and finished in 1909; this is located just west of Myrdal, at latitude 60° 45′ north, longitude 07° 03′ east. This connection between the capital and the west coast turned out to be a 250-mile project, the most difficult, impressive engineering feat in all of Norway. The tracks had to cross a roadless, nearly uninhabited region of precipitous mountains and perpetual snows, reaching 4,265 feet above sea level at Tangevatu, near Finse. The construction involved tremendous expenditures and was finished in 1909 after fifteen years of work. Inaugurated on 26 November 1909 at a great banquet with King Haakon VII in attendance (see illustration). This particular rail line was considered the most important economic achievement in Norway's history. Subsequent operations of the line proved that the use of standard 4-foot 8½-inch gauge tracks had been the correct decision.

During World War I, Norway remained neutral although the hostilities to the south had a profound effect on her commerce and industry. Naturally, the railways carried an enormous amount of traffic in the war years, and the supplies of all types of commodities became precarious. Coal stocks, for example, reached low levels and many locomotives had to be modified to burn wood; great piles of logs were common sights along the tracks. During World War I, the Norwegian State Railway (NSB) network consisted of 1,718 kilometers (1718.6 miles) of standard-gauge track and 996 kilometers (618.5 miles) of narrow-gauge. In addition, private companies owned 222 kilometers (137.8 miles) of standard-gauge railroads and 241 kilometers (149.6 miles) of narrow-gauge. Business in Norway boomed until 1920, when a depression set in, with falling prices and much unemployment.

With the introduction of competing over-the-road transport in the 1920s, railway traffic reached its peak in Norway in 1929. The need for low axle loads on all the railroads was a hindrance to increased rail speeds and greater operating efficiency. This challenge was met by railway engineers with an engine introduced in 1935, named Dovregubben, which combined great tractive power with light axle loading, representing Norwegian steam locomotive design at its best. See two illustrations.

When railways first came to Norway, the locomotive itself was a symbol of the transport revolution. The first engines had a maximum speed of fifty kilometers (31 miles) per hour. In 1914 State Railways' fastest engine reached a speed of ninety kilometers (56 miles) per hour. Until 1894 all locomotives, with the exception of a single narrow-gauge engine, were built abroad. In 1894, however, Norwegian locomotive works such as Thunes Mek, Vaerksted, and Hamar Jernstøberi, became regular suppliers. From the very beginning, locomotives were purchased in small series and in many different types. Virtually every new line was provided with its own individual varieties.

The Norwegian Railways were literally on the front line from the first day of World War II. They played an important part in moving Norwegian troops early in the conflict, and later there was an agonizing need for passenger and freight transport in the occupied regions due to ever-increasing pressure from the German occupation forces. During the war, the German military ruthlessly exploited the railroads in Norway, resulting in widespread destruction to the facilities and causing horrendous accidents, normally uncommon occurences in that country. When World War II ended, the NSB was left with run-down rolling stock and facilities, small coal reserves, and a depleted operating staff that had been hard-pressed during the conflict. The Germans had put about seventeen thousand prisoners-of-war to work building the Nordland line, which turned out to be a piece of unbelievably shoddy workmanship that had to be redone by the Norwegians afterward. The Germans did leave behind some series 6500 locomotives, built in Germany for the eastern front from 1941 to 1945.

Gradually, NSB provided the necessary capital investment to bring the railways back to some form of normalcy. By 1958 diesel locomotives finally replaced the big Dovregubbin engines. In mid-1969, steam locomotives were no longer seen on the main lines in Norway. The Oslo–Bergen line was shortened by twenty-one kilometers (thirteen miles) in 1964 by building the Ulriken tunnel (7.66 kilometers, or 4.75 miles, in length) and the shorter Arnanipa and Tunestviet tunnels. In 1970 all regular steam operations ceased, and in June 1971 the last three steam locomotives were removed from the NSB register, bringing a 117-year era to a close.

In 1973 on the Oslo–Drammen line, the largest railway tunnel in northern Europe, the 10.7-kilometer (6.6-mile) Luer tunnel was opened, shortening the trip by twelve kilometers. The largest project in the 1970s was the Oslo Central Station. It was subdivided into a series of separate plans: a new passenger terminal, a double-track tunnel beneath the city and a central marshaling yard at Alnabru.

In 1978 the Norwegian State Railways had 4,241 kilometers (2633.6 miles) of 1.435-meter (4-foot 8¼-inch) tracks in active operation.

PANAMA

IN 1846 THE COLOMBIA CONFEDERATION, A COALITION of Latin American states, signed an agreement with the United States granting rights of transit across the isthmus of Panama. Earlier, presidents Andrew Jackson and Martin Van Buren had instituted surveys in Panama and Nicaragua to determine the feasibility of railroad routes. In 1847 the United States negotiated separate steamship contracts to cover mail delivery by sea from Panama to California and Oregon, and from Panama to major east-coast cities. Early in 1848 Colombia granted a concession to build a railroad across Panama to the Pacific Mail Steamship Company. The concept of a Panama rail line received a tremendous boost when, on 24 January 1848, gold was discovered in California.

The Panama Railroad Company was incorporated during April 1849 with William H. Aspinwall as president; a stock issue in the amount of one million dollars to finance the construction of an interocean communication across Panama was immediately subscribed in the United States. A route survey for a forty-eight-mile Panama Canal. (See my previous book, *Seven Railroads*.)

Four photographs, of railroad interest, pertaining to the construction of the Panama Canal are included.

This is a 24 July 1910 picture of famous Culebra Cut in the Panama Canal, long before water filled this area. The occasion was a Quartermaster's Department Excursion to the site by canal workers and their wives and families.
(Courtesy: Panama Canal Commission)

This photograph, taken on 10 August 1910, shows a Panama Canal labor train on the dock at Cristobal located on the northern side of the Isthmus of Panama.
(Courtesy: Panama Canal Commission)

This photograph, taken in 1911 on the Panama Canal project site, shows part of a labor train used to transport workers. These were old French two-axle cars with nonswiveling trucks.
(Courtesy: Panama Canal Commission)

Another picture of a typical labor train at Tabernilla on the Panama Canal project is shown. This is a 1911 photograph.
(Courtesy: Panama Canal Commission)

Steam Locomotives in Panama

The first four locomotives supplied for the construction of the Panama Railroad, early in the 1850s, were type 4–4–0 engines built by the Niles Company of Cincinnati, Ohio. These engines had two pairs of cylinders, one on top of the other, following a design of George Escol Sellers. The bottom pair were connected to the drive wheels and the upper pair drove a special gear that gripped a raised rail in the middle of the track. A subsequent series of three type 4–4–0 engines, also furnished by Niles in the early 1850s, were wood-burners with inclined cylinders, weighing about seventeen tons.

The Portland Company of Portland, Maine, sent out three type 4–4–0 during October 1852. The first, named Nueva Granada, was inside-connected; the other two engines had outside connections to the drive wheels. Up to 1873, Portland supplied a total of twenty locomotives to the Panama Railroad, of which sixteen were type 4–4–0 and four were type 0–4–0. Ten of the engines fitted 5-foot 6-inch gauge rails and the balance were of a 5-foot gauge. The last 5-foot 6-inch gauge railroad to connect the Caribbean Sea with the Pacific Ocean was completed during June 1849, and actual work on a usable rail line was initiated during May 1850, starting on the north side of the isthmus.

Building a railroad across Panama was attended by many difficulties and dangers due to the harsh character of the land, the frightful privation and disease, law and order problems, and worker desertions and deaths. By September 1850 financial problems virtually suspended all track-laying efforts. However, in December 1851 hordes of travelers bound for Panama City and California started across the isthmus, and this gave the rail project renewed life. A new stock issue in New York was quickly sold out.

Despite horrendous problems, the rail line advanced south successfully to Panama City, where the job was officially completed on 27 January 1855 after four years and nine months of toil and tribulations. The finished system, at a cost of eight million dollars for a forty-eight-mile, single-track line, was considered the most expensive railroad ever built; however, from the investor's standpoint, then and later, it was the most financially rewarding rail system ever constructed. The early Panama railroad was credited with playing a unique role in helping open up the great American West by expediting great numbers of gold diggers on their way to California. Moreover, the railroad served as an important and indispensable tool in the subsequent construction of the mighty engine, named "Barbacoas," was delivered during August 1856, and the first 5-foot gauge engine, named "Atlantic," was built in April 1865. The type 4–4–0 Niles engines had 13 by 20-inch cylinders with 54-inch drive wheels. All were still in service at the time the French started their Panama Canal project in 1881.

The Rogers Works furnished the French Canal Company with twenty-six type 0–6–0 tank engines between 30 December 1882 and 12 November 1883. These all carried French names and had out-of-sequence numbers from 1 to 40. Cylinders were 15 by 22 inches, with drive wheels 44 inches in diameter. Engine weights were sixty thousand pounds. Water capacity was 965 gallons, and a ton of coal was carried.

In 1883 Hinkley furnished seven type 0–6–0 locomotives to the Panama Railroad; technical details were not available.

Also in 1883, H. K. Porter furnished eight type 0–4–2 tank engines (numbers 401–407) with the following specifications:

Cylinders	13 by 18 inches
Drive wheels	40-inch diameter
Engine weight	40,000 pounds

In 1884 Bourden, of Decauville, France, supplied ten type 0–4–0 tank engines for a 5-meter gauge line. These machines had the following specifications:

Cylinders	5¹¹⁄₁₆ by 8 inches
Drive wheels	16-inch diameter
Engine weight	10,000 pounds.

From 1882 to 1887, the Raismes firm of Cockrill, Belgium, supplied fifty-five type 0-6-0 tank locomotives known as the Belgians. Specifications for these engines are described in illustration Pa-7 (left locomotive). In 1886–87, Raismes also furnished forty-four type 0–6–0 tank engines with 16½ by 23½-inch cylinders and 47¼-inch diameter drive wheels. These were known as Chiriquis, which performed outstandingly during the digging of the Panama Canal.

The Baldwin Locomotive Works furnished six type 4–4–0 tank engines and five type 0–4–0 tank engines in the early 1880s. The type 0–4–0 ma-

A type 0–6–0 tank locomotive built originally by Raismes of Cockrill, Belgium in the period 1886–87. These were the so-called "Chiriqui's" that did wonderful service during the digging of the Panama Canal. The engines were taken over by the Isthmian Canal Commission when the United States started working on the canal. Original specifications were as follows:

Cylinders	16½ by 23½ inches
Drive wheels	47¼-inch diameter
Boiler working pressure	130 pounds per square inch
Tractive effort	14,450 pounds
Engine weight	77,000 pounds
No. designations	501–43.

(Courtesy: Panama Canal Commission)

A picture taken about 1913, of a culvert being constructed on the Panama Canal project site prior to the flooding of Gatun Lake. The locomotive, type 4–4–0, was Panama Railroad no. 51, named "Le Mares," built in 1883 by Cooke on their job no. 1529.

(Courtesy: Panama Canal Commission)

chines had 14 by 22-inch cylinders with 36-inch drive wheels, and weighed fifty thousand pounds. Stephenson gear was used. The construction was completed between October 1880 and October 1887. Capacities were: water, 780 gallons; coal, 1,100 pounds. The six type 4–4–0 engines had 16 by 24-inch cylinders with 53-inch drive wheels and weighed sixty-six thousand pounds in operating condition. These were supplied between January 1880 and September 1883.

Also in 1883, the Cooke Works delivered seventeen type 4–4–0 locomotives (nos. 41–57), many of which survived to the U.S. Panama Canal construction period under ICC control (Isthmian Canal Commission). These engines had 17-inch by 24-inch cylinders with 62⅜-inch drive wheels. When the French Canal effort ended, seven were transferred to the Panama Railroad and three to the

This illustration shows engine no. 299 on a monument site at the southern end of the Panama Canal Zone as photographed by the author in 1962. This was a Cooke Works type 2–6–0 engine built in 1906 for the Panama Railroad with the following specifications:

No. designations	201–300
Cylinders	19 by 24 inches
Drive wheels	54-inch diameter
Boiler working pressure	180 pounds per square inch
Tractive effort	23,980 pounds
Engine weight	124,500 pounds.

It is interesting to note that engine no. 299, originally constructed in Paterson, New Jersey and retired from Panama Railroad service in 1955, was removed from the monument site adjacent to the Balboa Railroad Station in 1979 and was transferred to Paterson where it became the centerpiece in a museum. The government of Panama protested the removal of this "historical piece" but finally lost its appeal.

(Courtesy: E. A. Haine)

Pictured is a 200-class, type 2–6–0, Cooke locomotive used in building the Panama Canal. Engine no. 239, shown near Miraflores in the Canal Zone, was part of an order for one hundred locomotives built by the Cooke Works in 1906; this was the largest single order for railway steam engines ever built for the Panama Railroad.
(Courtesy: Panama Canal Commission)

ICC. In 1906, one hundred type 2–6–0 tender engines, 200 class, were constructed by Cooke for the Panama Railroad—the largest single order ever placed by this railroad. Three of these locomotives were still in service in Panama in 1948. The specifications were as follows:

Cylinders	19 by 24 inches
Drive wheels	54-inch diameter
Engine weight	124,500 pounds.

In 1905 the Schnectady Works delivered twenty-four type 2–6–4 tank engines to the ICC (nos. 101–124), where they subsequently failed on most service assignments. In 1909 they were converted to type 2–6–0. All were sold around 1917 to the Chile Exploration Company. Specifications were as follows:

Cylinders	19 by 26 inches
Drive wheels	54-inch diameter
Engine weight	183,500 pounds.

The engine pictured no. 662, type 2–6–0, was built by the Brooks Works in 1908 with the following specifications:

No. designations	651–62
Cylinders	20 by 26 inches
Drive wheels	63-inch diameter
Boiler working pressure	200 pounds per square inch
Tractive force	28,100 pounds
Engine weight	146,600 pounds
Superheater	all but 4 so equipped.

(Courtesy: Panama Canal Commission)

Pictured are two steam locomotives which are described below. In 1907 the Baldwin Locomotive Works built forty type 2–6–0 tender locomotives for the Isthmian Canal Commission. These were numbered 301 to 340 and were constructed under nine different Baldwin shop orders. This class 300 engine, no. 311, shown on the right, had the following specifications:

Cylinders	19 by 24 inches
Drive wheels	54-inch diameter
Boiler working pressure	180 pounds per square inch
Tractive force	23,960 pounds
Engine weight	122,310 pounds

Also shown on the left, engine no. 704, was a rebuilt so-called "Belgian" locomotive. These were originally built in 1882–87 by Raismes of Cockrill, Belgium with the following specifications:

Wheel arrangement	0–6–0
Cylinders	15½ by 19½ inches
Drive wheels	47¼-inch diameter
Boiler working pressure	125 pounds per square inch
Engine weight	56.640 pounds
Series numbers	701–55.

(Courtesy: Panama Canal Commission)

Old French steam locomotives stored near Empire in the Panama Canal Zone in 1910 are pictured.
(*Courtesy: Panama Canal Commission*)

Pictured is a class 600 Brooks locomotive, no. 657, type 2–6–0, at the Mount Hope rail yards in the Canal Zone during June 1911. This Panama Railroad train was hauling old iced reefer cars behind box car 6052.
(*Courtesy: Panama Canal Commission*)

The Brooks Works in 1906 supplied twenty type 2–6–0 locomotives with the following specifications:

Cylinders	20 by 26 inches
Drive wheels	63-inch diameter
Engine weight	147,500 pounds.

In 1907 the ICC purchased from Baldwin forty type 2–6–0 tender locomotives, of which ten were transferred to the Panama Railroad in 1913. These had the following specifications:

Cylinders	19 by 24 inches
Drive wheels	54-inch diameter
Engine weight	122,310 pounds.

The Brooks Works furnished twenty super-heated type 2–6–0 locomotives to the ICC and twelve to the Panama Railroad in 1908. The latter were used on passenger and freight services until 1940. Also in 1908, twelve Brooks class 651 engines were delivered for dual service, numbered 651–662 (illustrations Pa-6 and Pa-12). These engines were sold to the Grand Trunk Western Railway in 1917 and converted to standard gauge. All but two were finally scrapped in 1934; numbers 892 and 893 were sold instead to the Detroit, Cairo, and Sandusky Railroad. The Brooks class 651 engines had these specifications:

Cylinders	20 by 26 inches

Drive wheels	63-inch diameter
Engine weight	146,600 pounds.

The H. K. Porter Company furnished the following type 0–6–0 locomotives in 1909 and 1910:

In 1908 the Davenport Works supplied five type 0–4–0 tank engines, 36-inch gauge, with 10 by 16-inch cylinders, 29-inch diameter drive wheels, and engine weights of 36,000 pounds.

Year	Gauge	Quantity	Drive wheels	Cylinders	Engine Weight (pounds)
1909	42-inch	10	40-inch	15 by 20 inches	66,800
1910	35-inch	10	24-inch	8 by 14 inches	23,000
1910	36-inch	5	24-inch	8 by 14 inches	28,000.

In 1908 also, Vulcan supplied five type 0–4–0 tank engines with 10 by 16-inch cylinders, 31-inch diameter drive wheels, and engine weights of 36,000 pounds.

In 1940 Schenectady furnished five engines to the Panama Railroad, numbers 701–705, with the following characteristics:

Cylinders	18 by 26 inches
Drive wheels	63-inch diameter
Engine weight	168,000 pounds.

In 1942, H. K. Porter supplied seven type 2–6–0 tender locomotives with these specifications:

Cylinders	20 by 24 inches
Drive wheels	54-inch diameter
Engine weight	159,400 pounds.

Disposition of excess railroad equipment in Panama seems to have started in 1913. Already mentioned was the transfer from ICC to the Panama Railroad of ten Baldwin engines in 1913, just before the completion of the Panama Canal. Also in 1913, Costa Rica received various locomotives and rolling stock for use on the narrow-gauge lines of the Pacific Railroad, the Northern Railroad, and the United Fruit Company line. In July 1917 the Alaska Railroad, then under construction, accepted the transfer of ten locomotives. Much equipment was sold to the A. B. Shaw Company of Chicago, which made subsequent sales to the Chile Exploration Company. In January 1922, the Alaska Railroad purchased seven 601 and seventeen class 201 locomotives: Cooke locomotives nos. 208, 221, 224, 225, 239, 242, 247, 265, 266, 270, 272, 275, 277, 280, and 285; Brooks locomotives nos. 601, 606, 610, 614, 618, 620, and 605. Also in 1922, additional locomotives were shipped to the United States War Department, the A. B. Shaw Company, and the Equitable Equipment Company of Pennsylvania.

This is an 4 April 1940 photograph of a Mogul, type 2–6–0, locomotive in use on the Panama Railroad. Five engines (701–5) were supplied by Schenectady in 1940 having the following general specifications:

Cylinders	18 by 26 inches
Drive wheels	63-inch diameter
Engine operating weight	168,000 pounds.

(Courtesy: Panama Canal Commission)

Pictured is a typical labor train in the famous Culebra
Cut of the Panama Canal, before it was flooded, on 20
June 1911.
(Courtesy: Panama Canal Commission)

This is an 18 October 1913 picture of the Panama Railroad bridge no. 57½ across the site of the Panama
Canal near Paraiso looking east. After the area was
flooded, a floating bridge remained at this location to
serve the West Bank rail trackage until the early 1920s.
(Courtesy: Panama Canal Commission)

This picture shows the storage of surplus class 600 steam locomotives at Dump No. 6 in the Canal Zone of Panama on 22 May 1915.
(*Courtesy: Panama Canal Commission*)

Another view of the Panama Canal Zone, Dump No. 6, on 22 May 1915 is presented. Stored are various class 300 Baldwin steam locomotives.
(*Courtesy: Panama Canal Commission*)

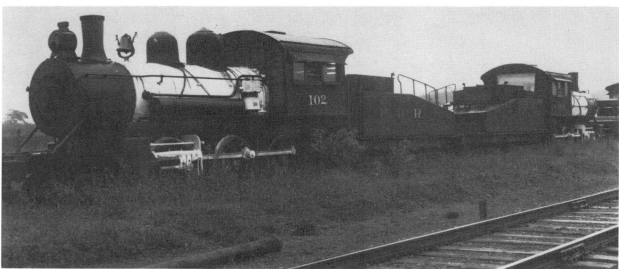

With the completion of the Panama Canal in August 1914, much heavy construction equipment, including steam locomotives, became surplus. Pictured are various locomotives stored at Dump No. 6 in the Panama

Canal Zone on 22 May 1915. Shown are two Mogul, type 2-6-0, locomotives, nos. 102 and 114.
(*Courtesy: Panama Canal Commission*)

PERU

THE PIONEER RAILROAD IN PERU, WHICH WAS claimed to be the first in South America, ran eight miles from the Pacific port of Callao to the capital city of Lima. After many years of delay and false starts, the line was completed on 17 May 1851. The system operated with steam locomotives until it was electrified early in the twentieth century as part of an overall Lima streetcar program. The Lima–Callao connection, known as the Lima Railways Company, was absorbed by the Central Railway of Peru, a government-controlled system, in 1934.

The second railroad in Peru was authorized on 18 December 1851, to join the coastal cities of Tacna and Arica, located in the southwestern corner of that country. This 18.5-mile stretch of standard-gauge track was finished in 1855. The line has had a long history of continous operation, although for some years after Peru lost the war with Chile in 1883, the railroad was managed by Chilean authorities. The line reverted in 1893 to Peruvian control and became a part of the National Railway of Peru on 1 January 1973.

Peru's first railway with really substantial commercial possibilities was the 107-mile connection between Peru's largest city, inland Arequipa, and the Pacific Ocean. This was the initial effort in Peru by Henry Meiggs, the famous railroad builder and entrepreneur. The job presented awesome engineering problems and the line had to be laid across extremely difficult desert terrain. The great railway adventure began on 27 May 1868, financed by British investments backed by Peruvian guano deposits. The Mollendo–Arequipa standard-gauge railway was completed on 24 December 1870, fully six months ahead of the schedule set forth in the original Meiggs contract with Peru. This railroad, later renamed the Southern Railway, has long served the export-import needs of this part of Peru. Early in the twentieth century, a new and better port was established near Mollendo, at Matarani, and a thirty-nine-mile branch line had to be added to the main line.

On 11 July 1870, Meiggs initiated work to extend the Arequipa–Mollendo road 179 miles east to Juliaca, at 12,550 feet above sea level and 286 miles inland from the Pacific Ocean. This line was completed in 1876, including a twenty-nine-mile branch from Juliaca to Puno on Lake Titicaca. All rail and iron for bridges were imported from England; however, British locomotives and rolling stock, first used on the line, were soon determined to be unfit for the punishing Andean grades, and American equipment was substituted.

Between 1872 and 1908 a combination of various lines, totaling 209.5 miles, was laid down connecting Juliaca and Cuzco, to the north. Originally started according to another contract with Meiggs, this construction was long delayed by financial obstacles, topographic barriers, political upheavals, and the subsequent death of Meiggs. The line was further extended for 93 miles between 1921 and 1960, to the vicinity of the famous Inca ruins at Machu Picchu.

A truly stupendous railway engineering achievement started by Henry Meiggs involved construction of the Lima–LaOroya railway. This momentous task projected a 129.3-mile railroad from near sea level at Lima to an altitude of almost sixteen thousand feet in the Andes highlands. Work commenced along the Rimac River on January 1, 1870. Overcoming awesome engineering difficulties, formidable geological obstructions (and fifteen zigzags, sixty-seven bridges, and sixty-five tunnels), the line finally reached Chicla during September 1877, at 12,500 feet above sea level, eighty-seven miles from the Pacific Ocean. At this point, Meiggs passed from the scene and the financial situation in Peru was also in a virtual state of collapse; further construction was delayed until 1890. The extension from Chicla to the Galera summit tunnel, at 15,685 feet, and down to La Oroya at 12,225 feet, was completed on 10 January 1893.

The Marococho rail line, providing an alternate route to La Oroya from the Galera tunnel, was constructed in 1902; parts of this line reached an altitude of 15,865 feet, the highest point attained by a railroad anywhere in the world.

The 120-mile Cerro de Pasco Railway, running from mines at a location of the same name at 14,250 feet above sea level, to La Oroya. This was finalized in 1904, and like most other railroads in Peru, was of standard gauge (4 feet 8½ inches). Still another rail system high in the Andes, seventy-seven miles from La Oroya to Huancayo along the Mantaro River valley, was completed by the Peruvian Corporation Ltd. in 1906. On 17 June 1908, a 3-foot gauge line was started from Huancayo and, after many problems, years, and delays, an 80.12-mile line to the cinnabar mines near Huancavelica was finished on 23 June 1926.

The railways described above, plus other coastal area lines in Peru, are fully detailed in my book, *Railways Across the Andes.*.

The following six illustrations spell out a bit of Peruvian railway history, mainly applicable to the famous Callao–Oroya–Huancayo railroad (Central Railway of Peru), which extends from the Pacific Ocean 215 miles into the high Andes mountains.

Pictured is the rail station at Callao as it looked in 1901. This is the western terminus of the Central Railway of Peru which extends 215 miles from Huancayo high in the Andes Mountains to the Pacific port at Callao.
(Courtesy: Central Railway of Peru)

A 1907 view of the Central Railway of Peru is shown. This is the Quita Sombrero Bridge at kilometer 93 (mile 58) on the famous Callao-Oroya Railway at an altitude of 2117 meters (6945 feet) above sea level. *(Courtesy: Central Railway of Peru)*

A type 0-4-0 tank locomotive used on the Central Railway of Peru in 1913 is pictured here. This engine was built by Beyer Peacock but no other data was available. *(Courtesy: Central Railway of Peru)*

This illustration shows a 1922 picture of a type 2-8-0 locomotive (no. 229) on a turntable on the Callao-Oroya section of the FCC railway of Peru. *(Courtesy: Central Railway of Peru)*

A main railroad station in Lima on the Central Railway of Peru is pictured. This photograph was taken in 1926.
(Courtesy: Central Railway of Peru)

Engine no. 104 is pictured at the Huancayo station high in the Andes Mountains (altitude 10,699 feet above sea level) located 346 kilometers (215 miles) on the Central Railway of Peru from the Pacific port of Callao. This was a 1935 photograph.
(Courtesy: Central Railway of Peru)

PORTUGAL

THE FIRST INDICATION OF A PROPOSED RAILWAY service in Portugal appeared in the London *Railway Chronicle* of 5 October 1844. According to that weekly, a plan had been laid before the Portuguese government for building a line from Lisbon to Oporto, through Santarém and Coimbra. The necessary capital was to be raised half in Portugal and half in Britain. The Portuguese government would guarantee a fixed rate of interest until the track was laid, and also grant various other privileges for a limited period. A month later, in its issue of 9 November 1844, the *Railway Chronicle* again referred to the scheme. By this time, the original plan had been changed and the first section was to be in the Alentejo region, connecting Évora and the larger towns in the north, and connecting east Alentejo, as well as Spain, with the city of Lisbon. The article indicated that negotiations were proceeding between influential British financiers and the government in Lisbon and an engineer of wide experience was to go out shortly to examine the terrain.

On 6 December 1844, a number of British merchants, bankers, and railway officials met in London to agree upon all the details of the Alentejo Railway, which was to be part of a system from Lisbon to the Spanish border. The first track would be laid between Évora and Alcácer do Sal. While a proposal to this effect was being worked out to be submitted to the Portuguese government, in London arrangements were made for engineers to come to Portugal to study local conditions and draw up a final plan for the line. However, months went by and spirits began to lag. In April 1845 still another

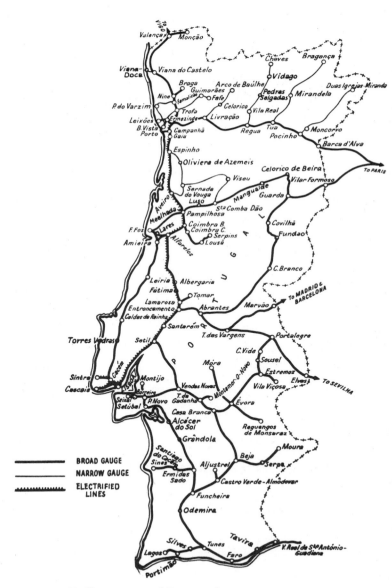

Railway map of Portugal.
(*Courtesy:* Janes World Railways)

scheme was submitted to the government, in the name of Benjamin de Oliveira and others, for a railway between Lisbon and Tomar with another up to Oporto. Eventually all these plans fell through, and no railway was constructed.

Almost ten years were to elapse before a viable railway was finally approved by the Portuguese government, and plans went ahead for its construction. On 7 May 1853, the reigning queen of Portugal, assisted by her consort, King Ferdinand, participated in ceremonies inaugurating work on the first railway. The official opening of Portugal's pioneer twenty-three miles of 1665-millimeter (5-foot 5-inch) track, between Lisbon and Carregado, took place with great fanfare on 28 October 1856.

In 1951 a number of leased concession railways were merged into a private concern known as the Portuguese Railway Company. At this time, there were 2,225 miles of gauge tracks (gauge was changed slightly after the initial truck) and 475 miles of narrow meter-gauge lines. The wide-gauge rails used on the Portuguese railroads were not compatible with other standard-gauge railways in Europe, which was a contributing factor to Portugal's minor role in international rail traffic. In the early 1970s, railroads in Portugal carried less than 10 percent of the domestic freight. In the period 1963 to 1973, the number of steam locomotives in use declined from 328 to 121, as diesel locomotion increased proportionately. In April 1974 the railways were nationalized, to become the Campanhia dos Caminhos de Ferro Portugueses (Portugal State Railways).

The most serious railway accident in Portugal was a wreck near Oporto on 26 July 1964, causing ninety-four deaths.

Janes World Railways in 1978, reported that Portugal had 2,807 kilometers (1,744 miles) of 1.665-meter (5-foot 5-inch) track and 759 kilometers (472 miles) of meter-gauge track.

Steam Locomotives in Portugal

Available photographs of steam locomotives used on the railways of Portugal are presented chronologically in the illustrations that follow.

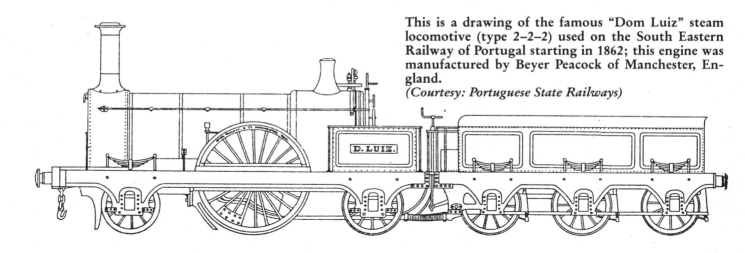

This is a drawing of the famous "Dom Luiz" steam locomotive (type 2–2–2) used on the South Eastern Railway of Portugal starting in 1862; this engine was manufactured by Beyer Peacock of Manchester, England.
(Courtesy: Portuguese State Railways)

Another drawing of an unusual steam locomotive used by the Lisbon Tramway Company starting in 1872 is presented. This engine, named "Lisboa," was the first of fifteen supplied by Sharp Stewart of Manchester, England. The engine had two cylinders driving a pair of powered wheels running on the railroad, with two guiding wheels each, front and aft, which operated on a central rail. Wheel arrangement was 1–1–2–1–1.
(Courtesy: Portuguese State Railways)

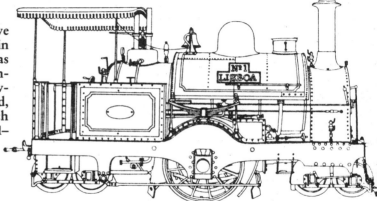

Pictured is a type 0–6–0 steam locomotive constructed by the Hanomag firm of Germany in 1885 for use on the railways of Portugal. This was engine no. 1117, part of a series from 1114 to 1131.
(Courtesy: Portugese State Railways)

A type 4–4–0 tender locomotive built by Beyer Peacock in 1891 for use on the Portuguese railways is shown. This was part of a series of engines numbered from 91 to 98.
(Courtesy: Portuguese State Railways)

Pictured is a type 0–6–2 tank locomotive built in 1891 by Beyer Peacock for operations on the railroads of Portugal. There were nine engines included in this order, numbered 1021 to 1029.
(Courtesy: Portuguese State Railways)

A type 0–6–0 tender locomotive built in 1895 by Soc. de Construction des Batignelles for use on the railways of Portugal. The order consisted of only two engines numbered 127 and 128.
(Courtesy: Portuguese State Railways)

This tank engine, type 2–4–0, was built for the railroads of Portugal in 1898 by Beyer Peacock. The series
included locomotives numbered 02012 to 02016.
(Courtesy: Portuguese State Railways)

The shunting locomotive, type 0–4–0, shown was constructed by John Cockrill of Belgium for use in the rail
yards of Portugal.
(Courtesy: Portuguese State Railways)

A type 0–6–0 steam locomotive used on the meter-gauge Tua line of northern Portugal is pictured. This tank engine was built by Kessler early in the twentieth century.
(Courtesy: Portuguese State Railways)

A tender locomotive, type 4–6–0, built in 1914 by Schwartzkopff of Germany for use on the Portuguese railways is shown. The order included fifteen engines numbered from 701 to 715.
(Courtesy: Portuguese State Railways)

Pictured is another Henschel-built 2–8–2 tank engine used on the meter-gauge railroads of Portugual. The locomotive dates from 1924.
(Courtesy: Portuguese State Railways)

Two pictures of a type 2–8–2 tank locomotive used on the meter-gauge Porto lines of Portugal are shown. This engine, number E-143, was built by Henschel in 1931.
(Courtesy: Portuguese State Railways)

A Mallet articulated tank locomotive, type 0–4–4–0, used on suburban service on the meter-gauge Porto line of northern Portugal is pictured here.
(*Courtesy: Portuguese State Railways*)

Pictured is an unidentified Mallet articulated steam locomotive widely used on the narrow-gauge railways of Portugal.
(*Courtesy: Portuguese State Railways*)

A Mallet type articulated tank engine used on various
narrow-gauge rail lines in Portugal is illustrated. No
technical or other data were available.
(Courtesy: Portuguese State Railways)

RHODESIA

CECIL RHODES, WHO INAUGURATED AND IN-spired so many ventures intimately linked with progress in Rhodesia and Zambia, realized from the start that rail communications were essential for settlement and development of the vast territories of Africa.

In 1891, while negotiations were proceeding for an Anglo-Portuguese treaty and its provisions for the building of a railway through Portuguese terri-tory (from Fontesvilla thirty-five miles (56.35 kilometers) to Beira on the Indian Ocean coast then to the eastern border of Rhodesia at Umtali), Rhodes consulted with George Pauling at Cape Town, South Africa. These discussions involved extending the Cape Railway system from Vryburg (about two hundred airline miles east southeast from Johannesburg) to Bulawayo in Rhodesia, 588 miles distant. Pauling's firm was responsible for a tremendous amount of rail construction in various parts of Africa, as well as in other parts of the world. In his memoirs, Pauling mentions signing a contract for the first stages of the long line that was eventually to connect Rhodesia with South Africa.

The next step was to complete the necessary ar-rangements for financing the initial stages of such a tremendous undertaking, and some time elapsed before actual work could be commenced. In fact, the Beira–Umtali railway was started first in Sep-tember 1892 and the Vryburg–Bulawayo line was begun eight months later.

Construction of the Beira–Umtali system was financed in sections as required for the extensions and branch lines. A number of companies were formed, seven in all; legally, these were separate entities, but were physically one unit, all sections of the system being under the same management. The various companies, in the order of their forma-tion, were:

Beira Railway Company Ltd. (July 1892)
Bechuanaland Railway Company (May 1893) Ti-tle later was changed to Rhodesia Railways Company Ltd. on June 1, 1899
Beira Junction Railway Company Ltd. (April 1895)
Mashonaland Railway Company Ltd. (April 1897)
Rhodesia–Katanga Junction Railway Company Ltd. (1908)
Blinkwater Railway Company Ltd.
Shabani Railway Company Ltd.
Victoria Falls Hotel Ltd.

VRYBURG TO BULAWAYO

Prior to the granting of a royal charter to the British South Africa Company on 29 October 1889, Rhodes obtained certain land rights north of Kimberly, South Africa, depending to no small ex-tent upon his promise to build a railway line to-ward Rhodesia. The Chartered Company financed the first 126 miles (202.86 kilometers) of track from Kimberly to Vryburg, but this section was taken over by the Cape government and did not actually become part of the Rhodesian railway system.

In May 1893 the Bechuanaland Railway Com-pany Ltd. was incorporated, with a share capital of 6,000 pounds sterling, and the Chartered Com-pany advanced 250,000 pounds for the Vryburg–

This sketch is depicting the scene on arrival at Bulawayo in 1897 of the first train from Vryburg; this was on the Bechuanaland Railway in South Africa. (*Courtesy:* Illustrated London News)

Palapye (Botswana) section. Land rights that had been granted to the Chartered Company were passed on to the Bechuanaland Railway Company. The imperial government declined to make any additional land grants but gave a subsidy of 20,000 pounds for ten years, the Chartered Company adding a subsidy of 10,000 pounds for a like period. The imperial government imposed certain rights of expropriation that caused much difficulty many years later in connection with negotiations for the conversion of debentures and the unification of the Rhodesia railways system.

No particular construction difficulties were experienced while building this line of 588 miles (946.68 kilometers from Mafeking to Bulawayo). The first extension, to Mafeking, was begun on 10 May 1893, and opened on 3 October 1894. A couple of years later the Matabele Rebellion, together with the cattle disease rinderpest, which swept southward through the subcontinent, made it a matter of grave urgency to get the line to Bulawayo quickly, it being well-nigh impossible to transport any goods to Rhodesia by ox wagon.

In September 1895 there was an issue of 900,000 pounds, 5 percent first-mortgage debentures of the Bechuanaland Railway Company for financing the line from Mafeking to Bulawayo. Further issues were made from time to time as work proceeded, with the Chartered Company guaranteeing the interest for twenty years. The issue amounted to two million pounds, the total discount and expenses of those various issues being 85,375 pounds.

By the end of 1896 a good start had been made, and Pauling gave Rhodes a personal challenge to do the final four hundred miles in as many days, a feat that was accomplished at an average cost of 3,500 pounds per mile (1.61 kilometer). The line was opened to Mochudi, some thirty-two miles (51.5 kilometers) north of Gaberones (now Gaborone), on 1 March 1897; to Palapye Road on 1 July; to Francistown on 1 September, and Bulawayo on 19 October. Pauling was understandably proud of his achievements in opening up rail communications in new countries, and it must have been an event of immense satisfaction to him, as it was to many others, when the first train steamed into Bulawayo on the afternoon of Tuesday, 19 October 1897, heralded by explosions of detonators, displays of flags and bunting, and the cheering of the pioneer settlers. See illustration.

For some time previously, *The Bulawayo Chronicle* had published regular bulletins reporting the progress of the line through the Bechuanaland Protectorate (now renamed Botswana) and now, after months of anticipation, Rhodesia was linked by rail with the Cape Peninsula, bringing Bulawayo within four or five days' journey from the coast.

From its inception in 1897, the Vryburg–Bulawayo section was operated on behalf of the Rhodesia Railways by the Cape Government Railway and its successors, the South African Railways, until various changes were made between 1959 and 1966.

THE BEIRA RAILWAY

Meanwhile, under terms of the Anglo-Portuguese Treaty of 1891, the Portuguese government had undertaken to have the line built from Fontesville in Mozambique (thirty-five miles, or 56.35 kilometers, from Beira), to the British sphere of influence, Bechuanaland. Exclusive rights were ceded by the Portuguese government to the Mocambique Company, which in turn granted a concession to Mr. Henry Theodore Van Laun for constructing a line according to the treaty. These rights were acquired by the Chartered Company and eventually brought to fruition through the medium of the Beira Railway Company, with the Portuguese government retaining the right to purchase the company's assets in 1916, or at the end of every successive ten-year-period.

The Beira Railway Company was incorporated in a form now obsolete in Great Britain for financial concerns. It was limited by guarantee, and divided into 600,000 profit-sharing shares of no par value. Of these shares, 295,000 were allocated to the Mocambique Company in part payment of the concession to build the railway, and the balance were offered as a bonus to subscribers of the first series of debentures. Between 1892 and 1896, three series of 6 percent debentures were issued, totaling 1,099,046 pounds. These issues were made at a discount of 214,820 pounds, for the prospects of the ultimate success of the venture were far from bright.

In September 1892 Pauling and Company began building, on behalf of the Beira Railway Company, a 2-foot gauge line from Fontesvill on the Pungwe River in Mozambique toward the eastern border of Rhodesia at Umtali. So great were the difficulties that it took more than five years of courageous struggle to complete the total section from Beira to Umtali, though it was only 205 miles (330 kilometers) in length. Not only did construction engineers face the problem of fetid swamps at the beginning and mountainous terrain at the inland end, but disease played havoc with man and beast alike and lions were a constant deadly risk.

By 1895 it was clear that the river link between Beira and Fontesvilla was most unsuitable owing to the ever-changing course of the waterway and the shifting sandbanks. Also, the Beira Railway Company could not finance the line connecting Fontesvilla with Beira because the company's bonds had dropped to a heavy discount, so meager were the hopes that its receipts would ever be sufficient to meet the debenture interest. Hence, the Beira Junction Railway Company came into being in April 1895, with a share capital of 62,500 pounds, and 250,000 pounds of six percent debentures were created—of which only 196,000 pounds could be placed at 52 percent of their face value plus a substantial bonus in shares at that time. The balance of the debentures was issued as occasion required, in settlement of funded interest and to meet expenses. This was quite a heavy burden of debt for a 35-mile (56.35-kilometer) narrow-gauge track.

The link-up with the port of Beira was completed in October 1896. George Pauling had put A. L. Lawley in charge of building the Beira–Umtali section, and a better engineer could scarcely have been chosen. Lawley was responsible for successfully getting the line first across the sixty-odd miles of marshy malarial flats (the alluvial region of the Pungwe and Revue Rivers), then up through the Amatongas Forest, ascending two escarpments to a final altitude of over thirty-five hundred feet (1,066.8 meters).

Eventually the line reached Umtali, in February 1898, four months after the first train steamed into Bulawayo over the southern section. Umtali has the distinction of having been brought to the railway, as the original site of the township was unsuitable from a railway construction point of view.

The narrow-gauge track of twenty-pound (9.07-kilograms) rails resembled a toy railway, but handled a large amount of traffic—including many contingents of Australians, New Zealanders, and Canadians brought in for the relief of Mafeking during the Boer War—before it was replaced in 1900 by the standard 3-foot 6-inch (1.07-meter) gauge line. Replacement took about six months, compared to the original construction period of five and a half years. Incidentally, funds for the conversion of the Beira–Umtali track to standard gauge were provided by the Mashonaland Railway Company, which had been incorporated on 13 April 1897 with a share of capital of 450,000 pounds, making an issue of 900,000 pounds, 5 percent debentures at 95 percent, with interest guaranteed by the Chartered Company for twenty-two years. The greater part of the proceeds of this issue was absorbed by the cost of widening the line.

ON TO SALISBURY

No time was lost in pushing ahead to fulfill Rhodes's scheme to give Rhodesia two routes to the sea, and in a little over twelve months after completion of the railroad to Umtali from Beira, the line was extended to Salisbury. This section of 170 miles (273.7 kilometers) of 3-foot 6-inch gauge line was built under the sponsorship of the Mashonaland Railway Company, and all supplies were transported from the Indian Ocean on the Beira Railway. The festivities arranged at Salisbury to celebrate the opening of the railway were not as ambitious as at some other places, but the town was decorated, and all enjoyed a three-day holiday, May 22 to 24, 1899.

THE LINK-UP

In the same month (May 1899), Rhodes addressed about a thousand shareholders of the Chartered Company in the hall of the Cannon Street Hotel in London, and put forth an ambitious scheme for the issue of 4.25 million pound debentures guaranteed as to principal, premium, and interest by the Chartered Company. The outcome was an issue, in May 1899, of 2,874,610 pound 4 percent guaranteed debentures, and on the first of June the Bechuanaland Railway Company's name was changed to Rhodesia Railways Limited. The extension from Bulawayo northeast to Gwelo also was begun in June 1899.

This line had reached a point near the present siding of Insiza when the Boer War broke out in October 1899, and construction came to a standstill owing to the immediate difficulties of obtaining permanent way material and stores. Rhodesia Railways therefore decided to continue the line from Salisbury, using the eastern rail route from Beira for necessary supplies. This extension was started in 1900 and proceeded at a reasonable pace to Gwelo, an important rail coaching center. The section was opened on 1 June 1902, with a link-up to the Insiza railhead effected five months later on 6 October. The entire through line from Bulawayo to Salisbury was opened for traffic on 1 December 1902. Meanwhile, on 1 August 1900, the Mashonaland Railway Company took over management of the whole line from Beira to Salisbury, by arrangement with the Beira Railway Company.

NORTHERN REGIONS

The dream Rhodes had of a Cape to Cairo route had an inspiring appeal, romantic as well as patriotic, and it had often been said that the glamor of taking part in the route's construction greatly assisted in the financial promotion of these railways. In March 1903, the balance of the 4.25 million pound debentures were issued, the net cash received for the whole issue being 4,071,180 pounds.

The original plan was to build the line northward from Gwelo, crossing the Zambezi River into the Mafungabusi district, then following the most direct route to Lake Tanganyika. This scheme was subsequently abandoned, however, because further survey indicated that the route would be particularly difficult and expensive and because discovery of extensive coal fields at Wankie meant that the main line was planned to extend from Bulawayo via Wankie and Victoria Falls.

Once again, somewhat difficult construction conditions were encountered; in certain areas the heat was intense, the country infested with lions, and fever rampant. Nevertheless, the railway reached Wankie in September 1903, and the colliery there was soon producing coal for sale. Eight months later, on 25 April 1904, the line reached Victoria Falls. The engine used for the opening ceremonies was decorated with palms and flowers and carried the legend: We've got a long way to go! (referring to Cairo). The whole line, Bulawayo to Victoria Falls, was opened to traffic on 20 June 1904.

THE FIRST BRANCH LINES

The need for branch lines to serve the growing mining industry arose long before the main line to the Congo border was completed. There was a great deal of activity in railway construction up to the time of the first world war, renewed in the late 1920s and early 1930s, and except in one instance, all were stimulated by mining developments.

Rails and rolling stock recovered from the original 2-foot (0.6-meter) gauge line from Beira to Umtali were used for a narrow-gauge line running about 84 miles (135.2 km) from Salisbury to the Ayrshire mine in the Sinoia district, which line had the distinction of being the first branch, begun in 1901 and opened on 1 November 1902. Known for many years as the Ayrshire or Lomagunda Branch, it was built by the Ayrshire Gold Mine and Lomagunda Railway Company Limited, to serve the mine, which began operations in 1900, but was closed down in 1908. The branch was purchased by the Mashonaland Railway Company Limited on 9 March 1905, extended some twelve miles (19.3 kilometers) to Eldorado Mine, and converted to 3-foot 6-inch (1.07)-miles) gauge. The work was completed as far as Benket in August 1913, and in Sinoia in June 1914.

Further branch lines were constructed and opened as follows:

Gwelo to Selukwe—25 August 1903
Heany Junction to Gwanda—25 August 1903
Westacre Junction to Matopos—7 November 1903
Gwanda to West Nicholson—1 March 1905
Lyndhurst Junction to Umvuma—19 June 1909
Gatooma to Eiffel Flats—16 May 1912
Mount Hampden to Shamva—23 April 1913
Umvuma to Fort Victoria—10 July 1914

Somabula to Shabani—11 May 1918
Ndola to Luanshya—22 January 1929
Mokambo to Mufulira—21 September 1929
Ndola to Nkana—2 July 1930
Maryland to Kildonan—2 July 1930
Sinoia to Zawi—1 August 1931
Nkana to Chingola—20 June 1931
Chambishi to Mufulira—1 April 1932

THE END OF THE PRIVATE COMPANY ERA

On 1 April 1947, the Rhodesian government acquired the assets of the Rhodesia Railways Limited for the sum of 23,642,266 pounds, and on 1 November 1949, via terms of the Rhodesia Railways Act, 1949, as amended, the railway undertaking became a statutory body known as Rhodesia Railways, established under the laws of Rhodesia and operating under the laws of Rhodesia, Zambia, and Botswana. In the same year, the Portuguese government exercised its right to expropriate the Beira Railway Company Limited—the section of line from Beira to Umtali—but Rhodesia Railways continued to operate the line until 1 October 1949.

Ten years later, on 1 December 1959, South African Railways purchased the line running from Vryburg, in what was then the Union of South Africa, to the southern border of Bechuanaland (Botswana), together with all lands and buildings and movable assets, other than locomotives, rolling stock, etc., for the sum of 1.35 million pounds sterling.

At the same time, Rhodesia Railways agreed to pay South African Railways, to operate and maintain the 200-mile (322-kilometers) section of line from the Bechuanaland–South African border at Ramatlhabama to Mahalapye, Rhodesia Railways was responsible for the line north of Mahalapye. The agreement had a twenty-year life but was subject to termination on six month's notice, and early in 1965, South African Railways signified their intention to terminate the agreement. As a result, Rhodesia Railways became responsible for maintaining and working this section of the line as of 26 September 1966, bringing to an end a particularly close association extending over a period of some sixty-eight years. That one administration should operate a major section of line for another railway administration in what amounted to a foreign county is in itself remarkable.

Another agreement of special importance was one toward the close of 1963 between the governments of Rhodesia and Zambia, providing for the ownership of Rhodesia Railways, upon dissolution of the federation, to pass in equal shares to the two governments. It is undoubtedly unusual, and possibly unique, for a statutory railway system to be owned jointly by two governments, and also to operate in the territory of yet another government, namely Botswana.

The intergovernmental agreement between Rhodesia and Zambia declared it to be the desire of both governments that Rhodesia Railways should continue as a single undertaking, with joint ownership and control by both governments. They set up a board of management, which functioned under a "Higher Authority" comprised of two ministers appointed by each of the two governments. Any decision of the Higher Authority had to be unanimous.

The agreement also covered innumerable important matters such as labor, rating, provision of new lines, and financial arrangements. Financial responsibility for the railway was accepted in equal shares by the two governments. When the federation did break up, the assets of Rhodesia Railways were valued at 100 million pounds, reflecting the enormous development that had occurred in the postwar years.

After a lull of two decades, a new upsurge of railway growth took place along with the general widespread development that followed World War II, and in 1955 a line of 199 miles (320.4 kilometers) was opened, connecting Bannockburn, on the Shabani Branch, with the Portuguese Railway at Malvernia, on the Rhodesia-Mozambique border, thus providing an urgently needed route to the port of Lourenco Marques (now Maputo).

The first good trains to run over this new route to the east coast left Bulawayo on 1 August 1955, and traffic quickly built up to considerable proportions. In July 1956 a weekly passenger service was introduced in both directions, with subsequent twice-weekly service. In the year ending 30 June 1964, this line carried more than 1.8 million tons (net) of traffic.

The links with the Mozambique ports of Beira and Maputo have not been used since the border was closed by President Machel in March 1976.

A still later major construction was officially opened by His Excellency Sir Humphrey Gibbs, KCMG, OBE, on 28 September 1964, forty-one mile (sixty-six-kilometer) first section of the Chiredzi branch line. It takes off from the

Bulawayo–Maputo (Lourenco Marques) main line at Mbizi to serve the rapidly developing low-veld areas, which have vast sugarcane fields and much agricultural potential.

Since the opening of the first section as far as Triangle, the line has been extended past Chiredzi to Nandi, a total distance of sixty-five miles (104.65 kilometers) from the mainline junction at Mbizi, and the future may well bring further rail extensions in the promising country of the Sabi Valley.

The construction of this new branch line, the first ever built primarily to serve agriculture, involved two major river bridges, one 1,389 feet (423.4 miles) across the Lundi River, and the other 1,097 feet (334.4 miles) over the Mtilikwe River.

These railways were renamed Zimbabwe Rhodesia Railways on 10 August 1979, then again renamed National Railways of Zimbabwe on 3 April 1980.

It must be remembered that while railways in Europe were built to serve settled populations and established industries, the railways of Rhodesia and other parts of Africa were built to open up new country to civilization and to facilitate development of known mining areas. There was then a much smaller African population than today, very few Europeans, and no industry. To imagine the pioneering railway construction in Africa is difficult, for, among other things, present-day engineers have the advantage of modern techniques and devices—such as heavy-duty earth-moving equipment and track-laying and ballasting machines—undreamed of in the days when a plate layer's principal equipment consisted of a pick and shovel, wheelbarrow, and a gun to shoot game as well as to protect himself from wild beasts and hostile tribesmen.

According to *Janes World Railways*, in 1978 Rhodesia had 3,239 kilometers (2,013 miles) of 1.067-meter (3-foot 6-inch) gauge railroad.

Steam Locomotives in Rhodesia

Since the late 1890s, when Rhodesia Railways came into being, the company has used fifteen main classes of steam locomotives and five classes of diesel-electric locomotives. The steam locomotives were divided into two distinct groups. First were the conventional, or straight, locomotives with a rigid frame throughout the length and (with the exception of a few tank engines) separate tenders. Beyer Peacock and Beyer Garratt locomotives were the second major type. Garratt locomotives are really two separate locomotive units with articulated joints supporting a boiler section and a cab section. The front locomotive unit carries a large water tank; the hind unit carries more water and the coal supply.

In the 1890s the original railway from Beira to Umtali was constructed to a 2-foot gauge, but soon was widened to the standard South African gauge of 3-feet 6-inches (1.067 meters). An example of one of the 2-foot gauge engines was displayed at Trade Fair Rhodesia a few years ago, and is now in the Rhodesia Railways Museum at Bulawayo. This locomotive was rediscovered at a sawmill near Lgusi on the rail line north of Bulawayo. Two engines actually were recovered; one was cannibalized to make the complete example now in the railway museum. The incomplete one was loaned to the Round Table Railway in Bulawayo and stands in Centenary Park.

Some confusion arises over engines 1 and 2. There were both Rhodesia Railways 1 and 2, and Mashonaland Railways 1 and 2. The Rhodesia Railways locomotives were purchased for working on the Beira wharves in 1929. No. 2 was named "Churchill." The others, much older, were dismantled in 1911. Engine no. 7, the well-known "Jack Tar," was introduced originally in 1896 by Pauling and Company and entered service with the Mashonaland Railways in 1900. It was first used in the work of broadening the gauge of the Beira line, then it went to Victoria Falls for the construction of the bridge. (It was reported to have killed a leopard during one of its early trips across the arch.) This locomotive was last used for shunting purposes in the railway works at Umtali. "Jack Tar" can now be seen at the Rhodesia Railways Museum in Bulawayo.

Engines numbered 8 to 50 are shown as class 7 in an old register. They were 4–8–0 type, with a tender that held 2,600 gallons of water and six tons of coal. A number of these machines were rebuilt as side-tank engines and designated class 6. In 1903 Rhodesia Railways purchased two Kitson-Meyer locomotives, which were numbered 51 and 52. Although at a quick glance these locomotives appeared conventional, they were quite the opposite. The boiler, cab, and bunker were supported on a frame that in turn rested on two power bogies. Each power bogie consisted of six coupled wheels, with the drive on the leading wheels of each unit. Their complete lack of speed, together with excessive coal and water consumption, proved such a serious handicap that they required a second tender, while the heat in the cabs led to constant complaints from the crews. They were consequently withdrawn in 1912 and dismantled; the boiler of one went into service at the Victoria Falls Hotel laundry. Engine no. 53 saw the introduction of the class 8 locomotive in 1904, and engine no. 80, the introduction of the class 9 locomotives in 1912. By 1914 Rhodesia Railways could boast some ninety-seven locomotives. The class locomotives commenced service in 1913, and in 1918 came the class 11 locomotives.

The seventh and subsequent classes of Rhodesian locomotives are pictured in illustrations, with appropriate captions.

During the 1960s a number of steam locomotive classes in Rhodesia were withdrawn from pickup and shunting work. These included class 9B straights and many renowned North British–manufactured class 12, type 4–8–2 machines, which were placed in "dead" storage in Bulawayo, Dabuka, and Gwelo. However, by the early 1970s, some class 12 locomotives of 1926 vintage (or older) were still to be found on mainline runs out of Bulawayo to Gwelo, to Victoria Falls, and on ballast loads on the section into Botswana. Most class 12 engines were eventually superseded by Garratt or diesel power on branch-line work to Seluke and Shabani, as well as on yard shunts. Garratt class 15 and 16A engines also took over yard shunting at Que Que and shuttled to and from the steelworks.

During 1973 steam motive power was eliminated in Salisbury and on sections out of the capital. In June 1973 the Salisbury steam sheds off Hatfield

Shown is the class 7 locomotive which had designation numbers 8 to 50 and 63 to 72. These engines had a 4–8–0 wheel arrangement and were built by the North British Locomotive Company starting in 1903. General specifications were:

Boiler pressure	160 pounds per square inch
Tractive effort	18,660 pounds at 75 percent boiler working pressure
Operating weight	83 tons
Overall length	54 feet 0¾ inches
Cab width	7 feet 1⅞ inches
Tender capacity	2600 gallons water; 6 tons coal.

(Courtesy: Rhodesia Railways)

Pictured is a seventh class locomotive, no. 43, at the time of the Rhodesian Diamond Jubilee in 1963.
(*Courtesy: National Railways of Zimbabwe*)

This illustration shows a class 12 or Mountain type locomotive, the most successful conventional engine ever used on the Rhodesian railway system. Fifty of these engines entered service in the period 1926–30 and, until 1978, they were the principal source of motive power on the "south line" from Bulwayo to Mahalapye in Botswana. These engines, built by the North British Locomotive Company, had a 4–8–2 wheel arrangement and carried the number designations 172–211 and 247–58. Subsequently there was a class 12 A (engines 198, 212, 213) and a class 12 B (316–35) with only minor changes.
(*Courtesy: National Railways of Zimbabwe*)

A class 12 locomotive crossing the famous Victoria Falls Bridge is shown here. Specifications were as follows:

Cylinders	20 by 26 inches
Drive wheels	4-foot 3-inch diameter
Boiler pressure	190 pounds per square inch
Tractive effort	32, 940 pounds at 85 percent boiler working pressure
Operating weight	131 tons
Overall length	65 feet 9 inches
First ten	equipped with Lentz poppet valves.

(Courtesy: National Railways of Zimbabwe)

A 1929 picture of a so-called "small" class of tank locomotive used on the Rhodesia Railways is presented. Originally six were purchased from Hudsell, Clark & Company for use on the Beira wharves in 1929. Engine no. 2, named "Churchill" is shown shunting supplies to the mechanical engineering shops at Bulwayo. Tractive effort at 75 percent boiler working pressure was 7858 pounds, and operating weight was 36 tons.
(Courtesy: National Railways of Zimbabwe)

Pictured is the class 16 Garratt type locomotives first introduced in 1929. These were decidedly larger than the 13–14 class engines having a 2–8–2 by 2–8–2 wheel arrangement. These were manufactured by Beyer Peacock in the period 1929–30 and later carried these identification numbers: 600–619. General specifications were:

Boiler pressure	180 pounds per square inch
Tractive effort	52,364 pounds at 85 percent boiler working pressure
Water capacity	5190 gallons
Coal capacity	11 tons
Overall length	81 feet 8 inches
Width across cab	10 feet.

(Courtesy: Rhodesia Railways)

Shown is a Rhodesia Railways class 17 Garratt locomotive manufactured by Beyer Peacock & Company in 1937 for the Sudan Railways. These type 4–6–4 plus 4–6–4 engines were similar to the class 15 and were purchased as used equipment from Sudan soon after World War II started when a shortage of motive power developed in Rhodesia. These engines were later sold to the Mocambique Railways. Originally the class 17 engines were numbered 271–80. General specifications were as follows:

Boiler pressure	180 pounds per square inch
Tractive effort	41,336 pounds at 85 percent boiler working pressure
Water capacity	4900 gallons
Coal capacity	12.5 tons
Operating weight	166.1 tons
Overall length	89 feet 11¼ inches
Cab width	9 feet 6 inches.

(Courtesy: Rhodesia Railways)

Pictured is a model of a Garratt locomotive, type 4–6–4 plus 4–6–4, class 15, four of which were manufactured by Beyer Peacock in 1940. These engines were initially used on the Capetown & Johannesburg mail trains between Bulwayo and Mafeking. Specifications were as follows:

Cylinders	17.5 by 26 inches
Drive wheels	4-foot 9-inch diameter
Tractive effort	42,700 pounds at 85 percent boiler working pressure
Operating weight	179.5 tons.

(Courtesy: Rhodesia Railways)

Road were finally closed. Accordingly, motive power furnished by class 12, 14, and 16A locomotives disappeared to other parts of the system. Also in June 1973, steam motive power was withdrawn on the south line to Mafeking. A class 15 locomotive, no. 406, left Bulawayo on 30 June 1973 with the final steam-hauled "mixed" train. What had been the territory of the classes 15 and 19 steam locomotives was now served by a miscellany of diesel-electric classes. Innumerable Garratts were set aside, but the class 19 Henschels, a small fleet of twenty-one engines, survived a short while longer on the Bulawayo–Thomson Junction and Bulawayo–Gwelo sections, after which they were relegated to shunting duties and subsequent withdrawal. Later, the program of terminating steam power reached a climax when no. 724, the first of the big class 20, Garratt 4–8–8 + 2–8–4 locomotives was set aside.

By the late 1970s there were indications that steam power might be restored as some stored locomotives were recalled for service. An active study was underway in an attempt to show the favorable economics of using steam, in view of worldwide oil crises. It also appeared that full-scale electrification of the Rhodesian Railways could never be justified. All in all, the general outlook appeared to gladden the hearts of many steam enthusiasts.

This illustration pictures the class 15 Garratt locomotives, type 4–6–4 plus 4–6–4. These engines, of a later series, were built by Beyer Peacock in 1947–52 and were numbered 384–423. General specifications were: tractive force 47,496 pounds at 85 percent boiler working pressure; operating weight 186.74 tons; boiler pressure 200 pounds per square inch; water capacity 7000 gallons; coal capacity 12.5 tons; overall length 92 feet 4 inches.
(Courtesy: Rhodesia Railways)

Three illustrations picture additional class 15 Garratt locomotives used on the Rhodesia Railways. No. 351 heads a freight train. Numbers 368 and 372 are shown pulling out of the rail station at Bulwayo. Also shown is a later Garratt, class 15A, no. 402, heading a passenger train.
(Courtesy: National Railways of Zimbabwe)

Pictured here is a conventional steam locomotive, class 19, type 4–8–2, no. 334, which was one of a follow-on to an order placed by the South African Railways with the German firm of Henschel in 1952. These engines were numbered 316–35. Actually the last was number 336 which was fitted with a condensing apparatus for the exhaust steam; subsequently it was involved in a collision and was rebuilt to the normal design. These locomotives were used on the south lines of Botswana until September 1966 as that section was operated by the South African Railways. The engine had a somewhat unconventional tender with a long cylindrical water tank. Water capacity was 6500 gallons and coal 12 tons. Operating weight with tender was 157 tons; tractive effort at 85 percent boiler working pressure was 36,090 pounds; overall length was 86 feet 8 inches.
(Courtesy: National Railways of Zimbabwe)

Shown is a class 16A Garratt locomotive put in service on the Rhodesian railways by Beyer Peacock in 1953. These carried the identification numbers 620–49. These engines had a 2–8–2 plus 2–8–2 wheel arrangement. General specifications were:

Boiler pressure	200 pounds per square inch
Tractive effort	58,183 pounds at 85 percent boiler working pressure
Operating weight	169.18 tons
Overall length	82 feet 5 inches
Width across cab	10 feet 8 inches.

(Courtesy: Rhodesia Railways)

A refurbished class 16A Garratt engine, no. 632, heading a short freight train somewhere in Rhodesia is pictured.
(Courtesy: National Railways of Zimbabwe)

The first Beyer Peacock Garratt locomotives, class 13, were purchased in 1926. These were originally used on the heavily graded sections of the Beira line which, until 1949, were operated as part of the Rhodesia Railways. In all, twelve type 2–6–2 plus 2–6–2 engines were secured from the above manufacturer. (This class is not illustrated).

Two illustrations show the class 14A, improved Garratt locomotives used initially in Rhodesia in 1929. These also operated on the Beira line, and some were sold to the Portuguese railway authorities when they took over in 1949. Various class 14 engines were still operating on the Rhodesian Railways in November 1978. Number designations were 215–20 and 231–40.

The class 14A locomotives manufactured in 1953–54 had a 2–6–2 plus 2–6–2 wheel arrangement, the same as class 14. These had a tractive effort of 39,168 pounds at 85 percent boiler working pressure. Operating weight was 131.67 tons. Boiler pressure was 180 pounds per square inch. Water capacity was 3600 gallons, and coal carried was 7 tons. The class 14A engines were numbered 508–25.
(Courtesy: Rhodesia Railways)

The 1957/58 or class 20 of Garratt articulated locomotives used on the Rhodesian Railways are shown here. These engines had a 4–8–2 plus 2–8–4 wheel arrangement and were manufactured by Beyer Peacock. They were the only Rhodesian locomotives equipped with a mechanical stoker. Designation numbers were from 700 to 720. Tractive force was 69,333 pounds at 85 percent boiler working pressure. Operating weight was 223 tons. Overall length was 95 feet 0½ inch. A subsequent series, class 20A was numbered 721-60 which weighed 225 tons.
(Courtesy: National Railways of Zimbabwe)

RUSSIA

IN 1833 THE FIRST RUSSIAN RAILROAD, A PRIVATE venture, was constructed in the Ural Mountains at Nizhnu Tagil; here the pioneer Russian locomotive was built by E. A. and M. E. Tcherepanov for the 5-foot 4.75-inch gauge tracks.

Commercial railroads in Russia came about through official czarist edicts. The first public railway, from St. Petersburg to Pavlovska, was built in the late 1830s under supervision of a Czech engineer named Franz Gerstner. The first section of the railroad, from Pavlovska to Tsarskoe Selo, was opened for horse traction on 30 October 1837. The materials, including rail for six-foot gauge tracks, came from England. The Russians ordered the first three steam locomotives from different British makers: Tayleur, Hackworth, and Stephenson. Stephenson's so-called patentee type 2–2–2 engine was built in 1836.

Subsequent rail lines in Russia adopted a gauge of five feet, which has been the standard ever since. Eventually, Moscow was connected with St. Petersburg, Warsaw, Kiev, and Sebastopol. Railroads were also constructed across the frozen tundra to locations near the Arctic Circle and, of course, through Siberia to the extremities of Asiatic Russia.

The construction of the 5,777-mile railroad across Siberia was considered one of Russia's greatest industrial efforts. As early as 1847, Perry M. Collins, an American adventurer, lawyer, and businessman, had advanced a proposal for the Amoor Railway to open the Siberian wilderness to world commerce. Unfortunately, the czar's government rejected the idea. From 1857 onward, authorities in Russia were subjected to countless petitions and requests from industrial concerns, engineering societies, and trade exponents for a railroad from west Russia to the Siberian east coast. In 1889 business interests at a huge trade fair in Nizhni-

The pioneer steam locomotive in Russia was constructed in the Ural Mountains area of Nishni Tagil by a small shop operated by Messers E. A. and M. E. Tcherepanov in 1833. This type 2–2–0 charcoal-fired engine is pictured. The machine was able to move a three-ton load about nineteen kilometers per hour. A model, as seen above, is presently on display in the USSR Railway Museum. Brief technical data were as follows:

Cylinders	7 by 9 inches (inside)
Boiler	
Length	5.5 feet
Diameter	3 feet
Fire tubes	20 in number.

(Courtesy: USSR Railways)

Novogorod, made personal appeals to Czar Alexander III for a "street of steel" from St. Petersburg to Vladivostok. By 1890, economic demands for a railway to open up Siberia to Russian industry and agriculture became apparent day by day. Moreover, there were many warning signals on the international horizon, especially with Japan making aggressive moves toward Korea and mainland China. The need for a modern communications link between the Russian eastern and western boundaries became evermore apparent. For essentially military and strategic reasons, Czar Alexander III on 29 March 1891 finally agreed to a railroad across Siberia.

Construction of the railway between European Russia and the Pacific Ocean was broken into several major sections. Intitial work on this tremendous project commenced on 19 May 1891, involving a 475-mile line from Vladivostok northward to Khabarovsk. A summary of subsequent rail construction activities in Russia-Siberia is spelled out in a table. This includes data on the so-called Chinese Eastern Railway, which was a Russian project (with Chinese approval) to build a short-cut line from central Siberia across Chinese Manchuria to Vladivostok. The story of the Trans-Siberian Railway is detailed in my book, *Seven Railroads*.

Summary Data—Siberian and Chinese Eastern Railways

Section	Miles	Years Of Construction	Total Cost	Cost Per Mile
Ussuri	475	1891-1897	$ 19,963,000	$ 42,027
West Siberian	900	1892-1895	20,417,000	22,686
Central Siberian	1140	1893-1898	43,632,000	39,666
Transbaikal	687	1895-1900	39,283,000	57,180
Irkutsk-Lake Baikal	40	1896-1900	1,554,000	38,850
Chinese Eastern	1045	1897-1903	192,493,000*	184,203
Circumbaikal	162	1901-1904	35,000,000	216,049
Amur	1200	1908-1916	150,000,000**	125,000
		Grand Total	$502,342,000	

* The cost of the Chinese Eastern Railway here included the eastern and western connections from the Trans-Siberian system, losses due to the Boxer Rebellion, all survey costs, costs of locomotives and rolling stock, and special projects such as boring the Khingan tunnel in western Manchuria.
** Partial payment up through 1913 only.

This is a table summarizing details of the Siberian and Chinese Eastern Railways construction data: 1891–1916.
(Courtesy: E. A. Haine, Seven Railroads, A. S. Barnes, 1979)

In modern times, most of the better Russian rail facilities have been concentrated west of the Ural Mountains. In 1970 the railways carried a major share of the country's traffic and were considered overloaded. The western region's railway network, which is extensive and dense, centers about Moscow's industrial hub. The east-west axis is served by the Trans-Siberian Railway system and by local branches and feeder trunk lines that extend south. Considerable traffic is imposed on the Trans-Caspian system, which swings eastward along the southern border from Krasnovoask on the Caspian Sea via Ashkhabad, Tashkent, and Alma-Ata, to join the Trans-Siberian line at Novosibirsk.

While the early railroad construction under the Czars was motivated by military strategy, under the Soviets, construction was mainly dictated by industrial considerations. In Russia the railways have a unique importance and are frequently guarded by railway troops. The national emphasis on railroads is indicated by the government-organized special schools devoted to training workers for all kinds of railway positions. The newspaper *Gudok (Whistle)* is published by the Rail Transport Workers Union and is primarily concerned with the railway industry. With the exception of the Turkestan–Siberian line, the Southern Siberian route, and the line from Vorkuta to Noril'sk, the Soviets have concentrated on making the existing rail lines more efficient through reconstruction, electrification, and double-tracking. In 1969 they announced that 95 percent of the rail lines had been converted from steam to diesel or electric locomotion.

Illustrated is a rail network map of Russia. In 1978, the U.S.S.R. had the following railway track lengths:

GAUGE (meters)	ROUTE LENGTH (kilometers)
1.520	135,324
0.60 to 1.0	2,863
1.435	73

Steam Locomotives in Russia

Russian railroad and locomotive supply from 1833 to the 1870s was largely in the hands of British, American, French, Belgian, and German manufacturers. From about 1880 to 1928, Russians did their own railroad and locomotive construction. A third phase, from 1928 to 1958, introduced basically larger locomotives, following American sizes and designs. A feature of Russian steam locomotion was use of a limited number of standard designs in order to facilitate production in large numbers.

Except for the earliest Russian-built engine mentioned at the opening of this chapter, the first com-

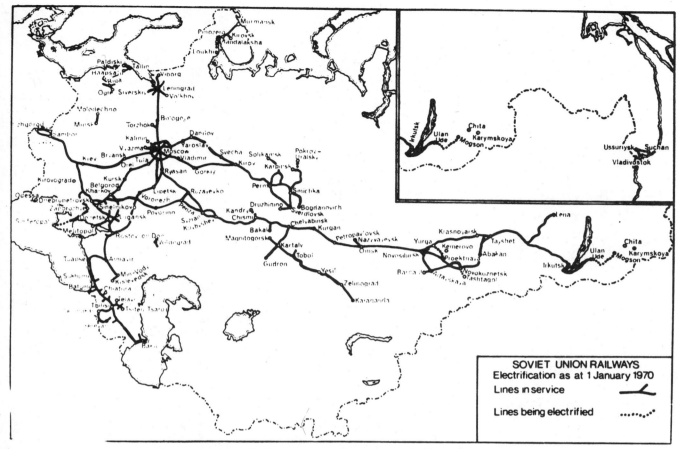

Railway map of Russia.
(*Courtesy:* Janes World Railways)

This Stephenson, type 2–2–2, locomotive built in 1836 was of the so-called "Patentee" design; it was one of the three first used on the pioneer railway of Russia. No technical data was immediately available. The engine was submitted to Russia in close competition with a similar engine designed and constructed by Hackworth in England. Both manufacturers claimed unheard-of engine speeds in their press notices.
(*Courtesy: O. S. Nock, The Dawn of World Railways 1800–1850*)

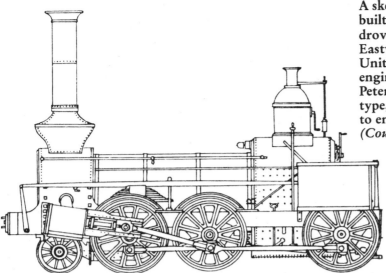

A sketch of the first 2–6–0 type steam locomotive ever built is shown. This was manufactured at the Alexandrovsk Works in Saint Petersburg early in the 1840s by Eastwick & Harrison who had recently departed the United States and set up operations in Russia. This engine was used to haul freight trains on the Moscow–Petersburg Railway. Constructed initially as a 0–6–0 type, it later had a set of leading bogie wheels installed to enhance stability and to distribute axle loading. *(Courtesy: USSR Railways)*

Pictured is a class C, type 0–6–0, steam engine used in freight service on the Poti–Tiflis Railway of Russia in the mid-nineteenth century. This wood-burning locomotive was built by the Yorkshire Engine Company of Sheffield, England.
(Hamilton Ellis, Pictorial History of Railways, *Middlesex, England: Hamlyn Group, 1968)*

The USSR Railway Museum has on display a model of a 2–4–0 passenger locomotive on which little is known concerning its past use. This engine was built at the Votkinski factory in 1870 for a 5-foot gauge railway. Cylinders were 1 foot 3.9 inches by 1 foot 3.9 inches; coupled wheels were 5 feet 6.1 inches in diameter. The boiler had 957.9 square feet of heating surface and generated steam pressure of 118 pounds per square inch.
(Courtesy: USSR Railways)

mercial railroads in Russia used locomotives mostly of British design and construction. Between 1833 and 1873, modestly proportioned locomotives, types 0–6–0, 4–4–0, 2–4–0, and 0–4–2, were furnished by a number of manufacturers. The three initial engines were supplied by Tayleur, Hackworth, and Stephenson from their respective English works. Stephenson's type 2-2-2 patentee engine was built in 1836. Hackworth's 2–2–0 engine was constructed in 1837 for steam-powered operations on the St. Petersburg–Tsarskoe Selo rail line.

In the early 1840s the first type 2–6–0 steam locomotive ever built was constructed in St. Petersburg by an American firm. The Yorkshire Engine Company of Sheffield, England, supplied a wood-burning type 0–6–0 engine in the mid-1850s for handling freight service on the Poti–Tiflis Railway.

Starting about 1870, a limited locomotive construction industry developed that was initially preoccupied with duplicating various engines purchased from abroad. Such a factory arose at Votkinshi, which built a series of 2–4–0 passenger engines.

It seems worthwhile to outline the extent to which Baldwin Locomotive Works furnished the Russian railroads with steam engines. An 1872 Baldwin contract with the Veronen Rostoff Railway called for eleven locomotives designed to burn low-grade Russian anthracite coal. Six locomotives sent to Russia were of the Mogul type, with cylinders measuring 19 by 24 inches and drive wheels 54 inches in diameter; five others were passenger engines, American-style, with 17 by 24-inch cylinders and 66-inch drive wheels. In addition, in 1874 Baldwin furnished one Mogul freight engine with 18 by 24-inch cylinders and one passenger engine with 16 by 24-inch cylinders—all for testing feasibility of burning anthracite coal in the engine boilers. These locomotives were bought by the technical department of the Russian government. Also in the same year, the Charkoff Nicolauff Railway purchased twelve Mogul freight engines with 19 by 24-inch cylinders.

In 1878, forty heavy Mogul-type locomotives with 19 by 24-inch cylinders and 54-inch drive wheels, were constructed by Baldwin for two Russian railways: Koursk Charkoff Azof and Orel Griazi. The engines were ordered on 16 December 1877, and delivery of the dismantled locomotives was completed on 13 February 1878. During 1895 and 1896, contracts were executed by Baldwin for several other railroads in Russia, and these totaled 138 units, all of the four-cylinder compound type. The Russian-Turkish War of 1878, causing widespread delays in shipments of steam engines from overseas, emphasized the great need for domestic

RUSSIA

Type 0–8–0 freight engines were built by the Russian Kolomna and Maltsevsk Works, starting in 1878 and continuing until 1892. These engines were characterized as follows:

Cylinders	19.7 by 24.6 inches
Coupled wheels	3-foot 11.2-inch diameter with Allan's link motion
Boiler	
Heating surface	1895 square feet
Working pressure	128 pounds per square inch
Operating weight	48 tons (engine)
Speed	45 kilometers per hour.

This illustration is a sketch duplicating a model of this locomotive on display in the USSR Railways Museum.

The Vladikavkaz Railway, which operated in southeast Russia, had great success with six type 4–6–0 engines manufactured by Kolomna Machine Building Works in 1892. These were compound locomotives with the following characteristics:

Cylinders	
Hi pressure	19.6 by 25.5 inches
Lo pressure	27.9 by 25.5 inches
Coupled wheels	6-foot diameter
Boiler	
Grate area	19.9 square feet
Heating area	1528.4 square feet
Boiler pressure	162 pounds per square inch
Speed	100 kilometers per hour.

In 1907 duplicate locomotives, with minor modifications, were manufactured in Russia at shops in Sormovski, Kharkov, Lugansk, and Kolomna. Oil-burning models were also built at Hanover, Germany by the Linden Locomotive Works. Pictured is a model of the original engine now preserved in the USSR Railway Museum. This picture illustrates the use of a platform railing, a typical Russian innovation, which was mandated by a czarist decree in 1870.
(Courtesy: USSR Railways)

production of transportation equipment. The first major locomotive works in Russia were the Kolomna and Maltsevsk factories, which turned out various engines in the period 1878 and 1892. Illustrated is a typical example of a Russian-built 0–8–0 freight and shunting engine.

A popular Russian locomotive was type 4–6–0, of which thousands were manufactured by the Kolomna Machine Building Works between 1892 and 1923. The same model was also built at factories in Lugansk, Kharkov, and Sormovshi. The Linden Locomotive Works at Hannover, Germany, built many duplicate engines, though of an oil-burning variety.

After a slow start and experimentation with various designs, 1892 saw the development of a two-cylinder, class N passenger engine, with drive wheels varying in diamater from 5 feet 7 inches to 6 feet 3 inches. About a thousand of these were manufactured over the following twenty-one years. A second standard, two-cylinder, class S engine was adopted in 1910, and nine-hundred of these passenger-train engines were built over the next eight years. General specifications of this engine were as follows:

Cylinders	$21\frac{5}{8}$ by $27\frac{9}{16}$ inches
Coupled drive wheels	6-foot diameter
Boiler grate area	41 square feet
Boiler steam pressure	185 pounds per square inch
Axle loading	15.8 tons.

The same basic passenger engine, with progressive design changes, was continued until 1951, by which time some four-thousand units had been produced. Specifications in 1951 were as follows:

Cylinders	22⅝ by 27⁹⁄₁₆ inches
Boiler grate area	50.9 square feet
Axle loading	20 tons.

In 1916 the Baldwin Locomotive Works furnished the International Engineering and Trading Company of Russia with a number of narrow-gauge, type 0–4–0 shunting engines, which are shown and described.

The story of freight locomotives in Russia is unique in that a greater number were produced here than in any other part of the world. There were three basic freight engine designs used on a grand scale:

1. Type 0–8–0, class C, constructed from 1891 to 1923. These had the general specifications set forth.
2. Type 0–10–0, class E, manufactured between 1912 and 1952.
3. Type 2–10–0, class Y, built during World War I and World War II. These were essentially the same as class E above, but of American manufacture. The following approximate

quantities were constructed: War I—900 units; War II—2,100 units (known as Ye).

In addition to the above locomotives, various other classes were designed and constructed in Russia. About five-hundred Mallet compound engines, types 2–4–4–0 and 0–6–6–0, were built between 1903 and 1916 for use on the Trans-Siberian Railway. Additional class E units were also manufactured over War I. These were type 0–10–0 engines built by outside firms: 500 units by a Swedish manufacturer, 500 units by various German builders.

Many thousands of high-boilered Russian class SU, type 2–6–2, medium passenger locomotives were built between 1925 and 1951.

Starting in 1928, the Russians upgraded their locomotives to a heavier style, based on experience with a few type 2–10–2 and type 2–10–4 engines purchased from the United States. In 1931 the Russians started building a class FD, type 2–10–2 engine for handling freight traffic. In 1932 a modified version of the class FD engine, known as class JS,

Shown is a fine photograph of a type 0–4–0 Baldwin switching engine, built in 1916 for the International Engineering & Trading Company of Russia. This was used on 2-foot 5.53-inch gauge tracks. Specifications were as follows:

Cylinders	7 by 12 inches
Coupled drive wheels	23-inch diameter
Boiler	

Grate area	3.8 square feet
Fire box	19 square feet
Tubes	140 square feet
Diameter	28 inches
Steam pressure	176 pounds per square inch
Operating weight	18,100 pounds
Tank capacity	185 gallons water; 14 cubic feet soft coal.

(Courtesy: Frederick Westing collection)

A class C, type 0–8–0, freight/passenger steam locomotive manufactured in vast numbers in Russia during the period 1891–1923 is shown here. Technical specifications, with variations between different series, were as follows:

Cylinders	19¹¹⁄₁₆ by 25⁹⁄₁₆ inches
Coupled wheels	3-foot 11.25-inch diameter
Boiler grate area	19.9 square feet
Operating steam pressure	156 to 213 pounds per square inch
Axle loading	13.5 to 14 tons
Number built	9000.

(Courtesy: USSR Railways)

Pictured is the most widely manufactured freight steam engine in the entire world. These were type 0–10–0, class E locomotives of which, it was reported, thirteen thousand units had been built with minor modifications over the period 1912–52 to serve various Russian railroads. After 1945 the design was copied and many engines were manufactured and used in the East Bloc countries. Specifications were as follows:

Cylinders	25⁹⁄₁₆ by 29⁹⁄₁₆ inches
Coupled wheels	4-foot 4-inch diameter
Boiler grate area	48 to 54.7 square feet
Working steam pressure	171 to 191 pounds per square inch
Axle loading	16.7 to 17.5 tons.

(Courtesy: USSR Railways)

Shown is another Russian class E, type 0–10–0 freight locomotive built in the period 1912–52.
(Courtesy: USSR Railways)

A decapod type locomotive (2–10–0 wheel arrangement), nine-hundred units of which were built by Baldwin and other American manufacturers in 1915–17 is pictured. These class Y engines resembled the Russian class E machines but were distinctly American in design. The locomotives were shipped from the United States west coast directly to Vladivostok where they naturally predominated on the Siberian railways. These freight engines proved so successful that 2100 machines known as class YE were delivered to the same Russian port in World War II as part of a lend-lease agreement. General specifications were as follows:

Cylinders	25 by 28 inches
Coupled drive wheels	52-inch diameter
Operating weight	200 tons
Track gauge	5 feet.

(Courtesy: Frederick Westing collection)

The USSR Railways has outstanding success using several thousand class Su locomotives in the period 1925–51. These were type 2–6–2 engines originally built at the Kolomna Works in 1925. Later on many units were constructed at the Lugansk, Sormovsk, Kharkov, and Kolomna Works. Pictured is a model of an early class Su model. These locomotives had the following characteristics:

Cylinders	22.6 by 27.5 inches
Coupled wheels	6-foot ⅞-inch diameter
Leading wheels	3-foot 5⅜-inch diameter
Trailing wheels	4-foot 4-inch diameter
Boiler	
Grate area	51.75 square feet
Firebox	199.1 square feet (Belpaire)
Superheater	785.1 square feet (Tchousoff)
Total heat surface	2974.8 square feet
Operating weight	147 metric tons
Piston valves	Trofimoff type
Axles	Hollow type.

(Courtesy: USSR Railways)

A Russian class FD type 2–10–2, heavy freight locomotive is shown. These were first built in 1931 by Voroshilovgrad Works (now Lugansk Works), three thousand units were constructed between 1931 and 1938. This engine was somewhat different in that the conventional hand rails around the normal Russian locomotives were not included in the design. Note skylight in roof of engineer's cab. The locomotive included such American features as bar frames, thermic syphons, and mechanical stokers. This is a model housed in the USSR Railway Museum. Specifications were as follows:

Cylinders	26.3 by 30 inches
Drive wheels	4-foot 11-inch diameter
Boiler	
Grate area	75.3 square feet
Working pressure	220 pounds per square inch
Operating weight	
134 tons (engine)	
101 tons adhesion	
Tender capacities	11,600 gallons water; 25 tons coal.

(Courtesy: USSR Railways)

This illustration shows a model of a Russian class JS-20 (named "Iosif Stalin"), type 2–8–4 locomotive, a passenger version of the class FD freight engine, type 2–10–2. These were first produced by the Kolomna Works in 1932 but were later mass-manufactured by the Lugansk Works. The prototype engines were long utilized to haul the famous "Red Arrow Express" over the October Railroad between Moscow and Leningrad. Specifications were:

Cylinders (2)	26 ⅜ by 30 ⅜ inches
Coupled drive wheels	6-foot 0⅞-inch diameter
Boiler	
Grate area	25.8 square feet
Superheater (not given)	
Total heat surface	1597 square feet
Working pressure	220 pounds per square inch
Operating weight engine	
133 tons	
81 tons adhesion	
Tractive effort	60,000 pounds
Design speed	115 kilometers per hour.

(Courtesy: USSR Railways)

The Russian locomotive on the right is another class JS ("Iosif Stalin"), type 2–8–4. See earlier illustration for details. The engine on the left, only partially visible, is a class S, type 2–6–2, which, with 6-foot drive wheels, was one of the most widely used passenger locomotives in Russia; over a period of almost forty years, from 1913 to 1951, about four thousand machines were manufactured. Specifications varied as follows:

Class S	
Cylinders	21⅝ by 27⁹⁄₁₆ inches to 22⅝ by 27⁹⁄₁₆ inches
Drive wheels	6-foot diameter
Grate area	41 to 50.9 square feet
Working pressure	185 pounds per square inch
Axle loading	15.8 to 20 tons.

(Courtesy: USSR Railways)

A head-on view of the class JS type 2–8–4, "Iosif Sta-lin" passenger locomotive widely used in Russia up to World War II is given here.
(Courtesy: USSR Railways)

This illustration shows another Russian class JS type 2–8–4, passenger locomotive first built in 1932. See an earlier illustration for complete details. See other illustrations for another view of the same class engine.
(Courtesy: USSR Railways)

The most massive Garratt type locomotive ever constructed is pictured. This engine, with a 4–8–2 plus 2–8–4 wheel arrangement and with 4-foot 11-inch drive wheels was built by Beyer Peacock of Manchester England, in 1932 for use on the Soviet railways. *(Courtesy: USSR Railways)*

A model of the Russian class SO-19, type 2–10–0, freight locomotive is shown. This machine was first used in 1934 simply as class SO, a modified class S, and was the last of what was considered to be purely Russian in design. In 1936–41 the class SO-19 engines appeared, on which were installed water condensing equipment; special condensing vans were provided as indistinctly seen on the far right of this picture. Some of the latter machines were built in Siberian plants after military hostilities started with Germany in

1941. Specifications were:

Cylinders	25.5 by 27.5 inches
Drive wheels	4-foot 4-inch diameter
Boiler	
Grate area	64.5 square feet
Superheater	1044 square feet
Total heat surface	2443 square feet
Operating weight	104 tons.

(Courtesy: USSR Railways)

was constructed for passenger service. This was a type 2–8–4 locomotive and is pictured in two illustrations.

Also in 1932, Russian railways tried out a Garratt-type locomotive with a 4–8–2 + 2–8–4 wheel arrangement. This engine was manufactured by Beyer Peacock and was considered the largest Garratt ever built.

About 1925, Russian manufacturers built a class S, type 2–6–2 locomotive, which was later modified to become class SO, type 2–10–0. About five-thousand of these units were produced in Siberian shops following the German invasion of western Russia in World War II.

After World War II, Russia produced three basic locomotive types.

1. Class L, type 2–10–0, also known as the Victory type, starting in 1945.
2. Class P36, type 4–8–4, for use with passenger express trains on the Moscow–Leningrad and Moscow–Brest lines.
3. Class LV, a modified and elongated class L, type 2–10–2 locomotive with a larger grate. This appeared in 1952. By 1956, when steam locomotion was ordered abandoned, only 100 such units had been produced.

The manufacture of steam locomotives in Russia ended about 1958, at which time approximately 70 percent of all rail traffic was still being handled by 36,000 steam engines. In European Russia at that time, the class L locomotives were seen in the greatest number.

This illustration pictures the last type steam locomotive designed and manufactured in large numbers by the Russians. This engine, designated as class SO, had a leading set of bogie wheels but otherwise resembled the last manufactured class E units. Approximately five thousand such locomotives were manufactured by the Russians during World War II, some in improvised plants hastily erected in Siberia during the German invasion of western Russia. Specifications follow:

Cylinders	25⁹⁄₁₆ by 27⁹⁄₁₆ inches
Coupled wheels	4-foot 4-inch diameter
Boiler grate area	64.5 square feet
Operating steam pressure	191 pounds per square inch
Axle loading	17.5 tons.

(Courtesy: USSR Railways)

Not illustrated is a Russian class L, type 2–10–0, freight locomotive designed and constructed after World War II. This was somewhat lighter than the heavy freight engine class FD. The class L engine had a maximum axle loading of 18 tons and therefore was widely used on a larger number of Russian railroads. This class was designed by L. S. Lebedianski, the Chief Designer, after whom the class was identified. This engine was readily adaptable to mass production and five thousand were manufactured up to 1957. Specifications were:

Cylinders	24.6 by 31.5 inches
Drivers	4-foot 11-inch diameter
Boiler	
Grate area	64.5 square feet
Superheater	1227 square feet
Total heat surface	2389.5 square feet
Operating weight engine	
103 tons	
91 tons adhesion	
Design speed	80 kilometers per hour.

This is a model housed in the USSR Railway Museum.

(Courtesy: USSR Railways)

The Russian class P36 passenger locomotives, type 4–8–4, arrived on the scene in 1950 with but a limited production. After four years an additional 250 units were manufactured. By this time a decision to phase out the steam locomotive had been made, otherwise many thousands of this successful class of engines would have been produced. These passenger engines, not illustrated, were two-cylinder design and had these specifications:

Cylinders	22⅝ by 31.5 inches
Coupled drive wheels	6-foot ¾-inch diameter
Boiler	
Grate area	72.6 square feet
Steam pressure	213 pounds per square inch
Engine weight	135 tons
Axle loading	18 tons
Number built	250 units.

(Courtesy: USSR Railways)

SOUTH AFRICA

A COMPLETE LACK OF NAVIGABLE WATERWAYS, coupled with the location of rich mineral resources in the interior of South Africa, made the development of an extensive railway system mandatory for heavy long-distance hauling. The direction of early railroad growth was inland from the ports in Cape Colony and Natal. While the plateaus of South Africa have been an advantage for railroad building, extensive escarpments and dissected marginal zones have proven to be a headache for railroad engineers. These problems were eventually overcome, although with heavy engineering and construction costs.

The first railway in South Africa appears to have been a private two-mile stretch of 4-foot 8½-inch gauge track that was opened on 26 June 1860, extending from Durban to "the Point," otherwise known as Durban Harbour or Natal Port. This small line was built by the Natal Railway Company and was taken over by the Natal government on 1 January 1897.

The first commercial railroad, another private venture, was built between 1859 and 13 February 1862—a line from Cape Town to the Eerste River. This line was lengthened another fifty-seven miles, from Stellenbosch to Wellington, and opened on 4 November 1863. On 19 December 1864 a railway from Salt River to Wynberg was opened, and on 4 April 1867 a rail line from Durban to Umgeni was completed. Railway construction in South Africa received a major boost with the discovery of diamonds at Kimberly in the early 1870s and the opening of the Witwatersrand gold field in 1886.

From about 1872 the government adopted a permanent rail gauge of 3 feet 6 inches.

The ambition of Cecil John Rhodes to establish a rail connection between Cape Town and Cairo, Egypt, brought about an agreed-upon standard gauge of 1.065 millimeters (3-feet 6-inches) over most of Africa, with the exception of fifty-nine hundred kilometers of meter-gauge rail in Kenya. Thus the rolling stock of countries south of the equator, despite international boundaries, remained completely interchangeable. This led to long-standing cooperation and business agreements between the South African Railways and various other South African nations with consequent progress in trade relations. In other words, rail transportation has been the basic catalyst in bringing about economically harmonious relations between the countries of the African subcontinent, insuring stability and prosperity through positive cooperation.

In 1873 Cape Colony nationalized the existing railway, then totaling about sixty miles, and in 1874 began building a line to the center of the diamond diggings at Kimberly, completing the last link in 1885. The discovery of gold in the Witwatersrand in the 1880s led the Cape Government Railways and the Natal Government Railways, which had started inland in the late 1870s, to try to reach this new source of traffic. Paul Kruger, president of the South African Republic (Transvaal), concerned over British-controlled economic forces moving toward his state, interrupted their advance at the Transvaal border. He then secured an agreement with Portugal for a line eastward from Johannesburg to Lourenço Marques (Maputo) in Mozambique, the closest port to Witwatersrand, thus making possible the last Cape and Natal links with Johannesburg. The first train from Cape Town reached Johannesburg in 1892. In the same year, another Cape Government Railways line to Johannesburg, from Port Elizabeth through Bloemfontein, was also opened; the Orange Free State section of this line was financed by Cape Colony. Three years later, in 1895, the first train service was initiated between Durban and Johannesburg.

In 1894 the Johannesburg–Lourenço Marques line was completed. The Transvaal government, in its agreement with Portugal, had guaranteed part of the Witwatersrand traffic to Mozambique in exchange for recruitment rights for laborers for the Witwatersrand mines. The new line soon drew a considerable amount of cargo from both the Cape and Natal lines. Frictions developed, which in part were responsible for the Anglo-Boer War of 1899–1902. In 1901, however, the British High Commission Authority, which at the time controlled most of the Transvaal, entered into a new agreement with Mozambique on mine labor recruitment. Mozambique was guaranteed 50 to 55 percent of the Witwatersrand traffic through Lourenço Marques. This arrangement was further confirmed in a Transvaal-Mozambique convention after the war, which provided a minimum of 50 percent of the traffic to Mozambique. The provisions of this postwar convention were reluctantly accepted by the Cape, Natal, and Orange Free State governments when the Union of South Africa was formed in 1910. At that time, the South African Railways and Harbours Administration was constituted from the formerly separate Cape Government Railways, Natal Government Railways, and Central South African Railways (the latter comprised the former Transvaal and Orange Free State Railways systems). Initially, each of these railways continued to operate independently, and a full merger was achieved only in 1916.

In 1938 a new Mozambique convention was negotiated that guaranteed that a minimum of 40 percent of the seaborne imports to the Witwatersrand would enter through Lourenço Marques and the Mozambique rail link to the Transvaal. In the mid-1960s, guaranteed percentages were not being met, and by 1968 South Africa had paid almost 4.4 million rand ($2.3 million) to Mozambique Railways as compensation. Although the South African government had urged businesses to utilize Lourenço Marques facilities more fully, the compensation amount continued to rise. In fiscal year 1967–68 it totaled over 1.3 million rand, compared with R 650,000 in 1965–66, and R 791,800 in 1966–67 (about 684,000, $342,000, and $416,736).

In modern times, large supplies of domestic coal and a lack of domestic oil production have necessitated the continuing and extensive use of steam locomotives, although the total number of steam engines has declined since the early 1960s. The steeply graded railways in South Africa used Garratt-type locomotives consisting of two powerful "chassis" united by a strong girder frame that carried the boiler. Similar engines built by Fairlie, Mallet, and others were also used. Most heavy passenger work was performed by Pacific-type locomotives, in addition to some class T, type 4–8–2 engines. Diesel engines were first used for mainline operations in 1958, especially in zones where the water was unsuitable or unobtainable for steam locomotives. In March 1969 the South African Railways had 324 diesels, more than double the number in 1961. Electric traction was also employed in the major suburban areas of Cape Town, Durban, and Pretoria-Johannesburg and on main lines, especially in Natal, where steep gradients gave electric traction a distinct advantage. Despite the strong emphasis on steam locomotives, their number steadily declined from 2,669 in March 1961 to 2,490 in March 1969. The 1968 Commission of Inquiry into the Coordination of Transport suggested further replacement of steam engines with diesel and electric engines as a way of increasing carrying capacity of the main lines.

In 1968 no direct rail connections existed between major east coast cities such as Durban and East London, and Durban had only one rail link with the interior. Because the bulk of freight came from or moved into southern Transvaal, railroad congestion was a problem there and on the rail links to various ports in South Africa.

In 1979 the South African Railways consisted of 23,377 kilometers (14,517 miles) of 1.065-meter (3-foot 6-inch) track, and 706 kilometers (438.4 miles) of 0.610-meter (2-foot) track.

The narrow-gauge facilities in 1979 used sixty-one steam locomotives and twenty diesel engines. On standard-gauge tracks, the following miscellaneous statistical data applied:

Distance electrified	13,751 kilometers (8544.4 miles)
Number of bridges	10,298
length of track on bridges	156.5 kilometers (97.24 miles)
Longest bridges	
Orange River	1,152 Bethulie meters
Orange River	1,067 Upington meters
Olifants River	1,050 meters (3444.0 feet)
Umfolozi River	533 meters (1748.2 feet)
Total number railway tunnels	178
Total length of tunnels	102.48 kilometers (63.68 miles)
Length of three longest tunnels	
Boughton-Cedara	6,023 meters (19755.4 feet)
Hidcote-Lowlands	4,029 meters (13215.1 feet)
Ermelo-Sheepmoor	3,896 meters (12788.88 feet)
Number of railway stations	1,007
Locomotives in service:	
Steam	1,770
Electric	1,817
Diesel-electric	1,267

South Africa's worst rail accident, a derailment, occurred near Durban on 4 October 1965, killing eighty-one people.

The highest summits on the railways of the South African Railways are at Belfast (6,463 feet sea level), Nederhost (6,871 feet above sea level), and Johannesburg, a meter-gauge line (5,715 feet above sea level).

The first South African transcontinental railway linked Cape Town with Durban, at Heidelberg in the Transvaal, on 10 October 1895.

Highlights of a Hundred Years

1853 Cape Town Railway and Dock Company formed.

1859 Natal Railway Company formed
31 March: Turning of first sod, Cape Town–Wellington railway.

1860 26 June: Opening of railway from Point to Durban.

1862 13 February: Opening of railway from Cape Town to Eerste River.
1 May: Opening of railway from Eerste River to Stellenbosch.

1863 4 November: Opening of railway from Stellenbosch to Wellington.

1864 19 December: Opening of railway from Salt River to Wynberg.

1867 4 April: Opening of railway from Durban to Umgeni.

1869 First tug, *The Gnu,* used in Table Bay.

1870 11 July: Table Bay Docks formally opened by Duke of Edinburgh.

1873 1 January: Transfer of the Cape Town–Wellington Railway to the government; leasing of Salt River–Wynberg Railway to the government.

1876 1 January: First sod turner of Durban–Pietermaritzburg railway line.
16 June: Cape main line extension to Worcester opened.

1877 1 May: Line opened from East London to King William's Town.

1879 26 August: Port Elizabeth railway reached Graff-Reinet.

1880 5 February: Line to Beaufort West opened.
5 May: East London Railway reached Queenstown. (Old Cape Eastern main line.)
1 December: Natal railway reached Pietermaritzburg.

1881 1 June: Line from Port Elizabeth to Cradock opened.

1882 Robinson Graving Dock, Table Bay Harbour, opened.
April: Electric lighting introduced on African Continent by Cape Government Railways at Table Bay Harbour.

1884 31 March: Cape Town and Port Elizabeth railway linked up at De Aar.
3 November: Cape railway reached Orange River from De Aar.

1885 2 September: East London railway reached Aliwal North.
28 November: De Aar–Kimberly railway line opened.

1886 21 June: Line opened to Ladysmith, Natal.

1887 21 June: Establishment of the Netherlands South African Railway Company (Nederlandsche Zuid-Afrikaansche Spoorwegmaatschappij—ZASM).

1888 Electric lighting of trains introduced by Cape Government Railways.

1890 Johannesburg Station, then known as Park Halt, ZASM.
17 March: First railway in Transvaal between Johannesburg and Boksburg, known as Rand Tram, subsequently extended to Springs and Krugersdorp.

1891 7 April: Natal main line opened as far as Charlestown. President Kruger attended.
1 July: Line between Portuguese border and Komatipoort opened.

1892 15 September: Arrival of first train at Johannesburg from Cape Town, via Bloemfontein.

1894 20 October: Railway from Delagoa Bay

reached Pretoria.

1896 2 January: Opening of complete service between Johannesburg and Durban.

1897 4 November: Formal opening of railway to Bulawayo from Cape Town.

1900 11 September: ZASM relieved of control of railways in Transvaal, which along with the railways of the Orange Free State, came under control of the Imperial Military Railways.

1902 1 July: Railways of Transvaal and Orange Free State placed under civil administration as Central South African Railways.

1906 4 April: Line between Klerksdorp and Fourteen Streams opened (now direct route from Cape via Kimberly to north).

1910 With union, the South African Railways came into being as a unit. Johannesburg became the seat of unified administration. (Total mileage, 7,039.)

1915 25 June: Union Railway System linked with that of South West Africa at Kalkfontein (Karasburg).

1925 Electric traction introduced in South Africa on Natal main line (Glencoe–Mooi River).

1928 June: Electrification Cape Town–Simonstown section completed.

1929 25 March: Union Limited de luxe trains introduced between Cape Town and Johannesburg.
16 April: Cape Town to Sea Point line closed.
31 August: Opening of line between Messins and Beit Bridge and of the Alfred Beit memorial rail and road bridge.

1933 4 December: Electrification of Salt River–Bellville section completed.

1936 6 February: Line between Postmasburg and Beeshoek opened.
1 May: Line between Point and Congella, Durban, opened.
30 June: Line between Beeshoek and Lohathla opened.

1937 15 March: Electrification completed on the first two Reef suburban sections, Germiston–Wattles and Germiston–Alberton.
3 October: Electrification of Glencoe–Volksrust section of the Natal main line brought into operation. Whole of Natal main line now electrified (327 miles).

1938 31 January: Roodepoort–Randfontein section opened for electric working; full electric service put into operation between Randfontein and Springs, Welgedag, as well as from Langlaagte to Pimville.
7 November: Introduction of electric passenger service between Johannesburg and Pretoria.

1939 Six luxury, air-conditioned, all-steel saloons placed in service on the Union Limited and Union Express deluxe trains. The Blue Train foreshadowed.

1940 February 5: Electrified Canada–Booysens–Village main line opened to traffic (Rand Mineral Line).

1941 July: All electrification work completed in connection with deviation from Krugersdorp to West Rand.

1942 The Blue Train, a luxury train, and other express trains, taken off as a wartime economy measure.

1946 February: Blue Train reinstated.

1947 Royal tour. The royal trains were first in the union to be completely equipped with radio communications.
2 June: Introduction of Orange Express between Cape Town and Durban.

1948 7 June: Line from Whites to Odendaalsrus (Orange Free State gold field) opened.

1950 A locomotive fitted with condensing equipment and tender successfully tested in semi-arid regions.
1 February: The two thousandth engine made by the North British Locomotive Company delivered to the railways of South Africa.
1 April: Extension of Ogies–van Dykadrif line to Broodsnyersplaas, in the eastern Transvaal, opened for all traffic.

1953 8 April: Opening of Bellville–Worcester electrified section of the Cape main line.

1954 14 May: Electrified section of main line opened between Worcester and Touws River.

1956 5 November: Minister B. J. Schoeman opened railway museum at Johannesburg station.
5 December: New double line between Vereeniging and Bloemfontein opened.

1958 28 August: Diesel power used for first time to haul a mainline passenger train in South Africa.

21 November: Breakthrough made on the "twin" of the 33¾-mile Boughton–Cedara tunnel, longest in Africa, permitting two-way travel. (The first breakthrough was July 17.)

1 December: Newly electrified Welverdiend–Klerksdorp section of Johannesburg–Cape Town main line brought into service.

Steam Locomotives in South Africa

The evolution of the railway system engine in South Africa was logically a part of the history of this country itself. As in many parts of the globe, the advent of the iron horse proved to be a major contributing element in the region's growth. The railroads, and thereby the steam locomotives, played a major role in building South Africa to the position it occupies today.

The following illustrations, accompanied by substantial captions, broadly chronicle the arrival and development of the steam locomotive in South Africa.

During 1904 the Vulcan Foundry, Ltd. of Newton-le-Willows, England supplied light class F engines to the design of P. A. Hyde, chief locomotive superintendent of the Central South African Railways, nos. 260–67. This class F engine is not illustrated. The class F, type 4–6–4, engines with side tanks were intended to replace the class B (ZASM) forty-six-ton machines used on the Springs-Randfontein passenger service. Electric headlights, complete with steam turbine and generator, were fitted in front of the chimney on top of the smokebox. These engines, at first, suffered from broken bar frames with the fractures occurring chiefly between the cylinders and leading drive wheels. Flitch plates, ½ inch thick, were fitted on each side of the frames to overcome the trouble. Generally these engines had pleasing exteriors and were aptly termed "chocolate boxes." Over the long haul the class F locomotives gave efficient service until they were finally scrapped in 1931. Not illustrated.

Specifications on the class F engines were as follows:

Cylinders	18 by 26 inches
Drive wheels	4-foot 6-inch diameter
Boiler	
Grate area	21.75 square feet
Total heating surface	1481 square feet
Boiler working pressure	200 pounds per square inch (later reduced to 180 pounds)
Tractive effort	20,060 pounds at 75 percent boiler working pressure
Operating weight	79 tons
Capacities	1800 gallons water; 3 tons coal

(Courtesy: South African Railways)

The last Pacific, type 4–6–2, engines procured from the North British Locomotive Company for use on the Central South African Railways in 1910 were similar to the CSAR class 10 Pacifics introduced in 1904. Ten units were purchased in 1910 of which five were saturated, nos. 747 to 751, and five were superheated types, nos. 752 to 756; these were respectively designated class 10A and Class 10B later on in the SAR system. This engine is not illustrated.

Specifications on the above were as follows:

Cylinders	20 by 28 inches
Drive wheels	5-foot 2-inch diameter
Boiler	
Grate area	35 square feet
Total heating surface	1588 to 1622.5 square feet
Superheater	384 to 446 square feet (Schmidt)
Boiler working pressure	180 pounds per square inch
Tractive effort	24,390 pounds at 75 percent boiler working pressure
Operational weight	123.8 tons (engine plus tender)
Tender capacities	4000 gallons water; 10 tons coal.

(Courtesy: South African Railways) LCN.18

A Class 12B, 4–8–2 type, Baldwin locomotive which was placed in service on the South African Railways in May 1920. Thirty of these engines, nos. 1931 to 1960, were purchased in broken-down units. Assembly was performed in the SAR workshops and a few were assembled by James Brown & Company at Durban (not illustrated). Specifications were as follows:

Cylinders	22.5 by 26 inches
Coupled drive wheels	51 inches
Boiler	
Grate area	40 square feet
Superheater	554 square feet
Heating surface	2508 square feet
Working pressure	190 pounds per square inch
Tractive effort	36,780 pounds at 75 percent boiler working pressure
Operating weight	145 tons plus 16 hundredweights (engine plus tender).

(Courtesy: SAR Publicity and Travel Department)

A Mountain type, 4–8–2 locomotive built by Baldwin for the South African Railways in 1925 is not illustrated. These were SAR class 15B engines known as "Big Bills." The engines were designed to operate between Beaufort West and Capetown, a distance of 340 miles, with a ruling gradient of 1 in 40 for about twenty-two miles, with severe curvatures on the Hex River Mountain section. Specifications follow:

Cylinders	23 by 28 inches
Drive wheels	4 feet 9 inches
Boiler	
Barrel diameter	6 feet 2¼ inches
Boiler centerline	8 feet 6 inches above rails
Grate area	48 square feet
Superheater	676 square feet (Schmidt)
Total heating surface	2780 square feet
Working pressure	200 pounds per square inch
Tractive effort	38,980 pounds at 75 percent boiler working pressure

Engine weight	104 tons plus 10 hun-
	dredweights
Tender weight	65 tons plus 9 hundredweights
	(working order)
Tender capacities	6000 gallons water; 12 tons
	(long tons) coal
Overall length	73 feet 3¼ inches.

(Courtesy: SAR Publicity and Travel Department)

A class 16D, 4–6–2, Pacific type locomotive built by Baldwin and placed in service on the South African railways in 1925 is not illustrated. These were built to incorporate the best in American and South African railway designs, to be employed on the difficult mountainous 956-mile run on gauge 3-foot 6-inch tracks between Capetown and Johannesburg. On 13 August 1925 engine no. 860 of class 16B, better known as "Big Bertha," made history after having hauled the "Union Limited" from Johannesburg to Capetown in twenty-nine hours. This continuous run for one engine set up a world record at that time. The above engines had these specifications:

Cylinders	22 by 26 inches
Drive wheels	5 feet
Boiler	
Grate area	45 square feet
Superheater	593 square feet
Heating surface	2686 square feet
Working pressure	195 pounds per square inch
Tractive effort	30,670 pounds at 75 percent
	boiler working pressure
Operating weight	155 tons plus 1 hundredweight
	(engine plus tender)
Tender capacities	6000 gallons water; 12 tons coal
Overall length	68 feet 3³⁄₁₆ inches.

(Courtesy: SAR Publicity and Travel Department) 9472

SOUTH AFRICA

Railway map of South Africa.
(Courtesy: South African Railways)

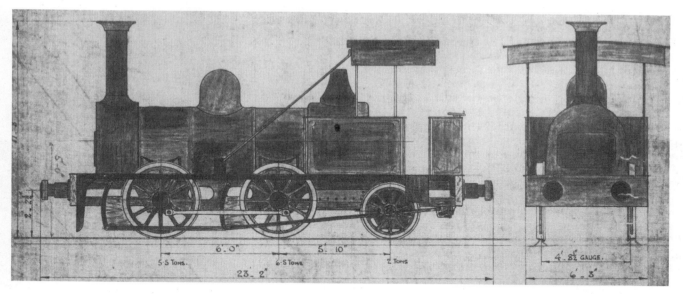

In South Africa, between 1849 and 1860, it was left to private enterprise to do the pioneering work, and the first attempts to introduce railway communications were made in the Cape of Good Hope. The Capetown and Dock Company, with headquarters in London and a management committee in Capetown, having a capital of 600,000 pounds sterling, made representations to the colonial government during 1853 and 1855, and finally provision was made by Act No. 10 of 20 June 1857, to construct a railway between Capetown and Wellington, a distance of fifty-seven miles. A beginning was made with the work in March 1859, to the plans and supervision of William George Brounger, chief engineer of the company. It was then decided to make the gauge of the track 4 feet 8½ inches to conform with the standard gauge laid in most parts of England. The line was opened to traffic in 1863.

Three tank locomotives were ordered in 1857 to help in the construction of the Capetown to Wellington railway; there were ordered from R. and W. Hawthorn of Leith Engine Works in Scotland. One of these engines was landed at Capetown on 8 September 1859. This machine had the following specifications:

Gauge	4 feet 8½ inches
Wheel arrangement	0–4–2
Cylinders	10 by 18 inches (inside)

Drive wheels	4-foot diameter
Trailing wheels	3-foot diameter
Link motion	Stephenson
Boiler pressure	120 pounds per square inch
Operating weight	14 tons
Weight on drive wheels	12 tons.

The other two tank engines arrived in South Africa in March and April 1859, respectively. Seven tender engines were later ordered from Robert Stephenson & Company of Newcastle, England. These also had a 0–4–2 wheel arrangement and were the first tender types to work in South Africa. Hand brakes with wooden blocks were fitted to the tender only; the remaining vehicles and the locomotive being unbraked. The Stephenson engines had the following specifications (not illustrated):

Cylinders	16 by 22 inches
Drive wheels	5-foot diameter
Boiler	
Firebox	85 square feet
Tubes	185 2¹⁄₁₆-inch diameter
Total heating surface	1210 square feet
Working pressure	120 pounds per square inch
Operating weight	
Engine	24 tons
Total	39 tons (engine and tender)
Tender water capacity	1250 gallons.

(Courtesy: South African Railways)

The Natal Railway Company was formed on 1 March 1859, with capital amounting to ten thousand pounds. The Natal Legislative Council passed the Natal Railway Company Law without much delay, giving powers to the new company to construct and maintain a 4-foot 8½-inch gauge railway between the Point and Durban. On 13 May 1860 the first engine imported by the Natal Railway Company, for the two-mile Durban-Point line, was landed at Durban. The engine was assembled, the body of the machine received a green paint and a high polish, while the wheels were painted a copper color. The name "Natal" was proudly displayed on a burnished brass plate on the side of the engine. It had a wheel arrangement of 2–4–0, and was officially described as being "about 24 horsepower." The chimney was of inverted conical shape, the wide opening of which was covered by wire mesh to retain sparks or fragments of wood-fuel. This was probably the first locomotive spark-arrestor used in South Africa. This little engine carried a small water tank underneath the coal bunker and footplate. A small donkey engine feed pump was attached to the bunker. The "Natal" engine on 26 June 1860 was the first locomotive in South Africa to haul a public train, about two miles between the Point and Market Square stations.

(Courtesy: South African Railways) 68234

Pictured is the earliest locomotive for the 3-foot 6-inch gauge rail of the Cape Government Railways. Cape Act No. 10, which was passed by the colonial parliament during December 1872, provided that the government undertake the construction and management of all railways in the Cape Colony starting on 1 January 1873. Subsequently, in 1873, the state purchased the Capetown–Wellington Railway and in 1875 the Salt River–Wynberg Railway. At this point it was decided to adopt 3 feet 6 inches as the standard gauge for the railways in South Africa. In 1874 the first of a long series of new locomotives for the 3-foot 6-inch gauge tracks arrived for use on the Cape Government Railways. By 1884 the state owned and operated 231 engines of various designs and types. One such engine was a type 4–4–0 tank engine supplied by Robert Stephenson & Company. This engine had the following characteristics:

Cylinders	13 by 18 inches (outside and inclined)
Drive wheels	4-foot diameter
Boiler	
Grate area	10 square feet
Firebox	46 square feet
Tubes	500 square feet
Total heat area	546 square feet
Working pressure	130 pounds per square inch
Tractive effort	6825 pounds at 75 percent boiler working pressure
Operating weight	24 tons
Water capacity	450 gallons
Coal capaicty	0.75 tons.

(Courtesy: South African Railways) 58531

Shown here is a photograph of a 4-foot 8½-inch gauge engine and train in the Capetown station in 1875. Note the double rails showing the conversion to 3-foot 6-inch gauge in progress. The tank engine appears to be "Perseverance" built by Kitson & Company of Leeds in 1875. Characteristics of this locomotive were:

Wheel arrangement	4–4–0
Cylinders	14 by 20 inches (outside)
Drive wheels	4 feet 6 inches
Boiler working pressure	120 pounds per square inch.

The name followed from the horse-drawn bus which operated between Pietermaritzburg and Durban during the early sixties. An interesting feature of the above engine was that the feed water pumps were attached to the back of the spectacle plates and were operated from the piston crossheads. Wooden brake blocks, operated by a hand brake on the driver's side of the cab, were provided. The lubrication of the cylinders was by gravitation from two tallow "cups" fitted to the sides of the smokebox immediately above the steam chests. It is recorded that the "Perseverance" engine was later converted into a stationary engine and was used for driving machinery in the Durban workshops, being finally scrapped about 1887. *(Courtesy: South African Railways)* 58532

The South Africa Cape Government Railways, organized in 1872, used various type 2–6–0 locomotives built in the period 1875–80 by Beyer, Peacock & Company, by Kitson & Company, and by Avonside Engine Company. Some Beyer Peacock engines had inclined cylinders, as shown, which is of a model preserved in the Railway Museum at Johannesburg. Specifications were as follows:

CGR First class   Rail gauge 3 feet 6 inches

Cylinders	12 by 20 inches
Coupled wheels	3-foot 3-inch diameter
Boiler	
Grate area	9.5 square feet
Heating surface	545 square feet
Boiler pressure	130 pounds per square inch
Tractive effort	7200 pounds
Operating weight	37.5 tons (engine plus tender)
Tender capacities	1700 gallons water; 2.5 tons coal.

(Courtesy: SAR Publicity and Travel Department)

Pictured is a type 2-6-0 tender locomotive furnished by Beyer, Peacock & Company in 1875-76 for the Western & Midland systems of the Cape Government Railways. The first order supplied eighteen engines, and in 1876 twenty more engines were furnished. Cowcatchers were fitted to all 3-foot 6-inch gauge engines imported into the Colony.

Specifications on the above engines were as follows:

Cylinders	12 by 20 inches
Drive wheels	3-foot 3-inch diameter
Boiler	
Grate area	9.5 square feet
Firebox	44 square feet
Tubes	492 square feet
Total heat surface	536 square feet
Working pressure	130 pounds per square inch
Tractive effort	7188 pounds at 75 percent boiler working pressure
Operating weight	39 tons (engine plus tender)
Tender capacities	1700 gallons water; 50 hundredweights coal.

(Courtesy: South African Railways) 68178

Early in 1875 the Hunslet Company of Leeds, England supplied a small saddle-tank engine for shunting purposes to East London. The machine was quite successful and five additional units were constructed by Kitson & Company in 1876 for use on the Cape Midlands system. In order to save wear and tear on tires, a ½ inch pipe supplied jets of water to the leading wheels when rounding curves, and this was found to materially diminish friction. The latter type 2-6-0 locomotives operated until 1941. Engine no. 0416 is pictured. Specifications were:

Cylinders (2)	12 by 20 inches (Stephenson's link motion used)
Drive wheels (6)	3-foot 3-inch diameter
Leading bissel wheels	2-foot diameter
Boiler	
Grate area	9.5 square feet
Firebox	49 square feet
Boiler tubes	483 square feet
Total heating surface	532 square feet
Working pressure	140 pounds per square inch
Tractive effort	7754 pounds
Operating weight	25 tons plus 13 hundredweights
Water capacity	520 gallons.

(Courtesy: South African Railways)

In 1877 the Natal Government Railways took over the Natal Railways by which time the rail gauge was being changed from the British standard of 4 feet 8½ inches to a narrow-gauge of 3 feet 6 inches. Illustrated is a model of a Beyer Peacock, type 2–6–0, tank locomotive. The prototype engine was part of an order for seven such engines built for the Natal Government Railways in 1877–79. Technical characteristics were as follows:

Cylinders	14 by 20 inches
Drive wheels	3-foot 3-inch diameter
Boiler	
Grate area	11 square feet
Total heating surface	639.5 square feet
Boiler working pressure	130 pounds per square inch
Tractive effort	9800 pounds
Operating weight	25.9 tons
Capacities	600 gallons water; 1 ton coal.

(Courtesy: South African Railways)

The severe gradients and curves of the eastern section of the Cape Government Railways rendered it necessary to experiment with more powerful locomotives, and during 1875 a "Fairlie" type was imported and placed in service between East London and Belstone, on the King-Williamstown line.

Pictured is a modified "Fairlie" engine ordered by the Cape Government Railways in 1880 from the Yorkshire Engine Company. The wheel arrangement was 0–6–0 plus 0–6–0. This photograph dates to 1903. The principal feature of this engine was that the boiler had two barrels and a central firebox common to both barrels. The cab was located in the center of the locomotive. Two power bogies supported the boiler and also carried the buffing and drawgear. The frame, by which the boiler was supported at its extremities, had a pivot under each of the saddles to which the boiler was attached. These pivots were carried on center bearings which formed part of the bogie frames.

Specifications of the above engines were as follows:

Cylinders (4)	11.5 by 18 inches (actuated by Walschaert gear)
Drive wheels	3-foot 3-inch diameter
Boiler	
Grate area	14 square feet
Boiler tubes	908 square feet
Firebox	90 square feet
Total heat area	998 square feet
Working pressure	135 pounds per square inch
Tractive effort	12,350 pounds at 75 percent boiler working pressure
Operating weight	36 tons
Water capacity	840 gallons (four side tanks)
Coal capacity	42 hundredweights.

(Courtesy: South African Railways) 73392

During 1880 the South African former standard-gauge tracks were removed, and nine broad-gauge engines were broken up, with the exception of the boilers which were converted to stationary units to drive workshop machinery. To cope with the constant increase in heavy traffic, thirty-six goods engines, type 4–6–0, were constructed in 1880 by Stephenson & Company and designated as class 04, the prefix "0" denoting that they belonged to an obsolescent type. In 1881 Neilson & Company built a number of similar engines. These tender engines, used on the Midland and Eastern rail system, had the following specifications:

Cylinders	15 by 20 inches (inside slide valves, Stephenson)
Drive wheels	
3-foot 2-inch diameter (six used on Eastern line)	
3-foot 6-inch diameter (thirty on Midland line)	
Boiler	
Fire grate	11.7 square feet
Firebox	65.0 square feet
Tubes (brass)	688.0 square feet
Total heating surface	753.0 square feet
Working pressure	130 pounds per square inch
Operating weight	55 tons plus 16 hundred-weights (engine plus tender)
Capacities	
Tender plus side tanks	2275 gallons water
Tender	6.0 tons coal.

(Courtesy: South African Railways) 60023

Shown is engine no. 84 built by Neilson & Company in 1882 and fitted with Joy's valve gear. This tender engine had a highly-polished dome, and the decorations were in honor of Queen Victoria's Jubilee. These four-coupled, type 4–4–0, engines were ushered into service on the Cape Government Railways early in 1883. Specifications were as follows:

Cylinders	15 by 20 inches
Drive wheels	4-foot diameter
Bogie wheels	2-foot 3-inch diameter
Boiler	
Grate area	11.25 square feet
Firebox	62.5 square feet
Tubes	690.0 square feet
Total heat surface	752.5 square feet
Working pressure	130 pounds per square inch
Tractive effort	9140 pounds at 75 percent boiler working pressure
Operating weight	47 tons plus 9 hundredweights (engine plus tender)
Tender capacities	1700 gallons water; 3 tons coal.

(Courtesy: South African Railways) P-1930

The first locomotive and tender designed and built in South Africa is pictured. This type 2–8–2 engine, with a side tank and tender, was designed by William Milne, locomotive superintendent, and built in the Durban workshops. The engine was numbered 48 but was later named "Havelock" after the governor of Natal, Sir Arthur Havelock. This engine was later converted to a 4–6–0 type and finally scrapped in 1905. Specifications were:

Cylinders	16 by 21 inches (outside, inclined)
Drive wheels	3-foot 3-inch diameter
Leading and trailing wheels	2-foot 1.5-inch diameter
Boiler	
Diameter	3-foot 10⅛-inch outside diameter
Length	11 feet
Tubes	174 1⅝-inch outside diameter
Fire grate area	14 square feet
Total heating surface	954 square feet
Working pressure	140 pounds per square inch
Tractive effort	14,473 pounds at 75 percent boiler working pressure
Operating weight	50 tons (engine plus tender)
Capacities	
Side tanks	880 gallons water
Tender	900 gallons water; 3.5 tons coal.

(Courtesy: South African Railways) 55003

In the period 1885–88 various tests were conducted on the Cape Government Railways to upgrade the design of the existing steam locomotives. Two experimental engines, designated class 03, type 4–4–0, were constructed by Neilson & Company in 1885 and numbered 53 and 646. These engines were used on the Eastern & Western rail system to test the best way to utilize colonial coal from miscellaneous locations. These operational studies resulted in new ideas for extended smokeboxes, wire netting spark-arrestors, and steam blowers. In 1888 Dubs & Company furnished twenty-four class 03 engines (nos. 93 to 116) to the detailed designs of Michael Stephens, chief locomotive superintendent. These engines were used for all classes of traffic until scrapped in 1923. In their day these locomotives were probably the most efficient in South Africa.

A typical class 03 locomotive pictured, had these specifications:

Cylinders	15 by 22 inches
Slide valves	Actuated by Stephenson link motion
Drive wheels	4-foot 1-inch diameter
Bogie wheels	2-foot 4-inch diameter
Boiler	
Grate area	13.0 square feet
Firebox	74.5 square feet
Tubes	689.0 square feet
Total heat surface	763.5 square feet
Working pressure	150 pounds per square inches
Operating weight	57 tons plus 17 hundred-weights (engine plus tender)
Tender capacities	1950 gallons water.

(Courtesy: South African Railways) M1162

A class 05 type 4–6–0, tender locomotive designed by Michael Stephens, chief locomotive superintendent of the Cape Government Railways is pictured. These engines, built by Dubs & Company in 1888, were described as "the first really efficient all-around six-coupled locomotives imported into the Colony." The class 05 machines were placed in service in 1890 and 1891 and gradually superceded the class 04 engines. A wire netting spark-arrestor as well as a Ramsbottom safety valve were fitted. The boiler centerline from the rail level was 6 feet 4.5 inches.

Specifications on the class 05 engines were:

Cylinders	16 by 24 inches
Coupled drive wheels	3-foot 10-inch diameter (later 4-foot 1-inch diameter)
Boiler	
Firegrate area	16–18 square feet
Firebox	90.96 square feet
Tubes	946.32 square feet
Total heating area	1037.28 square feet
Working pressure	150 pounds per square inch
Operating weights	
58 tons plus 6 hundred-weights (engine)	
28 tons plus 11 hundred-weights (tender)	
Tender water capacity	1950 gallons.

(Courtesy: South African Railways) 22911

The "Havelock" tender engine, the first locomotive designed and built in South Africa is pictured. From the experience gained with the latter type 2–8–2 engine, in 1888 forty so-called Dubs A, type 4–8–2, locomotives were constructed by Dubs & Company of Glasgow; these were a heavier and more powerful type of tank engine using a boiler working pressure of 140 pounds per square inch. When G. W. Reid was appointed locomotive superintendent in 1896, he immediately ordered a further sixty Dubs A engines but with the boiler pressure increased to 160 pounds per square inch.

Through the years these Dubs A locomotives proved satisfactory and worked the Natal mainline service. In 1905 further improvements were effected by D. A. Hendrie at which time the Belpaire type boilers were installed. The side tanks were accordingly moved further out to accommodate the wider firebox, and their capacity for water was increased from 1062 gallons to 1358 gallons. In 1926 it was found necessary to attach a tender to some of these engines in order to have an adequate supply of water and coal for shunting operations. Twenty-one engines were so altered (nos. 1415–35), and they were designated class 17. Alterations also entailed the removal of the trailing bissel bogie and the short coal bunker on the engine, and shortening the main frames.

Specifications on the class 17 locomotives were as follows (engine no. 1423):

Wheel arrangement	4–8–0
Cylinders	17 plus 21 inches
Drive wheels	3-foot 3-inch diameter
Leading wheels	2-foot 1¾-inch diameter
Boiler	
Firegrate area	24 square feet
Total heating surface	991.5 square feet
Working pressure	160 pounds per square inch
Tractive force	18,670 pounds at 75 percent boiler working pressure
Operating weight	77 tons (engine plus tender)
Tender capacities	2600 gallons water; 5½ tons coal
Engine side tank	1358 gallons water
Lengths	
Engine	29 feet 2 inches
Tender	23 feet 0 inches.

(Courtesy: South African Railways) 61698

The Netherlands Railway Company (NZASM, De Nederlandsche Zuid-Afrikaansche Spoorwegmaatschappij) was formed in 1887 for the purpose of promoting railways in the Transvaal and, more especially, between Pretoria and Delagoa Bay. On 20 July 1888 work commenced on various sections of a railroad from Johannesburg to Boksburg; this fifty-mile rail section was completed on 17 November 1890. The Pretoria–Delagoa Bay line was opened to traffic on 2 November 1894 and, by January 1895, service was initiated between Lourenco Marques, Mocambique and Pretoria. The NZASM also achieved a historic milestone when, on 2 January 1896, full rail service was established between Durban and Johannesburg. By August 1897 the NZASM had 717 miles of single track and by December 1897 locomotives in service totalled 226.

During 1889 E. Kessler of Esslingen, Germany designed and built six type 0–4–0 side-tank locomotives for the NZASM company. These were assembled at Elandsfontein (now Germiston) and were the first so erected in the Transvaal. These engines were finally scrapped in 1916, but number 1 was retained for monument display purposes on the station platform at Pretoria. Pictured is one of the above engines which had the following specifications:

Cylinders	11 by 15.75 inches
Drive wheels	2-foot 6-inch diameter
Wheel base	5 feet 3 inches
Working pressure	160 pounds per square inch
Tractive effort	7623 pounds at 75 percent boiler working pressure
Operating weight	14 tons.

(Courtesy: South African Railways) 20091

During 1890, construction engineers of the NZASM railway were faced with very difficult terrain between Waterval Onder and Waterval Boven. It was found necessary to adapt the Riggenbach rack track system to surmount a 4½-mile section having a 1 in 20 gradient. The rack consisted of two channel section beams with steel rack teeth fitted between them and spaced four inches apart and arranged to engage the gear wheels of the rack engine. A rack locomotive pictured, with a 0–4–2 wheel arrangement, was used. This had the following characteristics:

Cylinders	18.9 by 24.8 inches
Coupled drive wheels	3-foot 8-inch diameter
Slide valves	Actuated by Walschaert gear
Boiler	
Diameter	3 feet 8.25 inches
Length	10 feet 6 inches
Grate area	14.2 square feet
Tubes	156 1²⁵/₃₂-inches outside diameter
Total heating surface	833 square feet
Working pressure	175 pounds per square inch
Operating weight	32 tons.

Originally four engines were built, nos. 991 to 994, which had names as well as numbers. In the actual rack operations loads of 120 to 140 tons could be handled but occasionally two rack engines had to be employed on each train. These rack engines gave good service until the incline was abandoned in April 1908.
(Courtesy: South African Railways) 74414

In 1890 it was considered desirable to give a fair trial to American designed steam locomotives. Accordingly, in 1891, two Mogul type 2–6–0, class 01 engines were purchased from the Baldwin Locomotive works. These machines had bar frames and a leading pony truck. The picture shows a pop safety valve on the dome, a large whistle, the expansion lever and bracket on the firebox slide and frame. The engines were also later equipped with "finger-grate" fire bars, an innovation which had great success and eventually became standard for all South African locomotives. Cylinders were 18 by 22 inches and the drive wheels had a diameter of 4 feet. These engines were not too successful in the early stages since they did not steam well and were heavy on coal and oil. After various modifications they did give satisfactory service until scrapped in 1930.
(Courtesy: South African Railways) 68945

The Dutch ZASM Railway in the Transvaal in South Africa was opened in 1891. The first locomotives used came mostly from Emil Kessler in Germany. Pictured is an advanced type, a so-called forty-six-ton 0–6–4, side-tank locomotive. Difficulty was experienced in traffic with the rear bogie wheels fouling the firebox; there were also derailments, and many fundamental changes had to be made. A model of this engine is on display in the Railway Museum at Johannesburg. Specifications follow:

Cylinders	16¹⁵⁄₁₆ by 24¹³⁄₁₆ inches
Coupled wheels	4-foot 3⁹⁄₁₆-inch diameter
Boiler	
Grate area	15.6 square feet
Heating surface	936.2 square feet
Working pressure	160 pounds per square inch
Tractive effort	16,580 pounds
Operating weight	45.6 tons
Capacities	1503 gallons water; 4 tons coal.

(Courtesy: SAR Publicity and Travel Department)

The class 6, type 4–6–0, locomotives were designed by H. M. Beatty, and initially forty units were built by Dubs & Company in 1893–94. These engines rendered practicable an increase in speed on the Capetown–Johannesburg run. Also between Capetown and Worcester these engines did away with the necessity of attaching assisting engines to passenger trains. They were very successful engines, and repeat orders were placed in subsequent years as is indicated below. They were widely used on the Capetown–Simonstown suburban service continuously until the line was electrified in 1928. After Union they were used on all classes of traffic throughout South Africa except Natal. They had a splendid record for reliability and low cost repairs. Several of these locomotives were later sold for use in the Middle East.

In due course, between 1893 and 1904 a total of 230 engines were constructed by Dubs & Company and by Neilson Reid with minor modifications, comprising classes 6–6A, B, C, D, E, F, G, H, J, K, L, Y and Z.

Pictured are respectively class 6C and class 6H engines. These had the following specifications:

	Class 6C	Class 6H
Cylinders	17 by 26 inches	
Drive wheels	4-foot 6-inch diameter	
Leading bogie wheels	2-foot 4½-inch diameter	
Boiler		
Firegrate area	16.6 square feet	
Total heating surface	1041 square feet	
Boiler working pressure	160 pounds per square inch	
Tractive force at 75 percent boiler working pressure		
Class 6C	18,780 pounds	
Class 6H	19,740 pounds	
Operating weights	(not available)	
Tender capacities	*Class 6C*	*Class 6H*
Water	2600 gallons	3000 gallons
Coal	7½ tons	10 tons
Lengths		
Engine	30 feet 4 inches	30 feet 9 inches
Tender	21 feet 3 inches	22 feet 3 inches.

(Courtesy: South African Railways)

Shown are two locomotives heading a freight train on the South African Railways. The leading engine is class 6J, type 4–6–0, one of fourteen units placed in service in the period 1893–1902. The rear engine is class 8, type 4–8–0, of which twenty-three were placed in service by the Imperial Military Railways in 1902; these were manufactured by Neilson & Company. Subsequently, through 1904, 180 additional units were provided with minor modifications (classes 8A–F, X–Z). The original class 8 engines had these specifications:

Cylinders	18.5 by 24 inches
Drive wheels	4-foot diameter
Boiler	
Grate area	21.35 square feet
Heating surface	1184 square feet
Working pressure	180 pounds per square inch
Tractive effort	23,100 pounds at 75 percent boiler working pressure
Operating weight	96 tons plus 6 hundredweights (engine plus tender)
Tender capacities	3000 gallons water; 6 tons coal.

(Courtesy: SAR Publicity and Travel Department)

Pictured is a class 6A, type 4–6–0, locomotive (engine no. 462) which was a modification of the class 6 locomotive shown and described earlier. Dubs & Company of Glasgow, Scotland, built a number of the class 6A engines starting in 1895 (on 31 December 1911 on the SAR roster there were forty-nine units in service). These engines had the following specifications:

Cylinders	17 by 26 inches
Drive wheels	4-foot 6-inch diameter
Boiler working pressure	160 pounds per square inch
Valve gear	Stephenson
Tractive effort	16,690 pounds
Operating weights	
Engine	45 tons plus 15 hundredweights
Tender	30 tons plus 7 hundredweights
Tender capacities	2440 gallons water; 5.5 tons coal
Overall length	51 feet 3⅝ inches.

(Courtesy: South African Railways) 85600

The Cape Government Railway of South Africa had great success with a number of class 6, type 4–6–0, locomotives over the period 1893 to 1901. An additional series of fifty class 6B engines were turned out by Neilson, Reid & Company of Glasgow during 1897–1901. These were characterized as follows:

Cylinders	17 by 26 inches
Coupled wheels	4-foot 6-inch diameter
Boiler	
Grate area	16.6 square feet
Heating surface	1116 square feet
Boiler pressure	160 pounds per square inch
Tractive effort	16,690 pounds at 75 percent steam pressure
Operating weight	80.6 tons (engine plus tender)
Tender capacities	2600 gallons water; 5.5 tons coal.

A model of Class 6B shown, may be found in the Railway Museum at Johannesburg, South Africa. *(Courtesy: SAR Publicity and Travel Department)*

With the success of eight-coupled locomotives on the difficult parts of the Natal Railways, the Cape Government Railways Administration were convinced that comparable engines should be adopted for the coast sections of the Midland and Eastern sections. Accordingly thirty-eight class 7, type 4–8–0, locomotives, built by Neilson Reid (probably), were introduced in 1892. Subsequently these engines proved quite successful. One improvement the class 7 machines had over previous type 4–8–0 engines was the fitting of the first "Sight Feed" lubricator to locomotives in South Africa. Also the reversing gear was of the quick-threaded screw type which gradually superseded the reversing lever at about this time. In later deliveries performance was improved by fitting larger boilers. Thus the class 7 locomotives, and all later modifications, represented a considerable advance in design and power. Generally these machines were easy on the track and had good tracking qualities even under unfavorable conditions.

Pictured is a class 7A engine. Examples of classes 7B–7F locomotives (class 7 is not illustrated), are compared with the following specifications for Class 7:

Class 7 specifications only:

Cylinders	17 by 23 inches (later 17½ by 23 inches)
Drive wheels	3-foot 6¾-inch diameter
Boiler	
Grate area	17.5 square feet
Total heating surface	1010 square feet
Boiler working pressure	160 pounds per square inch (all later, 180 pounds)

(Courtesy: South African Railways) 7A-62227

The Pretoria–Pietersburg Railway Company in the Transvaal, incorporated in May 1896, finally completed this 176-mile railroad on 31 May 1899. Construction work was started with the first PPR engine, a twenty-six-ton saddle-tank type 0–6–0 machine manufactured by Hawthorn, Leslie & Company in 1893. This engine, named "Nylstroom," was placed in service in 1896. Pictured is a similar type locomotive named "Pietersburg" which arrived on the scene from Hawthorn Leslie in 1898. This same engine was still in service in South Africa during December 1944. The above engines had the following specifications:

Cylinders	14 by 20 inches
Drive wheels	3-foot 6-inch diameter
Boiler	
Firegrate area	8.3 square feet
Diameter	3-feet 4⅞-inches outside diameter
Length	8 feet 10⅝ inches
Tubes	130 1.75-inch outside diameter
Total heating surface	576.6 square feet
Working pressure	140 pounds per square inch
Tractive effort	9800 pounds at 75 percent boiler working pressure
Saddle tank capacity	620 gallons water
Bunker capacity	1.5 tons coal.

In 1898 Beyer Peacock supplied six type 2–6–4 side-tank locomotives which were heavier and more powerful than the two engines listed above. The latter engines for many years formed the main motive power of the PPR until they were finally scrapped in 1930.
(Courtesy: South African Railways) M47611

A class 7B, type 4–8–0, locomotive introduced to the South African Railways in 1900 is shown. See earlier illustration for details.
(Courtesy: South African Railways) 62229

During 1898 when the traffic on the Natal main line began to increase appreciably, the need arose for an engine which could haul on the worst grades fifty percent more loads than the Dubs A tank engines. Mr. Reid was requested to prepare a design having this tractive effort, but the limitations were somewhat severe. The maximum axle load was not to exceed fourteen tons with a construction gauge of 13 feet 0 inches high and 9 feet wide. The engine had to be designed to negotiate gradients of 1 in 30, compensated for curves of 300 feet.

Mr. Reid decided on a 4–10–2 wheel arrangement with 3-foot 9-inch diameter coupled wheels. Slide valves of the Richardson balanced type were placed between the frames; these valves were actuated by Allan straight-link motion, reversed by hand-wheel and quick-screw gear.

A single experimental engine was constructed by Dubs & Company in 1900. After comprehensive trials it was reported that the ten-coupled locomotive proved successful beyond anticipations, and management's aspirations for a more powerful locomotive were fully realized. It must be remembered that the turn-outs in those days were 1 in 7, which would present difficulty for a ten-coupled engine with a coupled wheelbase of 16 feet 8 inches. Altogether, the engine was a great advance on previous designs; to provide a workable design of ten-coupled locomotives for service on the Natal line at that time was no mean achievement.

Accordingly Dubs & Company secured an order for similar "Reid" engines in the number of twenty-five. Eventually one hundred such locomotives were received from Dubs; these were numbered 149 to 249, including the original trial engine. In 1901–02 the Imperial Military Railways obtained thirty-five engines of the same type built jointly by Dubs and by Neilson, Reid & Company. In 1905 the latter engines were purchased for use on the CSAR (Central South African Railways) and six-wheeled tenders were attached which increased the coal capacity to 5½ tons and gave additional water capacity of 1950 gallons. At Union in 1910 these engines were designated class 13. Alterations also included shortening the main frames, installing a trailing set of coupled wheels, and removing the trailing bissel bogie. The wheel arrangement then became 2–8–0.

Specifications on class 13 engine no. 1319 were as follows:

Cylinders	19 by 27 inches (outside of plate frames)
Drive wheels	3-foot 9-inch diameter
Boiler	
Firegrate area	21 square feet
Firebox	
Length	8 feet 11⅝ inches
Width	2 feet 4¼ inches
Total heating surface	1494 square feet
Boiler working pressure	175 pounds per square inch
Tractive effort	28,430 pounds at 75% boiler working pressure
Operating weight	84 tons plus 12 hundredweights (engine plus tender)
Tender capacities	1950 gallons water; 5½ tons coal
Engine tank capacity	1880 gallons water.

The above class 13 engines were still giving good service on shunting work after forty-four years on the job.

(Courtesy: South African Railways) 62263

Pictured is a class 06, type 2–6–2, tender locomotive, one of seven units delivered in 1902 by Neilson, Reid & Company. The design was a composite of features incorporated previously in various American and British engines. These engines, designated as class 6Z at Union, had bar frames and fireboxes 4 feet 1.25 inches wide with finger-bar rocking grates. They also had an extra long smokebox, low level blast pipes, and a large area spark-arrestor which minimized the ejection of live sparks. A roomy cab was provided in accordance with Cape tradition. Originally the engines were unsteady on the tracks at higher speeds and were converted to a 2–6–4 type by fitting a four-wheeled bogie under the firebox. These engines were scrapped in 1934 after thirty-three years of service. Specifications on the class 06 engines were:

Cylinders	18 by 26 inches
Drive wheels	14-foot 6-inch diameter
Slide valves	Richardson balanced type actuated by Stephenson link motion with rocker shafts
Boiler	
Grate area	25.5 square feet
Total heating surface	1462 square feet
Working pressure	180 pounds per square inch
Tractive effort	19,890 pounds at 75 per cent boiler working pressure
Operating weights	83 tons plus 14 hundredweights (engine plus tender)
Tender capacities	2640 gallons water; 5.5 tons coal.

(Courtesy: South African Railways) 6y

As a further extension of the class 6 locomotives introduced in 1902, the class 6J engines, built by Neilson Reid, were placed in service in 1902. This was a type 4–6–0 locomotive with the following specifications:

Cylinders	17 by 26 inches
Valve gear	Stephenson
Drive wheels	4-foot 6-inch diameter
Boiler working pressure	180 pounds per square inch
Operating weight	(not given)
Tender capacities	3000 gallons water; (10 tons coal
Lengths	
Engine	30 feet 9 inches
Tender	22 feet 3 inches.

(Courtesy: South African Railways) 62389

With the commencement of the Boer War in 1899, the British established the Imperial Military Railways in South Africa. Many different locomotives were commandeered and others procured to pursue the war effort. Among a variety of steam engines used in South Africa were forty class 8, type 4–8–0, machines designed by H. M. Beatty, chief locomotive superintendent of the CGR and constructed by the Neilson Company of Glasgow in 1902. These class 8 tender locomotives had the following specifications:

Cylinders	18.5 by 24 inches
Coupled drive wheels	4-foot diameter
Boiler	
Grate area	21.35 square feet
Firebox	131 square feet
Total heating surface	1184 square feet
Working pressure	180 pounds per square inch
Leading bogie wheels	2-foot 4.5-inch diameter
Tractive effort	23,100 pounds at 75 percent boiler working pressure
Operating weight	96 tons plus 6 hundredweights (engine plus tender)
Tender capacities	3000 gallons water; 6 tons coal.

The above engines gave excellent service, and several were still in operating service in January 1945. *(Courtesy: South African Railways)* 53821

The class 8 locomotives in South Africa were originally introduced in 1902. Up to and including 1904, modifications comprising classes 8, 8A, B, C, D, E, F, X, Y, and Z totalled 180 different engines. Pictured is a class 8AW engine with the following specifications:

Cylinders	20 by 24 inches
Drive wheels	4-foot diameter
Boiler working pressure	180 pounds per square inch
Tractive effort	27,000 pounds at 75 percent boiler working pressure
Operating weight	(not given)
Tender capacities	3000 gallons water; 10 tons coal
Lengths	
Engine	32 feet 7 inches
Tender	22 feet 3 inches
Manufacturer	Neilson Reid
Year	1902.

(Courtesy: South African Railways) 62396

The first recorded instance of a superheater and piston valve locomotive in South Africa was the class 6L engine designed by H. M. Beatty, chief locomotive superintendent of the Cape Government Railways in 1903. See illustration. Two type 4–6–0 engines were constructed with Schmidt superheaters by Neilson, Reid & Company of Glasgow. Oddly enough tests on the engines did not show any appreciable economies over saturated engines, and the class 6L engines were converted to the latter type in 1914 and finally scrapped in 1939. It was unfortunate that these South African first superheater trials did not reveal definite economies which were later demonstrated in other countries and caused superheating to be standard practice worldwide. However superheaters were again tried in 1921; from that time forward they were accepted and successfully used on SAR locomotives.

Specifications on the class 6L engines were:

Cylinders	18.5 by 26 inches
Drive wheels	4-foot 6-inch diameter
Boiler	
Diameter	4-foot 7⁹⁄₁₆-inch outside diameter
Length	11-foot 2⅛-inch
Tubes	158 2-inch outside diameter
Firegate area	18.75 square feet
Total heating surface	1068 square feet
Working pressure	180 pounds per square inch
Tractive effort	19,906 pounds at 75 percent boiler working pressure
Operating weight	
88 tons plus 7 hundredweights (engine plus tender)	
38 tons plus 13 hundredweights adhesion	
Tender capacities	3200 gallons water; 5 tons coal.

(Courtesy: South African Railways) 6L

In 1903 the Cape Government Railways had designed and constructed two class 5A, type 4–6–2, locomotives to cope with the increasing weight of passenger trains on the 1 in 80 grades between Beaufort West and DeAar. These engines, nos. 903 and 904 (722 and 721 at Union) were built by Kitson & Company of Leeds. These machines were similar to the Pacific type locomotives in America but were better known as Karroo types in South Africa. In general these locomotives gave successful performances and four additional units were ordered from Beyer Peacock in 1904, designated then as class 5B.

Specifications on the class 5A locomotives were as follows:

Cylinders	18.5 by 26 inches
Slide valves	Richardson, Stephenson link motion
Drive wheels	5-foot diameter
Boiler	
Length smokebox	8 feet
Boiler length	14 feet 6.25 inches
Firebox	110 square feet
Tubes	1317 square feet
Total heating surface	1427 square feet
Working pressure	180 pounds per square inch
Tractive effort	20,030 pounds at 75 percent boiler working pressure
Operating weight	92 tons plus 3 hundredweights (engine plus tender)
Tender capacities	2825 gallons water; 6 tons coal.

(Courtesy: South African Railways) 16373

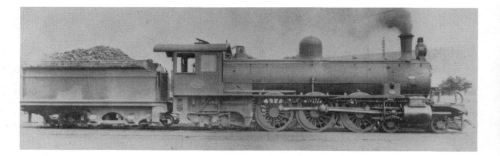

During 1903 P. A. Hyde, chief locomotive superintendent of the Central South African Railways, designed the class 10, type 4–6–2, locomotive for passenger traffic and the class 11, type 2–8–2, engine for freight traffic. These machines took advantage of the eighty-pound rails then gradually replacing the sixty-pounders on the main line. These were the heaviest and largest locomotives built for the 3-foot 6-inch gauge CSAR railroads at that time. Fifteen class 10 tender locomotives were ordered from the North British Locomotive Company in 1903 and placed in service during July 1904. Specifications were:

Cylinders	19.5 by 28 inches
Drive wheels	5-foot 2-inch diameter
Leading bogie wheels	2-foot 4.5-inch diameter
Trailing wheels	2-foot 9-inch diameter
Boiler	
Length	18 feet 6.5 inches
Diameter	4-foot 6.75-inch inside diameter
Grate area	35 square feet
Firebox (Belpaire)	
Length	7 feet 3 inches
Diameter	6-foot 1.5 inch
Tubes	157 2.25-inch outside diameter
Total heating surface	1842 square feet
Working pressure	190 pounds per square inch
Piston valves	10-inch diameter (actuated by Walschaert motion)
Tractive effort	24,470 pounds at 75 percent boiler working pressure
Operating weight	122 tons (engine plus tender)
Tender capacity	4000 gallons water; 10 tons coal
Engine numbers	650 to 664 (nos. 732 to 746 at Union).

(Courtesy: South African Railways) 81375

Pictured is a model of a locomotive built for use on the Natal Railways in South Africa in 1904 by the North British Locomotive Company. These followed the first design of D. A. Hendrie who had been appointed locomotive superintendent of the Natal Railways in 1903. These types 4–8–2 tank engines were numbered 250–74 and were later designated class G on the South African Railways system. These locomotives worked initially out of Durban but later were employed on SAR classification yards and on some industrial operations.

Specifications follow:

Cylinders	18 by 22 inches (inclined)
Coupled wheels	3-foot 6-inch diameter
Boiler	
Grate area	19 square feet
Heating surface	1223 square feet
Steam pressure	175 pounds per square inch
Tractive effort	22,280 pounds at 75 percent working pressure
Operating weight	60 tons plus 6 hundredweights
Capacities	1560 gallons water; 2.5 tons coal.

(Courtesy: SAR Publicity and Travel Department)

Another class 10, type 4–6–2, locomotive built in 1904 by the North British Locomotive Company is pictured. See earlier illustration for details. This is engine no. 655.
(Courtesy: South African Railways) P1481

Thirty-six class 11 locomotives were placed in service on the lines of the Central South African Railways in 1904. These engines, type 2–8–2, were built by the North British Locomotive Company and were used with heavy freight hauls. This machine is pictured in two illustrations, engines no. 938 and 729 respectively. Specifications were as follows:

Cylinders	20 by 26 inches
Piston valves	10-inch diameter (actuated by Walschaert motion)
Drive wheels	4-foot diameter
Leading and trailing wheels	2-foot 6-inch diameter
Boiler	
Grate area	37 square feet
Tubes	200 2¼-inch diameter
Firebox	Belpaire
Total heating surface	2278 square feet
Boiler working pressure	190 pounds per square inch
Tractive effort	32,500 pounds at 75 percent boiler working pressure
Operating weight	128 tons plus 3 hundredweights

	(engine plus tender)
Engine numbers	700 to 735 (nos. 912 to 947 at Union)
Tender capacities	4000 gallons water; 10 tons coal
Lengths	
Engine	38 feet 5 inches
Tender	26 feet 0 inches.

The above engines gave satisfactory service at moderate speeds, but the lightly-loaded (5 ton plus 12 hundredweights) leading bissel wheels gave problems on curves. These locomotives were still in active service in February 1945 on shunting and short-run duties. It is interesting to note that these engines were in advance of track limitations and several class 11 engines were actually staged for nearly a year before the chief civil engineer would allow them to run, as it took that length of time to carry out the complete program of track and bridge stengthening.
(Courtesy: South African Railways) 81377

A second view is given of the class 11 locomotives used on the Central South African Railway starting in 1904.
(Courtesy: South African Railways)

With David A. Hendrie's appointment as locomotive superintendent of the Natal Government Railway in January 1903, there emerged a new philosophy regarding steam locomotives. In the subsequent seventeen years of his service, Hendrie designed seventeen distinct types of railway steam engines. These were all sound in engineering practice and had enhanced external appearances as time went by.

Hendrie's first engine, a type 4–8–2 with side tanks, was designated class B (class G at Union) of which twenty-five units were built by Dubs & Company of Glasgow and placed in service in 1904, numbered 197 to 221. These machines, (not illustrated) worked the corridor trains out of Durban until the passenger train loads exceeded their capacity. They were later used for banking between Ladysmith and Van Reegen's pass, and for general service on the heavier branch lines. Six Hendrie class B engines were still operating on light shunting work during July 1944. The coupling and connecting rods were of I section which was the first recorded instance of their use in South Africa.

Specifications on the class B engines were as follows:

Cylinders	18 by 22 inches (outside, inclined)
Drive wheels	3-foot 6-inch diameter
Boiler	
Firegrate area	19 square feet
Tubes	232 1.75-inch outisde diameter
Total heating surface	1223 square feet
Working boiler pressure	175 pounds per square inch
Tractive effort	22,280 pounds at 75 percent boiler working pressure
Operating weight Capacities	60 tons plus 6 hundredweights
Side tanks	1560 gallons water
Hind coal bunker	2½ tons coal.

In 1904 Hendrie also designed two heavy tender engines of the class B vintage. One was for passenger and goods use and one for fast passenger service on the section of line north of Estcourt where grades and curvatures were not as severe as on lower sections of the line. This was a type 4–8–0 locomotive, designated class 1 at Union, of which engine no. 253 is pictured. Fifty of these engines were built by the North British Locomotive Company and placed in service in 1904–05.

Specifications on the class 1 locomotives were as follows:

Cylinders	20½ by 24 inches
Valve gear	Walschaert (first time used in Natal)
Drive wheels	3-foot 10-inch diameter
Boiler	
Barrel	5-foot 7½-inch diameter
Firebox (Belpaire)	9 feet 6 inches by 6 feet
Firegrate area	34 square feet
Total heating surface	2222.8 square feet
Boiler working pressure	200 pounds per square inch
Tractive effort	31,420 pounds at 75 percent boiler working pressure
Operating weight	105 tons plus 19 hundredweights (engine plus tender)
Tender capacities	3675 gallons water; 8¼ tons coal
Lengths	
Engine	33 feet 8 inches
Tender	22 feet 9 inches.

(Courtesy: South African Railways) 80827

Pictured is a class 8F locomotive with a 4–8–0 wheel arrangement; these were built by the North British Locomotive Company and placed in service in 1904. See other illustrations which picture and describe the class SAW and class 8FW engines. Class 8F engines in the number of ten were rostered for active service on 31 December 1911. Specifications on the class 8F locomotives were as follows:

Cylinders	18½ by 24 inches
Drive wheels	4-foot diameter
Boiler working pressure	180 pounds per square inch
Tractive force	23,110 pounds
Valve gear	Stephenson
Operating weights	(not given)
Tender capacities	3000 gallons water; 10 tons coal
Overall lengths	
Engine	31 feet 11 inches
Tender	22 feet 03 inches.

(Courtesy: South African Railways) 61690

In an earlier illustration a class 8AW locomotive was pictured. It was first introduced on the South African Railways in 1902. In 1904, one of various modifications and classes of this series, class 8FW, type 4–8–0, was placed in service; these were constructed by the North British Locomotive Company. In 31 December 1911 the SAR roster showed there were 195 units active comprising classes 8, 8A, 8B, 8C, 8D, 8E, 8F, 8X, 8Y and 8Z.

Specifications on class 8FW locomotives were as follows:

Cylinders	18.5 by 24 inches
Drive wheels	4-foot diameter
Boiler working pressure	180 pounds per square inch
Tractive effort	23,110 pounds
Valve gear	Stephenson
Operating weights	
Engine	59 tons and 5 hundredweights
Tender	36 tons and 9 hundredweights
Tender capacities	2855 gallons water; 10 tons coal
Overall length	54 feet 2¼ inches.

(Courtesy: South African Railways) 81371

Another Hendrie B locomotive which was designated class 1B is shown. After a few year's operations with the class 1 engines, six machines were altered by the addition of a trailing bissel bogie, thus converting the type 4–8–0 to type 4–8–2. At the same time it was stated that this modification was found necessary in order to ensure extra smooth running when working fast passenger trains. The latter engines were numbered 319 to 324 and at Union were renumbered 1440 to 1445 with a class 1B designation.

See an earlier illustration for technical details. *(Courtesy: South African Railways)* 5624

During December 1902, on the Eastern system of the Transvaal between Waterval Onder and Waterval Boven, it was found necessary to order two special rack engines to cope with the heavier loads. Gradients of 1 in 20 had to be overcome with a distance of 3.5 miles when hauling trains of 350 tons. By early 1905 the Vulcan Foundry, Ltd., Lancashire had supplied two side-tank rack locomotives, type 4–6–4. This CSAR rack engine had two distinct pairs of cylinders: the inner pair drove a coupled pair of rack wheels which were carried on a frame suspended from the leading and driving coupled wheel axles; the outside pair of cylinders drove the regular coupled adhesion wheels. A unique feature of this locomotive was the provision for using five distinct brakes as follows: (1) steam brakes on all coupled wheels and both bogies, (2) a hand brake on the coupled wheels, (3) a hand-operated brake on the crank discs of the rack engine, (4) The Le Chatelier counter pressure brake on the pistons, and (5) the counter pressure air brake also on the pistons.

Specifications were as follows:

Cylinders (2 pair)	18 by 20 inches
Drive wheels	3-foot 6-inch diameter
Boiler	
Firegrate area	33.5 square feet
Tubes	197 2-inch diameter
Total heating surface	1438.33 square feet
Boiler diameter	5-foot inner diameter
Working pressure	200 pounds per square inch
Tractive effort	
Adhesion engine	23,175 pounds
Rack engine	27,050 pounds
Total at 75 percent boiler working pressure	50,225 pounds
Capacities	
Side and bunker tanks	1200 gallons water
Bunker	2.5 tons coal.

Tests of these engines, carried out in 1905, showed that they could not maintain steam and had insufficient adhesive weight to prevent slipping on the steep gradient. They finally proved unsuccessful and were removed from service in 1906. They were scrapped at a later date, but the boilers were used at pumping stations. Owing to their failure, the old rack engines (NZASM, 32 tons) were kept in good order until the rack section was removed during 1908. *(Courtesy: South African Railways)* P3000P10

The Central South African Railways in January 1905 ordered two steam motor coaches for trials on passenger transport service. Due to the long delays in delivery, the work shops of CSAR fabricated a similar coach by combining an old nineteen-ton NZASM tank engine and a side-door suburban carriage. This powered motor coach is pictured. During 1906 it was reported that the running expenses per mile were very favorable, and the coach was found to be superior to the self-contained car in which the engine and boiler were embodied in the same vehicle. Two additional units which were identified as M3 and M4 were authorized in 1907. These machines ran on the Pretoria-Wonderboom rail line. Subsequently, in 1909, seven additional units, numbered M5 to M11, were constructed in the Pretoria workshops, and all gave excellent service. Coach no. 2, supplied later by Kitson & Company, was erected at the Salt River workshops and was placed in service on 10 August 1907 between Germiston and Elsburg and between Germiston and Rietfontein. Specifications on the latter coach were as follows:

Cylinders	11 by 16 inches
Drive wheels	3-foot 3-inch diameter
Piston valves	Actuated by Walschaert motion
Boiler	
Grate area	10.85 square feet
Tubes	180 1⅝-inch outer diameter
Total heating surface	510 square feet
Operating pressure	160 pounds per square inch
Tractive effort	6354 pounds at 75 percent boiler working pressure
Operating weight	47 tons plus 11 hundredweights
Capacities	500 gallons water; 1 ton coal
Overall length	75 feet 4¹³⁄₁₆ inches
Coach capacity	52 passengers.

(Courtesy: South African Railways) P3000P50

In 1906 the Natal Government Railways recognized the need for locomotives with higher tractive power. Accordingly Hendrie designed his class D engine with a 4–8–2 wheel arrangement. Five units were built by the North British Locomotive Company and placed in service in October 1909; these carried the designation numbers 330 to 334 (renumbered 1446 to 1450 at Union and then termed class 3). These engines regularly handled loads of 225 tons between Estcourt and Charlestown and also hauled goods traffic of fast perishable products. The "Hendrie D" boiler was the largest in South Africa at the time. The Walschaert valve motion was controlled by the "Hendrie" steam reversing gear. Pyle National Electric headlights were installed on these engines. The class D machines were mostly used for the movement of heavy down coal loads over the Estcourt-Highlands bank. Specifications were:

Cylinders	21 by 24 inches
Drive wheels	3-foot 9.5-inch diameter
Boiler	
Diameter	5 feet 7.5 inches outer diameter
Length	18 feet 6 inches
Grate area	34 square feet (Belpaire)
Tubes	237 steel 2.25-inch outer diameter
Total heating surface	2718 square feet
Working pressure	190 pounds per square inch (later 200 pounds)
Tractive effort	34,890 pounds at 75 percent boiler working pressure (later 33,150 pounds).

Shortly after Union twenty-five additional class D locomotives were constructed by the North British Locomotive Company. These were similar in all respects except that the tender coal capacity was increased from 6 to 8.25 tons and water capacity from 3500 gallons to 4000 gallons. The new operating weight for engine plus tender was 123 tons plus 3 hundredweights.

(Courtesy: South African Railways) 5674

A model of the first Mallet type locomotive used in South Africa is pictured. This was a type 2–6–6–0 compound engine built by the American Locomotive Company in 1909. These engines were principally utilized to bank heavy goods trains on the 1 in 25 grades of the main line between Estcourt and Highlands, South Africa. Later five more units were purchased. Characteristics were as follows:

Cylinders	
Hi pressure	17.5 by 26 inches
Lo pressure	28 by 26 inches
Coupled wheels	3-foot 9.5-inch diameter
Boiler	
Grate area	40 square feet
Heating area	2574 square feet
Boiler pressure	200 pounds per square inch
Tractive effort	44,810 pounds
Overall length	68 feet 2⅜ inches (engine plus tender)
Operating weight	129 tons plus 8.0 hundredweight (engine plus tender)
Tender capacities	4000 gallons water; 8.25 tons coal.

Under the South African Railways set-up these engines were designated as class MA locomotives. This model is on display in the Railway Museum at Johannesburg.
(Courtesy: SAR Publicity and Travel Department)

During 1909, the American Locomotive Company of Schenectady offered to supply a type 4–8–2 locomotive for experimental purposes, built on the line of American engines working over mountain roads in the United States. This offer was accepted by G. T. Wheatley, who was acting locomotive superintendent during Hendrie's visit overseas. This engine was placed in service in 1910 and numbered 335. At Union the locomotive was renumbered 1476, class 3A. The American D engine, as it was then known, marked the first introduction of the bar frame and superheaters for locomotives in Natal. At about this time, the advantages of superheaters were becoming apparent worldwide as the most practical means of improving engine power and efficiency. At this time it was claimed that superheating effected a saving of from ten to twenty percent in fuel and from fifteen to twenty-five percent in water. In many cases in South Africa these economies were obtained and were improved upon in later years. The engine no. 335 was fitted with a "Cole" superheater and when so equipped did show an appreciable economy in fuel and water consumption compared with engines not so fitted.

Specifications on the American D engine were as follows:

Cylinders	24 by 26 inches
Drive wheels	3-foot 9½-inch diameter
Boiler	
Firegrate area	36.25 square feet
Distance between tube plates	18 feet 7⅜ inches
Tubes	172 2¼-inch outer diameter
Boiler barrel	5 feet 4⅝ inches
Boiler centerline above rail level	7 feet 4 inches
Superheater area	457 square feet
Superheater tubes	15 5¼-inch outer diameter
Total heating surface	2417 square feet
Boiler working pressure	160 pounds per square inch
Tractive effort	36,400 pounds at 75 percent boiler working pressure
Operating weight	119 tons plus 7 hundredweights (engine plus tender)
Tender capacities	4000 gallons water; 8¼ tons coal.

The American D engine had too low an adhesion factor for the Natal line. Consequently it slipped badly in misty or rainy weather and was known as "Maud Allen" by the engine crews.
(Courtesy: South African Railways) 5669

In 1907, in order to provide additional locomotive power to handle mail service between Estcourt and Charlestown, D. A. Hendrie designed two type 4–6–2 tender passenger engines. These were built in the Durban workshops, placed in service in 1910, and designated as nos. 11 and 12. (At Union these were reclassified as class 2C, nos. 765 and 766.) This was the first recorded instance of modern type tender locomotives being completely designed and constructed in South Africa. These engines were equipped with Walschaert valve motion, the "Hendrie" steam reversing gear, and wide fireboxes carried down between the rear frames. The class C engines gave good service until scrapped in 1936. Last usage was with passenger and fast perishable products trains between Waterval Boven and Komatipoort.

Specifications on the class C engines were as follows:

Cylinders	19 by 24 inches (horizontal)
Coupled drive wheels	4 feet by 4.5 inches (later 4 feet 6 inches)
Boiler	
Grate area	29 square feet
Total heating surface	2322 square feet
Working pressure	185 pounds per square inch
Tractive effort	22,910 pounds at 75 percent boiler working pressure
Operating weight	110 tons (engine plus tender)
Overall length	60 feet 2.25 inches (engine plus tender).

(Courtesy: South African Railways) 54195

On the CSAR rail system, owing to heavy coal and goods traffic along the Witbank-Germiston section, it was decided to experiment with a Mallet type locomotive and, during March 1910, engine no. 1001 (no. 1617, class MD at Union) built by the American Locomotive Company was placed in service. This type Mallet articulated compound locomotive had two groups of six-coupled driving wheels with a 2–6–6–2 wheel arrangement. This was the heaviest locomotive working in South Africa, or on any 3-foot 6-inch gauge lines in the world at that time. See the illustration. Specifications were as follows:

Cylinders	
Hi pressure	18 by 26 inches (Walschaert motion)
Lo pressure	28.5 by 26 inches (Richardson slide valves)
Coupled drive wheels	3-foot 10-inch diameter
Boiler (Telescopic barrel)	
Minimum diameter	6 feet 0⅛ inches
Length	19 feet 10⅛ inches
Firegrate area	49.5 square feet
Tubes	271 2.25-inch outside diameter
Total heating surface	3325 square feet
Working pressure	200 pounds per square inch
Tractive effort	45,900 pounds at 75 percent boiler working pressure
Operating weight	157 tons plus 8.5 hundredweights (engine plus tender)
Tender capacities	5000 gallons water; 10 tons coal
Overall length	73 feet 7.25 inches.

The history of the Mallet type steam engine in South Africa was one of decreasing popularity since it did not perform on the Witbank-Germiston section as well as other nonarticulated types. The inferior performance of the Mallets was attributable to the small coupled drived wheels, compound cylinders, and long tortuous steam pipes and passages, slow operating speeds, frequent failures, and high maintenance costs. This engine was finally scrapped in October 1926.
(Courtesy: South African Railways) P2276

Pictured is a class 10C, 4–6–2 type, locomotive used on Reef traffic on the Central South African Railways. These engines, twelve in number built by the North British Locomotive Company and designated nos. 767–78, were placed in service during November and December 1910. The design was by G. G. Elliott, chief mechanical engineer. By April 1945 only two of the original class 10C engines were still in service. Specifications were:

Cylinders	18 by 26 inches
Coupled drive wheels	4-foot 9-inch diameter
Boiler	
Grate area	31.5 square feet
Diameter	4 feet 8½ inches (narrow point)
Total heating surface	1908 square feet
Working pressure	200 pounds per square inch
Tractive force	22,170 pounds at 75 percent boiler working pressure
Operating weight	114 tons (engine plus tender)
Drive wheels Axle loading	14 tons maximum.

(Courtesy: SAR Publicity and Travel Department)

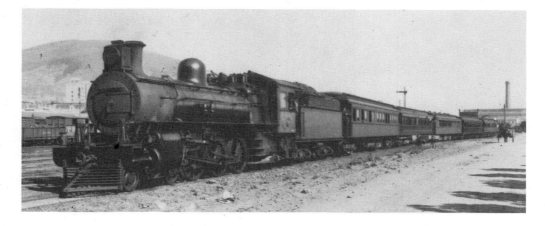

Another picture of a class 10C Central South African Railways, type 4–6–2 locomotive is shown. This engine is about to leave Capetown with the Transvaal Express in 1912. Specifications were previously given.
(Courtesy: SAR Publicity and Travel Department)

In order to meet the exacting requirements for fast passenger locomotives working in the Transvaal, it was decided to try out a type 4–6–2 Pacific engine. Such a machine, built by the American Locomotive Company, was placed in service in 1910; this was numbered 1002 (no. 779, class 10D at Union). Specifications were:

Cylinders	21 by 28 inches
Drive wheels	5-foot 2-inch diameter
Leading bogie wheels	2-foot 4.5-inch diameter
Trailing bissel wheels	2-foot 9.5-inch diameter
Boiler (Telescopic type)	
Diameter	5 feet 0.75 inches
Length	18 feet 0⅜ inches
Grate area	35 square feet
Superheater	353 square feet (Cole type)
Total heating surface	1981 square feet
Working pressure	170 pounds per square inch (later 180 pounds per square inch)
Tractive effort	26,890 pounds at 75 percent boiler working pressure
Operating weight	118 tons plus 13 hundredweights (engine plus tender).

This engine gave satisfactory service and was scrapped in 1931.
(Courtesy: South African Railways) 58649

With the introduction on the Central South African Railways of the class 10 locomotives in 1904 additional modifications were built (classes 10A, B, C, and D) up to 1911 by which time thirty-seven units were in operation.

Pictured is a class 10D, type 4–6–2, engine with the following specifications:

Cylinders	21 by 28 inches
Drive wheels	5-foot 2-inch diameter
Boiler working pressure	180 pounds per square inch
Tractive effort	26,890 pounds at 75 percent boiler working pressure
Operating weight	(not given)
Tender capacities	4000 gallons water; 10 tons coal
Lengths	
Engine	36 feet 7 inches
Tender	26 feet 0 inches.

(Courtesy: South African Railways) 62376

Shown is a class 4, type 4–8–2, locomotive designed by H. M. Beatty, chief locomotive superintendent of the Cape Government Railways. Two class 4 locomotives, nos. 1447 and 1448, built by the North British Locomotive Company were placed in service during March 1911. The locomotive and tender were designed for heavy mainline passenger traffic on the Cape Division.

The class 4 engines had flat-balanced type slide valves, arranged above the cylinders and were actuated by the Stephenson link motion through rocker shafts. The boiler and round-top firebox were designed to accommodate a combustion chamber, which was carried forward to two feet from the firebox into the boiler barrel; the latter at the hind end was increased in diameter to suit. Distance between the tube plates was eighteen feet. Engine no. 1447 was fitted with Ramsbottom safety valves while engine no. 1448

had installed the Cole's muffled type pop safety valves set at 180 pounds pressure.

Specifications on the class 4 locomotives were:

Cylinders	20½ by 28 inches (outside 4½-inch bar frames)
Drive wheels	4-foot 6-inch diameter
Boiler	
Grate area	37 square feet
Tubes	201 2¼-inch outside diameter
Total heating surface	2317 square feet
Boiler working pressure	180 pounds per square inch
Tractive force	29,240 pounds at 75 percent boiler working pressure
Operating weight	125 tons plus 11 hundredweights(engine plus tender)
Lengths	
Engine	40 feet 0 inches
Tender	22 feet 9 inches.

(Courtesy: South African Railways) 62202

The class 5A locomotives, Pacific type, pictured and described earlier were followed, in later years, by various modifications. Class 5R engines, type 4–6–2, were constructed by the Vulcan Foundry in England starting in 1912. Specifications of engine no. 781 which is shown here were as follows:

Cylinders	20 by 28 inches
Drive wheels	5-foot 2-inch diameter
Boiler working pressure	190 pounds per square inch
Tractive effort	25,750 pounds
Valve gear	Stephenson
Operating weights	
Engine	72 tons plus 9 hundredweights
Tender	49 tons plus 7 hundredweights
Tender capacities	4000 gallons water; 10 tons coal
Overall length	64 feet 1⅞ inches.

(Courtesy: South African Railway) 62211

With Union in South Africa in 1910, more powerful steam locomotives were necessitated by a rapid increase in traffic, the expansion of trade, and the introduction of many more new industries. In 1910 a class 12, type 4-8-2, large goods engine was designed to handle the heavy coal service between Germiston and Witbank. The first class 12 engine started operations during April 1912. Eight units were built by the North British Locomotive Company, nos. 1494-1501. In August 1913 the same British manufacturer furnished eight more engines, nos. 1502-9. Again in August 1915 the North British Locomotive Company built ten additional machines, nos. 1510-19. A further twenty class 12 engines, nos. 1859-70 were built by Beyer, Peacock & Company and placed in service during June 1921. Specifications were as follows (see engine no. 1494 illustrated):

Cylinders	22.5 by 26 inches
Drive wheels	4-foot 3-inch diameter
Boiler (Belpaire)	
Grate area	4 square feet
Boiler diameter	5-foot 7.5-inch inside diameter
Distance between tube plates	20 feet
Tubes	139 2.25-inch outside diameter
Flue tubes	24 5.5-inch outside diameter
Superheater area	554 square feet
Working pressure	190 pounds per square inch
Tractive effort	36,780 pounds at 75 percent boiler working pressure
Operating weights	
Engine	91 tons plus 19 hundredweights
Tender	50 tons plus 18 hundredweights

When the class 12 locomotives were introduced they were the largest nonarticulated types in South Africa. These mountain type engines worked successfully on the coal traffic routes referred to above, hauling fourteen hundred tons and returning to home base during a day's work, running a total round-trip distance of 320 miles.

The class 12 engines were remarkable, giving outstanding performance with low maintenance costs. They were still providing satisfactory service in June 1945. The only major alterations were: (1) fitting new cabs of increased width to provide additional comfort for the engine-man, and (2) fitting new SAR no. 2 boilers in 1935 when the class designation was changed to 12R.

(Courtesy: South African Railways) 49320

Another view of engine no. 1494, class 12, type 4-8-2, goods locomotive introduced into South Africa in 1912 is shown. See previous illustration for details.
(Courtesy: South African Railways) 12053

Pictured is class 7F locomotive, type 4–8–0, used on the South African Railways starting in 1913. See early illustration for details.
(Courtesy: South African Railways) 62231

On 30 May 1910, the same day the Union of South Africa was formed, the South African Railways were organized from the Cape Government and Natal Government rail systems. The top engineer was D. A. Hendrie, the former superintendent of the Natal Government Railway, who held this job until 1922. One of Hendrei's chief designs was the class 14, type 4–8–2, locomotive. A model of this class engine is shown and is on display in the Johannesburg Railway Museum. Sixty such engines were constructed, numbers 1701 to 1760, by Robert Stephenson & Company and Beyer, Peacock & Company over the period 1913–15. These were used primarily on the former Natal system. Specifications were as follows:

Cylinders	22 by 26 inches
Coupled wheels	4 feet
Boiler	
Grate area	37 square feet
Heating surface	2362 square feet
Boiler pressure	190 pounds per square inch
Superheater	521 square feet
Tractive effort	37,360 pounds at 75 percent steam pressure
Operational weight	141 tons plus 14 hundred-weights(engine plus tender)
Tender capacities	4250 gallons water; 10 tons coal.

(Courtesy: SAR Publicity and Travel Department)

The locomotive program for 1913–14 has been recorded as one of the most comprehensive in the history of South Africa. During this period 203 locomotives, comprising fifteen different classes, were on order. For the year 1914, ninety-five new engines, covering ten different classes, were placed in service. The total number of engines in operation was 1522 of which 1486 were on 3-foot 6-inch gauge tracks and thirty-six were on narrow-gauge 2-foot tracks. The average tractive force at 75 percent boiler working pressure increased during 1914 from 21,626 pounds to 22,262 pounds, while the number of engines of a tractive force of over 30,000 pounds increased from 216 to 295.

Experience gained with earlier engines gave rise to a new design for service in Natal on 1 in 30 gradients, which was designated as class 14, type 4–8–2. Sixty such machines were built by Stephenson & Company to the detailed design of D. A. Hendrie; twenty entered service during October 1913 (nos. 1701 to 1720) and forty more machines (nos. 1721 to 1760) were placed in service during June 1915. Subsequent modifications lead to a class 14A and to a class 14B machine.

During 1913 the design of the class 14 engines was further modified to change the drive wheel size from 4 feet to 4 feet 9 inches. These type 4–8–2 engines, now designated as class 15, were designed to haul either heavy goods or passenger traffic in the Orange Free State, where the curvatures and gradient were relatively easy. Ten units were placed in service after construction by the North British Locomotive Company during February and March 1914. Specifications were:

Cylinders	22 by 26 inches
Piston valves	Actuated by Walschaert gear
Drive wheels	4-foot 9-inch diameter
Boilers (Belpaire)	
Grate area	40 square feet
Tubes	131 2.25-inch outside diameter
Flue tubes	24 5.5-inch outside diameter
Superheater area	601 square feet
Distance between tube plates	21 feet 9 inches
Total heating surface	2578 square feet
Working pressure	185 pounds per square inch
Tractive effort	32,900 pounds at 75 percent boiler working pressure
Operating weight	143 tons plus 7 hundredweights (engine plus tender)
Tender capacities	4600 gallons water; 10 tons coal.

Later on the steel fireboxes of the class 15 engines had to be replaced by copper which brought about a redesignation to class 15A; the change was necessitated by the shortage of boiler water of satisfactory quality.

(Courtesy: South African Railways) 19425

In 1913 D. A. Hendrie, chief mechanical engineer of the South African Railways, changed the class 15 locomotive by modifying the boiler. To reduce the tube length of 21 feet 9 inches, a combustion chamber was installed reducing the distance between the tube plates to 19 feet. The new modification was called class 15A. These engines, Type 4–8–2, were originally fitted with steel fireboxes, but these were later refitted with copper types. The class 15A engine turned out to be one of Hendrie's best designs, and 119 units were eventually placed in service.

Five of the class 15A locomotives, nos. 1571–75, with the new boilers were constructed by the North British Locomotive Company and were placed in service during July 1914. Additional units were built as follows:

Engine numbers	Year into service	Builder
1781–1828	1914, 15, 16, 17, 19, 20	North British Locomotive Company
1839–58	1920–1921	NBLC (as above)
2011–25	1921	NBLC
1961–70	1921	Beyer Peacock
2080–2100	1925	J. A. Maffei

The class 15A engines were noted for their good steaming qualities and free running. Flangeless leading-coupled wheels were eventually arranged in place of the original flanged wheels. This modification was intended to give greater flexibility when negotiating the severe curves on the Hex River Mountain section. The class 15A engines worked between Kimberly and Capetown for many years until finally superseded by the more powerful types, classes 15E, 15F, and 23. It has been recorded that the 15A effected a reduction in the running time of the "Union Limited" in March 1922 by 2½ hours. These engines were a real utility type and gave a good account of themselves on passenger and goods operations.

Specifications on the class 15A engines were as follows:

Cylinders	22 by 28 inches
Valve gear	Walschaert's
Drive wheels	4-foot 9-inch diameter
Leading bogie wheels	2-foot 4½-inch diameter
Trailing bissel wheels	2-foot 9-inch diameter
Boiler (Belpaire)	
Grate area	40 square feet
Tubes	113 2¼-inch outside diameter
Flue tubes	21 5½-inch outside diameter
Superheater	466 square feet
Total heating surface	2026 square feet
Boiler working pressure	185 pounds per square inch
Tractive effort	32,990 pounds at 75 percent boiler working pressure
Operating weight	143 tons plus 6 hundredweights (engine plus tender)
Tender capacities	6000 gallons water; 12 tons coal
Lengths	
Engine	44 feet 1½ inches
Tender	27 feet 5 inches.

(Courtesy: South African Railways) 85042

The SAR Railways, in the period 1911–20, experienced an increasing demand for engines of a higher tractive effort. Much energy was exerted in designing more powerful engines which consequently involved larger boilers, cylinders, etc., which naturally increased operating weights. With axle-load limitations it was found necessary to utilize Mallet type locomotives to help solve this problem. During November 1911 five Mallet class MF, type 2–6–6–2, compound locomotives, nos. 1629 to 1633, were built by the American Locomotive Company, erected in the Pretoria workshops, and introduced to service on the Mermiston-Witbank section. These engines gave satisfactory performance up until they were scrapped in 1939. Later Mallet classes ME, MC, MC1, and MB were furnished by the North British Locomotive Company.

The need for engines with still higher tractive effort to cope with heavy traffic on branch lines gave rise to the design of the class MJ, type 2–6–6–0, Mallet compound engines. Eight such engines were ordered from J. A. Maffei of Munich, Germany during 1914; however, with the outbreak of World War I, only two units were delivered (nos. 1651 and 1652). Subsequently eight machines were ordered from the North British Locomotive Company, and these engines, nos. 1653–60, were placed in service during 1917–18. After World War I, in 1920 Maffei did deliver eight class MJ machines, nos. 1674–81. Specifications on the class MJ engines were as follows:

Cylinders	
Hi pressure	16.5 by 26 inches
Lo pressure	16.5 by 24 inches
Drive wheels	3-foot 6.5-inch diameter
Boiler (Belpaire)	
Grate area	40 square feet
Diameter	5 feet 1.5 inches
Tubes	151 2-inch outside diameter
Distance between tube plates	17 feet
Superheater tubes	18 5.5-inch outside diameter
Superheater	462 square feet (Schmidt)
Total heating surface	1913 square feet
Working pressure	200 pounds per square inch
Tractive effort	38,170 pounds at 75 percent boiler working pressure
Operating weight	138 tons plus 18 hundredweights (engine plus tender)
Tender capacities	4250 gallons water; 10 tons coal
Overall length	67 feet 5⅛ inches.

(Courtesy: South African Railways) P2222

During 1913 D. A. Hendrie designed a class 16 engine for passenger service. Twelve of these type 4–6–2 engines, used mainly on the Pretoria Johannesburg section, were built by the North British Locomotive Company (nos. 790 to 801) and were placed in service in 1914.

A new departure in South African locomotive practice was initiated by Hendrie in 1914–15 in respect to a four-cylinder noncompound passenger engine, type 4–6–2. Two units, nos. 851 and 852, were provided by the North British Locomotive Company during November 1915. The two outside cylinders drove the center coupled wheels, while the two inside cylinders were arranged to drive the leading coupled wheels through a cranked axle. Both sets of piston valves were actuated by one set of Walschaert gears. The last of these successful class 16A engines were scrapped in 1944.

Specifications on the class 16A locomotives were as follows:

Cylinders	14 by 26 inches
Drive wheels	5 feet
Boiler (Belpaire)	
Grate area	36 square feet
Tubes	119 2.25-inch outside diameter
Flue tubes	21 5.5-inch outside diameter
Distance between tube plates	19 feet 9 inches
Superheater area	473 square feet
Total heating surface	2121.5 square feet
Operating pressure	200 pounds per square inch
Tractive effort	25,480 pounds at 75 percent boiler working pressure
Operating weight	132 tons plus 5 hundredweights (engine plus tender).

(Courtesy: South African Railways) 49330

One of six 2-foot gauge class NG9, type 4–6–0, tender locomotives, nos. 42–47, built by the Baldwin Locomotive Works and placed in service in 1915 is pictured. These engines were assembled at the Uitenhage workshops. These were part of a series of locomotives built for the Defence Department for service in South West Africa; they were finally scrapped in 1929. Specifications on the class NG9 engines were as follows:

Cylinders	11.75 by 16 inches
Drive wheels	1-foot 9-inch diameter
Boiler working pressure	180 pounds per square inch
Tractive effort	9036 pounds at 75 percent boiler working pressure
Operating weight	41 tons plus 1 hundredweight (engine plus tender)
Tender capacities	1250 gallons water; 5 tons coal
Overall length	44 feet 4⅜ inches.

(Courtesy: South African Railways) P3219

During 1918 the effect of World War I conditions caused many railway problems in South Africa, especially with regard to steam locomotion. New engines were difficult to obtain, and spare parts were so scarce that repairs and general overhauls had to be postponed to the utmost in order to keep engines in some sort of service. By the end of March 1919, 187 locomotives and fourteen spare tenders were on order or authorized. At this point the number of engines in service on the SAR was 1556 on 3-foot 6-inch gauge tracks and fifty-two on narrow-gauge. The progressive increase in tractive effort since 1910 had been considerable, and the number of engines with tractive effort over 30,000 pounds increased from 161 in 1911 to 437 in 1918–19. During the war period and immediately afterwards various class 16B and class 16C, type 4–6–2, engines were placed in service; this list also included class 16 and class 16A machines.

During 1918 the American Locomotive Company delivered twenty Mountain type 4–8–2, class 14C engines, nos. 1761–80 and, in the following year, twenty more, nos. 1881–1900. These engines were actually constructed by the Montreal Locomotive Works of Canada. During December 1918 class 15B locomotives, type 4–8–2, nos. 1829–38 and nos. 1971–90 were supplied by the American Locomotive Works and again were actually built by the Montreal Locomotive Works. This class 15B engine is pictured. Specifications were as follows:

Cylinders	22 by 28 inches
Drive wheels	4-foot 9-inch diameter
Leading wheels	2-foot 4.5-inch diameter
Boiler (Belpaire)	
Grate area	40 square feet
Superheater area	446 square feet
Total heating surface	2028 square feet
Working pressure	185 pounds per square inch
Maximum axle loading	16 tons plus 11 hundredweights
Tractive effort	32,900 pounds at 75 percent boiler working pressure
Operating weight	142 tons plus 12 hundredweights (engine plus tender)
Tender capacities	4250 gallons water; 10 tons coal.

(Courtesy: South African Railways) 65436

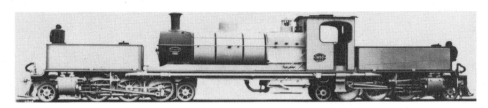

During 1914, as a result of aggressive new railway policies, the SAR ordered five Garratt articulated type locomotives. Three different designs were ordered to enable the Garratt principle to be studied under three different conditions. The construction of these engines by Beyer Peacock was held up because of World War I, and it was not until 1920 that they were finally received and placed into service. In cases where locomotives of exceptional tractive force were required and especially where the tracks, bridges, and curvatures did not allow development of the then existing designs, the number of coupled wheels required demanded the articulated types. Further, the use of articulated locomotives enables the capacity of a line to be approximately doubled without strengthening the track, bridges, and culverts, or improving the curvature. The most common type of articulated locomotive in South Africa, where considerations and requirements could not be met with orthodox designs, was the Garratt type. Here the operating economy, due to one engine crew for what is essentially a double engine, is obvious. Moreover, the Garratt runs equally well in either direction. The boiler is carried in a cradle suspended on pivot centers attached to the frames, each of which is free to align itself to the track curvatures. The firebox design and shape can also be extremely simple and can take advantage of the full moving structure gauge available. A greater depth of firebox is also possible than with ordinary types. Thus maximum boiler power is obtainable with the simplest forms of construction. The unusual length of the Garratt locomotive is a definite advantage where, due to restricted loads on bridges, weight spread-over is required. This type of locomotion became standard on all South African narrow-gauge lines.

During March 1920 the first Garratt locomotives were placed in service; these were all narrow-gauge engines. These proved quite successful with definite savings from reduced train mileage and trainsmen's hours. The original order of two Garratt experimental engines received the classifications GA and GB. Pictured is the class GB locomotive built by Beyer Peacock and placed in service during June 1921. Engine no. 1650, class GB type 2–6–2 plus 2–6–2, had these specifications:

Cylinders (4)	12 by 20 inches
Drive wheels	3-foot 6.75-inch diameter
Boiler	
Centerline above rail	7 feet
Working pressure	180 pounds per square inch
Tractive force	18,190 pounds at 75 percent boiler working pressure
Operating weight	71 tons plus 13 hundredweights
Maximum axle loading	7 tons plus 14 hundredweights.

The class GB locomotive worked passenger trains on the South Coast lines in Natal. It was noted for its good riding qualities and flexibility on light track having poor ballast and abounding with 300-foot curves. Following the success with the first class GB engine, six additional units were ordered from Beyer Peacock and placed in service in 1924. They embodied all improvements which experience had shown desirable. The Belpaire type boiler was provided with a superheater and the Gresley type air valve. Mechanical lubrication for the coupled wheel axle boxes were also provided. The latter engines first worked the Port Alfred and Aliwal North branch lines in the Cape Eastern Province, where the ruling gradients were 1 in 30 compensated. The weight of the engines on the second order were increased to 76 tons plus 1 hundredweight.

(Courtesy: South African Railways) 54091

Pictured is a model of a modified Fairlie steam locomotive; the prototype was built by the North British Locomotive Company in 1924 for the South African Railways, gauge 3 feet 6 inches. This engine, no. L 790, had a 2–6–2 plus 2–6–2 wheel arrangement with the following specifications:

Cylinders	14 by 23 inches
Coupled drive wheels	3-foot 6.75-inch diameter
Boiler	
Grate area	34 square feet
Feed	Two no. 10 injectors
Heating surface	
Tubes	1251 square feet
Firebox	155 square feet
Superheater	280 square feet
Total	1667 square feet
Working pressure	180 pounds per square inch
Tractive force	28,460 pounds at 75 percent boiler working pressure
Operating weight	99 tons plus 12 hundredweights
Water capacity	3000 gallons
Fuel capacity	225 cubic feet
Total wheel base	56 feet 8 inches.

(Courtesy: Museum of Transport, Glasgow) L790

The last engines designed by D. A. Hendrie were the class 12A, nos. 1520–39, 2111–25 and 2126–38, supplied by the North British Locomotive Company and nos. 1540–50 and 2103–10 by Henschel & Sohn A. G., Kassel, Germany. These engines were first placed in service during 1919 and marked the maximum size permissible at the time for type 4–8–2. Their performance fully justified Hendrie's efforts in that direction. These were designed primarily to supplement the class 12 engines then working between Germiston and Witbank.

See the illustration for a picture of the class 12A, type 4–8–2, tender locomotive built by Henschel & Sohn in 1927. Specifications were as follows:

Cylinders	24 by 26 inches
Drive wheels	4-foot 3-inch diameter
Boiler (Belpaire)	
Grate area	41 square feet
Tubes	159 2.25-inch outer diameter
Flue tubes	24 5.5-inch outer diameter
Distance between tube plates	18 feet
Superheater area	515 square feet
Total heating surface	2508 square feet
Working pressure	190 pounds per square inch
Tractive effort	41,840 pounds at 75 percent boiler working pressure
Operating weight	
Engine	99 tons plus 1 hundredweight
Tender	50 tons plus 18 hundredweights
Maximum axle loading	17 tons plus 6 hundredweights
Tender capacities	6000 gallons water; 12 tons coal.

(Courtesy: South African Railways) 83427

See earlier illustration and accompanying description which details the basic story on Garratt locomotives in South Africa; this covered a class GB engine. Subsequently many different Garratt modifications of this class engine were built (i.e., GD, GE, GF, GG, GL, GM, GO, etc.).

Shown is a class GF, type 4–6–2 plus 2–6–4, Garratt locomotive, of which sixty-five units were constructed. On the first order, engines nos. 2370–2406 were built by Hanomag and placed in service during December 1927. The second order, engines nos. 2407–25, was filled by Henschel & Sohn and placed in service during October 1928. The third order covered locomotives constructed by J. A. Maffei, and these were introduced to traffic during November 1928. These class GF engines were designed by Col. F. R. Collins for goods and passenger working on branch lines in all divisions of the Republic. The engines proved successful due mainly to the larger drive wheel diameters employed. They were capable of good speed, and their reasonably high tractive power made them a good utility type.

The Class GF engines worked a long time on the Johannesburg-Mafeking section. They also saw service in the Eastern Transvaal and Orange Free State as well as on the Natal North and South Coast lines. They were all eventually displaced by diesel power.

Specifications on the class GF Garratts were:

Cylinders (4)	16 by 26 inches
Valve gear	Walschaert's
Drive wheels	4-foot 6-inch diameter
Bogie wheels	2-foot 6-inch diameter
Boiler working pressure	185 pounds per square inch
Tractive effort	34,200 pounds at 75 percent boiler working pressure
Operating weight	
First order	143 tons plus 5 hundredweights
Second order	145 tons plus 11 hundredweights
Third order	147 tons plus 1 hundredweight
Water capacity	
Leading tank	3000 gallons
Beneath bunker	1000 gallons
Coal capacity	10 tons
Overall length	77 feet 1 inch.

About this time, articulated locomotives were in great favor in South Africa, and it has been stated that the Railway Board of the day was so impressed with results and possibilities that it instructed that no engines of nonarticulated types were to be ordered unless in exceptional circumstances. However, the retirement of Col. F. R. Collins in 1929 and the appointment of A. G. Watson as chief mechanical engineer brought about a change in this policy, and there was an interval of about ten years before another articulated design was adopted.

The later articulated designs were very different propositions from the earlier types of Garratts, especially with regard to accessibility, performance, and repair costs. In any case, it was well established that where the highest tractive efforts were essential, they could be obtained only by using this type of steam locomotive.

(Courtesy: South African Railways)

Pictured is another class 12A, type 4–8–2, locomotive.
This is engine no. 2131, part of a series built in 1927 by
Henschel & Sohn. See earlier illustration for details.
(Courtesy: South African Railways) 53825

In a continuing study of articulated types of steam
locomotives, the SAR designed various Garratt
modifications classed as GE, GEA, GG, G1, G2, GK,
and GD. During October 1927 the first order of the
class GCA locomotives, nos. 2190–2202, with a 2–6–2
plus 2–6–2 wheel arrangement, were placed in service
on the Natal South Coast line. These engines were
built by Freidkrupp of Essen, Germany to the
specifications and design of Col. F. R. Collins. They
were an improved type of class GC. Specifications
were as follows:

Cylinders (4)	14 by 24 inches
Drive wheels	3-foot 6.75-inch diameter
Boiler	
Grate area	34 square feet
Superheater area	331 square feet
Total heating surface	1388 square feet
Working pressure	180 pounds per square inch
Tractive effort	28,470 pounds at 75 percent boiler working pressure
Operating weight	104 tons and 16 hundredweights.

A second order for these engines was filled by Friedkrupp in August 1928, numbered 2600–2605. The latter engines were similar to those on the first order, but
operating weights were 105 tons and 16 hundredweights. This class of engines would have performed
better with larger cylinders and boilers. Trouble was
experienced with broken coupling rods, but this was
attributable to excessive speeds with relatively small
coupled drive wheels.
(Courtesy: South African Railways) P2274

During 1927 Col. F. R. Collins, SAR chief mechanical engineer between 1922 and 1928, introduced the three-cylinder locomotive designated class 18 with a wheel arrangement of 2–10–2. Two units built by Henschel & Sohn of Kassel, Germany, numbered 1360 and 1361, were placed in service December 1927 and January 1928, respectively. These engines, then being built in wide numbers in Europe and America, were noted for their more even turning movement, improved balancing, and better distribution of crank pin thrust loads. However, compared with SAR classes 12A and 15CA, the class 18 engines showed up unfavorably in regard to performance, mileage, and repair costs. Owing to the high fuel consumption the class 18 tenders did not carry sufficient coal to work a round trip on the Witbank-Germiston run.

The two outside cylinders were arranged horizontally outside the bar frames, while the third or inside cylinder was installed below the smokebox in an inclined position. Each of the outside cylinders was actuated by Walschaert gear, whereas the inside cylinder valve gear was controlled by the Gresley system actuated from the motions of the outside cylinder, through extensions on the piston valve tail rods. The three cranks were placed at an angle of 120 degrees to each other, allowing for the inclination of the inner cylinder. The third and fourth pair of class 18 driving wheels were flangeless. The drive for the outside cylinders was arranged on the third pair of coupled wheels. The inside cylinder actuated the second pair of drive wheels through a cranked axle. The valve gear gave frequent trouble due to wear and breakage of components. These troubles, together with excessive tire flange wear, resulted in the class 18 engines being shopped under 40,000 miles.

The class 18 engines were equipped with a mechanical stoker (Duplex D.4) which was operated by a 4-cylinder steam engine. The internal diameter of the boiler was the largest on any nonarticulated engine on the South African Railways. Also the total wheelbase was 38 feet 2½ inches, making it the largest of any nonarticulated engine in South Africa. The class 18 leading bissel bogie was combined with the leading coupled wheels on the "Krauss-Helmholtz" principle; this together with other rather sophisticated arrangements enabled this engine to negotiate curves of about 320 feet radius, notwithstanding its long wheel base.

Specifications on the class 18 were as follows:

Cylinders (3)	21¼ by 28 inches
Drive wheels	4-foot 9-inch diameter
Boiler	
Internal diameter	6 feet 3.75 inches
Combustion chamber	fitted
Distance between tube plates	20 feet 7 inches
Boiler centerline above rails	8 feet 6 inches
Grate area	60 square feet
Tubes	160 2¼-inch outside diameter
Flue tubes	34 5½-inch outside diameter
Superheater	850 square feet
Total heating surface	3231 square feet
Boiler working pressure	215 pounds per square inch
Tractive effort	63,650 pounds at 75 percent of boiler working pressure
Operating weight	187 tons and 5 hundredweights (engine and tender)
Maximum axle loading	19 tons
Tender capacities	6000 gallons water; 14 tons coal
Lengths	
Engine	47 feet 8 inches
Tender	28 feet 4 inches (8 wheels 2-bogie SAR type "H. T.").

(Courtesy: South African Railways)

In 1925 the SAR authorized an experiment with a modified type of Fairlie engine with a 2–6–2 plus 2–6–2 wheel arrangement. This articulated locomotive, supplied by the North British Locomotive Company, was viewed as a competitor and alternative to the Garratt type.

The above locomotive consisted of three distinct components—the upper main frame, extending almost over the whole length of the engine which carried the boiler; water tanks; coal bunker and cab. This superstructure was supported on two engine units by means of pivot centers located approximately at the center of the rigid wheelbase of each engine unit. This arrangement, it was claimed, reduced the wear between wheel flanges and rails. It was further claimed that the distribution of the loads on the axles, as fuel and water was expended, was less variable than could be obtained with the straight Garratt design. On the other hand, the distance between the power units had been increased in the same way as with the Garratt locomotive, thus allowing space for a liberal firebox and ashpan, resulting in a more efficient boiler, and also distributing the weight of the engine over a greater length than was obtainable with an orthodox Fairlie design.

As it turned out, the above modified Fairlie engine, or variations of it, were never entirely successful in South Africa. The heavy vertical loads carried by the pivots and concentrated on the center of the power units gave a lot of trouble, owing to broken frames and undue wear of the pivots. Further, the large overhang of the cradle frame longitudinally from the pivots caused vibration during running, thereby increasing the tendency for structural weaknesses to develop.

A further experiment was carried out in 1928 when ten class U engines were purchased from J. A. Maffei of Munich, Germany. This type 2–6–2 plus 2–6–2 engine embodied the Garratt design at the front end and the modified Fairlie design at the ear end. It has been stated that the reason for the hind end class U locomotives having been arranged on the modified Fairlie principle was to provide coal bunkers rigid with the boiler frames, to ensure a satisfactory arrangement for the mechanical stokers. However, subsequent designs of the class GL and GM Garratts have shown that this precaution was unnecessary. Specifications on the class U engines were as follows:

Cylinders (4)	18.5 by 26 inches
Drive wheels	4-foot 0-inch diameter
Boiler	
Grate area	60 square feet
Superheater area	633 square feet
Total heating surface	2806 square feet
Working pressure	180 pounds per square inch
Tractive effort	50,050 pounds at 75 percent boiler working pressure
Operating weight	164 tons plus 16 hundredweights
Maximum axle load	18 tons plus 12 hundredweights
Water capacity	5280 gallons
Coal capacity	14 tons.

Mechanical stokers were originally installed, but these were later removed since the engines were then being employed on comparatively short runs.

The above class U locomotives were somewhat sluggish, but an alteration to the exhaust passages performed in 1933, effected considerable improvement. The engineering staff and the running crews always referred to these engines as "U boats."
(Courtesy: South African Railways) P1979

During the twenty-five years prior to 1928, the bulk of the traffic handled on sixty-pound track on the South African Railways was hauled by classes 6, 7, and 8 locomotives. The various series of class 8 were especially good utility types, capable of good average speeds, reasonable haulage capacity, and freedom from breakdown and horrendous maintenance problems. However, with the increase in traffic, it became necessary to obtain newer and heavier type engines.

In 1928 four class 19 engines to the designs of Col. F. R. Collins were built by Schwartzkopff; these had the running numbers 1366 to 1369. During 1929 thirty-six class 19A engines, nos. 675–710 were ordered from the Swiss Locomotive Works, Winterthur, and placed in service. The latter machines had slightly smaller boilers than class 19 locomotives but with a lower axle load were better suited to some of the lighter SAR branch lines. The class 19A locomotive was also restricted on some lines to the use of the MP type tenders which carried 9.2 tons of coal and 4200 gallons of water. Specifications on the class 19A engines were as follows:

Wheel arrangement	4–8–2
Cylinders	19.5 by 26 inches
Drive wheels	4-foot 3-inch diameter
Boiler	
Diameter	4-foot 10.25-inch inside diameter
Distance between tube plates	20 feet 0⅜ inches
Firegrate area	36 square feet
Working pressure	200 pounds per square inch
Tractive effort	29,080 pounds at 75 percent boiler working pressure
Operating weight (engine)	75 tons plus 3 hundredweights.

(Courtesy: South African Railways) P2124

In 1929 the Class S, type 0–8–0, locomotives were introduced on the South African Railways intended for shunting work. Fourteen engines were built by Henschel & Sohn, and they achieved immediate respect for their rugged reliability. The class S engines had tenders of a rather unique design. The bunker walls were narrower at the top to allow better vision rearward for the crew—so important in shunting movements. The tender tank also had a curved top, which resulted in these tenders having an appearance entirely their own on the South African Railways. The class S engines spent nearly fifty years slogging in yards, mostly at Bramfontein and Johannesburg.

Specifications were as follows:

Cylinders	23¼ by 25 inches
Valve gear	Walschaert's
Drive wheels	4-foot diameter
Boiler working pressure	170 pounds per square inch
Tractive effort	35,890 pounds at 75 percent boiler working pressure
Operating Weight	133 tons plus 3 hundredweights (engine plus tender)
Tender capacities	6000 gallons water; 8 tons coal
Overall length	64 feet 10⁵⁄₁₆ inches.

The original class S boiler pressure was 215 pounds per square inch with a tractive force of 45,400 pounds at 75 percent boiler working pressure. However, the factor of adhesion was too low so the boiler pressure was reduced to 170 pounds per square inch given a tractive effort of 35,890 pounds at 75 percent boiler working pressure.
(Courtesy: South African Railways)

Dr. M. M. Loubser, chief mechanical engineer of the South African Railways between 1939 and 1949, designed a hefty standard boiler to replace the Belpaire type originally fitted to the class 12A engines. The 12A's, thus reboilered, became the class 12AR. The entire fleet of class 12A locomotives were not so reboilered. Derived from what was considered to be the finest SAR goods engine (class 12A), the class 12AR engines certainly proved to be invaluable for a wide variety of goods and passenger services.

For a number of years the class 12AR engines rendered sterling service on the Cape Eastern main line, hauling both goods and passenger trains on the section between East London and Queenstown. The Cape Midland system also used them to great advantage on like duties on the Port Elizabeth–Klipplaat section. The 12ARs have also been used in other parts of the Cape and in Natal, where they were utilized on various mainline duties, especially between Glenco and Vryheid.

The 12ARs have always presented a rather pugnacious appearance due to their massive boilers being mounted over comparatively small (4 feet 3 inch) coupled wheels, the image being accentuated by a rather long smokebox protruding towards the front buffer beam. Specifications on the class 12AR engines were as follows:

Builder	North British Locomotive Company
Wheel arrangement	4–8–2
Cylinders	24 by 26 inches
Drive wheels	4-foot 3-inch diameter
Valve gear	Walschaert's
Boiler working pressure	190 pounds per square inch
Tractive effort	41,840 pounds at 75 percent boiler working pressure
Operating weight	167.9 tons (engine plus tender)
Tender capacities	6000 gallons water; 12 tons coal.

(Courtesy: South African Railways) 83020

On the South African Railways in 1928 it developed that more powerful locomotives were required on the Pietermaritzburg-Durban section. It was decided to obtain two Garratt type engines, each with a tractive effort equal to two class 14 engines. In fact the class GL Garratt, as it became known, was very similar to two class 14 engines but with a single boiler on the Garratt principle. As it turned out, the class GL locomotive was the largest ever used in South Africa. The wheel arrangement was 4–8–2 plus 2–8–4.

The first order for two engines, nos. 2350 and 2351, was placed with Beyer Peacock according to design specifications by Col. Collins. The engines were required to haul abnormal loads between Durban and Cato Ridge, Natal, on which section there were about thirty-eight miles of continuous 1 in 66 gradient and no less than 154 curves, many of 494 feet radius. The track was equipped with eighty-pound rails. The engines were assembled in workshops at Durban and placed in service during October 1929.

These engines were such a phenomenal advance in locomotive practice that much experimental work had to be done before they could be placed in regular traffic. It was necessary to proceed cautiously owing to tunnel problems, since there were as many as eleven tunnels on this section, the longest, the Shongweni, being over a half-mile in length. The problem of preventing hot gases from the smokebox entering the cab when passing through was partially overcome by providing a "Sturtevant" blower, driven by a steam turbine which drew air from the front end of the engine and discharged it into the cab. Eventually a cowl was fitted over the top of the chimney to divert the hot gases, smoke, and steam away from the cab in a backward direction, the engine always running with the chimney trailing when ascending a gradient. Owing to limitations in the length of sidings and crossing-loops, the loads allowed originally were one thousand tons from Durban to Cato Ridge, and two thousand tons coastwise.

The performance of the two first engines was so satisfactory, the Railway Administration decided to place an order for six more engines with Beyer Peacock; engines nos. 2352–57 were placed in service during July 1930. These engines had "Clyde" type soot blowers, also self-cleaning smokeboxes, and L-4 duplex type mechanical stokers. The axle boxes were arranged for grease lubrication.

Specifications on the class GL locomotives were as follows:

Cylinders	22 by 26 inches
Valve gear	Walschaert's
Drive wheels	4-foot diameter
Leading bogie wheels	2-foot 4½-inch diameter
Carrier wheels	2-foot 9-inch diameter
Boiler	
Barrel diameter first course	7 feet
Grate area	75 square feet
Firebox	(steel, with 2 Nicolson thermic syphons)
Superheater	835 square feet
Total heating surface	3396 square feet
Boiler working pressure	200 pounds per square inch
Tractive effort	78,650 pounds at 75 percent boiler working pressure (highest ever in South Africa)
Operating weight	211 tons plus 1 hundredweight
Water capacity	
Leading tank	4650 gallons
Trailing tank	2350 gallons
Total	7000 gallons
Coal capacity	12 tons
Frames	Bar type
Overall length	90 feet 7⅞ inches.

On electrification of the Durban-Pietermaritzburg section, the class GL engines were transferred to the Glenco-Vryheid branch where they operated until about the mid-1970s. Again being displaced by electric traction, the GL's were transferred to Stanger for working traffic on the North Coast line to Empangeni. Later they were all withdrawn from service and scrapped except two earmarked for preservation. *(Courtesy: South African Railways)*

Pictured is a model of another class GL Garratt type 4–8–2 plus 2–8–4 steam locomotive. This was the most powerful Garratt railway engine ever constructed for any railway irrespective of the rail gauge. See earlier illustration for more details and technical specifications.

(Courtesy: Photo, Bassett-Lowke, Ltd.; data, South African Railways)

Class 16D, type 4–6–2, Pacific locomotives, built by Baldwin and known as "Big Berthas," were placed in service during 1925. In 1928 additional class 16D engines were ordered from Baldwin and Hohenzollern A. G. Running numbers of the latter machines were 843 to 850 and 868 and 873 respectively. These engines were classified as 16DA, having improved class 16A designs. In 1930 six more engines were ordered from Henschel & Sohn to a further improved design; these were numbered 874 to 879 and were still classified as 16DA. See illustration which pictures engine no. 876.

Engines 874–79 were originally built with wide fireboxes. Five of these new class 16DA's were provided with Walschaert's valve motion, but the sixth engine (no. 879) was fitted with Caprotti valve gear, and ran with this until 1940 when it was converted at the Bloemfontein mechanical workshops to Walschaert's motion.

The "wide box" class 16DA's all entered traffic with 5-foot coupled drive wheels and a boiler pressure of 195 pounds per square inch. However, four of the six engines (nos. 874, 875, 878, 879) subsequently had their coupled wheels increased in size to 5 feet 3 inches. The boiler pressure was also increased to 205 pounds per square inch which resulted in a tractive effort of 33,570 pounds at 75 percent boiler working pressure.

Initially these locomotives were stationed in Kimberly and worked fast passenger trains such as the Union Limited between Beaufort West, Kimberly, and Johannesburg. Together with the earlier 16DA's and the later 16E's, the wide-box 16DA's remained on the work already detailed until the arrival of air conditioned stock for the Union Limited in 1939. Together with their sister Pacifics, these engines were transferred to Bloemfontein to work passenger traffic in the Orange Free State, and up until 1953 they worked passenger trains through to Johannesburg. The "wide box" DA's also worked the Orange Express for quite a few years, especially between Bloemfontein and Kimberly.

However, the Pacific type locomotive lost favor on the SAR as it could not be regarded as a general mixed traffic type with accent on goods handling. Being regarded as a passenger locomotive, the class 16DA "wide box" was ultimately relegated to lesser and lesser duties such as pick-up goods work. Three of the latter engines have been preserved in addition to two of the narrow-firebox variety.

Specifications on the class 16DA engines were as follows:

Cylinders	23 by 26 inches
Drive wheels	see above
Working pressure	see above
Tractive effort	see above
Operating weight	160 tons plus 12 hundredweights
Tender capacities	6000 gallons water; 14 tons coal
Overall length	68 feet 4¹⁄₁₆ inches
Grate area	45 square feet (original), 60 square feet (final).

(Courtesy: South African Railways) 81940

Pictured is a class NG15 locomotive on the 2-foot gauge Port Elizabeth-Avontur line of South Africa on the Van Stadens Bridge in 1970. This engine is displaying a Diamond Jubilee plaque of the South African Historic Transport Association. Three class NG15 locomotives, type 2–8–2, bearing the identification numbers 17, 18, and 19 were built by Henschel & Sohn in 1931. A further order for three locomotives, numbered 117–19, was supplied by Henschel in 1937. Most of these locomotives were still in service in 1970. Specifications follow:

Cylinders	15.75 by 17.75 inches
Coupled drive wheels	2-foot 9⅞-inch diameter

Boiler

Internal diameter at smokebox end	3-foot 11.75 inch
Grate area	16.7 square feet
Superheater	180.0 square feet
Total heating surface	796 square feet
Working pressure	171 pounds per square inch
Tractive effort	16,610 pounds at 75 percent boiler working pressure
Operating weight	67 tons plus 16 hundredweights (engine plus tender)
Tender capacities	2860 gallons water; 5.5 tons coal
Overall length	54 feet 3³⁄₁₆ inches.

(Courtesy: SAR Publicity and Travel Department)

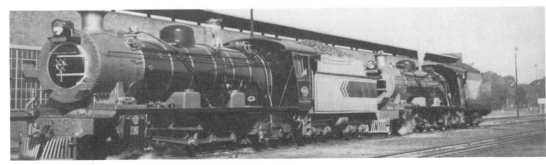

The original class 14 steam locomotive first entered traffic in 1913 and was designed by D. A. Hendrie, mechanical engineer of the South African Railways from 1910 to 1922, to suit conditions in Natal—sharp curvative combined with steep grades. That the 14's proved successful is an accepted part of locomotive history in South Africa.

The class 14R engines were a reboilered version of the original class 14 and were specially adapted for service in Natal. After reboilering in 1935 with Watson's standard no. 2 boiler, it did not take footplate men long to find a nickname for their pert locomotive. The new standard boilers looked so impressive with their nickel-plated boiler bands that the class 14R's became known as the "Striped Tigers."

By 1939 the entire Natal main line from Durban to Volksrust had been electrified, and naturally the services of the 14R's were no longer needed on the main line. However the 14's and 14R's spent some nine years working in company with the mighty class GL Garratts on the Durban-Cato Ridge section. Despite the loss of mainline duty there still remained the

"Old" Natal line between Booth and Cato Ridge via Botha's Hill as well as work further up and further down the coast as bridges were strengthened or replaced to take their mass. Eventually the 14R's worked right up the coast to Empangeni and southwards to Port Shepstone. Finally they were relegated to shunting work on the main lines.

Specifications on the class 14R locomotives were as follows:

Wheel arrangement	4–8–2
Builders originally	Robert Stephenson and Beyer Peacock
Cylinders	22 by 26 inches
Drive wheels	4-foot diameter
Valve gear	Walschaert's
Boiler working pressure	190 pounds per square inch
Tractive effort	37,360 pounds at 75 percent boiler working pressure
Operating weight	139 tons plus 13 hundredweights
Tender capacities	4250 gallons water; 10 tons coal
Length over couplers	65 feet 3⅞ inches.

(Courtesy: South African Railways) 85201

During 1935 A. G. Watson was appointed assistant general manager, technical, while also retaining the post of chief mechanical engineer with the South African Railways. Also in 1935 Mr. Watson designed the class 15E locomotive with a wheel arrangement of 4–8–2. Twenty engines of this type, nos. 2858–77 were built by Robert Stephenson & Company and twenty-four by Henschel & Sohn of Kassel, Germany. These engines were designed for heavy passenger and goods trains on mainline service. The class 15 locomotive was previously pictured and described.

Specifications on class 15E locomotives were as follows:

Cylinders	24 by 28 inches
Drive wheels	5-foot diameter
Valve gear	RC poppet
Boiler	
Standard	3B type
Grate area	63 square feet
Superheater	676 square feet
Tubes	3168 square feet
Firebox	206 square feet
Total heating surface	4050 square feet
Distance between tube plates	22 feet 6 inches
Boiler center above rails	9 feet 2½ inches
Boiler working pressure	210 pounds per square inch
Tractive effort	42,340 pounds at 75 percent boiler working pressure
Operating weight	109 tons (engine plus tender) (engines 2858–77)
107 tons plus 15 hundredweights	(engines 2878–2901)
Lengths	
Engine	42 feet 9 inches
Tender	30 feet 9 inches.

(Courtesy: South African Railways) 62287

In the early 1930s there was a worldwide tendency for railways to build so-called glamorous locomotives for prestige purposes, in addition to general workhorse types. Naturally these prestige engines were designed to haul crack passenger trains on their respective systems. It was with the foregoing in mind that A. G. Watson designed his class 16E engine. Mr. Watson intended the six class 16E's, ordered from Henschel & Sohn, exclusively to haul fast passenger trains like the "Union Limited" and "Union Express."

The 16E's (nos. 854–59) were placed in service in 1935 and were stabled at the Kimberly Locomotive Depot. They were assigned to express trains working on the section south to Beaufort West and north to Johannesburg. In effect the 16E represented the maximum development of the Pacific type locomotive on the South African Railways. The boiler had a centerline 9 feet 3 inches above rail level—the highest pitched boilers on the SAR. The coupled wheels at 6 feet were the largest ever used on a 3-foot 6-inch gauge railway anywhere in the world. Soon after being placed in traffic, engine no. 854 attained speeds on test in excess of 85 miles per hour with the regulator only half open and with a trailing load of 350 tons. The test engineers and the driver were satisfied that she would have exceeded 100 miles per hour if track conditions had been safe enough for the attempt. As it was, to avoid public concern, the attained speed was quoted at just around 70 miles per hour. Thus it follows that the full capabilities of the 16E could not be exploited on the SAR tracks with their maximum permitted speed on the main lines of 55 miles per hour. So, in a nutshell, while the 16E was in itself a magnificent example of a high-speed express passenger locomotive, its full potential could not be realized.

The 16E's remained in service on the Cape Northern system until the arrival, in 1939, of the all-steel air conditioned stock for the "Union Limited" which was later known as the "blue Train." The 16E's were considered insufficiently powered to handle the new steel trains, so the six 16E's were transferred to Bloemfontein, where they continued to work mainly passenger trains. Until 1953, they used to work through to Johannesburg, but subsequently they were confined to the sections to Kimberly and Noupoort. They did, in fact, work the "Orange Express" across to Kimberly for many years. They were finally relegated to pick-up goods work between Bloemfontein and Noupoort before being withdrawn from service in 1972. Basically, the demise of the class 16E locomotives as well as the earlier Pacific types was accelerated by the fact that eight-coupled engines could easily achieve the maximum of 55 miles per hour. In these circumstances special locomotives for handling passenger trains were not required.

Specifications on the class 16E engines were as follows:

Wheel arrangement	4–6–2
Cylinders	24 by 28 inches
Drive wheels	6-foot diameter
Boiler	
Fire grate	63 square feet
Superheater	592 square feet
Tubes	136 2.5-inch diameter
Flue tubes	36 5.5-inch diameter
Total heating surface	2914 square feet
Working pressure	210 pounds per square inch
Tractive effort	35,280 pounds at 75 percent boiler working pressure
Operating weight	167 tons plus 3 hundredweights (engine plus tender)
Tender ("JT" type) capacities	6000 gallons water; 14 tons coal
Overall length	71 feet 8³⁄₁₆ inches.

(Courtesy: South African Railways) 85696

A South African Railways class 19C, type 4–8–2, locomotive is shown. This was essentially a branch and secondary main-line engine built according to the design of A. G. Watson (chief mechanical engineer of SAR 1929–36) by the North British Locomotive Company and placed in service in 1935. The design of class 19C was arranged to permit a large degree of interchangeability of parts with class 19 and 19A locomotives. Various other fundamental changes were introduced by Watson. Fifty class 19C engines included a change from Walschaert gear to "R. C." (rotary cam) valve gears (poppet type). Specifications were the same as the class A engines, previously listed but with cylinder sizes and tractive effort changed as follows:

Cylinders	
Class 19A	19.5 by 26 inches
Class 19C	21 by 26 inches
Tractive effort at 75 percent boiler working pressure	
Class 19A	29,080 pounds
Class 19C	31,850 pounds.

(Courtesy: SAR Publicity and Travel Department) 62306

During 1934 A. G. Watson, then chief mechanical engineer of the SAR, designed a ten-coupled engine for use on the South West Africa rail system. Watson was restricted to a maximum axle load of eleven tons. A wheel arrangement of 2–10–2 type and 4-foot diameter coupled drive wheels, with driving and intermediate wheels flangeless, were decided upon. The tracks consisted of 40¼-pound section rails, laid in desert conditions practically without ballast.

Class 20 engine, no. 2485, was built in the workshops at Pretoria, although the bar frames and cylinders were imported. This was the third recorded instance of locomotives designed and constructed in the SAR workshops. The boiler used came from a discarded class 19A engine. The cylinders were identical with those of the class 19C and had the "R. C." (rotary cam) poppet valve gear. The coupled wheels were taken from scrapped class 8 engines. The main drive and valve gear drive came from a third pair of coupled wheels. Grease lubrication was provided for all coupled wheel axle boxes. The ten-coupled wheel arrangement in conjunction with the sharp curvature of the line necessitated special side play for the leading coupled wheel axle boxes and spherical bearings for

the leading crank pins. The trailing bogie was similar to that of the class 19C engine, but the design of the leading bissel type bogie necessitated certain proportions to suit the ten-coupled wheel arrangement.

Only one class 20 engine was ever built. It was found that the daily traffic offering in South West Africa was inadequate for the capacity of the engine, and there was some evidence that the latter was rather severe on the track. After only a short service the engine was transferred to the Union and was then worked on the Eastern Transvaal system.

Specifications on the class 20 locomotive were as follows:

Cylinders	21 by 24 inches
Drive wheels	4-foot diameter
Boiler working pressure	200 pounds per square inch
Tractive effort	33,080 pounds at 75 percent boiler working pressure
Operating weight	124 tons plus 8 hundredweights (engine plus tender)
Tender capacities	4250 gallons water; 10 tons coal
Lengths	
Engine	42 feet 2 inches
Tender	25 feet 11 inches.

(Courtesy: South African Railways) 43401

In 1935 A. G. Watson, chief mechanical engineer, designed a class 21, type 2–10–4, locomotive which, at the time, represented the maximum power obtainable for sixty-pound track without recourse to an articulated design. This was the first use of a 2–10–4 wheel arrangement on any SAR locomotives. One engine was built by the North British Locomotive Company who arranged to have a mechanical stoker installed. After trials on the rough Randfontein-Mafeking line, where it demonstrated a satisfactory performance, it was transferred to work on the Eastern Transvaal system where it handled excessive loads successfully. This engine was still in service in October 1946. Specifications on engine no. 2951 were as follows:

Cylinders	24 by 26 inches
Drive wheels	4-foot 6-inch diameter
Leading and trailing bogie wheels	2-foot 6-inch diameter

Boiler (Standard 3B)	
Grate area	63 square feet
Internal diameter (1st course)	6 feet 2.25 inches
Heating surface	
Firebox	206 square feet
Tubes	3168 square feet
Superheater	676 square feet
Total	4050 square feet
Working pressure	225 pounds per square inch
Tractive effort	43,700 pounds at 75 percent boiler working pressure
Operating weights	
Engine	106 tons plus 12 hundredweights
Tender	65 tons plus 16 hundredweights
Total	172 tons plus 8 hundredweights
Tender capacities	5750 gallons water; 10 tons coal.

(Courtesy: South African Railways) 45002

Pictured is another view of the class 21, type 2–10–4, locomotive built by the North British Locomotive Company in 1935. See previous illustration for technical details.
(Courtesy: South African Railways) 56032

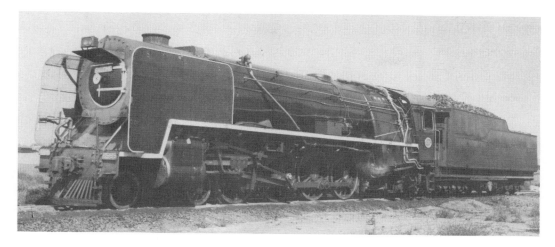

A. G. Watson, who was appointed assistant general manager, technical, while also retaining the post of chief mechanical engineer in 1935 made numerous important contributions to the art of the steam locomotive. At the time of his retirement in March 1936, additional locomotive power in the SAR was an urgent necessity, and the mechanical department was requested to submit proposals. It was felt that a general utility locomotive, capable of the highest performance possible within the axle load limits for eighty-pound track was required. The time available for designing was short, and no experimentation was possible, as any order placed would have to be followed quickly by other substantial orders for similar locomotives. On 8 May 1936, a design for a 4–8–2 type, class 23 engine, with a twelve-wheeled tender was submitted to the general manager.

The first order of twenty class 23 locomotives, nos. 2552 to 2571, was placed in 1936 with Henschel & Sohn (thirteen units), and the Berliner Maschinenbau A. G. (seven units). Before the above engines were delivered, the orders were increased by a further eighty-five and thirty-one machines respectively, making 136 engines in all. It is worth noting that the last of the class 23 engines were placed in service during August 1939, only one month before the outbreak of World War II. Specifications were:

Cylinders	24 by 28 inches
Piston valves	(12 inches) actuated by

	Walschaert motion
Drive wheels	5-foot 3-inch diameter (all flanged)
Boiler	
Centerline from rail	9 feet
Weight empty boiler	35 tons
Diameter	6-foot 2.25-inch inside diameter
Distance between tube plates	22 feet 6 inches
Grate area	63 square feet (rewired mechanical stokers)
Total heating surface	3400 square feet
Working pressure	225 pounds per square inch
Tractive effort	43,200 pounds at 75 percent boiler working pressure
Engine weights	
First order	110 tons plus 19 hundredweights
Second order	111 tons plus 2 hundredweights
Tender weight	
First order	104 tons plus 5 hundredweights
Second order	107 tons plus 14 hundredweights
Tender capacities	
First order	10,000 gallons water; 18 tons coal
Second order	9200 gallons water; 18 tons coal.

With the class 23 locomotives a twelve-wheeled tender was introduced to enable longer runs to be undertaken between stops because, as the engines had to work over the Karoo where the supply and quality of water was erratic, it allowed bad watering locations to be skipped.
(Courtesy: South African Railways) 81378

Shown is another side view of the class 23, type 4–8–2, locomotives introduced on the SAR lines in 1936. See previous illustration for technical data.
(Courtesy: South African Railways) 56069

Four illustrations picture one of the most widely used locomotives on the South African Railways: class 15F, type 4–8–2. This engine followed the early design of W. A. J. Day and in its later form, the detailed requirements of Dr. M. M. Loubser, chief mechanical engineer. During 1938 twenty-one class 15F engines were ordered for mainline freight and passenger services from Henschel & Sohn and forty-four from the North British Locomotive Company. The running numbers of these sixty-five engines were 2902 to 2966. The boiler was arranged for hand firing, but provision was made for fitting a mechanical stoker. During 1944, a further order for thirty class 15F engines, nos. 2967–96 was placed with Beyer Peacock. The war time need for these locomotives was very great. The last manufactured engines were austerity models in that planished steel boiler lagging was replaced by ordinary steel and stainless steel lagging bands, chromium-plated hand rails, radiused corners of firebox lagging, etc., were absent. Later models used vacuum brakes in place of the usual steam brakes on the engines. During 1945 a further order of sixty class 15F engines, nos. 2997–3056, was placed with the North British Locomotive Company, and in 1946 an additional order for one hundred class 15F locomotives, nos. 3057–3156, was placed with the North British Locomotive Company.

In 1945 it was arranged that naming engines, in vogue as early as 1860, should be resumed on some class 15F and class 23 engines. Accordingly various cities and towns of the Union were shown in both languages on suitable name plates on either side of the locomotive. For example: (all class 15F engines) no. 3046, "City of Bloemfontein"; no. 3044, "Kroonstad"; no. 3045, "Harrismith"; no. 3054, "Bethlehem." Eight additional engines were so named. Specifications on the class 15F locomotives were as follows:

Cylinders	24 by 28 inches
Coupled drive wheels	5-foot diameter
Boiler (standard type 3B)	
Grate area	63 square feet
Firebox	206 square feet
Tubes	3168 square feet
Superheater	676 square feet
Working pressure	210 pounds per square inch
Tractive effort	42,340 pounds at 75 percent boiler working pressure
Operating weight	178 tons (engine plus tender)
Tender (type "J. T.") capacities	6000 gallons water; 14 tons coal
Overall length	73 feet 5¹⁵⁄₁₆ inches.

(Courtesy: SAR Publicity and Travel Department)

The series of class 19 engines, type 4–8–2, starting in 1928 opened up a new era in steam locomotive power on the South African Railways. The class 19A engine, covered earlier was followed by progressively improved models, classes 19B, 19C, and 19D built with standard SAR no. 1A boilers. The class 19D engine was the end result of a long line of highly successful eight-coupled branch line locomotives. The 19D's were similar to the 19C's except the former had Walschaert's valve motion and piston valves in place of the rotary cam poppet valve gear fitted to the 19C's. The 19D's appeared in various forms and the original (1937) had domeless boilers. See two illustrations for typical class 19D engines. The class 19D locomotives were spread over a period of twelve years, 1937–39 and 1945–46. Suppliers were Friedkrupp, Borsig, Skoda, Robert Stephenson, and the North British Locomotive Company.

The 19D's saw service in almost every corner of the Republic and South West Africa. Although essentially branch line engines, they were by no means confined to such duties, since they performed a considerable amount of suburban passenger and mainline working.

After an inspection of the 19D's, Sir Nigel Gresley, a world-acclaimed British locomotive engineer, is reported to have said: "The design of this locomotive must surely be one of the best the world has ever seen." This statement was quite a feather in the cap of the mechanical engineering staff of the South African Railways who considered the "lean but tough" 19D's as worth their weight in gold to the Railway Administration.

Specifications of the class 19D locomotives were:

Cylinders	21 by 26 inches
Drive wheels	4-foot 6-inch diameter
Boiler working pressure	200 pounds per square inch
Tractive effort	31,859 pounds at 75 percent boiler working pressure
Operating weight	153 tons plus 19 hundredweights (with later torpedo type tender)
Tender capacities	6500 gallons (Torpedo type) water; 12 tons (Torpedo tender) coal
Overall length	86 feet 2⅜ inches.

(Courtesy: South African Railways) 45000

Another class 19D steam locomotive built by a variety of manufacturers and introduced to the South African Railways in 1937 is shown. See previous illustration for details.
(Courtesy: South African Railways)

Pictured is the famous Capetown–Durban Orange Express in 1956. This train is being pulled by a class 15F, type 4–8–2, locomotive on 3-foot 6-inch gauge tracks in the vicinity of Tulbagh Kloof. *(Courtesy: South African Railways)*

The class GEA Garratt, type 4–8–2 plus 2–8–4, locomotive was designed by Dr. M. M. Loubser, chief mechanical engineer of the SAR, built by Beyer, Peacock & Company, and placed in service in 1946–47. Fifty machines were constructed with the running numbers 4001–50. This engine was one of the most powerful in the world operating on sixty-pound track. In 1947 the class GEA locomotives were working on the Johannesburg-Zeerust line, the Mossel Bay-Oudtshoorn section, and were scheduled additionally for operations on the North Coast Line, Natal.

The class GEA locomotives, a modification of the older class GE engine, embodied the latest SAR practices known up to that time. The firebox had a round top instead of the Belpaire type and was fabricated from steel not copper. The superheater had an increased area. The extended wheel arrangement permitted increased coal and water capacities. Bar frames were provided instead of plate frames. The coupled drive wheels had a larger diameter, were flanged, and had a rigid wheelbase of 13 feet 4.5 inches, for each engine unit. Lubrication was furnished by two four-feed Wakefield Eureka type H-sight feed lubricators.

Stone's electric lighting equipment was fitted with a T. G. H.-type five hundred watt generator on the lefthand side boiler frame. Two twenty-one-inch diameter vacuum cylinders were provided on the front engine with steam and hand brakes on the rear engine. The class GEA engines had many other sophisticated additions too numerous to mention. Specifications were as follows:

Cylinders (4)	18.5 by 26 inches
Valve gear	Walschaert's
Drive wheels	4-foot diameter
Boiler	
Grate area	51.3 square feet
Diameter at smokebox tube plate	7 feet
Superheater (MLS Co.)	36 elements, 463 square feet
Total heating surface	2540 square feet
Working pressure	200 pounds per square inch
Smokebox	self-cleaning with SAR type spark-arrestor
Tractive effort	55,650 pounds at 75 percent boiler working pressure
Operating weight	185.5 tons (engine plus tender)
Tender capacities	5650 gallons water; 10 tons coal.

(Courtesy: South African Railways) 52463

Pictured is another view of a class GEA Garratt steam locomotive. See previous illustration for details.
(Courtesy: South African Railways)

This picture is an aerial view of two class GEA Garratt locomotives hauling the train used by the British royal family on their tour of South Africa in 1947. Specifications on this Garratt engine were listed earlier.
(Courtesy: SAR Publications and Travel Department)

During World War II recommendations were approved to construct a number of branch line locomotives in the SAR in their own mechanical workshops. Salt River was chosen as the workshop to undertake this construction, and twelve engines were finally built in 1947, nos. 374 to 385. These machines were type 0–8–0, designated class S1, designed to augment the class S engines already in service. Though not the first engines constructed in South Africa, the S1's were nevertheless a bold step forward, and they enjoyed immediate success in all sorts of shunting duties. A further twenty-five engines were then ordered from the North British Locomotive Company; these units entered service in 1951. Overall the S1's rendered excellent service in major yards throughout South Africa, although largely confined along the Witwatersrand and more especially at Germiston.

Specifications on the class S1 locomotives were:

Cylinders	23¼ by 25 inches
Valve gear	Walschaert's
Drive wheels	4-foot diameter
Boiler	
Grate area	42 square feet
Superheater	428 square feet
Total heating surface	1820 square feet
Boiler working pressure	180 pounds per square inch
Tractive effort	38,000 pounds at 75 percent boiler working pressure
Operating weight	140 tons plus 1 hundredweight
Tender capacities	6000 gallons water; 11 tons coal
Overall length	64 feet 6³⁄₁₆ inches.

(Courtesy: South African Railways)

In 1948 the North British Locomotive Company furnished one hundred class 15F, type 4–8–2, locomotives for use on the South African Railways. These were numbered 3057–3156. A model of no. 3057 is pictured. These engines had mechanical stokers, superheaters, and double-bogie tenders. Specifications were as follows:

Cylinders	24 by 28 inches
Coupled wheels	5-foot diameter
Boiler	
Grate area	63 square feet
Superheater	676 square feet
Total heating surface	3400 square feet
Boiler pressure	210 pounds per square inch
Tractive effort	42,340 pounds
Operating weight	182 tons plus 14 hundredweights (engine plus tender)
Tender capacities	5620 gallons water; 14 tons coal.

(Courtesy: Mitchell Library, Glasgow)

In South Africa the railways had a comparatively large mileage of forty-five-pound track and in South West Africa there were hundreds of miles of 40¼-pound track. The engines used on this type of rail were classes 6, 7, 8, GC, and GCA. With the increasing age of the latter equipment and with traffic increases, instead of laying sixty-pound rail, it was decided to order new locomotives capable of running on the existing systems. Dr. M. M. Loubser therefore designed the class 24 for this work. The wheel arrangement selected was 2–8–4, the first time it was used in South Africa. These engines were capable of traversing curves of three hundred-foot radius and sections of the branch lines laid with 40¼-pound rail. One hundred units of the class 24 engine were built by the North British Locomotive Company starting in 1949, and they acquitted themselves admirably until 1961 when diesel power was introduced.

Class 24's which became famous were those working the George-Knysna branch on the Cape Midlands system. Having had regular crews who took pride in their engines, these locomotives were truly resplendent with their polished brass fittings and copper pipes. See illustration: the name "Anneline" followed a practice, started in 1945, of naming locomotives after various cities and towns of the Union.

The Class 24 engines, and later the much larger class 25 locomotives, were equipped with Commonwealth one-piece cast steel locomotive beds (frames) in which the two cylinders and the smokebox saddle were cast in one unit.

Specifications on the class 24 engines were as follows:

Cylinders	19 by 26 inches
Drive wheels	4-foot 3-inch diameter
Leading bissel and 4-wheel trailing bogie	2-foot 6-inch diameter
Boiler	
Grate area	36 square feet
Superheater area	366 square feet
Tubes	76 2.5-inch diameter
Flue tubes	24 5.5-inch diameter
Total heating surface	1636 square feet
Working pressure	200 pounds per square inch
Tractive effort	26,600 pounds at 75 percent boiler working pressure
Operating weight	133 tons (tender plus engine)
Tender capacities	4500 gallons water; 10 tons coal
Overall length	74 feet 9¼ inches.

(Courtesy: South African Railways) 84942

The class 45 so-called Berkshire, type 2–8–4, locomotives were introduced on the South African Railways in 1948. These were designed for branch line operations on light forty-five-pound rail. The North British Locomotive Company built one hundred of these engines with designated numbers 3601 to 3700. Pictured is a representative model now housed in the Railway Museum at Johannesburg. Prototype specifications were as follows:

Cylinders	19 by 26 inches
Coupled wheels	4-foot 3-inch diameter
Boiler	
Grate area	36 square feet
Superheater	380 square feet
Total heating surface	1636 square feet
Boiler pressure	200 pounds per square inch
Tractive effort	27,600 pounds at 75 percent steam pressure
Operating weight	130 tons (engine plus tender)
Tender capacities	4500 gallons water; 9 tons coal
Tender type	Twelve-wheel Vanderbilt.

(Courtesy: SAR Publicity and Travel Department)

One hundred class S2, type 0–8–0, locomotives were built by Friedkrupp and placed in service on the South African Railways in 1952–53. Although basically designed as light shunters, especially for harbor work, the S2's were by no means confined to dock work; they were also used on other light shunting duty throughout the Republic. These shunters were equipped with torpedo tenders mounted on six-wheeled Buckeye bogies and, while the tender type was similar to that attached to class 24 engines, the coal bunker was cut inward to afford a clear view for the driver and fireman when running tender first. The S2 boiler was similar but a little longer than the boilers fitted to the class NGG 16 Garratts (2-foot gauge). Small wonder that these engines appeared so spindly when mounted on a 2-foot 6-inch gauge locomotive frame. However, a steam engine's appearance can be deceptive, and the S2's certainly earned their keep—their sharp staccato exhaust was a common sound in the ports and other parts of South Africa. Due to the very nature of their work the S2's remained in service for a considerable length of time.

Specifications on the class S2 locomotives were:

Cylinders	18 by 26 inches
Valve gear	Walschaert's
Drive wheels	4-foot diameter
Boiler working pressure	195 pounds per square inch
Tractive effort	25,600 pounds at 75 percent boiler working pressure
Operating weight	103 tons plus 18 hundredweights (engine plus tender)
Overall length	67 feet 9¼ inches.

(Courtesy: South African Railways)

This illustration pictures two SAR locomotives. On the right is the famous class 15F engine which was described earlier.

The engine on the left is a class GMAM Garratt, type 4–8–2 plus 2–8–4; these units were placed in service in the period 1953–58, and on 31 March 1979 there were eighty-seven such locomotives in active service.

The class GM Garratt engine was evolved starting in 1938 to increase the hauling capacity of trains on the Johannesburg-Mafeking line. The Johannesburg-Zeerust section, a distance of 149 miles, is the more difficult, as a considerable mileage consists of 1 in 40 grade and curves of five hundred feet radius. After leaving the Reef at an elevation of 5700 feet, the line, at a point twenty miles away, falls to a level of 4600 feet whilst in the next eleven miles, it again rises to over 5000 feet, to be followed later by a drop to 3585 feet. It was finally decided to build a Garratt type locomotive which was virtually two class 19D engines. The latter engine was the same as class 19C, but Walschaert valve gear with long valve travel was fitted in place of the R. C. gear. The final Garratt class GM engine had a separate water tank permanently attached, the only instance of such a practice in the world. Sixteen initial class GM locomotives were built by Beyer Peacock and were assembled in the Durban workshops. The coal bunker on the hind engine frame had a capacity of 10 tons and a type H. T. 1 mechanical stoker was installed. The front engine frame carried a water tank with a capacity of 1600 Imperial gallons. The auxiliary tank carried 6750 gallons of water. Cylinders of both front and hind engines were 20.5 by 26 inches. Coupled drive wheels were 4 feet 6 inches in diameter. Operating weight was 174 tons plus 10 hundredweights. Overall length was 93 feet 4.5 inches.

The class GM locomotive (not illustrated) was somewhat similar in appearance to the class GMAM engine pictured above. See a later illustration for details on the class GMAM machine.

(Courtesy: South African Railways) 65298

Take a 4–8–4 wheel arrangement, add a boiler almost 7 feet in diameter, plus a firebox with a grate area of 70 square feet, and you have a big locomotive by any standards! Use this engine on the 3-foot 6-inch gauge, and you have a veritable giant. This is an appropriate nutshell description of the South African Railways class 25NC engine. Her design was a real team effort, being divided between the SAR technical staff, the North British Locomotive Company, and Henschel & Sohn technical people, and the firm which supplied the cast-steel locomotive frames. However, the design work for the boiler was a South African effort. Tests were conducted using a class 23 locomotive boiler to formulate the design for the class 25NC boiler. The standard 3B boiler was rebuilt with a combustion chamber fitted to the firebox, thus reducing the length of the boiler tubes, resulting in a marked improvement in boiler tube and tube plate life. Another notable design characteristic was the provision of one-piece cast steel locomotive frames. In addition the 25NC's and the 25's were completely equipped with roller bearings; this included the axle boxes, side, and connecting rods. The tenders were equipped with water-bottom frames, which meant that there were no separate tank and frame as in previous models—in this instance the cast steel tender frame itself formed the bottom of the water space.

During the period 1953–55 the South African Railways placed in service 140 class 25 locomotives of which ninety were equipped with condensing equipment. The fifty remaining engines were called class 25NC (non-condensing). Prior to ordering any of these locomotives, considerable research was undertaken using a class 23 as a mobile test-bed. During the test period, an assortment of firegrates were tested while a combustion chamber was also fitted to the standard type 3B boiler. During the final stages, engineers from Henschel and the North British Locomotive Company were on hand to help out in the development.

The condensing apparatus was designed and supplied by Henschel who had considerable background with this type of equipment. The cast-steel locomotive

beds were supplied by the General Steel Castings Corporation in the United States. Erection of the final engines took place at Salt River, and they were placed in service on the Cape main line. The 25NC's started service with only a few "teething" problems. The condensing 25's gave trouble from the start. Most of this was involved with smokebox turbines which had nicked blades and went out of balance. The turbines were required to provide firebox drafts in the absence of the normal use of steam exhaust, the latter being diverted to the condensing van. Some problems were also experienced with inefficient separation of water and oil in the exhaust steam condensate. The latter mentioned problems were resolved with the help of Henschel engineers, and finally both engines started to give satisfactory service.

Both classes of engines had mechanical stokers and were equipped throughout with roller bearings. The locomotives were fitted with "Hadfield" reversing engines. The driver cabs had a layout which offered the crew a maximum of comfort and protection from the weather. The class 25NC locomotive had a massive tender on two six-wheeled bogies. The tender of the condensing 25 was even larger, due of course to the condensing equipment.

During September 1968 the 25 NC's were employed on passenger and goods trains between Kimberly-DeAar and Beaufort West, while the condensing 25's were utilized on the DeAar-Beaufort West section and also between Kimberly and Hotazel. Prior to electrification, the condensing 25's also worked on the Beaufort West-Touws River section, while the 25NC's also worked between Kimberly and Klerksdorp. Earlier still the 25 NC's worked through to Welverdiend, only about sixty miles from Johannesburg.

Specifications on the above engines were as follows:

Cylinders	24 by 28 inches
Valve gear	Walschaert's
Drive wheels	5-foot diameter
Leading wheels	2-foot 11-inch diameter
Trailing wheels	2-foot 6-inch diameter
Boiler	
Firegrate area	70 square feet
Tubes	158 2½-inch outer diameter, also 40 tubes 5½-inch outer diameter, Area 3059 square feet
Superheater	636 square feet
Circulators	37 square feet
Firebox	294 square feet
Boiler working pressure	225 pounds per square inch
Tractive force	45,360 pounds at 75 percent boiler working pressure
Operating weights	
Class 25NC	
Engine	117 tons plus 9 hundredweights
Tender	105 tons plus 11 hundredweights
Class 25	
Engine	121 tons plus 11 hundredweights
Tender van	113 tons plus 18 hundredweights
Tender capacities	
Class 25NC	10,500 gallons water; 18 tons coal
Class 25	water; (missing) 18 tons coal
Overall lengths	
Class 25NC	81 feet 5 inches
Class 25	107 feet 6 inches.

(Courtesy: South African Railways) 82488

This illustration is a 1970 photograph of a class 25NC locomotive hauling the famous "Blue Train" express in South Africa. See earlier illustration for details. *(Courtesy: South African Railways)* 76429

Pictured is a class 25 condensing locomotive hauling a freight train in South Africa in the 1970s. See an earlier illustration for technical and other information on this engine. *(Courtesy: South African Railways)* 66797

Shown here is a class 25NC steam locomotive, type 4–8–4, built by the North British Locomotive Company and Henschel & Sohn and introduced to traffic on the South African Railways in 1953. See previous illustration for details.
(Courtesy: South African Railways)

Some of the very last steam locomotives furnished for use in South Africa were classes GMA, GMAM, and GO Garratts. Pictured is a class GMA/M engine (the M in the classification denoted its use on main lines) which were supplied by Beyer Peacock, by the North British Locomotive Company, and by Henschel & Sohn in 1954. The wheel arrangement was 4–8–2 plus 2–8–4.

The class GMAM engines were ordered in part to prevent main line traffic on certain sections from grinding to a halt through a chronic shortage of motive power; such a section was the Witbank–Germiston when this line was being wired for electric traction. Steam came to the rescue, and the GMAM's provided in record time by the builders, helped existing motive power to keep traffic rolling. They also performed good work on the Waterval Boven–Komatipoort and the East London–Queenstown mainline sections.

Many GMAM's were subsequently converted to class GMA for use over sections laid with sixty-one-pound rail merely by reducing their coal and water capacities. The class GO engines were a lighter version of the same machine. It had noticeably smaller boilers, and both coal bunker and leading tank were of smaller proportions. Class GO locomotives had a lean appearance. A few were tried briefly on the Krugersdorp-

Zeerust section, but they did not prove successful. However they spent many years active on the Eastern Transvaal system, especially on the Belfast–Lydenburg–Steelpoort line and later on the Natal North Coast.

Specifications on the above Garratts were as follows:

Cylinders (4) GMA and GMAM	20½ by 26 inches
Cylinders (4) GO	18½ by 26 inches
Valve gear	Walschaert's
Drive wheels	4-foot 6-inch diameter
Boiler working pressure	200 pounds per square inch
Overall length	93 feet 10 inches (excluding tank car)

COMPARISONS OF CLASSES

	GMAM	GMA	GO
Tractive effort (Pounds at 75 percent boiler working pressure)	60,700	60,700	49,430
Operating weights (Tons plus hundredweights)	191 plus 8	187 plus 1	172 plus 2
Water capacity			
Gallons Leading tank	2100	1650	1660
Trailing tank car	6800	6800	6800
Coal capacity (tons)	14	11	11.

(Courtesy: South African Railways)

Pictured is one end of a Garratt locomotive used in South Africa. This engine, what appears to be a class GMA or GMAM machine, is shown to emphasize the tremendous size of these articulated engines.
(Courtesy: South African Railways)

Shown is an old photograph of George Pauling (1853–1919), famous South African engineer and contracting magnate. After working on various rail construction jobs in England, he went to South Africa in 1875 where he was first an assistant engineer on the Cape Government Railways. He later set up his own independent contracting business and carried out a lot of important rail construction projects in Africa. From 1882 to 1885 he constructed the rail line from Sterkstroom to Aliwal North. In 1884 he secured the contract for an extension from Beaufort West to Kimberly. After a short stint as a gold mining engineer, in 1886 he returned to railroad work about which time he met President Kruger in the Transvaal. Pauling built the "Rand Tram," the first rail line in the Transvaal in 1890. Subsequently, working for Kruger, he built the line from Vryburg to Rhodesia and also one from Beira. He later built lines to Salisbury from Umtali, from the south to Bulawayo, the Bulawayo section to Salisbury, and an extension to Victoria Falls and beyond. In the Union of South Africa he built the rail line to Caledon over Sir Lowry's Pass and various other lines. One of his last contracts covered a major portion of the Benguela Railway in Angola.
(Courtesy: Royal Commonwealth Society)

The sketch in this illustration shows construction work on the first part of the Transvaal Railway of South Africa in the early 1890s; this railroad was built under the supervision of the famous engineer and contractor, George Pauling.
(*Courtesy:* Illustrated London News)

	CLASSES			
	7	7A	7B	7F
Tractive force/ pounds at 75% BWP	18,600	20,990	20,990	22,240
Tender capacities				
(gallons) Water	2220	2850	2850	2800
(tons) Coal	5	8	8	6¼
Lengths				
Engine (Overall		29'8"	29'11"	30'0"
Tender 50 ft. 1 in.)		23'9"	23'9"	23'9"
Manufacturer—Probably	Neilson, Reid	Neilson Reid	Neilson Reid	North British Locomotive Co.
Date in service	1892	1896	1900	1913.

SPAIN

TWO RAILWAY LINES OPENED IN SPAIN IN THE 1840s: one from Barcelona on 28 October 1840, running seventeen miles northeast along the Mediterranean coast to Mataró, and a thirty-mile line south from Madrid to Aranjues. The 1,674-millimeter (5-foot 6-inch) gauge Barcelona–Mataró line was the more successful one, returning 22 percent the first year on the money invested. The latter railway was financed mainly by capital from France; in fact, up to the end of the nineteenth century, control of Spanish railroads was largely centered in Paris in the hands of Rothschild and Pereires interests. In general, English manufacturers lost out almost completely in the production and sale of rail, rolling stock, and locomotives used in Spain.

The main lines of the Spanish rail network, of a broad 5-foot 6-inch gauge, were established in the decade after 1855, and active building programs continued until 1900. A major hindrance to construction was the difficult topography, since only 22 percent of the railroad track was built over level ground. The terrain necessitated 4,000 bridges, 1,165 tunnels and nearly sixteen thousand crossings, which slowed the locomotives considerably. In 1856 work began on the difficult four-hundred-mile line between Valldolid and Irún, on the Biscay border with France. The early Catalan rail lines were bought out by the French Norte Company in 1866, which organization also acquired the Madrid–Zaragosa–Alicante system in 1898. Spanish historians and British railway people have both long maintained that French financiers and French engineers were the chief villains in the Spanish railway debacle in which much money was lost due to poor railroad design, graft, inadequate planning, and inept and dishonest contractors.

The peak periods of railroad construction in Spain were 1878–80, 1882–84, 1893, 1896, and 1899. From about 1904 to 1910, cheap narrow-gauge lines were constructed to fill transportation gaps between the main lines out of Madrid. By 1914, without adequate funds, the old railroad system began wearing out and required repairs and modernization. Moreover, the original private railways, which had been cheaply constructed using light rail, were found to be incapable of handling fast, heavy traffic. World War I brought all kinds of transport delays, accidents, and inadequacies. The economic boom of the 1920s permitted the government's railway council to provide up-to-date locomotives and rolling stock; during this period, of 1,106 locomotives in use on Spanish rail systems, 687 were locally made in the shops of Catalonia.

Depression in the 1930s forced cancellation of many orders for new railway engines and delayed a program of repairing and replacing worn rails, double-tracking the main lines, and eliminating a vast assortment of old-fashioned backup railroad equipment. By this time, as had occurred on many other world railways, over-the-road truck transport had captured a substantial portion of the shipping business.

The use of a 5-foot 6-inch rail gauge caused many problems in making connections with the international rail system. This was an especially troublesome problem at the French border; however, in 1969 an adaptor to the "Talgo" trains was devised that permitted direct through transportation to Paris and Geneva. The fast, efficient "Talgo" trains started operating in 1954 and were considered to be one of the world's most interesting innovations; these are so-called knucklebone types, low-slung with articulated carriages, and are as luxurious inside as modern aircraft.

In 1941, broad-gauge lines in Spain were nationalized and taken over by RENFE (Red Nacional de los Ferrocarriles Españoles) after the track and rolling stock of the private railroad lines had been decimated by the Spanish Civil War. In 1964 the World Bank lent $650 million to RENFE to finance the first stage of a ten-year modernization program. By 1972 there were 11,712 miles of railroad in Spain, of which about 3,000 miles were narrow-gauge, 1,675 miles were double-tracked, and 3,900 miles were electrified. Some private com-

panies still run by local narrow-gauge lines, but these are being gradually absorbed by RENFE as the private ninety-nine-year concessions expire.

In 1978 Spain had 13,509 kilometers (8,934 miles) of 1.676 meter (5-foot 6-inch) track.

The highest point on the Spanish railways is at Puerto de Navacerrada, where the summit on the 5-foot 6-inch gauge line is at 5,777 feet above sea level. The most southerly railroad in Europe is at Algeciras in southern Spain near Gibraltar.

The worst railway disaster occurred on 29 September 1957, in Leon Province, where a wreck in a tunnel killed between five hundred and eight hundred people.

Steam Locomotives in Spain

Representative steam locomotives used on the Spanish railways are set forth in the following thirty-three photographs, covering a period from 1854 to 1953.

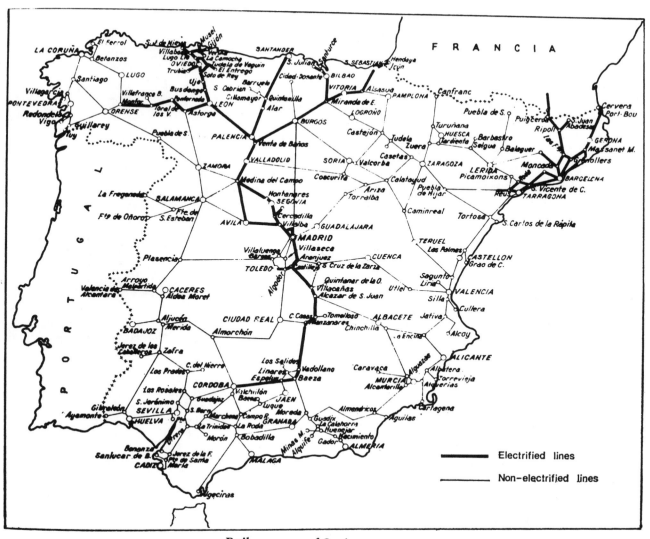

Railway map of Spain.
(*Courtesy:* Janes World Railways)

Pictured is a type 2–4–0 tank engine class 030 constructed in 1954 by Sharp & Stewart for use on the Barcelona & East Martorell Railway of Spain. Specifications were not available.
(Courtesy: RENFE) 1826B

In 1864 Neilson & Company furnished for the Utrera & Moron Railway of Spain a single type 2–2–2 tender locomotive (tender not illustrated in photograph). This engine was diverted from a large series of similar machines originally ordered by the East Indian Railway. Some specifications were as follows:

Gauge	5 feet 6 inches
Order number	E 280
Cylinders	15 by 22 inches
Drive wheels	6-foot 6-inch diameter
Boiler heating surface	1111 square feet
Working steam pressure	(not available)
Tener water capacity	1450 gallons.

(Courtesy: Mitchell Library, Glasgow)

Shown is a type 0–6–0 tank engine with tender unattached which carried the designations 030–0203/0204. Units numbers 1601 to 1605 were built by Creusot in 1867 for use on the Northern Railway of Spain. Specifications were:

Cylinders	350 by 440 millimeters
Drive wheels	1000-millimeter diameter
Boiler	
Grate area	0.82 square meters
Diameter	1200 millimeters
Length	3320 millimeters
Firebox	5.12 square meters
Tubes	54.45 square meters (116 at 50 millimeters)
Total heating surface	59.57 square meters
Working pressure	8 kilograms per square centimeter
Tractive effort	2803 kilograms
Horsepower	262
Engine weights	
Operating	27,600 kilograms
Empty	24,669 kilograms
Capacities	3 cubic meters water; 1000 kilograms coal (tender).

(Courtesy: RENFE) 2582B

In 1867 Dubs & Company furnished the Utrera & Osuna Railway with an unstated number of type 2–4–0 tender engines having the following characteristics:

Gauge	5 feet 6 inches
Work order no.	E 183
Cylinders	15 by 22 inches
Drive wheels	5-foot 8-inch diameter
Boiler heating surface	897.3 square feet
Working steam pressure	(not stated)
Operating weights	
Engine	28 tons plus 10 hundredweights
Tender	18 tons
Tender capacities	1200 gallons water; 135 cubic feet coal.

(Courtesy: Mitchell Library, Glasgow) D/E 183

The Tharsis Sulphur & Copper Company in 1867 bought four type 0–4–0 tank locomotives from Dubs & Company (nos. 1–4). These utility engines had the following specifications:

Gauge	4 feet 0 inches
Work order no.	E 231
Cylinders	12 by 22 inches
Drive wheels	3-foot 6-inch diameter
Boiler heating surface	540.3 square feet
Operating weight	19 tons
Capacities	540 gallons water; 35 cubic feet coal.

(Courtesy: Mitchell Library, Glasgow) D/E 231

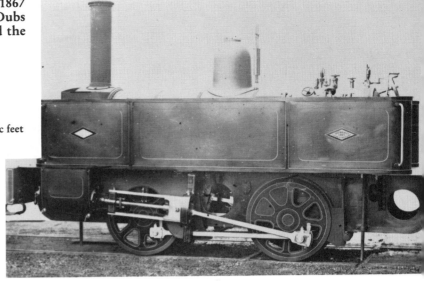

Pictured is an old locomotive, type 0–4–0, built in 1871 for use on the Andalusia Railway by Creusot & Neilson. This engine carried a designation of 020–0201. Specifications were as follows:

Cylinders	200 by 360 millimeters
Drive wheels	805-millimeter diameter
Boiler	
Grate area	0.41 square meters
Diameter	880 millimeters
Length	1810 millimeters
Firebox	2.47 square meters
Tubes	14.54 square meters (53 at 45 millimeters)
Total heating surface	17.01 square meters
Tractive effort	930 kilograms
Horsepower	131
Operating weight (engine)	9000 kilograms
Empty weight (engine)	6600 kilograms
Capacities	2 cubic meters water; 300 kilograms coal.

(Courtesy: RENFE) Neg. No. 163D

The Riotinto Company of Spain ordered from Neilson & Company in 1874 two type 0–6–0 tank locomotives (nos. 2–3). These machines had the following specifications:

Gauge	3 feet 6 inches
Work order no.	E 433
Cylinders	10½ by 18 inches
Drivers	3-foot diameter
Boiler heating area	485.76 square feet
Working steam pressure	120 pounds per square inch
Capacities	450 gallons water; 27 cubic feet coal.

(Courtesy: Mitchell Library, Glasgow) M/E 433(1)

Pictured is a Spanish railways type 0–8–0 locomotive manufactured by Sharp, Stewart & Company in 1878–80 for use on the Tarragona & Barcelona Railway. These tender engines bore the RENFE identification numbers 040–2011/2023. Specifications were as follows:

Cylinders	508 by 660 millimeters
Drive wheels	1388-millimeter diameter
Boiler	
Grate area	2.61 square meters
Diameter	1397 millimeters
Length	3965 millimeters
Firebox	12.64 square meters
Tubes (190 at 50 millimeters)	106.52 square meters
Total heating surface	119.16 square meters
Working pressure	8 kilograms per square centimeter
Tractive effort	6536 kilograms
Horsepower	835
Engine weights	
Operating	47,688 kilograms
Empty	42,882 kilograms.

(Courtesy: RENFE) Neg. No. 1825B

Shown here is a type 4–4–0 locomotive built in 1881 by Rich Hartmann-Chemnitz for use on the Western Railway of Spain. These engines bore the classification 220–2001/2005 and were numbered from 1 to 9. Specifications were as follows:

Cylinders	432 by 610 millimeters
Drive wheels	1860-millimeter diameter
Boiler	
Grate area	2.31 square meters
Diameter	1300 millimeters
Length	3500 millimeters
Firebox	10.44 square meters
Tubes (182 at 50 millimeters)	90.00 square meters
Total heating area	100.44 square meters
Working pressure	9 kilograms per square centimeter
Tractive effort	3550 kilograms
Horsepower	739
Engine weights	
Operating	41,800 kilograms
Empty	38,550 kilograms.

(Courtesy: RENFE) Neg. No. 2609B

Shown is a tender locomotive, type 0–6–0, class 030–2062/2064 constructed in 1883–84 by Creusot & Chemnitz for use on the Andalusia Railway. The engine numbers were 51–58 (constructed in the period 1860–61) and 91–98. Specifications on engine no. 97 were:

Cylinders	440 by 600 millimeters
Drive wheels	1430-millimeter diameter
Boiler	
Grate area	1.31 square meters
Diameter	1308 millimeters
Length	3902 millimeters
Firebox	7.86 square meters
Tubes (168 at 50 millimeters)	92.67 square meters
Total heating surface	100.53 square meters
Working pressure	8.5 kilograms per square centimeter
Tractive effort	4487 kilograms
Horsepower	419
Engine weights	
Operating	32,300 kilograms
Empty	28,800 kilograms.

(Courtesy: RENFE) Neg. No. 3.1.1.

The Zafra & Hullva Railway of Spain in 1884 bought eight type 0–8–0 tender locomotives from Dubs & Company (nos. 51–58). Specifications follow:

Gauge	5 feet 6 inches
Work order no.	E 1836
Cylinders	20 by 24 inches
Drivers	4-foot diameter
Boiler heating surface	1614.72 square feet
Working steam pressure	150 pounds per square inch
Tractive force	22,500 pounds
Operating weights	
Engine	47 tons plus 6 hundredweights
Tender	25 tons plus 8 hundredweights
Tender capacities	2000 gallons water; 230 cubic feet coal.

(Courtesy: Mitchell Library, Glasgow) D/E 1836

Neilson & Company in 1889 supplied six tender locomotives (nos. 1–6), type 2–6–0, to the Great Southern Railway of Spain. The locomotive shown in the photograph had the following specifications:

Gauge	5 feet 6 inches
Work order no.	E 636
Cylinders	18 by 24 inches
Drive wheels	4-foot 8-inch diameter
Boiler heating surface	1102 square feet
Working steam pressure	140 pounds per square inch
Operating weights	
Engine	46 tons plus 1 hundredweight
Tender	32 tons plus 7 hundredweights
Tender capacity	2500 gallons water; 200 cubic feet coal.

(Courtesy: Mitchell Library, Glasgow) N/E 636

Sharp, Stewart & Company in 1890 constructed two type 4–4–0 tank locomotives for use on the Cadagua Railway (nos. 1 and 2). Engine no. 1, named "Valmaseda," had the following general characteristics:

Gauge	3 feet 3⅜ inches
Work order no.	E 949
Cylinders	14 by 20 inches
Drivers	5-foot diameter
Water capacity	600 gallons

No additional data available.

(Courtesy: Mitchell Library, Glasgow) SSE 949

The Almansa, Valencia, & Tarragona Railway in 1891 purchased eight type 0–6–0 tender locomotives from Sharp, Stewart & Company (nos. 78–85). Engine no. 84 was used on the 5-foot 6-inch gauge tracks, had 19-by 26-inch cylinders, and 5-foot diameter drive wheels (Work order no. E 976).
(Courtesy: Mitchell Library, Glasgow) SS/E 976

This illustration shows a type 0–6–0 locomotive built in 1892 by Falcon-Loughboro for use on the F. C. de Triano Railway of Spain. This engine no. 6, carried the classification 030–0213. Specifications were:

Cylinders	356 by 559 millimeters
Drive wheels	1372-millimeter diameter
Boiler	
Grate area	1.39 square meters
Diameter	1041 millimeters
Length	2980 millimeters
Firebox	5.53 square meters
Tubes (116 at 50 millimeters)	54.47 square meters
Total heating surface	60.00 square meters
Working pressure	10 kilograms per square centimeter
Tractive effort	3333 kilograms
Engine weights	
Operating	28,500 kilograms
Empty	21,900 kilograms
Capacities	4.2 cubic meters water; 1600 kilograms (tender) coal
Horsepower	442.

(Courtesy: RENFE) Neg. No. 2608B

The type 0–6–0 engine pictured was used on the Western Railway of Spain. This class 030–0224, engine no. 161, was built by Cockrill in 1895. Specifications were:

Cylinders	370 by 520 millimeters
Drive wheels	1200-millimeter diameter
Boiler	
Grate area	1.07 square meters
Diameter	1100 millimeters
Length	3200 millimeters
Firebox	5.50 square meters
Tubes (136 at 45 millimeters)	55.00 square meters
Total heating surface	60.50 square meters
Working pressure	11 kilograms per square centimeter
Tractive effort	4244 kilograms
Horsepower	342
Engine weights	
Operating	28,580 kilograms
Empty	23,000 kilograms
Capacities	3.26 cubic meters water; 1000 kilograms (Tender) coal.

(Courtesy: RENFE) Neg. No. 850B

In 1896 Sharp, Stewart & Company supplied two type 2–4–0 tank engines to the Bilbao & Portugalete Railway (nos. 4 and 12). Locomotive no. 4 was used on 5-foot 6-inch gauge rail having cylinders 15 by 20 inches and drive wheels 4 feet 6 inches in diameter. The water and coal capacities were 1000 gallons and 1 ton plus 10 hundredweights, respectively. The work order number was E 1070. Name was "Sestao."
(Courtesy: Mitchell Library, Glasgow) SS/E 1070

In 1902 Dubs & Company constructed two type 2–6–2 tank locomotives for use on the lines of the Santander & Bilbao Railway (nos. 27–28). Pertinent specifications were as follows:

Gauge	3 feet 3⅜ inches
Work order no.	E 4221
Engine name:	"Cadacua"
Cylinders	15 inches by 20 inches
Drive wheels	3-foot 3-inch diameter
Boiler heating area	951 square feet
Working steam pressure	160 pounds per square inch
Tractive force	15,754 pounds
Operating weight	39 tons plus 7 hundredweights
Capacities	850 gallons water; 51 cubic feet coal.

(Courtesy: Mitchell Library, Glasgow) D/E 4221

The Cia Minera de Sierra Menera Railway of Spain in 1902 procured a single type 0–6–2 tank locomotive from Sharp, Stewart & Company (no. 1). This engine was named "Sagunto" and had the following general specifications:

Gauge	3 feet 3⅜ inches
Work order no.	E 1192
Cylinders	14 3/16 by 20 inches
Drivers	2-foot 11 7/16-inch diameter
Capacities	880 gallons water; 1 ton plus 5 hundredweights coal.

(Courtesy: Mitchell Library, Glasgow) SS/E 1192

In 1906 the F. C. Central Aragon Railway purchased five Mallet articulated type compound locomotives from the Swiss Winterthur manufacturer. These were type 0–6–6–0 engines which bore the classifications 060–4011/4014 and engine numbers 51 to 54. Specifications were:

Cylinders (4)
   Hi-pressure   400 by 600 millimeters
   Lo-pressure   600 by 600 millimeters
Drive wheels   1200-millimeter diameter
Boiler
   Grate area   2.5 square meters
   Diameter   1416 millimeters
   Length   4500 millimeters
   Firebox   11 square meters
   Tubes (207 at 50 millimeters) 145 square meters
   Total heat surface   156 square meters
   Working pressure   13 kilograms per square centi-
                           meter
Tractive effort   11,603 kilograms
Horsepower   950
Engine weights
   Operating   68,200 kilograms
   Empty   62,000 kilograms.

(Courtesy: RENFE) Neg. No. 2598B

In 1907 the North British Locomotive Company built two type 4–6–0 tender locomotives for use on the Medina Del Campo A Zamora Y Orense A Vigo Railway (nos. 60–61). These engines had the following specifications:

Gauge   5 feet 5¹³/₁₆ inches
Work order no.   L 200
Cylinders   19 by 26 inches
Drive wheels   5-foot 1½-inch diameter
Boiler heating surface   2113 square feet
Working steam pressure   170 pounds per square inch
Operating weights
   Engine   55 tons
   Tender   33 tons plus 11 hundredweights
Tender capacities   2730 gallons water; 5 tons coal.

This illustration pictures a model of a 2–8–8–0 prototype tank engine built in 1908 by Kitson-Meyer of Leeds, England. The original locomotive was used on the 5-foot 6-inch gauge Great Southern Railway of Spain. Specifications were as follows:

Cylinders (4) Hi-pressure	14.75 by 24 inches
Coupled drive wheels (8)	48-inch diameter
Boiler	
Length	15 feet
Diameter	5 feet 6 inches
Pressure	180 pounds per square inch
Capacities	
Tank	2300 gallons water
Bunker	2.5 tons coal
Operating weight	101 tons
Adhesion weight	90 tons.

(Courtesy: George Dow, World Locomotive Models)

In 1913 the Cia Minera de Sierra Menera Railway of Spain purchased two type 4–8–0 tender engines from the North British Locomotive Company (nos. 15–16). Machine no. 16, named "Casual," carried these specifications:

Gauge	3 feet 3⅜ inches
Work order	L 531
Cylinders	19 by 24 inches
Drive wheels	3-foot 9-inch diameter
Boiler heating area	1703 square feet
Working steam pressure	180 pounds per square inch
Tractive force	26,000 pounds
Operating weights	
Engine	63 tons plus 4 hundredweights
Tender	35 tons with 5 hundredweights
Tender capacities	3080 gallons water; 202 cubic feet coal.

(Courtesy: Mitchell Library, Glasgow) (L 531)

This 0–4–0 tank engine, named "Odiel," was used on the Tharsis Railway in the Rio Tinto copper mining area of Southern Spain in the 1920s. (*Courtesy: RENFE*)

The Tharsis Sulphur & Copper Company of Spain in 1930 purchased four type 2–8–0 tank locomotives from the North British Locomotive Company (nos. 44–47). Specifications follow on engine no. 46:

Gauge	4 feet
Class	H
Work order no.	L 871
Cylinders	20 by 22 inches
Drivers	3-foot 11¼-inch diameter
Boiler heating surface	1190.5 square feet
Working steam pressure	180 pounds per square inch
Tractive force	28,495 pounds at 85 percent boiler working pressure
Operating weight	59 tons plus 3 hundredweights
Capacities	(not stated) water; 2 tons plus 10 hundredweights coal.

(*Courtesy: Mitchell Library, Glasgow*) (L 871)

Pictured is a streamlined steam locomotive, type 4–8–2, built in 1939 by La Maquinista T. & M. for use on the Madrid, Zaragosa, Alicante Railway. These engines carried the classification 241–2101/2110 and were numbered 1801–10. Specifications were:

Cylinders	560 by 710 millimeters
Drive wheels	1750-millimeter diameter
Boiler	
Grate area	5.0 square meters
Diameter	1800 millimeters
Length	5790 millimeters
Firebox	19.20 square meters
Tubes (85 at 60 millimeters plus 42 at 143 millimeters)	186.60 square meters
Total heating surface	205.80 square meters
Working pressure	20 kilograms per square centimeter
Tractive effort	16,917 kilograms
Horsepower	2400
Engine weights	
Operating	117,500 kilograms
Empty	107,500 kilograms.

(Courtesy: RENFE) Neg. No. 1828B

A streamlined steam locomotive built in Spain by the La Maquinista T. & M. in 1942 is pictured. This was a type 2–10–2 engine classified as 151–3101/3120 and bearing the identification numbers 5001 to 5020. This machine was used on the main lines of Spain to haul heavy freight trains. Specifications were:

Cylinders	570 by 750 millimeters
Drive wheels	1560-millimeters diameter
Boiler	
Grate area	5.30 square meters
Diameter	2000 millimeters
Length	6325 millimeters
Firebox	26.15 square meters
Tubes (150 at 55 millimeters plus 48 at 133 millimeters)	267.57 square meters
Total heating surface	293.72 square meters
Working pressure	16 kilograms per square centimeter
Tractive effort	25,000 kilograms
Horsepower	2700
Engine weights	
Operating	144,710 kilograms
Empty	130,710 kilograms.

(Courtesy: RENFE) Neg. No. 352D

Shown here is a Mikado type 2–8–2 locomotive (class 141) introduced for service on the railways of the RENFE in 1953. Specifications were as follows:

Cylinders	(not available)
Drive wheels	1560-meters
Boiler	
Superheater	72.00 square meters
Total heating surface	207.50 square meters
Working pressure	15 kilograms per square centimeter
Tractive effort	14,790 kilograms
Horsepower	2000
Operating weights	
175,000 kilograms (engine plus tender)	
104,500 kilograms (engine only)	
72,000 kilograms adherence.	

(Courtesy: RENFE) Neg. No. 133D

In 1953 the Spanish National Railways (Red Nacionale De Los Ferrocarriles Espanoles) purchased twenty-five type 2–8–2 tender locomotives from the North British Locomotive Company (nos. 141–2101 to 141–2125). These Mikado engines carried the following specifications:

Gauge	5 feet 6 inches
Work order no. L 5	(second series)
Cylinders	570 by 710 millimeters
Drive wheels	1560-millimeter diameter
Boiler heating surface	2795 square feet
Working steam pressure	15 kilograms per square centimeter
Operating weights	
Engine	99 tons plus 19 hundredweights
Tender	61 tons plus 18 hundredweights
Tender capacities	5950 gallons water; 11 tons plus 4 hundredweights coal.

(Courtesy: Mitchell Library, Glasgow) L 5 (2d Series)

This type 0–4–0 shunting engine was used on the JOP
Huelva Railways of Spain; the locomotive was built
by the Orenstein & Koppel firm in Germany.
(*Courtesy: RENFE*)

Pictured is a 2–6–2 tank engine built by Beyer Peacock
for use on the meter-gauge Alcoy & Gandia Railway
of Spain.
(*Courtesy: RENFE*)

Pictured is a type 2–8–0, class 140, freight locomotive
in 1962 on the railways between Grenada and Lorca in
southeastern Spain. No other data were available.
(Courtesy: RENFE)

SUDAN

SUDAN, ONCE A BRITISH PROTECTORATE IN northern Africa, initiated a railway under Egyptian auspices in the early 1830s. The rail line started at Wadi Halfa', on the Egypt-Sudan border, and ran a few miles southeast. In 1885 the British built a military railroad south along the White Nile from Wadi Halfa' to Akasha, about seventy miles, as part of a campaign to speed relief for General Gordon's forces at Khartoum. This line was later extended about one hundred miles farther south to Kerma; however, all this rail was lifted in 1905 when the rail line from Wadi Halfa' to Abu Hamad, across the Nubian Desert, was finally completed.

The railway from Wadi Halfa' to Abu Hamad by 1911 was extended to Atbarah and Shandi, then on to Khartoum at the junction of the Blue and White Nile rivers. A branch line was built later, running southwest from Abu Hamad to Karima, about 115 miles distant, but it was constructed ten to fifteen miles north of the White Nile and consequently did little or nothing for people living near that river.

Between 1910 and 1920, a rail line was constructed reaching southeast from Khartoum roughly parallel to the Blue Nile to Wad Madani and Sannar—about 150 miles. This railroad from Khartoum to Sannar greatly diminished the value of this part of the Blue Nile for normal river navigation.

In 1911 a line was completed from Sannar west about seventy-five miles to Kusti on the White Nile. A line was also extended about fifty-five miles from Sannar east to the Raha River, with a crossing near Al-Hawata. Another railroad was later pushed west from Kusti to Ar-Rahad, about 130 miles, with a forty-mile branch to Al Ubayyid. Later still, a long rail extension was laid from Ar-Rahad west about 375 miles, terminating at Nyala in the western Sudan.

In 1923 a rail line was built northeast from Al-Hawata to Al-Qadarif and then northeast and north to Kassala, near the Ethiopian border—a total of about 175 miles. A rail line running south from Sannar along the Blue Nile to a dam site near Ar-Rusayris (about 125 miles) was completed in 1955.

At present, the headquarters of the Sudan Railways Corporation, a national government railway system, is located at Hadid Atbarah. In 1978 *Janes World Railways* reported that the Sudan Railways had a route length of 4,780 kilometers (2,970 miles) of 3-foot 6-inch gauge rail in active use.

The Sudanese railways were principally equipped with British steam locomotives, but some Baldwin machines were procured around the turn of the twentieth century. Such English manufacturers as Neilson, Kitson, Beyer Peacock, Robert Stephenson, and the North British Locomotive Company were involved. The following twenty-four illustrations outline the history of the steam locomotive in Sudan from 1898 to 1955.

In 1898 Neilson, Reid & Company constructed three tender locomotives for the Egyptian War Office for use in the Sudan. These engines had a 4–8–0 wheel arrangement and were numbered 33, 34, and 35. Specifications follow:

Gauge	3 feet 6 inches
Cylinders	17 by 23 inches
Coupled drive wheels	3-foot 6¼-inch diameter
Boiler heating area	1078 square feet
Boiler working pressure	160 pounds per square inch
Operating weights	
Engine	46 tons plus 12 hundredweights
Tender	33 tons plus 17 hundredweights
Tender capacities	2600 gallons water; 256 cubic feet coal.

(Courtesy: Mitchell Library, Glasgow) E 180

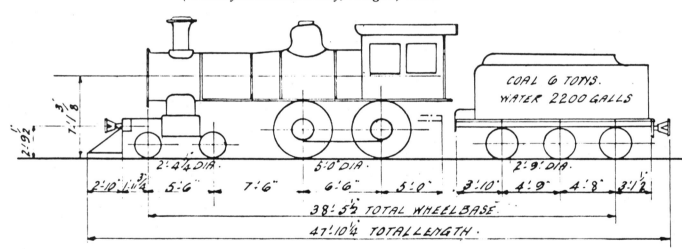

In 1898 the Baldwin Locomotive Works furnished the Sudan Railways with a number of class 36, type 4–4–0, tender locomotives. Specifications of the enginee were as follows:

Rail gauge	3 feet 6 inches
Cylinders	15 by 24 inches
Coupled drive wheels	5-foot diameter
Bogie wheels	2-foot 4.25-inch diameter
Tender wheels (6)	2-foot 9-inch diameter
Boiler	
Grate area	13.58 square feet
Tubes	877 square feet
Firebox	86 square feet
Total heating surface	963 square feet
Working pressure	165 pounds per square inch
Tractive force	11,137 pounds at 75 percent boiler working pressure
Operating weight	
57 tons (engine plus tender)	
22 tons adhesion	
Tender capacities	2200 gallons water; 6 tons coal
Overall length	47 feet 10.25 inches.

(Courtesy: Sudan Railways)

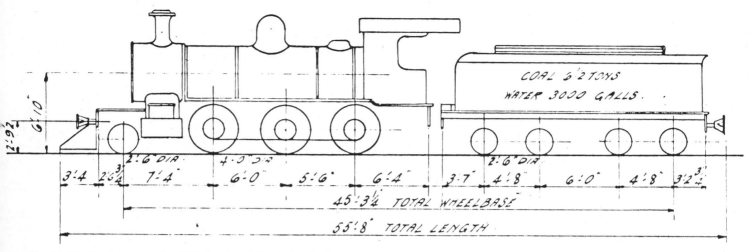

The Baldwin Locomotive Works furnished the Sudan Railways in 1900 several class 40, type 2–6–0, tender locomotives. A drawing of these engines is shown. Specifications were as follows:

Rail gauge	3 feet 6 inches
Cylinders	17 by 22 inches
Drive wheels	4-foot diameter
Bogie wheels	2-foot 6-inch diameter
Tender wheels (8)	2-foot 6-inch diameter
Boiler	
Grate area	16.6 square feet
Tubes	990.63 square feet
Firebox	100.88 square feet
Total heating surface	1091.51 square feet
Working pressure	160 pounds per square inch
Tractive effort	15,895 pounds at 75 percent boiler working pressure
Operating weight	
71.3 tons (engine plus tender)	
30.4 tons adhesion	
Tender capacities	3000 gallons water; 6.5 tons coal
Overall length	55 feet 8 inches.

(Courtesy: Sudan Railways)

Kitson & Company of Leeds, England supplied the Sudan Railways in 1902 with several class 51, type 4–4–0, tender engines which are shown in the drawing. Specifications were:

Cylinders	15 by 24 inches
Drive wheels	4-foot 4-inch diameter
Bogie wheels	2-foot 4-inch diameter
Tender wheels (6)	3-foot 1-inch diameter
Boiler	
Grate area	15.2 square feet
Tubes	767.7 square feet
Firebox	5.5 square feet
Total heating surface	853.2 square feet
Working pressure	150 pounds per square inch
Tractive effort	11,683 pounds at 75 percent boiler working pressure
Operating weight	
64 tons plus 10 hundredweights (engine plus tender)	
21 tons plus 13 hundredweights adhesion	
Tender capacities	2400 gallons water; 6 tons coal
Overall length	48 feet 5.5 inches.

(Courtesy: Sudan Railways)

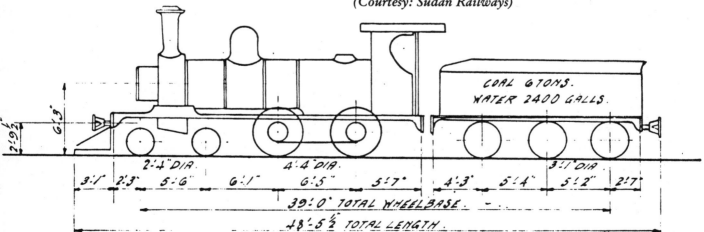

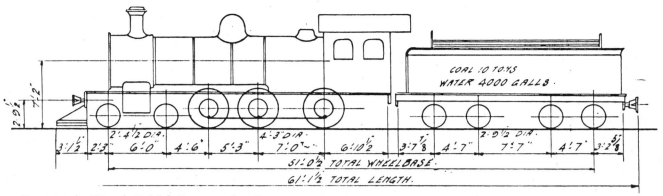

In 1904 the North British Locomotive Company supplied the Sudan Railways with several class 57, type 4–6–0, tender locomotives. Specifications were:

Cylinders	18.5 by 24 inches
Drive wheels	4-foot 3-inch diameter
Bogie wheels	2-foot 4.5-inch diameter
Tender wheels (8)	2-foot 9.5-inch diameter
Boiler	
Grate area	25.9 square feet
Superheater	262.5 square feet
Tubes	
Small	418.88 square feet (196 2-inch outside diameter)
Large	588.96 square feet
Firebox	104.60 square feet
Total heating surface	1112.44 square feet
Working pressure	175 pounds per square inch
Tractive force	22,680 pounds at 85 percent boiler working pressure
Operating weight	
99 tons plus 11 hundredweights (engine and tender)	
41 tons plus 12 hundredweights adhesion	
Tender capacities	4000 gallons water; 10 tons coal
Overall length	61 feet 1.5 inches.

See a drawing of the above engine.
(Courtesy: Sudan Railways)

In 1904 the North British Locomotive Company furnished a second series of type 4–6–0 tender engines; these were class 69 locomotives, slightly smaller and less powerful than the class 57 machines, and were designed, apparently, for passenger service. The valve gear used Stephenson's link motion, and vacuum brakes were installed. Specifications were:

Cylinders	17 by 22 inches
Drive wheels	4-foot 6-inch diameter
Bogie wheels	2-foot 4.5-inch diameter
Tender wheels (8)	2-foot 9.5-inch diameter
Grate area	17.3 square feet
Tubes (153 2-inch outer diameter)	971.5 square feet
Firebox	110.0 square feet
Total heating surface	1081.5 square feet
Working pressure	175 pounds per square inch
Tractive effort	15,453 pounds at 75 percent boiler working pressure
Operating weight	91 tons plus 17 hundredweights (engine plus tender)
	37 tons plus 17 hundredweights adhesion
Tender capacities	3600 gallons water; 6 tons coal
Overall length	56.5 feet.

See a drawing of the above engine.
(Courtesy: Sudan Railways)

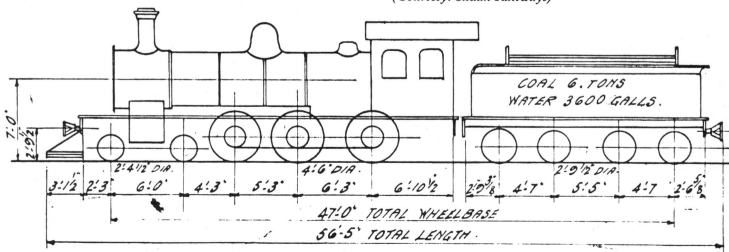

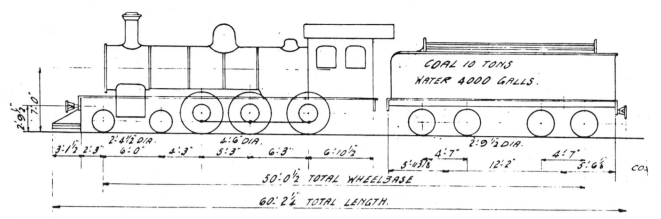

COAL 10 TONS
WATER 4000 GALLS.

50'0½ TOTAL WHEELBASE

60'2¼ TOTAL LENGTH.

The Sudan Railways in 1907 purchased additional type 4–6–0 tender engines from the North British Locomotive Company; these are shown in the outline drawing. These class 86 locomotives were quite similar to the class 69 locomotives previously described. Specifications were as follows:

Cylinders	17 by 23 inches
Drive wheels	4-foot 6-inch diameter
Bogie wheels	2-foot 4.5-inch diameter
Tender wheels (8)	2-foot 9.5-inch diameter
Boiler	
Grate area	18.8 square feet
Tubes (153 2-inch outer diameter)	971.5 square feet
Firebox	105.0 square feet
Total heating surface	1076.5 square feet
Working pressure	175 pounds per square inch
Tractive force	16,156 pounds at 75 percent boiler working pressure
Operating weight	
93 tons plus 12 hundredweights (engine plus tender)	
36 tons plus 17 hundredweights adherence	
Tender capacities	4000 gallons water; 10 tons coal
Brakes	Vacuum type
Valve gear	Stephenson's link motion, 3 fitted Marshall gear
Overall length	60 feet 2.25 inches.

(Courtesy: Sudan Railways)

In 1907 Beyer, Peacock & Company of Manchester, England submitted several type 4–6–0 tender locomotives which, as class 96, were more powerful than earlier class engines 57, 69, and 86. The engines were apparently used on freight services on the Sudan Railways which maintains temperatures as high as 120° F. with high humidities and some altitudes reaching to 3035 feet above sea level. Specifications were as follows:

Cylinders	18 by 24 inches
Drive wheels	4-foot diameter
Bogie wheels	2-foot 4.5-inch diameter
Tender wheels (8)	2-foot 9.5-inch diameter
Boiler	
Grate area	2.4 square feet
Tubes (196 2-inch outer diameter)	1282.7 square feet
Firebox	102.0 square feet
Total heating surface	1384.7 square feet
Working pressure	175 pounds per square inch
Tractive force	21,262 pounds at 75 percent boiler working pressure
Operating weight	
97 tons plus 7 hundredweights (engine plus tender)	
39 tons plus 7 hundredweights adhesion	
Tender capacities	4000 gallons water; 10 tons coal
Overall length	60 feet 7.75 inches.

See engine drawing.
(Courtesy: Sudan Railways)

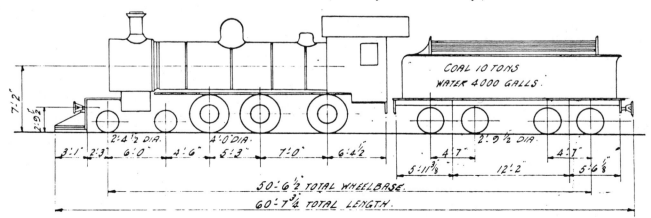

COAL 10 TONS
WATER 4000 GALLS.

50'6½ TOTAL WHEELBASE.

60'7¾ TOTAL LENGTH.

The Sudan Government Railways in 1908 acquired five type 2–6–0 tender engines (not illustrated) from Kitson & Company of Leeds, England. These were numbered 100–104. Specifications were:

Cylinders	16.5 by 22 inches
Drive wheels	4-foot 3-inch diameter
Bogie wheels	2-foot 7-inch diameter
Tender wheels (8)	2-foot 9.5-inch diameter
Boiler	
Grate area	17 square feet
Tubes	965 square feet
Firebox	107 square feet
Total heating surface	1072 square feet
Working pressure	175 pounds per square inch
Tractive force	15,414 pounds at 75 percent boiler working pressure
Operating weight	82 tons plus 2 hundredweights (engine plus tender)
Tender capacities	3500 gallons water; 8 tons coal
Overall length	55 feet 0⅜ inches.

(Courtesy: Sudan Railways)

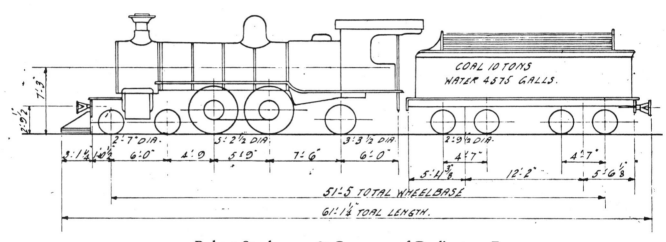

Robert Stephenson & Company of Darlington, England built several class 110, type 4–4–2, tender locomotives in 1910 for express services on the Sudan Railways. Specifications were:

Cylinders	18 by 26 inches
Drive wheels	5-foot 2.5-inch diameter
Bogie wheels	
Front	2-foot 2-inch diameter
Rear	3-foot 3.5-inch diameter
Tender wheels (8)	2-foot 9.5-inch diameter
Boiler	
Grate area	24.75 square feet
Tubes (194 2-inch outer diameter)	1406 square feet
Firebox	112 square feet
Total heating surface	1518 square feet
Working pressure	175 pounds per square inch
Tractive effort	17,690 pounds at 75 percent boiler working pressure
Operating weight	105 tons plus 7 hundredweights (engine plus tender)
Tender capacities	4575 gallons water; 10 tons coal
Overall length	61 feet 1.25 inches.

    See drawing.
(Courtesy: Sudan Railways)

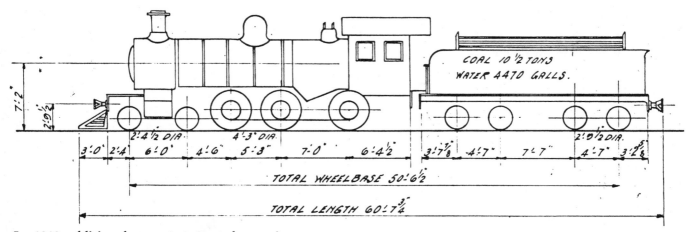

In 1910 additional type 4–6–0 tender engines were purchased for use on the railways of Sudan. These were supplied by Beyer Peacock and identified as class 99. Specifications were as follows:

Cylinders	18 by 24 inches
Coupled drive wheels	4-foot 3-inch diameter
Bogie wheels	2-foot 4.5-inch diameter
Tender wheels (8)	2-foot 9.5-inch diameter
Boiler	
Grate	23.6 square feet
Tubes (196 2-inch outer diameter)	1282.7 square feet
Firebox	102.0 square feet
Total heating surface	1384.7 square feet
Working pressure	175 pounds per square inch
Tractive effort	20,012 pounds at 75 percent boiler working pressure
Operating weight	98 tons plus 17 hundredweights (engine plus tender)
Tender capacities	4470 gallons water; 10.5 tons coal
Overall length	60 feet 7.75 inches.

See drawing.
(Courtesy: Sudan Railways)

In 1911 the North British Locomotive Company furnished the Sudan government three type 4–6–0 tender locomotives (nos. 105, 106, and 107) having these specifications:

Gauge	3 feet 6 inches
Cylinders	18 by 24 inches
Drivers	4-foot 3-inch diameter
Boiler heaing area	1384 square feet
Boiler working pressure	180 pounds per square inch
Tractive force	20,580 pounds
Operating weights	
Engine	51 tons plus 7 hundredweights
Tender	51 tons plus 17 hundredweights
Tender water capacity	4600 gallons.

(Courtesy: Mitchell Library, Glasgow) L 420

In 1911 the Sudan Railways purchased several class 120, type 4–6–2, tender locomotives from the North British Locomotive Company. These were superheated models with the following specifications:

Cylinders	18 by 24 inches
Drive wheels	4-foot 6-inch diameter
Bogie wheels	
Front	2-foot 4.5-inch diameter
Rear	3-foot diameter
Tender wheels (8)	2-foot 9.5-inch diameter
Boiler	
Grate area	22 square feet
Superheater	220 square feet
Tubes	
100 2-inch outer diameter	834.95 square feet
14 5-inch outer diameter	292.19 square feet
Firebox	110.58 square feet
Total heating surface	1237.72 square feet
Working pressure	175 pounds per square inch
Tractive force	21,420 pounds at 85 percent boiler working pressure
Operating weight	
99 tons plus 18 hundredweights (engine plus tender)	
33 tons plus 17 hundredweights adhesion	
Tender capacities	Not available
Overall length	62 feet 9.5 inches.

Not illustrated.
(*Courtesy: Sudan Railways*)

The Sudan government in 1911 purchased from the North British Locomotive Company, four type 4–6–2 tender engines (nos. 120–23) with the following characteristics:

Gauge	3 feet 6 inches
Cylinders	18 by 24 inches
Coupled drivers	4-foot 6-inch diameter
Boiler heating surface	1520 square feet
Boiler working pressure	180 pounds per square inch
Tractive force	19,440 pounds
Operating weights	
Engine	54 tons plus 1 hundredweight
Tender	45 tons plus 17 hundredweights
Tender capacities	4000 gallons water; 315 cubic feet coal.

(*Courtesy: Mitchell Library, Glasgow*) L 419

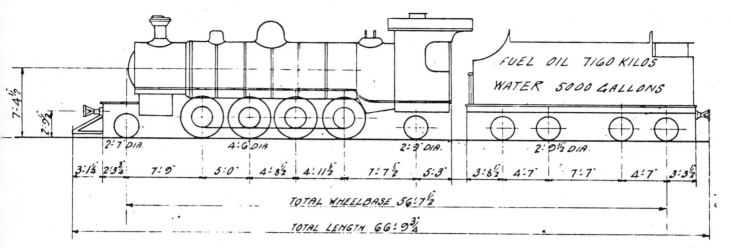

FUEL OIL 7160 KILOS
WATER 5000 GALLONS

7'-4½" 2'-9½"

2'-7" DIA.   4'-6" DIA.   2'-9" DIA.   2'-9½" DIA.

3'-1½" 2'-3¾" 7'-9"   5'-0" 4'-8½" 4'-11½" 7'-7½" 5'-3" 3'-8½" 4'-7" 7'-7" 4'-7" 3'-3½"

TOTAL WHEELBASE 56'-7½"

TOTAL LENGTH 66'-9¾"

In 1920 the Sudan Railways embarked on a program of using substantially heavier freight engines when the North British Locomotive Company constructed a number of class 150, type 2–8–2, tender machines. These locomotives had superheaters, steam and vacuum brakes, and were equipped with Walschaert's gear; also oil replaced coal as a fuel source. Specifications on the engine shown in the drawing were as follows:

Cylinders	21 by 27 inches
Drive wheels	4-foot 6-inch diameter
Bogie wheels	
Front	2-foot 7-inch diameter
Rear	2-foot 9-inch diameter
Tender wheels (8)	2-foot 9.5-inch diameter
Boiler	
Grate area	33.1 square feet
Superheater	372 square feet
Tubes	
107 2-inch outer diameter	870 square feet
24 5.25-inch outer diameter	512 square feet
Firebox	155 square feet
Total heating surface	1537 square feet
Working pressure	180 pounds per square inch
Tractive force	33,737 pounds at 85 percent boiler working pressure
Operating weight	130 tons plus 7 hundredweights (engine plus tender)
Tender capacities	5000 gallons water; 7160 kilograms fuel oil
Overall length	66 feet 9.75 inches.

(Courtesy: Sudan Railways)

In 1923 Robert Stephenson & Company of Darlington, England constructed a number of class 180, type 2–8–2 freight engines for use on the Sudan Railways. The outline drawing shows the above engine which had the following specifications:

Cylinders	19 by 24 inches
Drive wheels	4-foot 3-inch diameter
Bogie wheels	
Front	2-foot 7-inch diameter
Rear	2-foot 9-inch diameter
Tender wheels (8)	2-foot 9.5-inch diameter
Boiler	
Grate area	26 square feet
Superheater	260 square feet
Tubes	
83 2-inch outside diameter	652 square feet
18 5-inch outside diameter	371 square feet
Firebox	142 square feet
Total heating surface	1165 square feet
Working pressure	180 pounds per square inch
Tractive force	25,992 at 85 percent boiler working pressure
Operating weight	109 tons plus 7 hundredweights (engine plus tender)
Tender capacities	4000 gallons water; 7160 kilograms fuel oil
Overall length	63 feet 3⅜ inches
Valve gear	Walschaert's
Brake gear	Steam and vacuum.

(Courtesy: Sudan Railways)

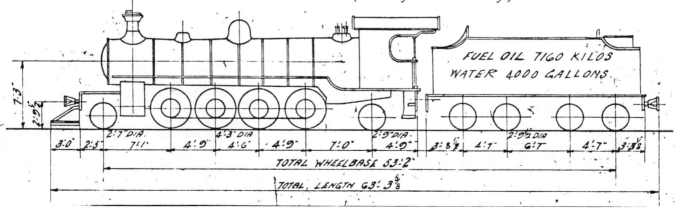

FUEL OIL 7160 KILOS
WATER 4000 GALLONS.

7'-3" 2'-9½"

2'-7" DIA.   4'-3" DIA.   2'-9" DIA.   2'-9½" DIA

3'-0" 2'-5" 7'-1"   4'-9" 4'-6" 4'-9"   7'-0" 4'-9" 3'-8½" 4'-7" 6'-7" 4'-7" 3'-3½"

TOTAL WHEELBASE 53'-2"

TOTAL LENGTH 63'-3⅝"

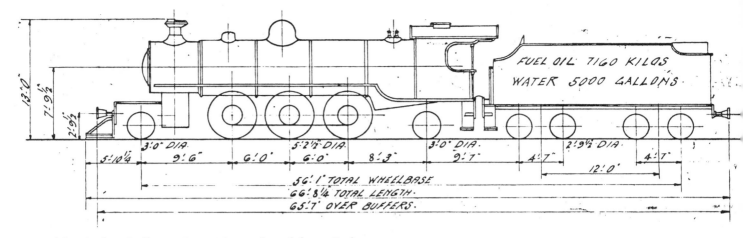

The Sudan Railways in 1925 purchased from Robert Stephenson & Company a number of class 200, type 2–6–2, superheated tender locomotives. The engine in the drawing had the following specifications:

Cylinders	21 by 27 inches
Drive wheels	5-foot 2.5-inch diameter
Bogie wheels (front and rear)	3-foot diameter
Tender wheels (8)	2-foot 9.5-inch diameter
Boiler	
Grate area	33.1 square feet
Superheater	372.0 square feet
Tubes	
107 2-inch outside diameter	870 square feet
24 5.25-inch outside diameter	512 square feet
Firebox	155 square feet
Total heating surface	1537 square feet
Working pressure	180 pounds per square inch
Tractive effort	29,149 pounds at 85 percent boiler working pressure
Operating weight	127 tons plus 5 hundredweights (engine plus tender)
Tender capacities	5000 gallons water; 7160 kilograms fuel oil
Overall length	65 feet 7 inches (over buffers)
Valve gear	Walschaert's
Brake gear	Steam and vacuum.

(Courtesy: Sudan Railways)

In 1927 the North British Locomotive Company constructed ten type 4–6–2 tender engines for the Sudan Government Railways (nos. 220–29) Specifications follow:

Gauge	3 feet 6 inches
Cylinders	18 by 24 inches
Coupled drivers	4-foot 6-inch diameter
Boiler heating surface	1385 square feet
Boiler working pressure	189 pounds per square inch
Tractive force	19,440 pounds
Operating weights	
Engine	58 tons
Tender	48 tons plus 6 hundredweights
Tender capacities	4000 gallons water; 360 cubic feet fuel.

(Courtesy: Mitchell Library, Glasgow) L 831

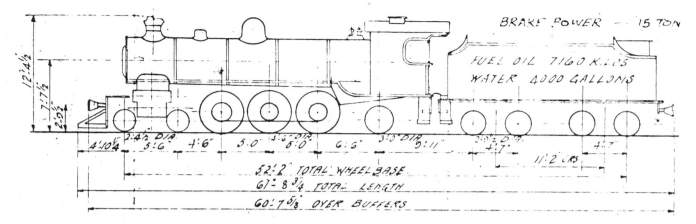

The Sudan Railways in 1927 purchased a series of Pacific type 4–6–2, class 220, tender locomotives from the North British Locomotive Company and Kitson & Company (Kitson built engines identified as 230 to 235). Specifications were:

Cylinders	18 by 24 inches
Drive wheels	4-foot 6-inch diameter
Bogie wheels	
Front	2-foot 4.5-inch diameter
Rear	3-foot diameter
Tender wheels (8)	2-foot 9.5-inch diameter
Boiler	
Grate area	26 square feet
Superheater	260 square feet
Tubes	
83 2-inch outside diameter	627 square feet
18 5.25-inch outside diameter	356 square feet
Firebox	142 square feet
Total heating surface	1125 square feet
Working pressure	180 pounds per square inch
Tractive force	22,032 pounds at 85 percent boiler working pressure
Operating weight	106 tons plus 6 hundredweights (engine plus tender)
Tender capacities	4000 gallons water; 7160 kilograms fuel oil
Overall length	60 feet 7⅝ inches
Brake power	15 tons
Valve gear	Walschaert's
Brake gear	Steam and vacuum.

    See drawing.
(Courtesy: Sudan Railways)

In 1937–38 the Sudan Railways added to their rolling stock a number of class 100, type 4–6–4 plus 4–6–4, Beyer Garratt engines built by Beyer Peacock. The engines shown in the outline drawing had these specifications:

Cylinders (4)	16.75 by 26 inches
Drive wheels (6)	4-foot 9-inch diameter
Bogie wheels (16)	2-foot 9-inch diameter
Boiler	
Grate area	43.2 square feet
Superheater	440.0 square feet
Tubes	
180 2-inch outside diameter	1169 square feet
36 5.25-inch outside diameter	607 square feet
Firebox and arch tubes	184 square feet
Total heating surface	1960 square feet
Tractive force	43,520 pounds at 85 percent boiler working pressure
Operating weight	168 tons plus 16 hundredweights
Water capacity	
Front tank	4300 gallons
Rear tank	2700 gallons
Total	7000 gallons
Buker capacity	10 tons coal
Overall length	89 feet 11.25 inches.

(Courtesy: Sudan Railways)

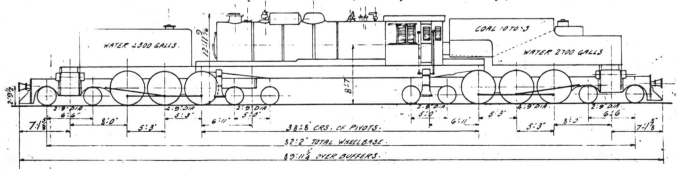

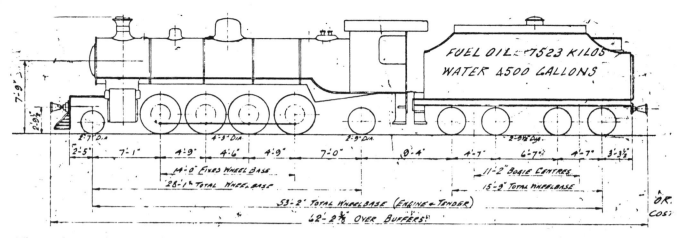

The Sudan Railways in 1952 acquired from the North British Locomotive Company a number of class 310, type 2–8–2, heavy freight tender engines with the following specifications:

Cylinders	19 by 24 inches
Drive wheels	4-foot 3-inch diameter
Bogie wheels	
Front	2-foot 7-inch diameter
Rear	2-foot 9-inch diameter
Tender wheels (8)	2-foot 9-inch diameter
Boiler	
Grate area	26 square feet
Superheater	260 square feet
Tubes	
83 2-inch outside diameter	627 square feet
18 5.25-inch outside diameter	356 square feet
Firebox	142 square feet
Total heating surface	1125 square feet
Working pressure	180 pounds per square inch
Tractive force	25,992 pounds at 85 percent boiler working pressure
Operating weight	113 tons plus 17 hundredweights (engine plus tender)
Tender capacities	4500 gallons water; 7523 kilograms fuel oil
Overall length	62 feet 2⅜ inches
Valve gear	Walschaert's
Brake power	15.48 tons
Brake gear	Steam and vacuum.

    See drawing.
(Courtesy: Sudan Railways)

The Sudan Railways in 1952 purchased from the North British Locomotive Company nineteen type 2–8–2 oil-fired tender engines (nos. 310–28). Specifications were as follows:

Gauge	3 feet 6 inches
Cylinders	19 by 24 inches
Coupled drivers	4-foot 3-inch diameter
Boiler heating surface	1385 square feet
Boiler working pressure	180 pounds per square inch
Tractive force	25,992 pounds
Operating weights	
Engine	61 tons plus 7 hundredweights
Tender	49 tons plus 10 hundredweights
Tender capacities	4500 gallons water; 1840 gallons oil.

(Courtesy: Mitchell Library, Glasgow) L1 2d series

In 1955 the North British Locomotive Company furnished the Sudan Railways with a number of type 4–8–2 heavy tender locomotives which are not illustrated. Specifications were:

Class 500	
Cylinders	25.5 by 26 inches
Drive wheels	4-foot 6-inch diameter
Bogie wheels	
Front	2-foot 5.4-inch diameter
Rear	2-foot 9.5-inch diameter
Tender wheels (8)	2-foot 9.5-inch diameter
Boiler	
Grate area	40 square feet
Superheater	542 square feet
Tubes	
122 2.25-inch outside diameter	1258 square feet
36 5.25-inch outside diameter	769 square feet
Firebox	203 square feet
Total heating area	2230 square feet
Working pressure	190 pounds per square inch
Tractive force	35,940 pounds at 85 percent boiler working pressure
Operating weight	147 tons plus 19 hundredweights (engine plus tender)
Tender capacities	6272 gallons water; 7000 kilograms fuel oil
Overall length	71 feet (over buffers)
Brake power	15.75 tons
Valve gear	Walschaert's
Brake gear	Steam and vacuum
Maximum trailing load	1400 tons.

(Courtesy: Sudan Railways)

In 1955 the North British Locomotive Company supplied the Sudan Railways with forty-two type 4–8–2 oil-fired tender steam locomotives (running numbers 500–541). Specifications follow:

Gauge	3 feet 6 inches
Cylinders	21½ by 26 inches
Drive wheels	4-foot 6-inch diameter
Boiler heating surface	2772 square feet
Boiler working pressure	190 pounds per square inch
Tractive force	35,940 pounds
Operating weights	
Engine	(not stated)
Tender	(not stated)
Tender capacities	6260 gallons water; 1700 gallons oil.

(Courtesy: Mitchell Library, Glasgow)

SWEDEN

THE DAWN OF RAILWAY DEVELOPMENT CAME TO Sweden between 1854 and 1856, and construction continued until World War II, after which little further expansion took place. The oldest parts of the present Swedish State Railways opened on 1 December 1856; these were rail lines running several miles from Gothenburg to Jonsered, and from Malmö about ten miles to Lund, in the far south of Sweden. An illustration shows an early Swedish rail station.

Already in 1854, a Swedish legislature voted mandatory government ownership of railways. Moreover, the government showed considerable foresight in developing several guiding principles relating to the construction and operation of railways in Sweden:

1. New railways must not follow existing shipping routes, whether coastal or canal.
2. Except for terminal points, railroads were to be built in sparsely settled areas.
3. All rail activities and construction would follow a master plan.
4. Each railway line had to be operated as an individual entity, covering its own operating and maintenance expenses.

The first two rules led to the growth of new communities, especially at railway junctions. The last rule, unfortunately, hurt some poorly managed railroads with low or nonexistent profits, and occasioning long-term shutdowns in periods of financial setbacks or bad weather, or in the case of serious rail accidents.

Railway construction in Sweden was very slow. Generally, it was decreed that the state would lay down and administer the main lines and leave the building of branch and smaller lines to private initiative. Early government rail development activities were entrusted to one Nils Ericson, an energetic, farsighted planner who had worked on the Göta Canal in his youth. He was able to visualize a total, ideal rail system connecting centers of population as well as pioneer locations for future industrial growth. Such action was stimulated in 1864 when a moratorium on local taxes and tolls was declared, and manufacturing and service centers developed at various railroad junctions; the towns of Bjuv, Olofström, Hässleholm and Höganäs were examples of this kind of pioneering activity.

When Ericson severed his connections with the Swedish Railways, about 1862, the essential rail network was already largely planned. By this time, the Gothenburg–Stockholm line was finished, as well as a number of shorter railroads. For defense and economic purposes, various rail lines along the east coast were located somewhat inland, with branch lines providing short connections with seaports along the Gulf of Bothnia.

In 1898 a vital decision was made to build a rail line from Boden, in the far northeast near the border with Russian Finland, through the iron-mining areas to the frontier with Norway. The Norwegians were then to build a connection across their territory to Narvik on Ofoten Fjord, from which the iron ore of the Swedish Kiruna-Gällivare fields could be exported to world markets.

The major periods of railway construction in Sweden were from 1870 to 1882 and 1897 to 1910. As in other parts of the world, financing railroads was attended by more problems than the actual building. However, up to 1914, with large loans from foreign investors, the Swedish government was able to spend 400 million kroner ($1,071,600), which covered about 33 percent of all track laid down. The balance was covered by home loans.

In general, early Swedish railroad construction (1860 to 1914) utilized mostly English rail. Rolling stock came both from England and Germany until 1914, by which time Swedish industries were able to successfully duplicate all types of rail equipment.

Railways in Sweden were nationalized following a government edict enacted in 1939. By 1970 the state owned and operated 93 percent of all railroads, consisting of 10,300 miles of track, of which 40 percent was electrified. A map of the Swedish railroads is provided.

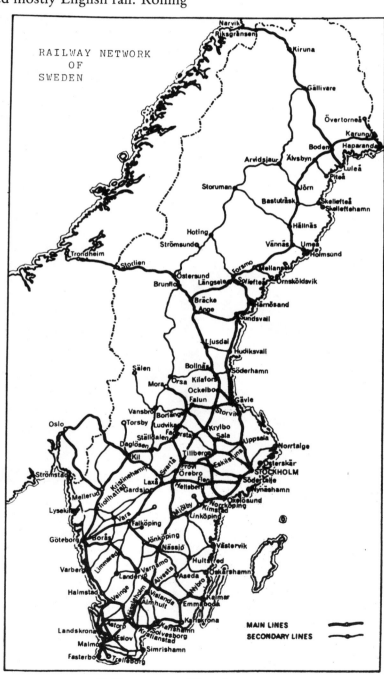

Railway map of Sweden.
(*Courtesy:* Janes World Railways)

Steam Locomotives in Sweden

The first railway engine in Sweden was of local manufacture, built in 1847 at Eskilstuna by the Munktells Mechanical Works, under the watchful eyes of the building contractor for the Norberg Railway, Frederick Sundler. The engine is pictured and described.

The pioneer commercial railroads in 1856 were equipped with locomotives made in England. With two exceptions, they were produced by Beyer Peacock. Illustrated is a typical early engine used on the Swedish State Railways (SJ). Beyer Peacock delivered mixed-traffic locomotives used on early railways in the period 1856–73. These carried the names of Swedish royalty.

Various private railways in the southern regions opened early, with engines and rolling stock purchased from miscellaneous foreign manufacturers. Shown is a locomotive built in 1885 for the Malmö–Trelleborg Railway by Hannoversche Maschinenbau A.G.

An early and continuing Swedish locomotive manufacturer was Nydqvist & Holm. One of their productions, a class Kd, type 0–6–0 freight engine, appeared in 1890. A model of this machine is pictured and described.

A typical tank engine, class S13p, type 2–6–0, built by Nydqvist & Holm in 1894 is shown.

A passenger express locomotive that saw long-term passenger service in Sweden was the class Cc, type 4–4–0 machine built by Nydqvist & Holm

The first Swedish railway engine, named "Förstlingen," a 0–4–0 tank type, was constructed for the Norberg Railway in 1847 by Munktells Mechanical Works of Eskiltuna. The outside cylinders were located between the axles, the piston rods being lengthened in both directions, with connecting rods driving each pair of wheels. In 1853 this locomotive was modified with the cylinders driving only one pair of wheels. The gauge was also changed from 3 feet (Swedish) to the standard-gauge width of 4 feet 8½ inches. In the modified form specifications were as follows:

Cylinders	8.3 by 15.5 inches
Coupled wheels	2-foot 4.3-inch diameter
Operational weight	5.6 tons.

This locomotive was also used in the construction of the Nora–Ervalla Railway and later provided service on the finished line. The engine was withdrawn from active service in 1856. Pictured is the original locomotive as it is preserved in the Swedish Railway Museum at Gävle.

(Courtesy: Swedish Railway Museum, Gävle)

The Swedish State Railways, which opened in 1856, used British manufactured locomotives built by Beyer, Peacock & Company. A prototype engine is pictured, which is a model now on display in the Swedish Railway Museum. An original order of twenty, type 2–2–2, locomotives was filled between 1863 and 1864. These had 15 by 20 inch cylinders and coupled wheels 6 feet 1.1 inch in diameter. Boilers had 941 square feet of heating surface and generated a boiler pressure of 100 pounds per square inch. Steam was distributed using slide valves actuated by Allan straight-link motions. Operational weight was 24.4 tons.
(Courtesy: Swedish Railway Museum, Gävle)

This is an old-time sketch of a railroad station at the Swedish town of Toreboda. Represented is a Beyer Peacock locomotive used on the railroads of Sweden about 1856.
(Courtesy: Swedish State Railways)

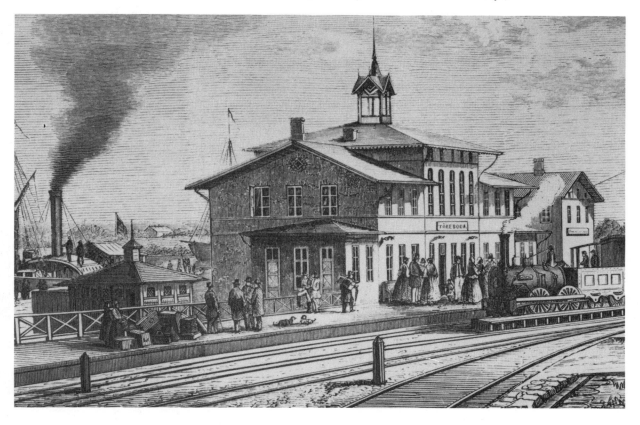

The first mixed traffic locomotives on the Swedish State Railways were class B, type 2–4–0, bearing the names of various Swedish princes. They were delivered by Beyer, Peacock & Company of Manchester, England, between 1856 and 1873. The "princes" were considered fast and handy engines. Shown is no. 3, named "Prins August", with coaches from the 1850–60 period, being filmed for the hundred-year Swedish celebrations in 1956.

Locomotive no. 3 had the following specifications:

Cylinders	394 by 508 millimeters
Drive wheels	1684-millimeter diameter
Steam pressure	7 kilograms per square centimeter
Operating weight	37.8 tons (engine plus tender)
Tender capacities	4.58 cubic meters (1210 U.S. gallons) water; 1.4 tons coal.

(Courtesy: Swedish State Railways)

In the southern part of Sweden at Scania, there existed a number of private railways with varying types of rolling stock. Some were built as light railroads, so-called steam tramways, as in Denmark and on the Continent. Pictured is the former Malmö–Trelleborg Railway locomotive no. 2, named "Hvellinge," which was built by Hanomag in 1885. The machine was sold to the Hvellinge-Skanör-Falsterbo Railway in 1904. The type 2–4–0 locomotive shown had the following specifications:

Cylinders	267 by 451 millimeters
Drive wheels	1143-millimeter diameter
Steam pressure	10 kilograms per square centimeter
Operating weight	18.2 tons (engine plus tender)
Tender capacities	2.0 cubic meters (528 U.S. gallons) water; 0.6 ton coal.

(Courtesy: Swedish State Railways)

The Swedish firm of Nydqvist & Holm built quite a number of class Kd, 0–6–0 type, freight locomotives for use on the Swedish State Railways; the first of these appeared in 1890. Cylinders were 16.7 by 22 inches, and the coupled wheels had a diameter of 4 feet 6.5 inches. Grate area was 17.8 square feet, heating surface was 1020 square feet, developing a steam pressure of 143–57 pounds per square inch. Operating weight of engine and tender was about 60 tons. An engine model, pictured, is housed in the Swedish Railway Museum at Gävle.
(Courtesy: Swedish State Railway)

A 1950 photograph of a mixed train, on the Gotland Railway, rolling along outside the ancient town of Visby in Sweden is presented. This tank engine, no. 3076, class S13p, type 2–6–0, was withdrawn in 1951. The locomotive was originally built by Nydqvist & Holm, of Trollhättan in 1894. Limited specifications on the above machine are as follows:

Cylinders	310 by 400 millimeters
Steam pressure	11 kilograms per square centimeter.

(Courtesy: Swedish State Railways)

A model locomotive housed in the Swedish Transport Museum is shown. It represents a class Cc, 4–4–0, passenger locomotive long used on the Swedish State Railways. The prototype was built in 1896 by Nydqvist. The first ten units had narrow engineer cabs, but this was changed later when they were equipped with one-section side-sheets with a shield to the tender. Specifications were as follows:

Cylinders	16.3 by 22 inches
Coupled wheels	6-foot 2-inch diameter
Boiler	
Grate area	21.2 square feet
Heating area	1160 square feet
Boiler pressure	
143 pounds per square inch (first ten units)	
157 pounds per square inch (later units)	
Operational weight	40 tons plus 9 hundredweights.

(Courtesy: Swedish State Railways)

The Mogul type locomotives, widespread in Sweden, were a development from the "English era." The machine pictured was manufactured by Nydqvist & Holm in 1900 for the Östra Skånes Railways and was scrapped in 1951 as SJ engine no. 1669. Note the double brake equipment, vacuum and air, a common sight in Sweden during the years 1920–40. Locomotive no. 16, type 2–6–0, had these specifications:

Cylinders	440 by 610 millimeters
Drive wheels	1530-millimeter diameter
Steam pressure	10 kilograms per square centimeter
Operating weight	56.1 tons (engine plus tender)
Tender capacities	9 cubic meters (2378 U.S. gallons) water; 2.1 tons coal.

(Courtesy: Swedish State Railways)

Pictured is the model of a class Ke shunting engine, introduced to the Swedish State Railways early in the twentieth century. The original prototype was constructed by Ljunggrens of Christianstad in 1903. This was a tank modification of the earlier class Kd freight locomotive. The engine was occasionally used to handle suburban passenger traffic, although its highest operating speed was only 39 miles per hour. This type 0–6–0 tank engine, class Ke, had the following characteristics:

Cylinders	16.7 by 22 inches
Drive wheels	4-foot 6.5-inch diameter
Boiler	
Grate area	16⅔ square feet
Heating surface	908 square feet
Working pressure	157 pounds per square inch
Operating weight	39 tons plus 17 hundredweights.

(Courtesy: Swedish State Railways)

The Swedish State Railways put in service twenty-six class A, type 4–4–2, locomotives, manufactured in 1906 by the Trollhättan factory of Nydqvist & Holm. These engines were characterized as follows:

Cylinders	19.6 by 23⅝ inches
Coupled wheels	6-foot 2-inch diameter
Boiler	
Grate area	28 square feet
Heating surface	1432 square feet
Superheater	353 square feet (Schmidt)
Steam pressure	170 pounds per square inch
Tractive effort	13,700 pounds
Operating weight	59.5 tons (engine only)
Tender capacities on original 6-wheeled type	3080 gallons water; 4.5 tons coal.

The model is on display in the Railway Museum at Gävle, Sweden.

(Courtesy: Swedish State Railways)

A model of a class E, 0–8–0 locomotive used on the Swedish State Railways early in the twentieth century is illustrated. These freight locomotives were built by Nydqvist & Holm during the period 1907–20 and were first used on the Norrlands lines. They were later used on some passenger train service. General specifications were as follows:

Cylinders	19.6 by 24.2 inches
Coupled wheels	4-foot 6.6-inch diameter
Tractive effort	19,800 pounds
Operational weight	82.7 tons.

(Courtesy: Swedish State Railways)

The narrow-gauge 1067-millimeter (42-inch) system of the Blekinge Coastal Railway in southern Sweden used some rather large locomotives built by two Swedish manufacturers in 1907 and 1917. The line was taken over by the Swedish State Railways in 1942 at which time the 1907 engines became class L2t, and the 1917 engines became class L3t. One of these engines is preserved in the National Railway Museum at Gävle. Two engines of this class are shown with a train awaiting departure at Karlskrona in 1938. Referring to the locomotives in the picture, the right engine, no. 13, was built by Nydqvist & Holm in 1907 and had these specifications:

Cylinders	400 by 500 millimeters
Drive wheels	1170-millimeter diameter
Steam pressure	10 kilograms per square centimeter
Operating weight	38.1 tons (engine plus tender)
Tender capacities	5.2 cubic meters water; 1.5 tons coal.

The left engine was constructed by Helsingborgs mek Verkstad, Sweden, in 1917. Specifications were as follows:

Cylinders	400 by 500 millimeters
Drive wheels	1300-millimeter diameter
Steam pressure	11 kilograms per square centimeter
Operating weight	43.3 tons (engine plus tender)
Tender capacities	5.6 cubic meters water; 1.9 tons coal.

(Courtesy: Swedish State Railways)

starting in 1896. This is illustrated by a model on display at the Swedish Railway Museum.

A Mogul-type passenger engine with 2–6–0 wheel arrangement was widely used in Sweden starting in 1900. These also were built by Nydqvist & Holm. A typical machine is pictured and described.

Class Ke, type 0–6–0 tank engines were first built in Sweden in 1903 to meet the increasing needs for modern shunting equipment.

In 1906 the Swedish class A, type 4–4–2 locomotive first appeared from the Nydqvist & Holm shops; this was extensively used for handling freight trains. A model of the class A engine in the Railway Museum at Gävle is shown with a tender and two two-wheel bogies. This type of tender superseded the six-wheel vehicle starting in 1910.

Class E locomotives, type 0–8–0, of which about 130 were produced by Nydqvist & Holm in 1907–20, were also designed for freight hauls.

Of the private railroads in Sweden, the southern lines normally used a gauge of 1.067 millimeter (3 feet 6 inches). One such rail line was the Blekinge Coast Railroad. In 1907 Nydqvist & Holm constructed a number of heavy locomotives, type 2–6–2, for use on this railroad, and in 1917 additional machines were produced by the Helsingborg Mechanical Works.

In 1908 a tank engine—type 2–6–2, class Sa—was built to handle suburban passenger and freight traffic.

In 1908 and 1909, five class R locomotives, type 0–10–0, freight-hauling giants, were constructed by Motala Mechanical Works and by Nydqvist & Holm. These engines were put to work on the iron-ore line running from Luleå to Kiruna, in Sweden, and on to Narvik in Norway. After electrification of the line, the machines were transferred to handle heavy freight traffic on the northern trunk line between Långsele and Krylbo.

In 1909 a heavy express locomotive, type 4–6–0, designated class B, was introduced to the Swedish State Railways. A model on display in the Swedish Railway Museum is pictured.

A Mallet articulated compound engine was used in 1910 on an 891-millimeter (35-inch) gauge line in

This illustration shows the model of a Swedish State Railways suburban-traffic tank engine of the class Sa, with a 2–6–2 wheel arrangement. This locomotive was introduced in 1908. Forty-six were built by Falun up to 1916. Specifications were as follows:

Cylinders	19.6 by 22.8 inches
Coupled wheels	6-foot 0.2-inch diameter
Tractive effort	15,620 pounds
Operational weight	62.7 tons.

(Courtesy: Swedish State Railways)

This illustration is a 1920 picture, taken near Abisko, of a Swedish State Railways class R, type 0–10–0, freight locomotive. These were considered the most powerful ever built and used in Sweden. Five such machines were constructed as follows: two by Motala in 1908 and three by Nydqvist & Holm in 1909. The engines were originally used to pull heavy ore trains running anywhere along the Luleå–Kiruna–Riksgränsen line in Sweden and the port at Narvik in Norway. Later, when traction reverted to electric locomotives, these engines were transferred to other freight assignments in Sweden. Note American type of headlamp and the huge snow plow. The New York air pump, visible in the photograph, was replaced by an ordinary Knorr pump when the engines were transferred to other duties. In recent times the last three engines were laid away in controlled storage, possibly for future military usage. Specifications were as follows:

Cylinders	640 by 700 millimeters
Drive wheels	1300-millimeter diameter
Steam pressure	12 kilograms per square centimeter
Tractive effort	40,400 pounds
Tender capacities	20 cubic meters (5283 U.S. gallons) water; 4 tons coal.

(Courtesy: Swedish State Railways)

Pictured is a model of the class R, type 0–10–0, freight locomotives described in the previous illustration.

(Courtesy: Swedish Railway Museum, Gävle)

Shown is a model presently displayed in the Swedish Railways Museum of 4–6–0 heavy express locomotive which was first used on the Swedish State Railways in 1909. The original was constructed by Motala and designated as a class B engine. Specifications were as follows:

Cylinders	23¼ by 24⅜ inches
Coupled wheels	5-foot 6-inch diameter
Boiler	
Grate area	28 square feet
Heating surface	1682 square feet
Firebox	137 square feet
Superheater	481 square feet
Steam pressure	170 pounds per square inch
Operational weight	116.5 tons (engine plus tender)
Tender capacity	4000 gallons water; 6 tons coal.

(Courtesy: Swedish Railway Museum, Gävle)

This is a picture of a lumber train on the 891-millimeter (35-inch) line of the Dala–Ockelbo–Norrsundet Railway, now extinct, in northern Sweden; this railroad was plagued with many severe curves and heavy gradients. Three Mallet compound engines, type 0–6–0 plus 0–6–0, were purchased in 1910 from the Atlas Works in Stockholm. These engines were able to handle the heavier demands of larger and longer trains at that time. Of the three locomotives originally built, numbered 1, 8, and 12, engines nos. 8 and 12 are preserved in Sweden. Specifications were as follows:

Cylinders	330/500 by 500 millimeters compound
Drive wheels	1000 millimeters
Working pressure	12 kilograms per square centimeter
Operating weight	57.7 tons (engine plus tender)
Tender capacities	8 cubic meters (2113 U.S. gallons) water; 2 tons coal.

(Courtesy: Swedish State Railways)

This is a type 4–6–0 locomotive used on the private line of the Bergslagernas Railways, starting in 1910. Engine no. 63, class H3, is shown accelerating out of Gothenberg with the so-called Dala-Express. This machine later became SJ class A6, no. 1789 on the Swedish State Railways. Note the unusual smoke deflector, typical of the Bergslagernas steam equipment. The above locomotive, built by Nydqvist & Holm of Trollhättan, Sweden, in 1912 had these specifications:

Cylinders	520 by 610 millimeters
Drive wheels	1720-millimeter diameter
Steam pressure	12 kilograms per square centimeter
Operating weight	94.4 tons (engine plus tender)
Tender capacities	13.8 cubic meters (3646 U.S. gallons) water; 5.9 tons coal.

(Courtesy: Swedish State Railways)

northern Sweden, the now-extinct Dala–Ockelbo–Norrsundet Railway. The Mallet engines easily conquered the severe curves and heavy grades on this line.

The small private railways in Sweden used a wide variety of nonstandard rolling stock. A few large private companies, often amalgamations, also existed, such as the Bergslagernas Railway. This rail line actually designed some of its own locomotives, many of which were bought and used by other railroads. An example of the stock used on this line was the class H3, type 4–6–0 locomotive, introduced in 1910. This engine is pictured and described.

The most famous, heaviest, fastest, and possibly the best-looking steam locomotive in Sweden was the compound class F, type 4–6–2. The first twelve hundred of these Pacific engines were delivered by Nydqvist & Holm between 1914 and 1916, intended for express service on the Stockholm–Gothenburg–Malmö line. These big, four-cylinder compound locomotives were sold to Denmark in 1937 when the Swedish main lines were electrified. In Denmark, with few grades and only light curves, they proved even more successful—so much so that twenty-four more were built up to 1950 by Frichs Locomotive Works, using the original plans.

During the years 1900 to 1920, the Swedish State Railways constructed and used a great assortment of standard classes and types of steam locomotives for express, freight, mixed-traffic, shunting, and

when the main lines of Sweden were electrified. In 1963 the first engine of this class, SJ no. 1200, was returned to Sweden for preservation; some others have also been preserved in Denmark. Specifications were as follows:

Cylinders	
Lo pressure	24.8 by 25.9 inches (outside)
Hi pressure	16.5 by 25.9 inches (between frames)
All were inclined 1 in 9.15	
Coupled wheels	6 feet 2 inches
Boiler	
Grate area	38.8 square feet
Heating surface	2770 square feet including superheater
Diameter	5 feet 7 inches
Length	17 feet 4.6 inches
Working pressure	185 pounds per square inch
Operational weight	142.75 tons (engine plus tender)
Tender	Double bogie type with semicircular sections
Tender capacities	5466 gallons water; 6 tons plus 8 hundredweights coal.

(Courtesy: Swedish State Railways)

suburban service. The engine classes were designated as A, B, E, J, S, N, R, and F. All of these classes were used throughout Sweden and became well-known, with a distinctive "Swedish" profile. Also shown is another standard locomotive, class J, which was used with suburban passenger traffic.

Soon after World War I, the Swedish State Railways (SJ) found it necessary to renew its motive power, especially the freight locomotives. Since railway steam engines were relatively inexpensive in bankrupt Germany, SJ chose to purchase the Prussian standard, class G8. Twenty such machines were ordered in 1918 from Linke-Hofman-Werke of Breslau, Germany. These engines worked well,

Many standard steam locomotives were built and used in Sweden in the period 1900–1920; these carried the class designations: A, B, E, J, S, N, R, and F. All had a distinctive "Swedish" appearance. Pictured is a typical Swedish engine, class B, no. 1287, type 4–6–0. This is shown working a passenger train near Ånge in the 1930s. The original machines were built by Nydqvist & Holm in 1916 and had the following specifications:

Cylinders	590 by 620 millimeters
Drive wheels	1750-millimeter diameter
Steam pressure	12 kilograms per square centimeter
Operating weight	116.8 tons (engine plus tender)
Tender capacities	20 cubic meters (5283 U.S. gallons) water; 6 tons coal.

(Courtesy: Swedish State Railways)

A standard tank engine, class J, type 2–6–4, was widely used in Sweden for local passenger work. Note the inside cylinders which were common in Sweden due to the early British influence. The totally enclosed cab was also a typical Swedish feature because of the harsh winter conditions. Pictured is a class J engine taking a rest at Alvesta in 1951. This locomotive, no. 1389, was built by Motala Verkstad in 1918 and had these specifications:

Cylinders	420 by 580 millimeters
Drive wheels	1300-millimeter diameter
Steam pressure	12 kilograms per square centimeter
Operating weight	62 tons (engine plus tender)
Tender capacities	10 cubic meters (2642 U.S. gallons) water; 4 tons coal.

(Courtesy: Swedish State Railways)

The Prussian class G8 locomotives purchased from Germany by Sweden after World War I did a fairly good freight hauling job after new Swedish boilers were installed. Pictured is an SJ class G2 (the figure "2" indicating locomotives with the new boilers), type 0–8–0, engine no. 1425, on a turntable at the Sävenäs locomotive depot in Gothenberg in 1948. The special smokestack, developed in Finland, indicated the engine was a wood-burner. Specifications were:

Cylinders	600 by 660 millimeters
Drive wheels	1350-millimeter diameter
Steam pressure	14 kilograms per square centimeter
Operating weight	115 tons (engine plus tender)
Tender capacities	16.5 cubic meters (4359 U.S. gallons) water; 7 tons coal.

(Courtesy: Swedish State Railways)

except that the boilers did not hold up and Swedish standard types had to be substituted. Some machines also received a pair of leading wheels to enhance running qualities. SJ later authorized an additional series of the same design, to be built by Swedish firms.

In the 1930s, both the state railways and the private Grängesberg-Oxelösund Railways (TGOJ) tried various experiments with turbine locomotives. The TGOJ line decided to try out a noncondensing type, of which three were built by Nydqvist & Holm from 1930 to 1936. The huge TGOJ engines hauled ore trains from Grängesberg to Oxelösund until the line was electrified in 1953–54. Generally, the turbine engines proved quite satisfactory but had higher maintenance costs than regular steam locomotives of the same size.

The last steam engines for Sweden were class S, type 2–6–0 Baltic tank machines built in 1952. In modern times, a serious scarcity of Swedish coal and petroleum, plus a plentiful supply of hydroelectric energy, mandated an early demise for

In the 1930s the Grängesberg–Oxelösund Railway had built three noncondensing type turbine steam locomotives. These huge engines handled ore trains from Grängesberg to Oxelösund. Pictured is a TGOJ class M3t, type 4–8–0, turbine freight engine on a test run after delivery in 1934. All three machines were constructed by Nydqvist & Holm in the period 1930–36 and were retired into a preserved status in 1953–54 when electric traction took over. Specifications on engine no. 71 were as follows:

Turbine	
Drive wheels	1350-millimeter diameter
Steam pressure	13 kilograms per square centimeter
Operating weight	117.6 tons (engine plus tender)
Tender capacities:	15 cubic meters (3963 U.S. gallons) water; 5 tons coal.

(Courtesy: Swedish State Railways)

the steam locomotive. The mainline conversion to electric traction starting in 1937 led to the sale of many Pacific-type locomotives to Denmark. By 1965 about half the Swedish State Railways had been electrified. Since then, electric rail cars have been used to move passengers and diesel traction has handled freight traffic on the secondary lines. It has been alleged that Sweden has reconditioned and stored a large number of serviceable steam locomotives as part of a military contingency plan. On occasion, some of these engines are taken out for test runs.

SWITZERLAND

THE CONTROL OF IMPORTANT ALPINE PASSES and ancient routes through the Rhône and Danube waterways gave Switzerland a key position in trans-Alpine traffic through the centuries. As an example, the main artery of European communication across the Alps, the St. Gotthard route, ran through Swiss territory.

The first railway in Switzerland opened on 15 June 1844 and ran from Basel to St. Ludwig. The second railroad opened in 1847, and this ran northwest from Zürich to Baden, a distance of about fifteen miles. The first locomotive was of the Stephenson long-boiler design.

Early railway endeavors in Switzerland were hindered by confusion, lack of financing, and a fear of construction problems in such difficult environment. Another serious obstacle to rail progress was the autonomous nature of the various cantons, which had imposed trade restrictions and arbitrary duties on goods moving into their domains. With the establishment of the Swiss Confederation in 1848, these tariff barriers were largely invalidated, and shortly thereafter Robert Stephenson was commissioned to evaluate the use of railways in this small country. English surveyors in the 1850s suggested various routes, recommended that local interests be sacrificed for the general public good, and advised against private ownership and operation. However, in order to avoid a huge public debt, the authorities finally decided that any railway development should be based on a private enterprise approach, which soon brought on a rash of financial speculations. Another major weakness was the lack of a central railway policy, which severely hampered chances of a successful, coordinated, planned communications system in Switzerland. By 1860, under private auspices of four different companies, 663 miles of railroad were laid down. See illustration showing the Bern station. Subsequent operations were haphazard, few profits resulted, and interest payments on invested capital had to be suspended. In order to salvage the situation, in 1862 the central government proposed buying all the railways outright, but failed to actually make these acquisitions. In time the private owners managed to put their houses in order, and the economic picture took on a much brighter outlook.

As railway business expanded, connections with adjoining countries became an obvious and paramount objective. The French Mont Cenis and the Austrian Brenner lines were opened in 1867. International communications agreements were worked out between Switzerland and Italy in 1869, and with Germany in 1871. Also in 1871, the great 7.79-mile Mont Cenis tunnel linking France with Italy was opened at a cost of $15 million, culminating work that had started in 1857. After the Mont Cenis tunnel was completed, railway authorities in Switzerland adopted this engineering idea and late in 1871 formed the St. Gotthard Railway Company to build and operate a north-south alpine route in that country. Soon it was decided to construct the 9.32-mile St. Gotthard tunnel from Göschenen, Switzerland, to Airolo, Italy. Work started on 4 June 1872 and was completed on 28 February 1880; the first ballast train traveled through the tunnel on 24 December 1881, and the facility was

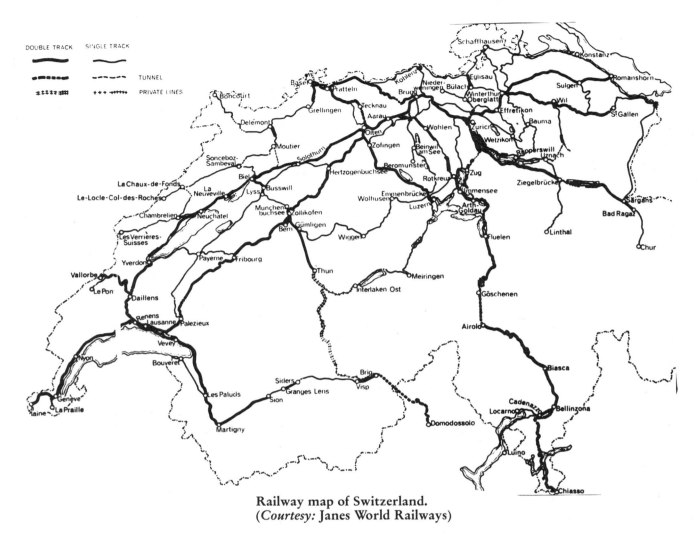

Railway map of Switzerland.
(*Courtesy:* Janes World Railways)

officially opened on 27 May 1882, at latitude 46°35′ north, longitude 8°36′ east.

The St. Gotthard tunnel, built at a cost of $11.9 million, was the world's longest railroad tunnel until the 12.3-mile Simplon tunnel was constructed during the period 1898–1905, at a cost of $21 million. That tunnel under the Alps, at latitude 46°15′ north and longitude 8°08′ east, was opened in 1906 and connected Brig, Switzerland, and Iselle, Italy. The original Simplon single-track tunnel was supplemented by a separate double-track boring excavated between 1912 and 1922, which opened on 16 October 1922.

Pictured is Louis Favre of Genoa, Italy, the prime contractor in the construction of the famous Saint Gotthard Tunnel between Switzerland and Italy. He won the contract in 1871 but in the excruciating process of carrying it out lost his life and financially wrecked his company.
(*Courtesy: Swiss Federal Railways*)

An artist's sketch of the main railway station at Bern, Switzerland, in 1860 is shown. The overall roof, which enclosed most of the rail terminal, is typical of many railroad stations built in various parts of Europe in the nineteenth and early twentieth centuries.
(Courtesy: Swiss Federal Railways)

Of course, the advent of the original Simplon tunnel offered the most direct route for rail traffic between France and Italy, and the Simplon Express was inaugurated in 1906, running from Paris to Lausanne, Brig, Simplon, and Milan. Service was extended to Venice in 1907 and to Trieste in 1912. When World War I broke out in 1914, operations on the Simplon Express were terminated. The war also interrupted service on the famous Orient Express, since part of this system ran through German territory. After the war, the Allies chose to avoid east-west operations through Germany, and consequently the Simplon Orient Express was inaugurated after service was extended from Trieste to Belgrade to Istanbul. In January 1923 the Simplon Orient Express was again terminated when French and Belgian troops occupied the Ruhr valley in retaliation for Germany's failure to pay war reparations. Consequently, Germany would not allow any international trains to proceed through her

The northern entrance to the Saint Gotthard Tunnel at Göschenen, Switzerland is pictured. This 9.32-mile tunnel connection with Airolo, Italy, was bored over the period 1872–80 with a fearful loss of 310 lives and 877 others incapacitated. The work cost 57.6 million francs ($11.2 million); the tunnel was officially opened on 27 May 1882. Travel time from Lucerne to Milan was reduced from twenty-seven to five and a half hours.
(Courtesy: Swiss Federal Railways)

Pictured is an artist's conception of the first train through the Gotthard Tunnel, arriving from Switzerland at Airolo, Italy, on 13 March 1880.
(*Courtesy:* Illustrated London News)

Pictured is an artist's conception of the final breakthrough in constructing the Saint Gotthard Tunnel on 29 February 1880. The 9.3-mile railroad tunnel, built over the period 1872–80 to connect Göschenen, Switzerland, with Airolo, Italy, was finally opened to traffic on May 27, 1882.
(*Courtesy: Swiss Federal Railways*)

This illustration shows a group of workers at the north end of the Simplon Tunnel in 1899 then under construction. The rail tunnel, 12.3 miles long, was built 1898–1905 and connected Brig, Switzerland, with Iselle, Italy.
(Courtesy: Swiss Federal Railways)

Pictured are workers inside the Simplon Tunnel, date about 1900. This 10.3-mile tunnel was opened in 1906 connecting Switzerland and Italy under the Alps Mountains.
(Courtesy: Swiss Federal Railways)

The north or Brig, Switzerland, end of the Simplon
Tunnel under the Alps Mountains which connected
with Iselle, Italy, is shown. This 12.3-mile tunnel, built
at a cost of $21 million, was the world's longest when
it opened on 1 June 1906. A second parallel section
opened on 16 October 1922.
(Courtesy: Swiss Federal Railways)

This is a sketch of typical Alpine tunnel workers,
thousands of whom participated in building the Mont
Cenis, Saint Gotthard, and Simplon tunnels, and
many other railroad tunnels, starting in Europe in
1872.
(Courtesy: Swiss Federal Railways)

This illustration shows the north end of the 3.893-mile Albula Tunnel on the Rhaetian Railway in Switzerland which opened to traffic on 1 July 1903. (*Courtesy: Swiss Federal Railways*)

territory. As a result, a new route was adopted for international travel, using the Arlberg tunnel (in Austria), which allowed passage through Basel and Zürich. Thus was born the Arlberg Orient Express. After World War II hostilities had ceased, services on the Arlberg Orient Express were the first to be restored, on 27 September 1945. Two months later the Simplon Orient Express resumed runs to Trieste, Belgrade, Sofia, and Istanbul.

Switzerland's mountainous terrain necessitated many railroad tunnels. The major ones are described below.

A tunnel called Albula, handling the meter-gauge Rhaetian Railway, was opened on 1 July 1903. This boring had a length of 3.64 miles and was located at an altitude of 5,981 feet above sea level at latitude 46°34' north, longitude 09°48' east.

Another Alpine tunnel, named Loetschberg, with a length of 9.08 miles, was opened on 15 July 1913. It was located at latitude 46°25' north, longitude 07°43' east.

An Alpine tunnel through the final ridge of the Jura Mountains, the Grenchenberg tunnel, with a length of 5.33 miles, was opened in 1915, somewhat reducing distances on the Loetschberg Railway.

This photograph shows various curves on the Albula section of the meter-gauge Rhaetian Railway of Switzerland; this section is located in southeast Switzerland in the general vicinity of Saint Moritz. (*Courtesy: Swiss Federal Railways*)

The south entrance to the Loetschberg Tunnel which was constructed between 1906 and 1912 through the Bernese Alps in Switzerland is shown. It has a length of nine miles plus 140 yards and facilitated rail operations on the Berne–Loetscherberg–Simplon Railway which opened in 1913.
(Courtesy: Swiss Federal Railways)

Shown is the north end of the double-track Loetschberg Tunnel at Goppenstein, Switzerland. This nine mile plus 140 yard tunnel connected Italy and Switzerland. The boring started in 1906 and was finished on 15 July 1913. The tunnel under the Bernese Oberland Mountains stands at an altitude of 4070 feet above sea level.
(Courtesy: Swiss Federal Railways)

The mountainous terrain in Switzerland has always necessitated thousands of bridges and viaducts to facilitate the progress of the railroads. A typical viaduct is pictured on the Loetschberg Railway near Frutigen in southwest Switzerland.
(Courtesy: Swiss National Tourist Office)

Still other tunnels were constructed in the difficult Swiss terrain. Between 1910 and 1915, a 3.8-mile railroad tunnel known as Mont d'Or was bored through the Jura Mountains at a cost of $4,060,000. This connected the western border of Switzerland with France and is located at latitude 46°43′ north, longitude 06°20′ east.

In 1916 the Hauenstein tunnel, with a length of 5.04 miles, was bored to bypass the Hauenstein Upper tunnel, which was located at a higher, more difficult elevation. The upper tunnel had been the first built in Switzerland, constructed under the guidance of Thomas Brassey between 1854 and 1858. The new Hauenstein tunnel furnished an easier rail route between Basel and Olten in northern Switzerland. The Hauenstein tunnel is located at latitude 47°24′ north, longitude 07°54′ east.

Another tunnel, named Ricken, connects Lake of Zürich and the Toggenburg area. It has a length of 5.34 miles and was under construction from 1904 to 1910. The Ricken tunnel is located at latitude 47°13′ north, longitude 08°34′ east.

Switzerland also has a railroad tunnel with a higher elevation than any other in Europe. Named Jungfrau, it has a length of 4.43 miles and was opened 1 August 1912, after sixteen years of toil and tribulation. This boring is unique in that it represents a terrific average grade of 15.91 percent between its entrance altitude of 7,612 feet above sea level and its exit altitude of 11,332 feet. The tunnel has Abt-rack rail and is used by the Jungfrau Railway, which runs between Eigerletscher and Jungfraujoch in south-central Switzerland, at latitude 46°34′ north, longitude 8° east.

Switzerland has the steepest rack railway in the world—the Pilatus railway, with a gradient of 1 in 2.1.

Switzerland's only steam mountain railway is the Brienzer and Rothorn Railway with a 2-foot 7.5-inch gauge and Abt track. This opened in 1892 and has a summit at 7,707 feet above sea level.

The highest railroad summits in Switzerland are four meter-gauge lines.

The first production diesel-electric railway engines were five 200-horsepower machines built in 1914 by Sulzer in Switzerland for the Prussian & Saxon State Railways.

In Switzerland, 70 percent of the Federal rail system and the entire Rhaetian, plus several other meter-gauge systems, use steel sleepers in their railroad construction.

The worst train wreck in Switzerland, a collision near Basel on 14 June 1891, killing one hundred people.

This is a picture of the meter-gauge Jungfrau Railway which opened during August 1912. The tunnel starts at Eigerletscher at 7612 feet above sea level and ends at Jungfraujoch at 11,332 feet above seal level. The tunnel is four miles plus 750 yards in length, and the Abt rack system is used throughout. This railroad has been described as the highest in Europe.
(Courtesy: Swiss Federal Railways)

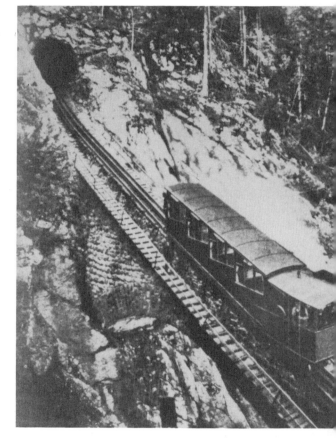

The steepest rack railroad in the world is pictured. The Mount Pelatus Railway in Switzerland was opened on 4 June 1884 and used steam locomotion until it was electrified on 15 May 1937. This railroad has a gradient of forty-eight percent. A special rack system, devised by Edward Locher, had horizontal teeth on each side of the rack rail to prevent any slippage or derailment. The gauge was 800 millimeters or 2 feet 7.5 inches.
Courtesy: Swiss Federal Railways)

This pictures a scenic section of the 2-foot 7.5-inch gauge Brienzer–Rothorn Railway, the only steam-operated mountain railway in Switzerland. This section is located in south central Switzerland and the Brienzer See is in the (light) background.
(Courtesy: Swiss Federal Railways)

Altitude (feet)	Summit Name	Railway Name
7,403	Bermina Hospice	Rhaetian
6,711	Oberalp Pass	Furks–Oberalp
5,981	Albula Tunnel	Rhaetian
5,358	Wolfgang	Rhaetian

The first gas-turbine engine was applied to rail traction in 1941, when a 2,140-horsepower gas-turbine electric locomotive was built by Brown Bovere for the Swiss Federal Railways. This was 53 feet 9 inches long and weighed ninety-two tons.

In 1974 Switzerland had about thirty-two hundred miles of railway which included eighteen-hundred miles of the Swiss Federal Railways and about nine hundred miles of narrow-gauge line. In private operations, totaling about fourteen hundred miles, the Rhaetian meter-gauge system was largest, with 245 miles of track. There were two other meter-gauge systems—the Brig–Visp–

Zermatt Railway and the Furka–Oberalp Railway. The second-largest private operation in the country was the standard-gauge Bern–Loetschberg–Simplon Railway of about 155 miles. See map of the Swiss rail network.

In 1974 there were fourteen rack-and-pinion rail systems comprising a distance of about sixty miles, and fifty funicular railways totaling about thirty miles.

The Swiss Federal Railways had about 670 tunnels, including the world's longest, the Simplon, as well as the St. Gotthard and the Loetschberg. Bridges on this government system totaled 5,455, with a combined length of fifty-three miles.

Steam Locomotives in Switzerland

The pioneer steam locomotives in Switzerland were predominantly British; however, as time passed, other manufacturers from many nations provided equipment. Eventually, the Swiss made many of their own engines.

This illustration sketches the first locomotive used in Switzerland in 1847. This was a Stephenson long-boiler engine which operated on the Zurich-Baden 14.5 mile rail line nicknamed "Spanish Bun Railway." The long-boilered design was patented in 1841 and was an attempt to improve fuel efficiency and cut down airflow through the furnace and boiler to minimize the discharge of live sparks out the smokestack.
(*Courtesy:* O. S. Nock, The Dawn of World Railways 1800–1850)

Shown is a photograph of a type class D ⅓, type 4–2–0, locomotive originally built by Stephenson in 1847 for use on the Zurich–Baden fifteen-mile railway in Switzerland. This reproduction of Stephenson's famous long-boiler design was produced in 1947. The original engine weighed 30 tons and attained a maximum speed of 40 kilograms per hour.
(Courtesy: Swiss Federal Railways)

The Swiss Western Railway commenced service in 1855 between Yverdon on Lake Neuchâtel and Morges on Lake Geneva. One of its first locomotives was named "Liberte et Patrie" which was constructed by Cail & Cie in Paris in 1858. This was a type 2–4–0 engine with 15.7 by 24 inch cylinders; coupled drive wheels had a diameter of 5 feet 6.4 inches; the operating weight of engine and tender was 40 tons. A model of the prototype, shown in the illustration is housed in the Swiss Transport Museum at Lucerne.
(Courtesy: Swiss Federal Railways)

The following representative photographs give a general picture of the development and use of the steam locomotive in Switzerland.

The second railway in the country—Zürich to Baden—which opened in 1847, used the Stephenson railway engine shown and described. Illustrated is a working reproduction (1847) of the original Stephenson locomotive.

The French influence on steam locomotion in Switzerland was demonstrated on many railways, especially those near the border between the two countries. For example, the Swiss Western Railway opened a section of about twenty-five miles between Yverdon on Lake Neuchâtel and Morges on the north central shore of Lake Geneva in 1855. An Englishman, Charles Vignoles, its first chief engineer, recommended the French type 2–4–0 passenger locomotive, which is pictured, with general specifications.

Engerth-type engines, which had wide success on Austrian mountain grades in 1854, were also used on the Central Railway and the Wohlen–Bremgarten Railway of Switzerland, starting in 1857.

A type 0–4–6 locomotive used on the Central Railway in 1858 is illustrated.

French Bourbonnaise, type 0–6–0 tender engines were used extensively on the Swiss railways, especially the Jura–Simplon line, between 1858 and 1892. With the opening of the Gotthard tunnel in 1882, the Esslingen Works built an additional series of Bourbonnaise, type 0–6–0 engines.

Pictured is a Stephenson, type 2–4–0 steam locomotive built in the period 1868–70, for use on the Jura–Simplon Railway.

Between 1886 and 1888, a 2.83-mile rack railway was built up Mount Pilatus near Lucerne. A model of the Locker-type framework and gearing of the original locomotive, plus other details of this railroad, are shown and described.

This old photograph shows an Engerth type 0–4–4, steam locomotive built in the period 1857–58 for use on the Central Railway of Switzerland. A series of twenty-five engines of this type were supplied of which some later bore Swiss identification numbers 5680 to 5699. Weights were from 45 to 50 tons, and maximum speed was 75 kilometers per hour. Specifications on this engine, named "Sargans," were as follows:

Cylinders	408 by 561 millimeters
Drive wheels	1375-millimeter diameter
Boiler	
Grate area	1.0 square millimeters
Firebox	6.5 square millimeters
Heating surface	78.9 square millimeters
Working pressure	10 atmospheres
Operating weight	46.7 tons
Capacities	4.6 cubic meters water; 3.0 tons coal
Maximum speed	60 kilograms per hour.

(Courtesy: Swiss Federal Railways)

Pictured is a type 0–4–6, class Ec2/5 locomotive which operated in Switzerland on the Central Railway starting in 1858. Specifications were as follows:

Cylinders	421 by 580 millimeters
Drivers	1590-millimeter diameter
Boiler	
Grate area	0.9 square millimeters
Firebox	7.2 square millimeters
Heating surface	105.7 square millimeters
Working pressure	7.5 atmospheres
Operating weight	47.0 tons
Capacities	4.9 cubic meters water; 2.0 tons coal
Maximum speed	60 kilograms per hour.

(Courtesy: Swiss Federal Railways)

This picture shows a Bourbonnaise class D 3/3, type 0–6–0, tender steam locomotive built for the Swiss railways in the period 1858–92. This series of engines later on carried the Swiss railway identification numbers 3351 to 3399. These engines varied in weight from 54 to 62 tons and could travel at a maximum speed of about 50 kilometer per hour. Specifications were:

Class D3/3	
Cylinders	450 by 650 millimeters
Drive wheels	1320-millimeter diameter
Boiler	
Grate area	1.3 square millimeters
Firebox	7.7 square millimeters
Number tubes	194
Length tubes	4295 millimeters
Total heat surface	126.8 square millimeters
Working pressure	10 atmospheres
Operating weight	54.4 tons (engine plus tender)
Tender capacities	5.8 cubic meters water; 2.7 tons coal.

(Courtesy: Swiss Federal Railways)

In 1881–82 the Esslingen Works built a number of 0–6–0 type tender locomotives for use on the newly opened Gotthard Railway. These engines were employed on passenger as well as freight service between Lucerne and Chiasso. The engines had the following characteristics:

Cylinders	18.9 by 24.4 inches
Coupled wheels	4-foot 4.4-inch diameter
Horsepower	600
Engine speed	55 kilometers per hour
Operating weight	70 tons (engine plus tender).

A model of the above locomotive is pictured and is displayed in the Swiss Transport Museum at Lucerne, Switzerland.
(Courtesy: Swiss Federal Railways)

Shown is a class B2/3, type 2–4–0, steam locomotive built by Stephenson in the period 1868–70 for use on the Jura–Simplon Railway of Switzerland. Originally six units were furnished which later carried the Swiss identification numbers 1074 to 1079. These engines had a maximum speed of 70 kilometers per hour. Specifications were:

Cylinders	400 by 610 millimeters
Drive wheels	1686-millimeter diameter
Boiler	
Grate area	1.0 square millimeters
Firebox	6.0 square millimeters
Total heating surface	100.1 square millimeter
Number tubes	145
Tube length	4350 millimeter
Working pressure	8 atmospheres
Operating weight	40.0 tons (engine plus tender)
Tender capacities	4 cubic meters water; 2.7 tons coal.

(Courtesy: Swiss Federal Railways)

The railway up Mount Pilatus, near Lucerne, was constructed in 1886–88. It is 2.83 miles long and rises 5370 feet, with a maximum gradient of 1 in 2.08. The gauge of the rails is 31.5 inches (800 millimeters). For this railway, Dr. E. Locker devised a system in which a pair of horizontal toothed wheels gear with a double horizontal rack, and the model represents the framework and gearing of one of the locomotives built at the Swiss Locomotive Works, Winterhür.

The underframe is carried on four flangeless wheels 15.75 inches in diameter. The engine is placed at the lower end and has two horizontal outside cylinders, 8.62 inches in diameter by an 11.75-inch stroke. The connecting rods drive a horizontal crank shaft, upon the middle of which a spur pinion is fixed, and this, by a spur wheel and two pairs of bevel wheels, drives the vertical shafts that carry at their lower ends the toothed driving wheels. The latter are fitted with guiding rings below, which roll upon the central rail that supports the rack and also prevent the wheels from rising out of gear. The gear ratio is 3.8 to 1, and the tractive factor 206. At the front end of the frame is placed another pair of toothed wheels similar to the driving pair, and these are used to guide the car and also to actuate the automatic brake. The boiler is of the usual locomotive type, but is placed transversly; it has a heating surface of 215 square feet and a grate area of 4 square feet, the steam pressure is 176 pound per square inches.

The normal speed of the engine is 2.25 miles an hour and, on the downward journey, is controlled by three brakes. These consist of (a) a hand-applied band brake on one of the engine crank discs, (b) a cylinder air brake, and (c) an automatic brake which comes into action if the speed exceeds 3 miles an hour. Clips are fitted embracing the running rail, to guard against derailment by wind. The water tank carried 176 gallons, and the coal bunker holds 2.5 hundredweights. The weight of the loaded car is 10.5 tons.

The permanent way consists of flat-footed rails bolted to channel-iron cross sleepers which are fixed to a continuous masonry bed. The rack is formed of steel bars with teeth milled along each side; these are bolted to the top of a continuous saddle-shaped rail which is itself bolted to chairs riveted to the cross sleepers.

Scale 1:16

(Courtesy: London Science Museum)

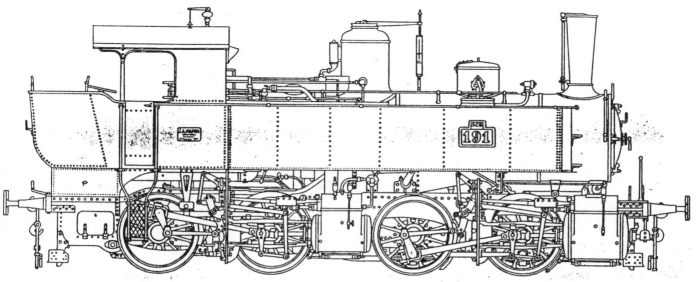

This illustration is a drawing of a Mallet type 0–4–0 plus 0–4–0, class C4 tank engine which was designed in 1890 and constructed in 1894 by J. A. Maffei for use on the Swiss Central Railway.
(*Courtesy: Swiss Federal Railways*)

Shown is a Mallet type 0–6–0 plus 0–6–0 tank locomotive, class Ed 2 × 3/3, used on the railways of Switzerland including the Gotthard line. This engine, no. 151, was designed in 1890 and built by Maffei in 1894. Maximum speed was 45 kilometers per hour. Specifications were as follows:

Cylinders
   400 by 640 millimeters
   580 by 640 millimeters

Drivers	1230-millimeter diameter
Boiler	
Grate area	2.2 square meters
Firebox	9.3 square meters
Heating area	154.3 square meters
Working pressure	12 atmospheres
Operating weight	87.2 tons (tank type)
Capacities	7.0 cubic meters water; 4.3 tons coal.

(*Courtesy: Swiss Federal Railways*)

Various Mallet tank engines were designed and built for Swiss railways from 1890 to 1894 (see two illustrations).

Pictured and described is a popular type 4–4–0 tank locomotive utilized on the Jura–Simplon Railway starting in 1891.

The North Eastern Railway of Switzerland operated for a long time with a domeless type 2–4–0 steam engine built by the Swiss Locomotive Works at Winterthur. These engines, built in 1892, were of compound design. See illustration.

A model of the framework and gearing of an Abt-rack locomotive built in 1896 for the mountain Snowdon Railway is shown.

The Swiss Northern Railway introduced a series of class A2/4, type 4–4–0 locomotives between 1898 and 1902. See illustration.

Pictured is a class D4/4, type 2–6–0 locomotive used on the Gotthard Railway starting in 1901.

From 1904 to 1909, a series of four-cylinder compound, type 4–6–0 locomotives were constructed by the Swiss Locomotive Works at Winterthur. These class A3/5 engines were operated successfully on express service on the following sections of the Jura–Simplon Railway: Lucerne–Basel, Lausanne–Brigue, and Geneva–Bern–Olten. These sections had all came under control of the Swiss Federal Railways in 1903. See two illustrations.

In 1908 J. A. Maffei of Germany constructed a series of four-cylinder compound locomotives for use on the Gotthard Railways. These were a modification of the class A3/5 engines built earlier by the Swiss Locomotive Works. In 1909, the Gotthard system was absorbed by the Swiss Federal Railways, after which Schmidt superheaters

A type 4–4–0 tank locomotive built in 1891 for use on the Swiss Jura–Simplon railway is shown. Engine no. 5469, class Eb2/4, attained a speed of 75 kilometers per hour. Specifications were as follows:

Cylinders	410 by 612 millimeters
Drivers	1255-millimeter diameter
Boiler	
Grate area	1.3 square meters
Firebox	7.3 square meters
Total heating surface	101.2 square meters
Working pressure	10 atmospheres
Operating weight	29.8 tons
Water capacity	5.3 cubic meters
Coal capacity	2.0 tons.

(Courtesy: Swiss Federal Railways)

In 1892 the Swiss Locomotive Works at Winterthür built a number of 2–4–0 locomotives for passenger service on the North Eastern Railway. This was a two-cylinder compound model with the following characteristics:

Cylinders	
Hi Pressure	15.7 by 24.4 inches
Lo Pressure	22.8 by 24.4 inches
Coupled wheels	5-foot 2.4-inch diameter
Engine horsepower	550
Speed	55 kilometers per hour
Operating weight	60 tons (engine plus tender)
Adhesive weight	27 tons
Bogie	Bissel type.

A model of this locomotive, housed in the Swiss Transport Museum, is shown.
(*Courtesy: Swiss Federal Railways*)

were installed to replace the inefficient steam-drying equipment first used to heat steam. See two illustrations.

A combination adherence and rack-rail locomotive built in 1909 for use on the Riggenbach rack-and-pinion rail system in Switzerland is illustrated.

Shown is a class B3/4, type 2–6–0 tender locomotive. Sixty-nine such engines, built between 1905 and 1916, had a long history of service on the Swiss Federal Railways.

Pictured is a class Eb3/5, type 2–6–2 locomotive built from 1911 to 1916 and widely used on various parts of the Swiss Railways.

Shown in an illustration is Swiss Federal Railways engine no. 2978, a class C5/6, type 2–10–0 machine that was the last standard-gauge steam locomotive built in Switzerland. This was one of a series of similar engines built between 1913 and 1917.

The centennial celebration of the Waldenberg Railway took place during June 1980. At that time, two class G3/3 tank engines were removed from mothballs to participate in the ceremonies (see three illustrations).

The zenith of steam locomotion was reached on the Swiss railroads in 1914. In this year, 1,588 locomotives were in operation. Of this total, 1,226 were owned and operated by the Swiss Federal Railways, and 362 by private railways. The last narrow-gauge adhesion steam locomotive was constructed in 1926, no. 1068, a class HG3/3 engine built for the Brunig line. It is presently preserved at Meiringen. A similar machine is shown. In 1936 the last rack-and-pinion steam engine was a class H on the Brienz–Rothorn Railway. In 1968 all steam traction on the Swiss Federal Railways was officially terminated.

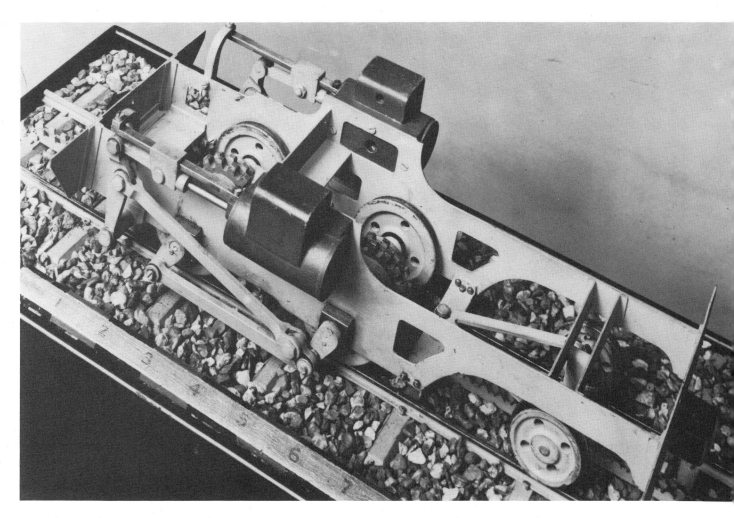

This model represents the framework and gearing of one of the rack locomotives built at the Swiss Locomotive Works, Winterthür, in 1896 for use on the Snowdon Mountain railway, which is 4.67 miles long with a maximum gradient of 1 in 5.5 and a gauge of 31.5 inches. The rack is of the form patented by R. Abt in 1882, in which two narrow rectangular bars, having teeth cut in them, are placed vertically side by side on chairs with the teeth stepped, thus ensuring smoothness of motion.

The engine is carried on six wheels; the four leading wheels are 25.71 inches in diameter, running loose on their axles, and the trailing wheels 20.47 inches in diameter, are arranged on a Bissell truck. The rigid wheelbase is 4.43 feet and the total 9.85 feet. There are two horizontal outside cylinders 11.81 inches in diameter by a 23.62-inch stroke, placed above the footplate midway along the engine, with the valve chests above them. The piston rods are continued forward to the crossheads and the motion is communicated to cranks on the central axle through connecting rods and rocking levers pivoted low down on the frame. The two leading axles are coupled by rods, and each carry a double pinion gearing with the rack. The tractive factor is 146. The boiler has a heating surface of 397 square feet and a grate area of 10 square feet; its axis is inclined at 1 in 11 to the rails. The steam pressure is 200 pounds per square inch.

The engine pushes its load up the inclines, there being no couplings, whilst on the descent three methods of braking are available. These consist of (a) brake blocks gripping grooved drums on the driving axles; (b) an automatic gear which applies a steam brake to two of the drums when the speed of the engine exceeds five miles an hour; and (c) by the compression of air in the cylinders, air being drawn in through the exhaust ports, compressed, and expelled through a special regulating valve. The latter method is generally used, and water jets are introduced into the cylinders to cool the air. Water is carried in side tanks having a capacity of 440 gallons, while the coal bunker holds 10 hundredweights. The weight of the engine in working order is 17.22 tons, its load of 18.5 tons being conveyed at a speed of 4 to 5 miles an hour.

The rack bars are bolted to rolled steel chairs which are bolted to transverse steel sleepers. The rails are flat-footed and weigh 41.25 lb. per yard.

Scale 1:16.

(Courtesy: London Science Museum)

This picture shows one of a series of twenty-five class A2/4, type 4–4–0, steam engines built for the railroads of Switzerland in the period 1898–1902. These engines originally carried the identification numbers NOB 101–25. Maximum speeds were about 90 kilometers per hour. Specifications were:

Cylinders	460 by 660 millimeters
Coupled drive wheels	1830-millimeter diameter
Boiler	
Grate area	2.2 square meters
Firebox	10.5 square meters
Total heat surface	128.6 square meters
Working pressure	13 atmospheres
Operating weight	81.3 tons (engine plus tender)
Tender capacities	12.0 cubic meters water; 6.0 tons coal.

(Courtesy: Swiss Federal Railways)

This old photograph shows a tender type steam locomotive, class D4/4, one of a series numbered from 141 to 145, which was used on the Gotthard line of Switzerland starting in 1901. Maximum speed of this engine was 45 kilometers per hour. Specifications were:

Cylinders	520 by 630 millimeters
Drive wheels	1230-millimeter diameter
Boiler	
Grate area	2.1 square meters
Firebox	11.6 square meters
Total heat surface	176.8 square meters
Working pressure	15 atmospheres
Operating weight	86.3 tons (engine plus tender)
Capacities	10.0 cubic meters water; 5.0 tons coal.

(Courtesy: Swiss Federal Railways)

In Switzerland in 1902 a series of successful 4–6–0 compound locomotives were constructed by the Swiss Locomotive Works at Winterthür for the Jura-Simplon Railway which, in 1903, became part of the Swiss Federal Railways. An additional series of the same locomotive, with minor improvements, was built in the period 1904–9. These had the following characteristics:

Class A3/5
Cylinders
   Hi pressure — 14⅜ by 26 inches
   Lo pressure — 24.5 by 26 inches
Coupled wheels — 5-foot 10-inch diameter
Bogie wheels — 2-foot 9.5-inch diameter
Boiler
   Grate area — 28 square feet
   Heating surface — 1792 square feet
   Steam pressure — 2.3 pounds per square inch
Operating weight — 101.5 tons (engine plus tender)
Tender capacities — 3742 gallons water; 5 tons coal
Wheel arrangement — 4–6–0.

A model pictured is exhibited in the Swiss Transport Museum at Lucerne.
(*Courtesy: Swiss Federal Railways*)

Pictured is compound locomotive no. 742, class A3/5, type 4–6–0, part of a series numbered 703–809 built between 1904 and 1909 for use on the Swiss Railways. Engine no. 742 had a horsepower of 1350 and attained a maximum speed of about 100 kilometers per hour. See also the prior illustration. Specifications were:

Cylinders — 360 by 660 millimeters, and 570 by 660 millimeters
Coupled drive wheels — 1780-millimeter diameter
Boiler
   Grate area — 2.6 square meters
   Total heat surface — 157.7 square meters
   Firebox — 14.6 square meters
   Number tubes — 217
   Length tubes — 4200 millimeters
   Working pressure — 15 atmospheres
Operating weight — 105.7 tons (engine plus tender)
Tender capacities — 17.8 cubic meters water; 7 tons coal.

(*Courtesy: Swiss Federal Railways*)

In 1908 a series of four-cylinder, 4–6–0 locomotives were constructed by J. A. Maffei of Munich, Germany, for the Swiss Gotthard Railway. Specifications were as follows:

Cylinders	
Hi Pressure	15.5 by 25⅛ inches (between frames)
Lo pressure	25 by 25⅛ inches (outside)
Coupled wheels	5-foot 3⅜-inch diameter
Boiler	
Grate area	36 square feet
Heating surface	2540 square feet
Steam pressure	220 pounds per square inch
Operating weight	115.25 tons (engine plus tender)
Tender capacities	3750 gallons water; 4.75 tons coal.

Pictured is a model exhibited in the Swiss Transport Museum at Lucerne. See also next illustration.
(Courtesy: Swiss Federal Railways)

Pictured is a powerful compound steam locomotive, built in 1908, which was widely used to surmount the heavy grades on the Swiss Gotthard Tunnel route. See prior illustration for specifications.
(Courtesy: Swiss Federal Railways)

A class HG3/3 combination adherence and rack rail steam locomotive constructed in 1909 for use on a Riggenbach system of the Swiss Railways is pictured. Engine no. 1063 weighed 31.6 tons and travelled at 45 kilometers per hour on regular 1000-millimeter gauge tracks and 16 kilometers per hour on rack rails. This locomotive was cut open for working demonstrations and is on display in the Swiss Transport Museum at Lucerne. Specifications were:

Cylinders	380 by 400 millimeters
Drive wheels	790 millimeters
Boiler	
Grate area	1.3 square meters
Total heating surface	66.9 square meters
Working pressure	14 atmospheres
Operating weight	31.6 tons
Capacities	3.0 cubic meters water; 0.8 tons coal.

(Courtesy: Swiss Federal Railways)

The Swiss Locomotive Works at Winterthür (SLM) built sixty-nine machines of a class B 3/4, type 2–6–0, between 1905 and 1916. Pictured is engine no. 1367 of this class which went into service on 17 June 1916. This engine was discarded on 31 December 1964 when the Swiss lines were electrified finally. The locomotive was preserved in 1977–78 but is still used on occasion for special trips and excursions. Specifications were as follows:

Manufacturer's number	2557
Cylinders (2)	540 by 600 millimeters
Coupled drive wheels	1529-millimeter diameter
Boiler	
Grate area	2.3 square meters
Total heating surface	152.5 square meters
Working pressure	12 atmospheres
Operating weight	93 tons (engine plus tender)
Horsepower	990 at 70 kilometers per hour
Tender capacities	16 cubic meters water; 6 tons coal.

(Courtesy: Swiss Federal Railways)

Shown is a Swiss tank locomotive, class Eb3/5, numbered from 5801 to 5834, built between 1911 and 1916. This 2–6–2 type engine, no. 5819, developed 990 horsepower and attained a maximum speed of 75 kilometers per hour. Specifications were:

Cylinders	520 by 600 millimeters
Coupled drive wheels	1520-millimeters diameter
Boiler	
Grate area	2.3 square meters
Total heating surface	152.5 square millimeters
Working pressure	12 atmospehers
Operating weight	74.9 tons
Capacities	7.7 cubic meters; 2.5 tons coal.

(Courtesy: Swiss Federal Railways)

The final standard-gauge locomotive, type 2–10–0, no. 2978, built for the Swiss Federal Railways is shown. This engine was the last of class C 5/6 (the series was numbered 2951 to 2978) built between 1913 and 1917. Specifications were as follows:

Cylinders (4)	690 by 640 millimeters, and 470 by 640 millimeters
Drivers	1330-millimeters diameter
Boiler	
Grate area	3.7 square meters
Total heating surface	273.7 square meters
Number tubes	176
Length tubes	5000 millimeters
Working pressure	15 atmospheres
Horsepower	1350
Operating weight	128.4 tons (engine plus tender)
Tender capacities	18 cubic meters water; 7 tons coal
Maximum speed	65 kilometers per hour.

(Courtesy: Swiss Federal Railways)

Pictured is a class G3/3, type 0–6–0, tank locomotive,
engine no. 5, named "T. Thommen," built in 1902 by
the Swiss Locomotive Works at Winterthür (SLM).
The engine was withdrawn from service in 1954 and
stored. A couple of these engines were removed from
storage and participated in the hundred-year celebration of the Waldenberg Railway in June 1980. See also
the two final illustrations.
(Courtesy: Swiss Federal Railways)

This illustration shows another class G3/3, type 0–6–
0, tank engine, no. 6, which was wtihdrawn from storage to take part in the one hundred-year commem-
oration of the Waldenberg Railway in June 1980.
(Courtesy: Swiss Federal Railways)

Pictured is an emblem or medallion which was widely
distributed in Switzerland in celebration of the one
hundred-year anniversary of the Waldenberg Railway, 7 June 1980.
(Courtesy: Swiss Federal Railways)

TAIWAN

IN APRIL 1887, WITH THE APPROVAL OF THE CHInese imperial government (Ching dynasty), the governor of Taiwan, Liu Ming Chuan, initiated work on the island's first railway, and groundbreaking ceremonies took place in downtown T'aipei. In 1888, a railroad project was begun to build the 78.1-kilometers (48.5-mile) section between T'aipei and Hsinchu; this part was completed in 1893. In 1891, the 28.6-kilometer (17.8-mile) T'aipei–Chilung section was finished; this is located at the north end of the island.

After the Sino-Japanese conflict in 1894, the island of Formosa (Taiwan) was ceded to Japan. During the long period of Japanese occupation (1894–1945), most of the railroads in Taiwan were laid down, showing a heavy Japanese influence as a result.

By 1908, railway traffic from the far north at Chilung had been connected with Kaohsiung in the far south, a distance of 297.3 kilometers (184.5 miles), along the west coast, via T'aichung.

In 1922 the so-called Coast Line, built parallel to the earlier west-coast line, ran 91.2 kilometers (146.8 miles) from Chunan to Chunghau. All the rail lines on the west coast of Taiwan were constructed to a gauge of 3-feet 6-inches.

In 1924 the Ilan line, a branch road 95 kilometers (58.9 miles) in length, was inaugurated from Chilung to Suao on the northeast coast. The East Line, a separate 2-foot 6-inch gauge railroad running north-south near the east coast, was completed in 1926 linking T'aitung and Hualien—a distance of 175.7 kilometers (109.1 miles). In 1935 second tracks were laid from T'aipei to Chunan, 91.7 kilometers (56.8 miles), and also from T'ainan to Kaohsiung, 46.7 kilometers (29 miles).

In 1945, with the unconditional surrender of Japan, Taiwan was restored to the Republic of China. A second track from Peitou to Hsinpeitou on the Tanshui Line was installed in northern Taiwan in 1946. The Hsinchu–Chutung branch line was finished in 1947, and Chutung to Hohsiung in 1950. In 1951 the Neiwan branch line from Hsinchu (27.9 kilometers or 17.2 miles) was completed. In 1953, a second track on the Linpien–Fangliao section was laid down, and in this year the "class" system of passenger traffic was discontinued.

Diesel expresses began operating between T'aipei and T'aichung in 1954, and between T'aipei and Kaohsiung in 1956. A branch line, 14.1 kilometers (8.75 miles) in length, was opened in 1959 between Tungshih and Fengyuan. In 1965 Chungho was linked to Panchiao by a 6.5-kilometer (4 miles) branch line. In 1967 Taoyuan and Linkou in the far northwest, were linked by a branch line 19.2 kilometers (11.8 miles) long, with Taoyuan on the main line.

As of December 1977 fifteen rail lines made up the Taiwan Railway Administration network; these had a total of 1,007.5 kilometers (626 miles) of track. All were of 3-foot 6-inches gauge except for 157.7 kilometers (98 miles) of the East Line, which used 2-foot 6-inch gauge tracks.

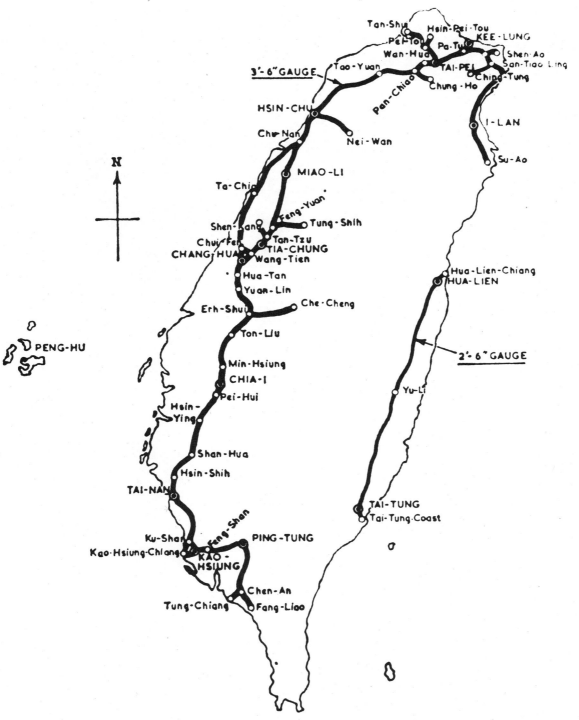

N

3'-6" GAUGE

Tan-Shui
Hsin-Pei-Tou
Pei-Tou
Pa-Tu
KEE-LUNG
Wan-Hua
Shen-Ao
Tao-Yuan
TAI-PEI
San-Tiao-Ling
Pan-Chiao
Ching-Tung
Chung-Ho

HSIN-CHU
I-LAN
Che-Nan
Nei-Wan
Su-Ao
MIAO-LI
Ta-Chia
Feng-Yuan
Tung-Shih
Shen-Kang
Tan-Tzu
Chui-Fen
TIA-CHUNG
Hua-Lien-Chiang
CHANG-HUA
Wang-Tien
HUA-LIEN
Hua-Tan
Yuan-Lin
Erh-Shui
Che-Cheng
Ton-Liu
2'-6" GAUGE
PENG-HU
Min-Hsiung
CHIA-I
Pei-Hui
Yu-Li
Hsin-Ying
Shan-Hua
Hsin-Shih
TAI-NAN
TAI-TUNG
Tai-Tung Coast
Ku-Shan
Feng-Shan
PING-TUNG
Kao-Hsiung-Chiang
KAO-HSIUNG
Chen-An
Tung-Chiang
Fang-Liao

Railway map of Taiwan.
(*Courtesy:* Janes World Railways)

Steam Locomotives in Taiwan

Repeated requests to the Taiwan Railway Administration finally brought forth eight locomotive photographs; however, I was subsequently unable to secure any caption material whatsoever. The pictures are nevertheless included for any historical value they may have to interested railway buffs. The Science Museum of London was able to furnish only one photograph of a railway steam engine used in Taiwan—one built by the North British Locomotive Company in 1906.

This illustration pictures a type 4–4–0 tender locomotive furnished to the railways of Taiwan by the North British Locomotive Company in 1906. This engine used on 3-foot 6-inch gauge tracks had the following specifications:

Cylinders	16 by 22 inches
Drive wheels	4-foot 6-inch diameter
Bogie wheels	2-foot 4-inch diameter
Boiler	
Firegrate	17 square feet
Firebox	98 square feet
Tubes	899 square feet
Total heating surface	997 square feet
Boiler working pressure	160 pounds per square inch
Tractive effort	12,515 pounds
Operating weight	
Engine total	33 tons plus 10 hundredweights
On coiupled wheels	22 tons plus 4 hundredweights
Tender	
Water capacity	2300 gallons
Fuel sapce	110 cubic feet
Operating weight	25 tons plus 10.5 hundredweights.

(Courtesy: Science Museum, London)

The following eight photographs were furnished by the Taiwan Railways Administration without any caption information.

THAILAND

THE ORIGINAL RAILWAYS IN THAILAND WERE constructed to supplement thirty-seven hundred miles of canals and river waterways, which in 1978 still carried about half of that country's freight traffic. The first rail line in Thailand was finished in 1892 and ran northeast from Bangkok, finally reaching Nakhon Ratchasima in 1900, a distance of 264 kilometers (164 miles). The original system was standard-gauge, i.e., 4 feet 8½ inches, but when construction to the south was begun, it was decided in 1900 to use meter-gauge tracks to link smoothly with the system in Malaysia. Eventually, about 580 miles of track were laid from Bangkok south, and two connections were established with the Malayan Railway at Padang Besar and at Sungai Kolok. Subsequently, starting in 1919, the standard-gauge network in the north was converted to meter-gauge, which project was completed in April 1930.

In modern times, Thailand's railways radiate from Bangkok south to Malaysia, as indicated; to Cambodia in the southeast; to Udon Thani in the northeast, and to Chiang Mai in the north. The Japanese built a junction line to Burma during World War II, but this was dismantled after the conflict. (David Fogarty's article, "Building The Death Railway," in the October 1981 issue of *The Retired Officer* gives an overview of the short-lived Burma branch line.) Although the rail system in Thailand has always been under government control, beginning as the Royal State Railway of Siam, it became an autonomous organization called the State Railway of Thailand (RSR) in 1951.

On 30 September 1979, RSR had a total of 3,735 kilometers (2,321 miles) of route track and 4,418 kilometers (2,745 miles) of total trackage open to traffic. This system crossed 2,578 bridges, totaling 55,371 meters or 1.4 percent of the total length of running track. Also in 1979, the Thailand rail network served 444 rail stations with 39 steam engines, 190 diesel locomotives, 46 diesel rail cars, 924 passenger cars, and 7,506 freight cars. The railways employed 29,378 people (26,944 permanent and 2,434 temporary employees) in that year.

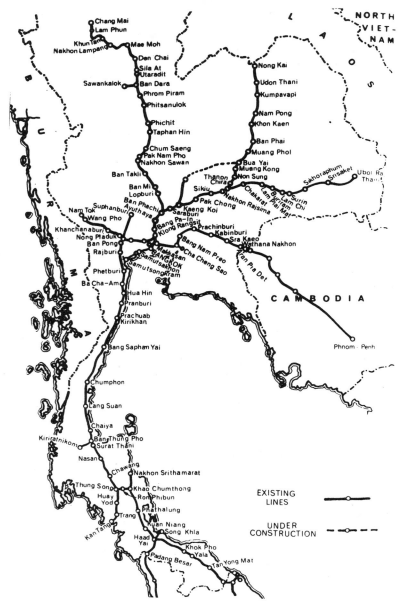

Railway map of Thailand.
(*Courtesy:* Janes World Railways)

Steam Locomotives in Thailand

With no commitments to any colonial powers, Thailand has always been able to purchase her steam locomotives solely according to her internal railway requirements and to select steam engines from all the world's manufacturers. Thailand always had a reputation for high maintenance, operational, and appearance standards for her locomotives and rolling stock.

Steam locomotives used in Thailand between 1893 and 1951 are tabulated. One of the first two tank locomotives on the initial rail line is shown. This had an 0–6–0 wheel arrangement and was manufactured by Hunslet & Son, England. It was used on standard-gauge tracks for shunting purposes and railroad construction work.

In 1895 and 1896, six tank locomotives were purchased from Dubs & Company of England for the standard-gauge (1.435-meter, or 4-foot 6½-inch)

One of the first two tank locomotives, nos. 7 and 8, used in Thailand in 1893. These were type 0–6–0 engines manufactured by Hunslet & Son in England. (*Courtesy: State Railway of Thailand*)

Also in 1894 the Nagara Rajasema Railway received from Dubs & Company four type 2–4–0 tank locomotives equipped with auxiliary tenders (nos. 1–4). These unusual combination engines had the following specifications:

Gauge	4 feet 8½ inches
Work order no.	E 3129
Cylinders	10 by 18 inches
Drive wheels	4-foot 3-inch diameter
Boiler heating surface	395 square feet
Working steam pressure	160 pounds per square inch
Operating weights	
Tank engine	28 tons plus 8 hundredweights
Tender	15 tons plus 4 hundredweights
Tender capacities	1220 gallons water; 140 cubic feet fuel
Tank engine capacities	670 gallons water; 120 cubic feet fuel.

(*Courtesy: Mitchell Library, Glasgow*) D/E 3129

In 1894 the Nagara Rajasema Railway of Siam purchased from Dubs & Company four type 0–6–0 tender locomotives (nos. 5–8). Wood-burning engine (no. 5) is shown in the photograph; this had the following specifications:

Gauge	4 feet 8½ inches
Work order no.	E 3125
Cylinders	15 by 20 inches
Drivers	3-foot 2¼-inch diameter
Boiler heating surface	725 square feet
Working steam pressure	169 pounds per square inch
Tractive force	14,119 pounds
Operating weights	
Engine	26 tons plus 19 hundredweights
Tender	21 tons plus 4 hundredweights
Tender capacities	1800 gallons water; 280 cubic feet fuel.

(Courtesy: Mitchell Library, Glasgow) D/E 3125

Shown is one of six tank locomotives, type 2–4–0, built by Dubs & Company of England in 1895–96 for use on standard-gauge tracks in Thailand.
(Courtesy: State Railway of Thailand)

Over the period 1906–9, George Egestoff of Germany supplied twelve type 2–6–0 locomotives for use on standard-gauge tracks of Thailand. Pictured is engine no. 215
(Courtesy: State Railway of Thailand)

In the period 1902–13 Krauss & Company of Germany supplied six type 2–4–2 locomotives for use on the initial meter-gauge rail lines in Thailand.
(Courtesy: State Railway of Thailand)

line running northeast from Bangkok.

In the period 1902–13, six type 2–4–2 locomotives with tenders, numbered 125 through 131, were procured from Krauss & Company of Germany. These were used on the first meter-gauge lines.

From 1906 to 1909, Thailand railways purchased twelve type 2–6–0 locomotives (numbered 209 through 221) from George Egestoff in Germany.

Between 1910 and 1915, six type 0–6–0 tank locomotives, numbered 51 through 56, were secured from Henschel & Sohn, Germany. These were first used on standard-gauge tracks for shunting purposes but later were modified to operate on meter-gauge lines. In the same period, Thailand used seven type 0–6–0 engines, numbered 57 through 63, manufactured by the Brush Electrical Engineering Company of England. Engine no. 62, which was used on meter-gauge tracks, is featured.

In 1912 the North British Locomotive Company

Between 1910 and 1915 Henschel & Sohn of Germany supplied six 0–6–0 tank engines for use on standard-gauge tracks on the Thailand railroads. Engine number 55 is shown.
(Courtesy: State Railway of Thailand)

The Brush Electrical Engineering Company of England in 1910 built seven type 0–6–0 tank locomotives for use on the meter-gauge rail lines of Thailand. Shown is engine no. 62.
(Courtesy: State Railway of Thailand)

furnished twelve type 4–6–0 tender locomotives to the Royal Siamese State Railways. See illustration.

Between 1913 and 1921, forty-two class E locomotives, type 4–6–0, manufactured by North British Locomotive Company, were delivered to Thailand. Numbered 156 through 197, these were later converted from coal- to oil-burning types and fitted with smoke deflectors. Shown is a model of locomotive no. 156, which had the following specifications:

Cylinders	14.5 by 22 inches
Coupled wheels	4-foot diameter
Boiler working pressure	180 pounds per square inch
Boiler heating surface	915 square feet
Operating weight	58 tons
Tractive force	13,009 pounds.

In the 1920s Baldwin supplied a number of steam rail cars that are described. In 1922 Baldwin also introduced the type 2–8–2 tender locomotives on the Siam State Railways meter-gauge lines. In 1928–29 Baldwin furnished twenty-six three-

The Royal Siamese State Railways in 1912 purchased twelve type 4–6–0 tender locomotives from the North British Locomotive Company (nos. 8–19) for use on the southern railways. No. 8, shown in the photograph, had these specifications:

Gauge	3 feet 3⅜ inches
Work order no.	L 501
Cylinders	14½ by 22 inches
Drive wheels	4-foot diameter
Boiler heating surface	918 square feet
Working steam pressure	180 pounds per square inch
Tractive force	13,000 pounds
Operating weights	
Engine	33 tons plus 7 hundredweights
Tender	24 tons plus 13 hundredweights
Tender capacities	2000 gallons water; 400 cubic feet wood fuel.

(Courtesy: Mitchell Library, Glasgow) L501

The Royal Siamese State Railway in 1915 procured five type 4–6–0 engines from the North British Locomotive Company for use on the southern lines of Siam. These were class E locomotives similar in type to the 4–6–0 machines purchased in 1912 but with mechanical improvements. Specifications follow:

Gauge	3 feet 3⅜ inches
Work order no.	L 641
Cylinders	14½ by 22 inches
Drivers	4-foot diameter
Boiler heating surface	918 square feet
Working steam pressure	180 pounds per square inch
Tractive force	13,000 pounds
Operating weights	
Engine	33 tons plus 7 hundredweights
Tender	24 tons plus 13 hundredweights
Tender capacities	2000 gallons water; 400 cubic feet wood fuel.

(Courtesy: Mitchell Library, Glasgow) L641

The model of a class E, type 4–6–0, locomotive used on the Royal State Railways of Thailand is pictured. Forty-two of these engines were built over the period 1913–21 by the North British Locomotive Company for use on the Thailand meter-gauge rail lines. Specifications are tabulated in the text.
(Courtesy: State Railway of Thailand)

This steam rail car was built in the 1920s by Baldwin for use on the Royal State Railways of Siam. The boiler was fired with oil, and a tank had a capacity of 800 gallons of fuel. Water capacity was 2000 gallons. In the picture the car body itself is missing. A steam operated brake actuated the leading bogie wheels and the drive wheels while a vacuum brake was used to control the rear car truck. Specifications were as follows:

Cylinders	10 by 12 inches
Drive wheels	40-inch diameter
Boiler diameter	48 inches
Total car weight	99,186 pounds.

(Courtesy: State Railway of Thailand)

A Mikado type locomotive, the first engine ever constructed for the Royal Siamese State Railways by Baldwin in 1922. This was used on their meter-gauge railroads. Specifications were:

Cylinders	17 by 24 inches
Drive wheels	43.6-inch diameter
Engine weight	118,600 pounds.

(Courtesy: Frederick Westing collection)

cylinder, type 4–6–2 locomotives (not illustrated).

During World War II, the Japanese built a number of type 4–6–2 engines for military use in Thailand. The Japanese also delivered about forty-five class C56, type 2–6–0 engines for their armed forces.

In 1946–47 Baldwin's Mikado-type locomotives with a 2–8–2 wheel arrangement, together with tender—known as MacArthurs—were widely used in Thailand. The MacArthur engines consisted mostly of a series of sixty-eight locomotives, numbers 380 through 447, declared surplus after World War II. They had originally been used on the Ben-

gal to Assam Railway of India during the war.

In 1949–50, Thailand purchased from the Association of Railway Industry in Japan twenty-one tender locomotives of the Pacific 4–6–2 type (numbers 821–849), and, later, sixty-nine more Pacific-type locomotives (numbers 901–969) from the same source. Illustrated is Thailand's last steam engine, no. 850, purchased from the above Japanese manufacturer in 1951. This was another Pacific type and had originally burned wood as fuel. It was later converted to burn oil by the Mechanical Engineering Department of the Thailand Railways.

Pictured is one of ninety Pacific, type 4–6–2, locomotives purchased from the Association of Railway Industry of Japan over the period 1949–50 for use on the Thailand railroads.
(Courtesy: State Railway of Thailand)

The last steam engine purchased in 1951 by Thailand from the Japanese manufacturer, the Association of Railway Industry is pictured. This was a wood-burning Pacific, type 4–6–2, locomotive which was later converted to fuel oil.
(Courtesy: State Railway of Thailand)

TURKEY

THE FIRST RAIL LINE IN TURKEY, CONSTRUCTED under British concession , linked Izmir with Aydin through the Menderes Valley. This eighty-mile railroad opened in 1866 and helped to develop Southwestern Anatolia. In 1873, a fifty-eight-mile stretch of track was finished from Haydarpasa to Izmit (latitude 40°46′ north, longitude 29°55′ east). The first stage of the Orient Express route, from Istanbul to Edirne, a distance of 198 miles, was also inaugurated in 1873.

The first general plan for a rail system of any significance dates from 1869, but this plan was modified in 1872. Foreign companies furnished the capital and received a subsidy from the Turkish government. In return, the foreign construction and operating firms were to make certain annual payments. Unfortunately, the contract clauses providing for these compensations were so carelessly drawn that it became expedient for the alien enterprises to protract the work for extended periods.

Turkey lost some early rail lines following the Russo-Turkish War of 1878. In that year, there were about 711 miles of active railways in the country.

From about 1885, Turkey experienced a great increase in railway construction activity mostly by foreign concession holders. On 12 August 1888 the first direct connection between Vienna and Istanbul was opened, which finally breached the veil of mystery that separated Turkey from the west. With the start of this Orient Express service, contacts between Europe and Asiatic Turkey rapidly increased and passenger and freight traffic mounted by leaps and bounds. The arrival of the Orient Ex-

press naturally brought more and more western influence, which also stimulated pan-Islamic reactions. Not to be outdone by European interests, Muslims worldwide pressed for their own rail construction projects. In 1900 the Hejaz Railway, which had been formed earlier, opened a railroad linking Damascus in Syria with Medina in Turkey. This was made possible by extensive donations from thousands of mideastern adherents to Islam.

In 1902 the Germans were granted the most notorious concession by Sultan Abdul Hamid's government—the right of the Baghdad Railway to cross Turkey. Moreover, the Germans were guaranteed a fixed payment per kilometer of track laid, so, as it turned out, the extensive and serpentine route through the difficult Turkish terrain brought about excessive fee payments. Also, the Germans were granted exploitation rights for all mineral, forest, and water resources within a zone extending 12.5 miles on both sides of the railroad right-of-way. The concession was to run ninety-nine years, but the defeat of German and Turkish military forces in World War I, of course terminated the agreement.

As of 1913, the Ottoman Empire in Europe and Asia held about 3,882 miles of active railway track. With the start of Turkey's status as a republic in 1923, the nation's first great transportation expense involved the purchase of the privately owned railroads built and operated by German, French, Belgian, and British firms. These amounted to about twenty-five hundred miles of track. Then, without resorting to any foreign capital, the republic increased the rail routes to 4,750 miles by 1948. In the interim, from 1923 to 1938, Kemal Ataturk, the

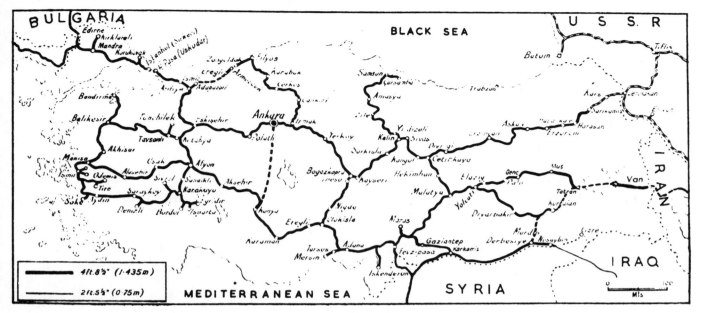

Railway map of Turkey.
(*Courtesy:* Janes World Railways)

Turkish nationalist leader, was able to further extend the railroads, at considerable cost, with a spur to Izmir from the original German-built single-line Baghdad Railway. He also ordered construction of rail extensions to the Russian frontier and to the Black Sea, as well as linking Ankara with Izmir. These connections were funded by substantial Turkish capital expenditures between World Wars I and II, which helped to open large and otherwise isolated tracts of Anatolia. The city of Sivas was linked with Ankara, Samsun, Malatya and Erzincan. The railway also provided the easiest access to the small town of Divigi and the important nearby iron mines.

Between 1938 and 1948, the Turks doubled rail service by increasing rolling stock and operating efficiency. In 1940 new railways provided a more integrated network. These included the lines from Eregli and Zonguldak to Ankara, Kayseri, and Adona, and the series of lines that later linked Samsun on the Black Sea with Kayseri, Erzurum, Malatya, Adona, and Kurtalan in the oil-rich southeast. In 1948 a new ten-year construction program was worked out, with United States advisers, which called for about two thousand miles of additional track by 1958. Until recently, the Turkish railroads were constructed with national defense as the primary consideration, trade and popular travel being secondary matters.

In 1963 there were 873 steam locomotives providing rail services in Turkey, along with 67 diesel and 3 electric locomotives. In 1972 there were 819 engines in use, plus 154 diesels and 12 electric locomotives. The total number of personnel on Turkish railroads in 1963 was 60,858; in 1972 the number was 63,502.

In 1978 *Janes World Railways* reported that route mileage in Turkey totaled 5.128 kilometers (3,186 miles) of 1.435-meter (4-foot 6½-inch) gauge track.

Steam Locomotives in Turkey

The accompanying fifteen illustrations present a representative number of steam locomotives used on the railways of Turkey between 1874 and 1937.

Tank engine no. 2251, used on the Turkish railways was a type 0–4–0 built by Krauss in 1874. General specifications were:

Boiler power	438 horsepower
Tare weight	17.85 tons
Operating weight	25.12 tons
Maximum axle loading	12.62 tons
Maximum speed	40 kilometers per hour.

(Courtesy: TCDD Railways, Turkey)

Sharp, Stewart & Company in 1889 constructed for the Ottoman Railways of Turkey an unstated number of type 0–6–0 tender locomotives. Specifications follows:

Gauge	4 feet 8½ inches
Cylinders	18 by 24 inches
Order no.	E 936
Drivers	4-foot 6½-inch diameter
Boiler heating surface	1022 square feet
Working steam pressure	(not stated)
Tender water capacity	2500 gallons.

(Courtesy: Mitchell Library, Glasgow) SS/E936

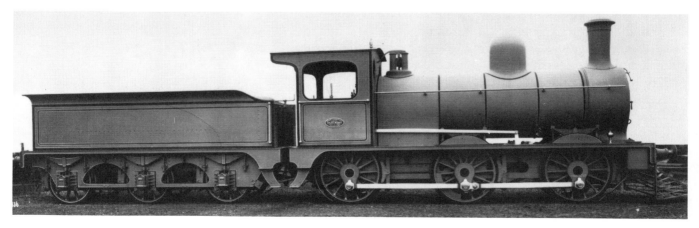

In 1890 the Ottoman Railways of Turkey purchased from Neilson & Company an unstated number of type 4–4–0 tender locomotives (work order no. E 671). These engines carried the following specifications:

Gauge   4 feet 8½ inches
Cylinders   17½ by 24 inches
Drivers   6-foot 1½-inch diameter
Boiler heating surface   1067.6 square feet
Working steam pressure   160 pounds per square inch
Operating weights
  Engine   38 tons plus 4 hundredweights
  Tender   29 tons plus 10 hundredweights
Tender capacities   2500 gallons water; 4 tons coal

(Courtesy: Mitchell Library, Glasgow)

Pictured is tank engine no. 0412, type 0–6–2, locomotive built by Stephenson in 1911 for use on the Turkish railways. This engine had the following general specifications:

Boiler power   999 horsepower
Tare weight   51.8 tons
Operating weight   61.2 tons
Maximum axle loading   16.5 tons
Maximum speed   64 kilometers per hour.

(Courtesy: TCDD Railways, Turkey)

An old type 2–4–0 tank locomotive, no. 3351, built in 1912 by Maffei for use on the Turkish rail system is shown. General specifications were:

Boiler power	445 horsepower
Tare weight	29.5 tons
Operating weight	39 tons
Maximum axle loading	13 tons
Maximum speed	45 kilometers per hour

(Courtesy: TCDD Railways, Turkey)

A Henschel locomotive built in 1937 for the Turkish Railways is pictured. General specifications were:

Boiler power	1896 horsepower
Tare weight	95.9 tons
Operating weight	106.5 tons
Maximum axle loading	18.5 tons
Maximum speed	70 kilometers per hour.

(Courtesy: TCDD Railways, Turkey)

Two photographs of similar type 0–6–0 locomotives built by Nohab in 1929 for use on various Turkish railways are shown. Specifications were:

Boiler power	471 horsepower
Tare weight	37.5 tons
Operating weight	48 tons
Maximum axle loading	13–16 tons.

(Courtesy: TCDD Railways, Turkey)

This illustration shows a locomotive roundhouse
somewhere in Turkey in 1960.
(Courtesy: TCDD Railways, Turkey)

Five illustrations show miscellaneous locomotives
which operated on various Turkish railways. These
were not specifically identified.
(Courtesy: TCDD Railways, Turkey)

BIBLIOGRAPHY

Alan, Ray. *Spanish Quest.* London: Collier-Macmillan, 1969.

Alexander, Edwin P. *American Locomotives.* New York: Bonanza Books, 1950.

Allen, Cecil John. *Switzerland's Amazing Railways.* London: Thomas Nelson, 1965.

——. *Modern Railroads.* London: Faber & Faber, 1959.

Allen, G. Freeman. *The Fastest Train in the World.* New York: Scribners, 1978.

Anderson, Robert F. *Denmark: Success of a Developing Nation.* Cambridge, Mass.: Schenkman, 1975.

Bagnall, G. Philip. *The Railway Clearing Houses.* London: Allen & Unwin, n.d.

Baldwin Locomotive Works. *History of the Baldwin Locomotive Works.* Philadelphia, 1924.

Barsley, Michael. *The Orient Express.* New York: Stein & Day, 1967.

Baxter, Eric. *The Study Book of Railways.* London: Bodley Head, n.d.

Beasley, W. G. *The Modern History of Japan.* New York: Praeger, 1974.

Behrend, George. *Grand European Expresses.* London: Allen & Unwin, 1962.

Berghans, E. *A History of the Railways.* London: Barrie & Rockliff, 1964.

Bernard, Jack F. *Up From Caesar.* Garden City, N.Y.: Doubleday, 1970.

Berridge, P. S. A. *Couplings to Khyber.* London: David & Charles, 1974.

Blainey, Geoffrey. *The Tyranny of Distance.* London: Macmillan, 1968.

Blake, Robert. *A History of Rhodesia.* New York: Alfred Knopf, 1978.

Bonjour, E.; Offer, H. S.: and Potter, G. R. *Switzerland.* Oxford, England: Clarendon Press, 1952.

Cady, John F. *Thailand, Burma, Laos, Cambodia.* Englewood Cliffs, N.J.: Prentice-Hall, 1948.

Calvert, Peter. *Mexico.* New York: Praeger, 1973.

Carr, Raymon. *Spain: 1808–1939.* Oxford, England: Clarendon Press, 1966.

Casserley, H. C. *Preserved Locomotives.* Shipperton, England: Ian Allan, n.d.

Cerny, Louis. *Meter-Gauge Steam in India.* N.p.: Joliet, 1974.

Clark, Sydney. *Austria.* New York: Dodd, Mead & Company, 1972.

Clyde, Paul H., and Beers, Burton F. *The Far East.* Englewood Cliffs, N.J.: Prentice-Hall, 1966.

Comstock, Henry B. *The Iron Horse.* New York: Thomas Crowell, 1971.

Cookridge, E. H. *Orient Express.* New York: Random House, 1978.

Crowley, Frank, ed. *A New History of Australia.* New York: Holmes & Meir, 1974.

Croxton, A. H. *Railways of Rhodesia.* Newton Abbot, England: David & Charles, 1973.

Cumberland, Charles C. *Mexico.* New York: Oxford Press, 1968.

Cumberland, K. B., and Fox, James W. *New Zealand: A Regional View.* Auckland: Whitcombe & Tombs, 1958.

Derry, T. K. *A History of Modern Norway.* Oxford, England: Clarendon Press, 1973.

Devere, Irwin R., and Potter, J. R. *The Belt System of Locomotive Repairs*. Calcutta: Railway Board, G.I., 1932.

Donnison, F. S. V. *Burma*. New York: Praeger, 1970.

Dow, George. *World Locomotive Models*. New York: Arco Publishing, 1973.

Ellis, C. Hamilton. *The Lore of the Trains*. N.Y.: Crescent Books, 1971.

———. *The Splender of Steam Engines That Passed*. London: Allen & Unwin, n.d.

———. *Railway History*. London: Hamlyn, 1974.

———. Steam Railways. London: Eyre & Methuen, 1975.

———. *Pictorial Encyclopedia of Railways*. London: Octopus, 1971.

Fenino, F., and Broncard, Y. *The Last Steam Locomotives of France*. London: Ian Allan, 1977.

Ferns, H. S. *Argentina*. New York: Praeger, 1969.

Fryer, Donald, W., and Jackson, James C. *Indonesia*. London: E. Benn, 1977.

Gloag, G. L. *Railways of Spain*. London: Faber & Faber, 1923.

Haine, Edgar A. *Railways Across the Andes*. Boulder, Colo.: Pruett Publishing, 1981.

———. *Seven Railroads*. Cranbury, N.J.: A. S. Barnes, 1979.

HaLasz, Zoltan, ed. *Hungary*. New York: Corvina Press, 1963.

Hale, Hugh Marshall. *Old Rhodesian Days*. London: Frank Cass, 1928.

Harrison, Joseph. *The Locomotive Engine*. Philadelphia: George Gebbie, 1872.

Hatada, Takashi. *A History of Korea*. Santa Barbara, Calif.: ABC, Inc., 1969.

Henry, Robert Selph. *Trains*. New York: Bobbs-Merrill, 1957.

Hind, John R. *The Book of the Railway*. London: Collins, 1927.

Hirota, Naotaka. *The Lure of Japan's Railways*. Tokyo: Japan *Times*, 1969.

Howard, Robert West. *The Great Iron Trail*. New York: Putnam, 1962.

Hughes, Hugh. *Steam Locomotives of India*. Harrow, England: Continental Railway Circle, 1977.

Hungerford, John B. *Hawaiian Railroads*. Reseda, Calif.: Hungerford Press, 1963.

Janes World Railways. Bridgeport, Conn.: Key Book Service Inc., 1980.

Jelavich, Charles and Barbara. *The Establishment of the Balkan National States*. Seattle: University of Washington Press, 1977.

Jensen, Oliver. *Railroads of America*. New York: American Heritage, 1975.

Jones, W. Glyn. *Denmark*. New York: Praeger, 1970.

Kalla-Bishop, Peter, ed. *The Golden Years of Trains*. New York: Crescent Books, 1975.

Kay, George F. *Steam Locomotives*. London: Hamlyn, 1974.

Kemp, A. R. *Rhodesia Railways*. Bulawayo: Rhodesia Railways, 1965.

Kennedy, J. *A History of Malaya*. London: St. Martin's Press, 1962.

Kitchenside, G., *Steam*. London: David & Charles, 1975.

Lant, Agnes C. *The Romance of the Rails*. New York: R. M. McBride, 1929.

Larsen, Karen. *A History of Norway*. Princeton, N.J.: Princeton University Press, 1948.

Latourette, Kenn Scott. *The Chinese*. New York: Macmillan, 1941.

Lewis, Bernard. *The Emergence of Modern Turkey*. London: Oxford University Press, 1961.

Levy, Allen. *A Century of Model Trains*. New York: Crescent Books, n.d.

Little, Tom. *Modern Egypt*. New York: Praeger, 1967.

Mallinson, Vernon. *Belgium*. New York: Praeger, 1970.

Marshall, John. *Rail Facts and Feats*. New York: Two Continents Publishing Group, 1974.

Marshall, L. G. *Steam on the RENFE*. London: Macmillan, n.d.

McBride, H. A. *Trains Rolling*. New York: Macmillan, 1953.

McDowell, Bart. *Journey Across Russia*. Washington, D.C.: National Geographic Society, 1977.

Mead, W. R. *Finland*. New York: Praeger, 1968.

Meyer, Michael C. *The Course of Mexican History*. New York: Oxford University Press, 1979.

Miller, W. *The Balkans*. New York: Putnam, 1899.

Morgan, Bryan, ed. *The Great Trains*. New York: Crown Publishers, 1973.

Nock, O. S. *Railways of Southern Africa*. London: Black, 1971.

———. *The Dawn of World Railways*. New York: Macmillan, 1972.

———. *The Golden Age of Steam*. London: Black, 1973.

———. *Railways of Western Europe*. London: Black, 1975.

———. *Railways: Then and Now.* London: Bratford Publishing, 1975.

Pangborn, J. G. *The World's Railways.* New York: Bramhall House, 1974.

Pennoyer, A. Sheldon. *Locomotives in Our Lives.* New York: Hastings House, 1954.

Perceval, Michael. *The Spaniards.* New York: Praeger, 1969.

Phillips, Lance. *Yonder Comes the Train.* New York: A. S. Barnes, 1965.

Pike, Douglas. *Australia.* London: Cambridge University Press, 1962.

Plowden, David. *Farewell to Steam.* New York: Bonanza Books, 1966.

Powell, F. W. *The Railroads of Mexico.* Boston: Stratford, 1921.

Ratta, H. C. *Steam Locomotive Guide.* Calcutta: Atma Ram & Sons, 1961.

Riverain, Jean. *Trains of the World.* Chicago: Follett, 1964.

Roberts, R. H. *Romania.* New Haven: Yale University Press, 1951.

Sahani, J. N. *Indian Railways, 1853–1953.* New Delhi: Railway Board, 1953.

Said, Beshir M. *The Sudan.* London: DuFours Editions, 1965.

Scobie, James R. *Argentina.* New York: Oxford University Press, 1971.

Scott, Franklin D. *Sweden.* Minneapolis: University of Minnesota Press, 1977.

Shaw, A. G. L. *The Story of Australia.* London: Faber & Faber, 1960.

Shirer, William L. *The Challenge of Scandinavia.* Westport, Conn.: Greenwood Press, 1955.

Sinclair, Angus. *Development of the Locomotive Engine.* New York: Angus Sudans, 1907.

Singleton, Fred. *Twentieth-Century Yugoslavia.* New York: Columbia University Press, 1976.

Snell, J. B. *Early Railways.* New York: Putnam's, 1964.

Stavrianos, L. S. *The Balkans Since 1453.* Hinsdale, Ill.: Dryden Press, 1958.

Swengel, F. M. *The American Steam Locomotive.* Chicago: Midwest Rail Publications, 1967.

Talbot, Fred Arthur. *Railway Conquest of the World.* Philadelphia: Lippincott, 1911.

Theroux, P. *The Great Railway Bazaar.* London: Hamish Hamilton, 1975.

Turnbull, Clive. *A Concise History of Australia.* London: Thames & Hudson, 1965.

Walpert, Stanley. *A New History of India.* New York: Oxford University Press, 1977.

Ward, Russel. *A History of Australia.* New York: Harper & Row, 1977.

Watters, R. F., ed. *Land and Society of New Zealand.* Wellington: Reid, 1965.

Westing, Fred. *The Locomotive that Baldwin Built.* Seattle: Superior Publishing Co., 1966.

Westwood, J. N. *Locomotive Designer in the Age of Steam.* London: Sedgwick & Jackson, 1973.

———. *Railways of India.* London: David & Charles, 1974.

White, E. L. *The Wheels Spin.* London: Collins, 1936.

Wright, Gordon. *France in Modern Times.* Chicago: Rand McNally, 1960.

Wvorinen, John H. *A History of Finland.* New York: Columbia University Press, 1965.

Zaffo, George, and Eagleson, Mike. *The How and Why Wonder Book of Railroads.* New York: Wonder Books, 1964.

Zill, Ron. *The Twilight of World Steam.* New York: Grosset & Dunlap, 1973.

INDEX